A LEVEL
MATHEMATICS

Duncan Graham,
Christine Graham and Allan Whitcombe

Letts

EDUCATIONAL

Every effort has been made to trace copyright holders and to obtain their permission for the use of copyright material. The authors and publishers will gladly receive information enabling them to rectify any reference or credit in subsequent editions.

First published 1984
Revised 1988, 1993, 1995
Reprinted 1986, 1991, 1994, 1996, 1997, 1998

Letts Educational
Aldine House
Aldine Place
London W12 8AW
Tel: 0181-740 2266

Text © Duncan Graham, Christine Graham
and Allan Whitcombe 1995

Design and illustrations © BPP (Letts Educational) Ltd 1995

British Library Cataloguing in Publication Data

A CIP record for this book is available from the British Library.

ISBN 1 85758 338 8

Printed and bound in Great Britain by
WM Print Ltd, West Midlands, WS2 9NE

Letts Educational is the trading name of BPP (Letts Educational) Ltd

Preface

The key aim of this book is to assist students in their study and revision of A-level, AS-level and Scottish Higher mathematics and AS-level statistics or mechanics. It has been written for students who are studying mathematics at school, college, evening class or at home, and who are taking either linear or modular courses.

Most students of A-level mathematics study single-subject mathematics leading to one A-level. Typical combinations are:

> pure mathematics + mechanics;
> pure mathematics + statistics;
> or pure mathematics + mechanics + statistics.

If you are one of these students this book has been designed with you specifically in mind.

If you are one of the smaller number of students studying double-subject mathematics leading to two A-levels this book will cover at least a half of the work you have to do. Subject combinations are as above but with wider coverage and greater depth .

This book should act as a course companion from the beginning and throughout any A-level mathematics course (or its equivalent) and could be used as a study-aid, workbook and revision aid. It is not intended to provide a complete guide to the subject since the book is designed to complement a textbook rather than duplicate it.

Students preparing for an AS-level examination in pure mathematics, mechanics or statistics will also find that this book is an invaluable aid to their study. Most, if not all, of the requirements of their chosen syllabus will be found to be fully covered in the appropriate study units.

This book has been produced after analysing the most recent appropriate mathematics syllabuses of all the Exam Boards in England, Wales, Northern Ireland and Scotland. Most of the mathematics required by these syllabuses has been divided into 96 Study Units, and Table I (p. xii) shows which topics are in which syllabuses. Table II (p. xvi) analyses the methods of examination of each syllabus.

The largest section of the book is Part II, containing the Study Units and Question Banks. Each Study Unit contains essential information, worked examples and questions from recent specimen and examination papers relating to that Unit. The essential information omits proofs and other similar material which may be found in most standard texts. The material has been presented in a clear and concise fashion so as to be easily accessible to the student.

Part I 'Working for A/AS level' includes a guide on how to use the book, information on study skills, revision and examination technique, and reference chapters on mathematical modelling, coursework and graphics calculators.

The majority of Study Aids/Revision Guides claim to offer a complete coverage of A-level syllabuses, but seem to have few, if any, advantages over a traditional textbook. In this Letts Study Guide the authors have made a genuine attempt to break the mould of the standard presentation of such material with their fresh, unique presentation. They are convinced that all students, including those who feel unsuccessful with conventional texts, will gain substantial assistance with their study of A- and AS-level mathematics and its examination from the use of this book. Students working on modular courses will find this approach especially helpful.

Acknowledgements

During the preparation of this latest edition our co-author, Allan Whitcombe, suddenly died. We are therefore extremely grateful to all the people (including Allan) who helped us to make this edition available in time for the start of the new A-level modular courses in the autumn of 1995.

We wish to thank especially, Hendrina Ellis, without whose organisational and other skills we would never have achieved our objective; Steve Davies who gallantly took up the challenge of producing the tables of analysis; Bruce M. McKenzie for his invaluable advice and careful checking of answers; Dr Ted Graham for writing the chapter on mathematical modelling; and Mark Patmore for writing the chapters on coursework and graphics calculators.

We should like to reiterate our thanks to others who over the years also contributed to previous editions of the book: John Earle and Sue de Pomerai for their invaluable assistance as consultants for a previous revision of the book; Rod Parsons, Chris Aylott and Dave Crocker for their comments on the original manuscript; the late Norma Whitcombe for general help and encouragement, and other members of our families whose patience and understanding have been appreciated; and to Wayne Davies and the staff of Letts Educational.

We are most grateful to the following Exam Boards for permission to use questions from their specimen and recent examination papers: the Associated Examining Board, the University of Cambridge Local Examinations Syndicate, the University of London Examinations and Assessment Council, the Northern Examinations and Assessment Board (formerly the JMB), the Northern Ireland Council for the Curriculum Examinations and Assessment, the Oxford and Cambridge Schools Examination Board, the University of Oxford Delegacy of Local Examinations, the Scottish Examination Board and the Welsh Joint Education Committee.

None of the above boards can accept responsibility for the accuracy or method of working in the answers given. These are solely the responsibility of the authors.

Duncan and Christine Graham
August 1995

CONTENTS

iv

Part I WORKING FOR A /AS LEVEL

HOW TO USE THIS BOOK

Part I is general advice for your course – how to identify your syllabus, study skills, how to revise, examination technique – plus useful reference chapters on mathematical modelling, coursework and graphics calculators, together with a glossary of symbols.

Part II makes up the bulk of the book. It contains the Study Units and the Questions Banks.

Part III contains the answers to the Study Unit questions and is followed by the Index.

Identifying your course

To use this book most effectively you need to know which Study Units are in your course, and which are not. Therefore you need to identify the syllabus you are studying. The following questions should help you to do so (check with your teacher if you need to).

- What is the name of your Exam Board?
- Which type of course (linear or modular) are you taking?
- Which qualification (AS- or A-level) do you want to gain?
- What is the name or reference number of your syllabus?
- Which of these sections are you studying: Pure Mathematics, Mechanics, Statistics?
- Which modules (if any) are you taking?
- Which options (if any) have you chosen?

Finding out about your syllabus

Table I (p. xii–xv) tells you which Units are in which syllabuses. It is organised into Pure Mathematics, Mechanics and Statistics. Find your Exam Board on the top line, locate your syllabus and look down the column.

- is blank □ — ignore that Unit because you do not need it;
- has a dot ▣ — study that Unit because it is on your syllabus;
- has a letter ▣ — look for the letter(s) in the table footnotes to find out what to do about that Unit.

(It may help to use marker pen to identify your column and Study Unit names, and then highlight your Unit pages.)

Table II (p. xvi–xix) tells you the method of examination of all the Exam Boards. In the lefthand column, find your Exam Board, locate your syllabus and read across to find details of the examination you will be sitting.

If your syllabus is not in the tables, either ask your teacher or write to your Exam Board for details. Syllabuses sometimes change from year to year, if in doubt consult your teacher.

AS/A-level core for Mathematics

From the summer of 1996 all AS- and A-level subjects that are called 'Mathematics' (or have 'Mathematics' as the first word in their title) must cover the 'core material for Mathematics' on their syllabuses. This 'core material' is defined in a document produced by the Schools Examinations and Assessment Council (SEAC). Most topics in the core material are in Pure Mathematics, a few in Statistics and none in Mechanics.

In this book topics in the core material are in Units P1 to P24 and S1 to S7. Core material is indicated by a 'C' in Table I.

Study Units

The mathematics in this book has been divided into 96 Study Units, which are grouped into three sections: Pure Mathematics, Mechanics and Statistics.

Each Study Unit is presented on a double page spread, with notes and simple illustrations – the ⒤ s – on the lefthand page; and Worked examples, Guided examples, Exercises and Exam questions on the righthand page. (Some notes run over to the righthand page.) The diagram on p. x–xi identifies the main features of a Study Unit.

Answers to questions in the Study Units are given in Part III.

Question Banks

A Question Bank containing past examination questions is provided after each of the Pure Mathematics, Mechanics and Statistics Study Unit sections. The answers are worked out in some detail and given immediately after each Question Bank.

When you feel that you have mastered a number of Study Units and have successfully answered the Exercise/Exam questions, you can practise the knowledge and skills you have gained by answering some questions from the relevant Question Bank.

Ways of using this book

The authors anticipate that students will use this course companion in three ways: as a study aid, as a workbook and as a revision aid.

If you use it as a study aid, you can use the Study Units to reinforce, or teach yourself, the essential features of each topic introduced in your course and the section on 'Study Skills' to improve your approach to study itself.

If you use it as a workbook, you can use the carefully graded types of questions, i.e. Illustrations, Worked Examples, Guided Examples and Exercises, in each Unit, and the Question Banks, to help you to improve understanding of each topic, check progress and develop problem-solving techniques.

If you use it as a revision aid, you can use the syllabus analysis and the Study Units as the basis of your revision programme and the sections on Revision Strategy and Examination Techniques to improve your approach to revision and examinations.

You may use this book in one or more of these ways or, alternatively, you may have your own ideas on how to integrate this book into your course of study.

> **MODULAR COURSES IN MATHEMATICS**
>
> Until recently most maths students took one or more external exams at the end of the course. To describe this 'traditional' structure we now use the word 'linear'.
>
> Students who follow a **linear course** usually study the whole of their syllabus before taking the external exam(s). They take all the exams at one session and the questions on the papers may cover any topic in the syllabus. If a student passes these exams he or she is awarded an appropriate pass grade; but failing them results in no qualification at all.
>
> Since autumn 1995 AS- and A-level maths candidates have also been able to opt for a **modular course** and/or scheme of assessment. The Exam Board divides the mathematics syllabus into several smaller parts (the modules). By combining modules in different ways the Board covers the specifications of the different syllabuses it offers (see Table II). So each student studies the modules that give the AS- or A-level award he or she wants.
>
> A student may study one or more modules at a time. After studying the topics in a module a student may take an exam based solely on that module.(Exam Boards offer papers on each of their modules at different times of the year, so a candidate may sit the papers for a module when he or she feels confident of success. If a student fails a module exam, he or she may resit the paper(s) at a later session.) The grade gained for each module is banked at the Exam Board. When enough credits have been obtained they may be 'cashed in' for the appropriate AS- or A-level award.

DIFFERENCES BETWEEN GCSE AND A/AS LEVEL

Mathematics is different

In many other subjects studied at this level, students find it disconcerting that it is possible to be asked almost the same question at GCSE and A level but that different answers are required. Obviously the difference must be in the standard expected and students often have difficulty in assessing the correct level for their work. Mathematics is different: this same question/different answer situation cannot arise in an A-level mathematics course.

Different context

In mathematics a few of the topics studied at GCSE will be reconsidered at A level to a greater level of understanding but, in general, you will be studying mostly new topics and a much wider syllabus. Most of the mathematics you studied at GCSE is 'Pure Mathematics' but the majority of students at A level follow a course which includes both 'Pure Mathematics' and 'Applied Mathematics'; the 'Applied Mathematics' is usually mechanics and/or statistics. It will be assumed that you are able to use the mathematical background and expertise developed during a GCSE course as a working part of mathematical knowledge. You will be expected to work hard on your own to acquire the new basic concepts to which you will be introduced and to develop a thorough understanding of the fundamental principles so that you can apply them in a variety of situations. Much more than for GCSE, you will need to be able to prove standard results underlying principles used. There is not always a single 'correct' method to solve a problem but you will learn to appreciate also that there is often an 'elegant' solution which may be preferred.

Different study skills

The major difficulty that most students experience is in adjusting to the transition from the more formal, probably highly structured pattern of most GCSE teaching to the more independent approach usually encountered at A level. For GCSE you probably relied on your teacher to organise your work and on your class notes, and perhaps a single textbook, to provide your information. At A level you will be expected to organise your own work to a much greater extent, to use a wider range of sources of information to supplement your course notes, to maintain the necessary self-discipline to work industriously throughout your course and to have the essential motivation and determination to succeed.

Motivation

It is important to appreciate that, at this level, you have deliberately chosen to follow this course and to be aware of your own reasons for doing so. You may have chosen to study A-level mathematics because mathematics is your 'best' subject, your most 'interesting' subject, needed for another course you wish to follow, a requirement for the job you want to do … but, whatever the reason for your choice, it must be strong enough to sustain your motivation to study. Good motivation is usually associated with an interest in a subject and you will find that you will be able to increase your own motivation if you can broaden your mathematical interests. One way to do this is to try to learn more about mathematics in general, about its history, its great scholars, its applications, its relationships with other subjects. You can do this by reading around the subject and looking out for 'mathematical' features in television and radio programmes, etc. Besides acquiring a more extensive knowledge of mathematical ideas and methods, your mathematical maturity will increase and you will begin to appreciate the beauty and immense power of mathematics. The abilities which you will acquire, enabling you to analyse information and organise structures, will be found useful in many aspects of life.

STUDY SKILLS

If you can develop good study skills your learning will be more efficient and more effective.

Your study plan

Whether you are studying at school, college, evening class or at home, you will have to spend a lot of time working on your own, possibly without much guidance. A personal study plan is essential if you are to make the best use of your time. It should be an extension of your school/college timetable, and should cover not only study periods but any other activities which feature regularly in your week. Try to spread your work sensibly throughout the week on each of the subjects you are studying. Use your study plan to meet deadlines for assignments set on your course(s).

To be most productive your study periods should be from one to three hours long with planned short breaks of 5–10 minutes duration every hour to help you to maintain concentration. These breaks will be most effective if you can do something different, such as leaving your work room, making a drink, etc., rather than just sitting at your desk. Each study period should be followed by a longer break for recreation and relaxation and these are as much a part of your study plan as the study periods.

When to study

When you study is a matter of personal preference and the time you have available. Some students are 'early birds', doing their best studying in the morning, some are 'late birds', studying best at night. You should find out, if you do not know already, when you do your 'best work' and, if it is possible, fit this into your study plan.

Where to study

You will find studying easier if you have a room, or part of a room, which you can identify as your own study place. Not only will this have a positive psychological effect on you, since you will associate the place with study and find it easier to settle down to work, but also on your family and friends, since they will associate it with your study and, hopefully, not disturb you unnecessarily. It is important that you find it comfortable and attractive: it should not be too warm but well ventilated and away from distractions. A desk or table, on which you can spread your books, is ideal for working on and the light should be good, the best form of lighting being a reading lamp. Keeping all your books, files, paper, calculator and other essential equipment readily available in this one place will save you a great deal of valuable time during your study periods.

Your study periods

Mathematics is a subject which you cannot study by simply reading: you need to 'do mathematics' to understand it. Private study periods will usually be spent either working on notes or on problems but to make them as productive as possible vary the topic and/or activity and set yourself definitive objectives. By starting each session with a brief review of the previous session on the same topic, you will find that it acts as a 'mental warming up' time and reinforces the previous session's study.

Making notes

As soon as possible after each lesson/lecture, you should write up your lesson/lecture notes whilst the topic is still fresh in your mind. The actual process of making notes will help you to understand the topic you are studying and encourage you to concentrate on what you are learning. Remember that your notes are for your use and will eventually form the basis of your revision plan, so the way you organise them must be concise and presented in a form which is best for you.

Every time you work through your lesson/lecture notes, your textbook(s) and this book, you should be jotting down notes and trying to work through the mathematics for yourself. Making card-index files, small notebooks or charts on themes such as key terms, formulae, etc., are excellent notemaking activities which you will find extremely useful during your revision time.

Understanding the topic you are studying is essential but if, after making reasonable efforts to do so, you still cannot understand something, do not worry about it: make a note of it and ask about it later. Do not allow worrying about one topic to ruin the rest of your work schedule for a study session.

Problem solving

Problem solving is one of the most important aspects of your mathematics course so you will need to spend a large part of your private study time tackling problems, either for homework assignments or on your own account to improve your understanding of a topic and your ability to answer questions.

It is a good idea, if possible, to attempt problems set for homework assignments more than a day before they are due to be handed in. This will give you the opportunity, if needed, to sort out any difficulties you may encounter, either by consulting this book, your textbook, your teacher or simply by giving yourself time to 'sleep on it'. Persevere with your problem solving: do not give in too easily, but on the other hand do not waste time on a problem that is not yielding to your strategy and on which you do not have any alternative strategies to try. Leaving a problem and coming back to it can often be fruitful, the break giving you new insight into its solution.

You will find that working through the notes provided in the appropriate Study Unit in this book will remind you of the basic principles, notation, formulae, units, etc. needed in your problem solving sessions. Working through the examples in each Study Unit, stage by stage, will help to develop your problem solving technique. As you work through each section of a Study Unit, cover the solution to each Illustration (marked ⅰ), try to answer the question yourself and then compare your working with that given. When you feel that you understand a topic, try to answer the Worked and Guided Examples, before referring to the given solution for guidance.

You can then try the questions in the Exercises and Exam questions, those marked with an * being easier. There is no need to restrict yourself to questions from your own Exam Board. Answers are given in Part III, p. 252.

Finally, after completing a number of Study Units, you could try some questions from the Question Bank. Detailed answers to these are given in the Question Bank Answers (following each Question Bank).

Learning

Mathematics is a very demanding discipline. To understand some of the basic ideas and concepts will involve you in some hard thinking and for the first time in your intellectual development you may be aware of consciously directing your critical powers to discover the nature of any misunderstandings which you may have.

There are a large number of identities, formulae and equations in mathematics and most probably your Examination Board will provide a book of formulae for you to use. There is no reason why many of these formulae should not be committed to memory. If you make an attempt to memorise new results when you first see them it is not such a daunting task as it may appear and the effort pays handsome dividends when you do not constantly have to refer to a formulae book when solving problems. However, if you are not confident in your memorising abilities, regular use of the formulae book will help you to get to know where in the book a formula appears so that you can check.

At A-level you may also be asked to prove results and standard bookwork: make sure that you understand the 'bookwork' and can produce these proofs when necessary.

REVISION STRATEGY

Revision should be an on-going process which starts very early in your course. The amount of knowledge to be accumulated and the variety of skills and techniques to be developed are large and they are best assimilated gradually and consolidated as you go along. Regular revision is really a part of the learning process but, of necessity, becomes more concentrated as the examination approaches.

Regular reviews

Research has shown that, although factual recall declines rapidly after the first session, the use of regular reviews keeps the level of recall much nearer to its original very high level. It is important, therefore, that the strategy of regular reviewing should be a continuous and integral aspect of a planned study programme. If you review each section of work one session, one week, one month, or three months after you have originally studied it, then you will have revised each topic at least four times before you reach your final intensive revision programme.

Final revision programme

At the start of your final revision programme (say 3 months before your actual examination) you must get organised and the best way to do this is to devise a revision timetable. The strategy involved is basically the same as that used throughout the study of your A-level course. Plan your time carefully, give yourself definite objectives for each session, revise actively, test yourself regularly, make notes, practise problem solving. Use revision sessions to study topics you have worked on before as revision is simply the process of reminding you of topics and techniques previously understood. You will appreciate how well-organised notes will help you during your revision. Write out important definitions, proofs, formulae and equations, checking them against your notes or this book. Rework previously solved problems without looking at your previous solution, then attempt questions that you have not looked at before. Make special revision notes for quick reference on cards to keep in your pocket and charts to hang on the wall of your study room. Practise your examination technique.

Examination practice

You should identify the sort of examination you are going to sit by looking up the details of your syllabus in Table II (p. xvi to xix). You should have identified your syllabus already using Table I. Analyse recent examination papers (booklets of past examination papers can be bought direct from your Board, address on p. xxix, or your teacher may have a stock of them). Work out how long you have for each question and become familiar with the style of questions.

During your ordinary study periods you will have attempted many questions but seldom given yourself strict time restrictions. In examinations the timing of your answers to questions is vitally important. Practise answering examination questions in mock examination conditions, allowing yourself only the normal available examination time and the equipment you are permitted to take into the examination room. To obtain 'mock examination' practice save one or two complete examination papers so that you can use them as final test papers 'against the clock'.

Examination nerves are common and understandable but will be lessened if you have followed a sensible course of study and revision. You may not do yourself justice if you have a poor examination technique. The hints on the next page should help you to tackle the examination with greater confidence.

EXAMINATION TECHNIQUE

Before the day

Before the actual day of your examination make sure you know:

- the date, day, time and place of each paper of your examination;
- how to get to your examination centre if it is not well known to you;
- your candidate number;
- your examination centre number;
- the telephone number of your examination centre.

Prepare any equipment you will need for your particular examination:

- pens which are comfortable to use and ink,
- sharp pencils, a pencil sharpener and rubber,
- drawing instruments such as a ruler, compasses, protractor, set squares,
- calculator (if allowed) and spare batteries (check that you know how to replace them quickly),
- an accurate watch or small clock.

On the day

Before the examination Check that you have all the equipment you will need before setting off for your examination centre with plenty of time to spare. If you are delayed, contact your examination centre (have the telephone number with you) to explain what has happened. Arrive at the examination room early; a late start to an examination cannot be a good start.

Just before the start Listen carefully to the invigilator. There may be some changes or special instructions which you were not expecting or some errors in the paper. Fill in any details such as candidate number and examination centre number when the invigilator instructs you to do so.

Reading the instructions When the invigilator says that you may begin, read the instructions on your examination paper very carefully. Make sure that it is the correct examination paper! Although you will be familiar with the style and format of past papers for your examination, these can change without notice. Note these in particular:

- the number of sections and questions you have to do;
- how much time you have to do them in;
- which questions (if any) are compulsory;
- what choice of questions (if any) do you have;
- how to present your answers.

Planning your time Quickly calculate the length of time you should spend on each question. You will have practised doing this for past papers but make sure that you use the instructions on your actual examination paper, not the ones you are expecting. Try to allow about 10 minutes at the end for checking your paper.

Choosing the questions Read through the whole examination paper carefully, checking that you have read every page. If you have a choice of questions:

- cross the ones you can't do;
- tick those you can definitely do;
- choose the correct number to do;
- mark the order in which you are going to attempt them, attempting your best question(s) first.

Try to answer full questions if you can but you can sometimes pass an examination by answering a lot of part questions. Indeed, questions are often structured—the first part being easier to answer than later parts. Some Examination Boards list the marks to be awarded for each question or part question. This information will help you to decide which questions or part questions to do.

Answering the questions Before you attempt to answer a question, read it all again carefully, jotting down points such as formulae and information relating to that question. These hints should help you when writing an answer.

1. Make sure that your writing is legible.
2. Draw a large clearly labelled diagram if appropriate.
3. Present your solution in a neat, logical and concise way.
4. Show all your working; many marks are given for working, not answers.
5. Solve the problem which has been set and not the one you think is being posed.
6. Do not do things you are not asked for; for example, do not do proofs unless specifically requested.
7. State any principles, results, formulae, etc. used and indicate your reasons for using them.
8. Check any formulae you use with the formula sheet, if provided.
9. Use and state the correct units, e.g. $m\ s^{-2}$, $N\ s$, etc.
10. Always do a rough estimate of any calculation to check that your answer is sensible.
11. When using a calculator, make sure that each calculation is shown clearly in your answer.
12. Give your final answer to the required degree of accuracy.
13. In questions saying 'hence or otherwise', try 'hence' first since it is usually easier and uses the suggestion given in the first part of the question.
14. If you get 'stuck', re-read the question carefully to check that you have not missed any important information or hints given in the question itself.
15. When you have completed your solution, re-read the question to check that you have answered all parts.

Examination discipline It is important that you try to keep to the times you have allocated to answering a question or section and that you answer the correct number of questions. If you answer less than the number required you are limiting the number of marks available to you.

In short-answer papers or sections, which are often compulsory, if you cannot see how to solve a problem fairly quickly, leave it and return to it later if you have time. A fresh look at a question often helps.

In longer-question papers or sections do not overrun your time allocation on any question by more than a minute or so. Do not be lured into thinking 'just a few more minutes and I'll have the answer'. In most examinations, the first parts to many questions are easier than the later parts so it is usually easier to gain more marks by attempting all the questions required than by completing a question.

Different Examination Boards have different policies regarding candidates who have answered too many questions. This can vary from year to year so check on your board's policy. If you answer too many questions and your board:

1. Marks all your questions and ignores your worst marks—hand in all your answers.
2. Ignores your last questions—cross out the questions you feel you have done badly, leaving only the correct number to be marked.

At the end Before handing in your examination paper check that:

- any 'front sheet' is completed according to the instructions;
- every loose page is clearly marked with your examination number, etc;
- every answer is numbered correctly;
- pages are numbered clearly and in order.

LAYOUT OF A STUDY UNIT

Look at the items ① – ⑭ in order, to find out the things you need to know about the organization of a Study Unit.

① Study Unit title

② Study Unit contents

③ Section heading

④ Section notes

⑤ Bold
— a keyword or phrase

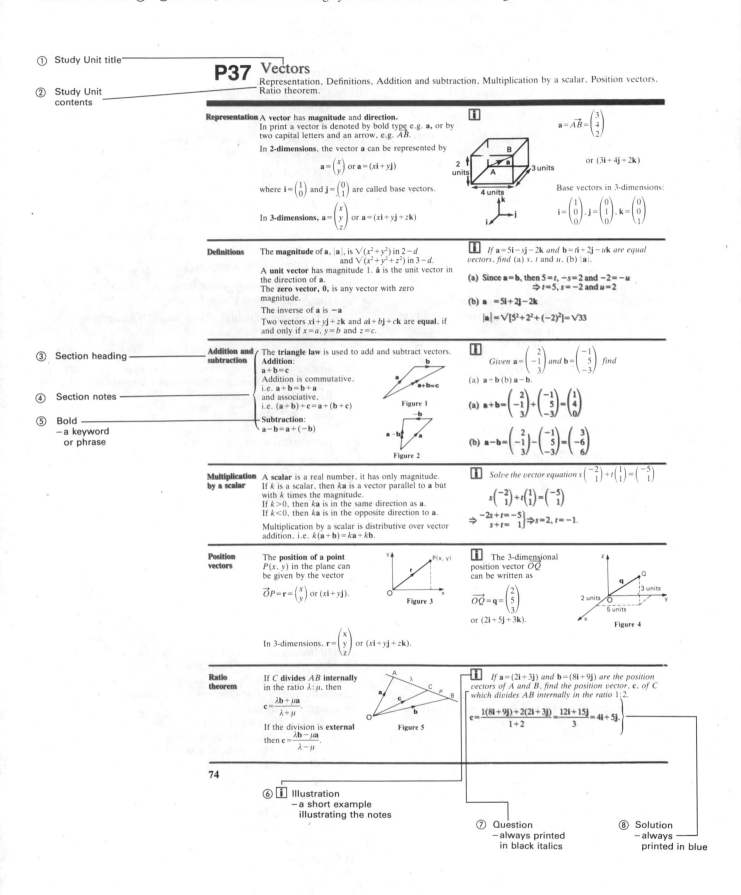

P37 Vectors

Representation, Definitions, Addition and subtraction. Multiplication by a scalar. Position vectors. Ratio theorem.

Representation A **vector** has **magnitude** and **direction**.
In print a vector is denoted by bold type e.g. **a**, or by two capital letters and an arrow, e.g. $\vec{AB}$.

In **2-dimensions**, the vector **a** can be represented by
$$\mathbf{a} = \begin{pmatrix} x \\ y \end{pmatrix} \text{ or } \mathbf{a} = (x\mathbf{i} + y\mathbf{j})$$
where $\mathbf{i} = \begin{pmatrix} 1 \\ 0 \end{pmatrix}$ and $\mathbf{j} = \begin{pmatrix} 0 \\ 1 \end{pmatrix}$ are called base vectors.

In **3-dimensions**, $\mathbf{a} = \begin{pmatrix} x \\ y \\ z \end{pmatrix}$ or $\mathbf{a} = (x\mathbf{i} + y\mathbf{j} + z\mathbf{k})$

$$\mathbf{a} = \vec{AB} = \begin{pmatrix} 3 \\ 4 \\ 2 \end{pmatrix}$$
or $(3\mathbf{i} + 4\mathbf{j} + 2\mathbf{k})$

Base vectors in 3-dimensions:
$\mathbf{i} = \begin{pmatrix} 1 \\ 0 \\ 0 \end{pmatrix}$. $\mathbf{j} = \begin{pmatrix} 0 \\ 1 \\ 0 \end{pmatrix}$. $\mathbf{k} = \begin{pmatrix} 0 \\ 0 \\ 1 \end{pmatrix}$

Definitions The **magnitude** of **a**, |**a**|, is $\sqrt{(x^2+y^2)}$ in $2-d$ and $\sqrt{(x^2+y^2+z^2)}$ in $3-d$.
A **unit vector** has magnitude 1. $\hat{\mathbf{a}}$ is the unit vector in the direction of **a**.
The **zero vector, 0,** is any vector with zero magnitude.
The inverse of **a** is $-\mathbf{a}$
Two vectors $x\mathbf{i} + y\mathbf{j} + z\mathbf{k}$ and $a\mathbf{i} + b\mathbf{j} + c\mathbf{k}$ are **equal**, if and only if $x = a$, $y = b$ and $z = c$.

ⅰ *If $\mathbf{a} = 5\mathbf{i} - s\mathbf{j} - 2\mathbf{k}$ and $\mathbf{b} = t\mathbf{i} + 2\mathbf{j} - u\mathbf{k}$ are equal vectors, find (a) s. t and u. (b) |a|.*

(a) Since $\mathbf{a} = \mathbf{b}$, then $5 = t$, $-s = 2$ and $-2 = -u$
$\Rightarrow t = 5$, $s = -2$ and $u = 2$

(b) $\mathbf{a} = 5\mathbf{i} + 2\mathbf{j} - 2\mathbf{k}$
$|\mathbf{a}| = \sqrt{[5^2 + 2^2 + (-2)^2]} = \sqrt{33}$

Addition and subtraction The **triangle law** is used to add and subtract vectors.
Addition:
$\mathbf{a} + \mathbf{b} = \mathbf{c}$
Addition is commutative.
i.e. $\mathbf{a} + \mathbf{b} = \mathbf{b} + \mathbf{a}$
and associative.
i.e. $(\mathbf{a} + \mathbf{b}) + \mathbf{c} = \mathbf{a} + (\mathbf{b} + \mathbf{c})$
Subtraction:
$\mathbf{a} - \mathbf{b} = \mathbf{a} + (-\mathbf{b})$

Figure 1

Figure 2

ⅰ *Given $\mathbf{a} = \begin{pmatrix} 2 \\ -1 \\ 3 \end{pmatrix}$ and $\mathbf{b} = \begin{pmatrix} -1 \\ 5 \\ -3 \end{pmatrix}$ find*
(a) $\mathbf{a} + \mathbf{b}$ (b) $\mathbf{a} - \mathbf{b}$.

(a) $\mathbf{a} + \mathbf{b} = \begin{pmatrix} 2 \\ -1 \\ 3 \end{pmatrix} + \begin{pmatrix} -1 \\ 5 \\ -3 \end{pmatrix} = \begin{pmatrix} 1 \\ 4 \\ 0 \end{pmatrix}$

(b) $\mathbf{a} - \mathbf{b} = \begin{pmatrix} 2 \\ -1 \\ 3 \end{pmatrix} - \begin{pmatrix} -1 \\ 5 \\ -3 \end{pmatrix} = \begin{pmatrix} 3 \\ -6 \\ 6 \end{pmatrix}$

Multiplication by a scalar A **scalar** is a real number. it has only magnitude.
If k is a scalar, then $k\mathbf{a}$ is a vector parallel to a but with k times the magnitude.
If $k > 0$, then $k\mathbf{a}$ is in the same direction as a.
If $k < 0$, then $k\mathbf{a}$ is in the opposite direction to a.
Multiplication by a scalar is distributive over vector addition. i.e. $k(\mathbf{a} + \mathbf{b}) = k\mathbf{a} + k\mathbf{b}$.

ⅰ *Solve the vector equation $s\begin{pmatrix} -2 \\ 1 \end{pmatrix} + t\begin{pmatrix} 1 \\ 1 \end{pmatrix} = \begin{pmatrix} -5 \\ 1 \end{pmatrix}$*
$s\begin{pmatrix} -2 \\ 1 \end{pmatrix} + t\begin{pmatrix} 1 \\ 1 \end{pmatrix} = \begin{pmatrix} -5 \\ 1 \end{pmatrix}$
$\Rightarrow \begin{matrix} -2s + t = -5 \\ s + t = 1 \end{matrix} \Rightarrow s = 2, t = -1$.

Position vectors The **position of a point** $P(x, y)$ in the plane can be given by the vector
$\vec{OP} = \mathbf{r} = \begin{pmatrix} x \\ y \end{pmatrix}$ or $(x\mathbf{i} + y\mathbf{j})$.

Figure 3

In 3-dimensions, $\mathbf{r} = \begin{pmatrix} x \\ y \\ z \end{pmatrix}$ or $(x\mathbf{i} + y\mathbf{j} + z\mathbf{k})$.

ⅰ The 3-dimensional position vector $\vec{OQ}$ can be written as
$\vec{OQ} = \mathbf{q} = \begin{pmatrix} 2 \\ 5 \\ 3 \end{pmatrix}$
or $(2\mathbf{i} + 5\mathbf{j} + 3\mathbf{k})$.

Figure 4

Ratio theorem If C divides AB **internally** in the ratio $\lambda : \mu$, then
$$\mathbf{c} = \frac{\lambda \mathbf{b} + \mu \mathbf{a}}{\lambda + \mu}.$$
If the division is **external** then $\mathbf{c} = \frac{\lambda \mathbf{b} - \mu \mathbf{a}}{\lambda - \mu}$.

Figure 5

ⅰ *If $\mathbf{a} = (2\mathbf{i} + 3\mathbf{j})$ and $\mathbf{b} = (8\mathbf{i} + 9\mathbf{j})$ are the position vectors of A and B, find the position vector. c. of C which divides AB internally in the ratio 1:2.*
$$\mathbf{c} = \frac{1(8\mathbf{i} + 9\mathbf{j}) + 2(2\mathbf{i} + 3\mathbf{j})}{1 + 2} = \frac{12\mathbf{i} + 15\mathbf{j}}{3} = 4\mathbf{i} + 5\mathbf{j}.$$

74

⑥ **ⅰ** Illustration
— a short example illustrating the notes

⑦ Question
— always printed in black italics

⑧ Solution
— always printed in blue

x

⑨ **WE** Worked example
– shows you how to
solve the question
and how to set out
your working

⑪ **EX** Exercise – questions and
past examination questions
for you to practice answering
(answers in Part III, p. 252)

Vectors

Worked example, Guided example and Exam questions

WE *In the diagram, ST = 2TQ, $\vec{PQ} = a$, $\vec{SR} = 2a$ and $\vec{SP} = b$.*

(a) *Find in terms of a and b:*

(i) $\vec{SQ}$

(ii) $\vec{TQ}$

(iii) $\vec{RQ}$

(iv) $\vec{PT}$

(v) $\vec{TR}$

(b) *What do your answers to (iv) and (v) tell you about the
the points P, T, R?*

(a) (i) $\vec{SQ} = \vec{SP} + \vec{PQ} = b + a$ (or $a+b$ by commutativity)

(ii) $\vec{TQ} = \frac{1}{3}\vec{SQ} = \frac{1}{3}(a+b)$

(iii) $\vec{RQ} = \vec{RS} + \vec{SQ} = -2a + (a+b)$
$= b - a$

(iv) $\vec{PT} = \vec{PS} + \vec{ST}$

$= -b + \frac{2}{3}\vec{SQ}$ (since $\vec{ST} = \frac{2}{3}\vec{SQ}$, i.e. $\vec{ST} = 2\vec{TQ}$)

$= -b + \frac{2}{3}(a+b) = \frac{2}{3}a - \frac{1}{3}b$

$= \frac{1}{3}(2a-b)$

(v) $\vec{TR} = \vec{TS} + \vec{SR}$

$= -\frac{2}{3}(a+b) + 2a$

$= \frac{4}{3}a - \frac{2}{3}b = \frac{2}{3}(2a-b)$.

(b) Since $\vec{PT} = \frac{1}{3}(2a-b)$ and $\vec{TR} = \frac{2}{3}(2a-b)$, $\vec{PT}$ and $\vec{TR}$
are both multiples of the same vector $(2a-b)$. Hence PT and
TR are parallel and T is common to both lines, so, P, T, R lie
on the same line, i.e. they are co-linear.

GE (a) $\vec{OS}$ and $\vec{OT}$ represent the vectors $\lambda i + \mu j$ and $\mu i + \lambda j$ where λ
and μ are scalars and i and j are unit vectors in two mutually
perpendicular directions Ox and Oy. Show that $|\vec{OS}| = |\vec{OT}|$.
Given that OS and OT are two adjacent sides of a rhombus
OSUT, find the vectors represented by the diagonals OU and
ST.

(b) $\vec{PQ}$ and $\vec{PR}$ are represented by the sides PQ and PR of the
triangle PQR, Show that

$$\vec{PQ} + \vec{PR} = 2\vec{PS}$$

where S is the midpoint of QR.
Hence, or otherwise, find the position of the point O within the
triangle PQR such that

$$\vec{OP} + \vec{OQ} + \vec{OR} = 0$$

(a) Use the definition of the magnitude of a vector to show
that OS = OT.
Sketch the rhombus OSUT. Use, $\vec{OU} = \vec{OS} + \vec{SU}$ and
$\vec{ST} = \vec{SO} + \vec{OT}$ to find the required vectors.

(b) Use the ratio theorem to express $\vec{PS}$ in terms of $\vec{PQ}$ and
$\vec{PR}$. Hence, required result.
Consider a point O on RT (where T is the midpoint of PQ).
Write down $\vec{OP} + \vec{OQ}$ using the result just established. Hence
show that

$$\vec{OP} + \vec{OQ} + \vec{OR} = 0,$$

where O is the point which divides RT in a certain ratio. State
what this point O is called.

EX 1 The vector **p** has magnitude 7 units and bearing 052°, and
the vector **q** has magnitude 12 units and bearing 163°. Draw
a diagram (which need not be to scale) showing **p**, **q** and the
resultant **p + q**. Calculate, correct to one decimal place, the
magnitude of **p + q**.
(L)

2 From an origin O the points A, B, C have position vectors
a, **b**, 2**b** respectively. The points O, A, B are not collinear.
The midpoint of AB is M, and the point of trisection of AC
nearer to A is T. Draw a diagram to show O, A, B, C, M, T.
Find, in terms **a** and **b**, the position vectors of M and T. Use
your results to prove that O, M, T are collinear, and find
the ratio in which M divides OT.
*(L)

3 Given that **OA = a, OB = b, OP = $\frac{1}{3}$OA** and that Q is the
midpoint of AB, express **AB** and **PQ** in terms of **a** and **b**. PQ
is produced to meet OB produced at R, so that **QR** = nPQ
and **BR** = kb. Express **QR**: (i) in terms of n, **a** and **b**;
(ii) in terms of k, **a** and **b**. Hence find the value of n and of k.
*(C)

4 The position vectors of three points A, B and C relative to
an origin O are **p**, 3**q** − **p**, and 9**q** − 5**p** respectively. Show
that the points A, B and C lie on the same straight line, and
state the ratio AB:BC. Given that OBCD is a
parallelogram and that E is the point such that **DB** = $\frac{1}{3}$**DE**,
find the position vectors of D and E relative to O.
*(C)

5 The points A, B and C have position vectors **a**, **b** and **c**
respectively, referred to an origin O.
(a) Given that the point X lies on AB produced so that
$AB:BX = 2:1$, find **x**, the position vector of X, in terms of
a and **b**.
(b) If Y lies on BC, between B and C so that $BY:YC = 1:3$,
find **y**, the position vector of Y, in terms of **b** and **c**.
(c) Given that Z is the mid-point of AC, show that X, Y
and Z are collinear.
(d) Calculate $XY:YZ$.
(L)

6 O, A and B are three non-collinear points; the position
vectors of A and B with respect to O are **a** and **b**
respectively. M is the mid-point of OB, T is the point of
trisection of AB nearer B, AMTX is a parallelogram and
OX cuts AB at Y. Find, in terms of **a** and **b**, the position
vectors of:
(a) M; (b) T; (c) X; (d) Y.
(O & C)

7 The vertices A, B and C of a triangle have position vectors
a, **b** and **c** respectively relative to an origin O. The point P is
on BC such that $BP:PC = 3:1$; the point Q is on CA such
that $CQ:QA = 2:3$; the point R is on BA produced such
that $BR:AR = 2:1$. The position vectors of P, Q and R are
p, **q** and **r** respectively. Show that **q** can be expressed in
terms of **p** and **r** and hence or otherwise show that P, Q and
R are collinear. State the ratio of the lengths of the line
segments PQ and QR.
(J)

8 The points P and Q have position vectors **p** and **q**
respectively relative to an origin O, which does not lie on
PQ. Three points R, S, T have respective position vectors
$r = \frac{1}{2}p + \frac{3}{4}q$, $s = 2p − q$, $t = p + 3q$. Show in one diagram
the positions of O, P, Q, R, S and T.
(J)

⑫ * indicates an
easier question

⑬ No asterisk
– A-level
question

⑭ (L) – board which
set the question

75

⑩ **GE** Guided example – suggests a method
for solving the question (the answer(s)
are given in Part III, p. 250)

xi

Table Ia Analysis of Examination Syllabuses: Pure Mathematics

Board	AEB 0880		CAMB 8472 linear	CAMB 9200 linear	CAMB 8521 mod.	CAMB 8522 9501/2 mod.	CAMB 9501/2 mod.	ULEAC		NEAB			3136 SMP 16-19	4136 SMP 16-19	OXF 9850	OXF 9850	OXF 9850	OXF 8770 Nuffield	OXF 9870 Nuffield	O&C MEI	O&C MEI	O&C	O&C MEI	O&C	O&C
Level	AS	AS/A	AS	A	AS	AS/A	A	AS/A	A	AS/A	A	A	AS	A	AS	A	A	AS	A	AS/A	A	A	AS/A	A	A
Paper number		P1	P1/2	P1-4	P1/2	P1-3	P4	P1	P2	P1	P2/3	P4			P1/2	P1-4	P1	P1/2	P1-3	P1, 4	P2	P3	P1/2	P3	P4/5
Notes								1		1									*		1	2		2	*
P1 C Rational and irrational numbers	•	•	•	•	•	•		•							•	•				•					
P2 C Errors and accuracy	•	•	•	•	•	•		•		•				•	•	•		•	•	•				•	
P3 C Solving simple linear equations	•	•	•	•	•	•		•		•				•	•	•		•	•	•				•	
P4 C Quadratics	•	•	•	•	•	•		•		•				•	•	•			•	aa		•		•	
P5 C Solving equations	•	•	•	•	•	•		•		•				•	•	•		•	•	•				•	
P6 C Inequations	•	•	•	•	•	•		•		•	•	•	•	•	•	•	•	•	•	•				•	
P7 C Polynomials	•	•	•	•	•	•		j	•	j				•	•	•		•	•	•				•	
P8 C Indices and logarithms	•	•	•	•	•	•		•		•	•	•	•	•	•	•		•	•	•				•	
P9 C Exponential growth and decay		•	•	•	•	•		•						•	•	•		•	•	•				•	
P10 C Coordinates and graphs	•	•	•	•	•	•		•		•				•	•	•		•	•	•	•			•	
P11 C Functions	•	•	•	•	•	•		•		•				•	•	•		•	•	•				•	
P12 C Simple curves	•	•	•	•	•	•		•		•		•		•	•	•		•	•	•	•			•	
P13 C Trigonometrical functions	•	•	•	•	•	•		•		•				•	•	•		•	•	•				•	
P14 C Plane triangles	•	•		•	•	•		l	•		•		•	l	•		•	•	•	l				•	
P15 C 3D figures	q		q	q	q	q			d	q				d	q				gg	•	q			d	
P16 C Trigonometrical identities	•	•		•		•				•					•	•		•	•	•	•	•	•		
P17 C Sequences	•	•	•	•	•	•		•		•					•	•		•	•	•				•	
P18 C Series	•	•	•	•	•	•		•		•					•	•		•	•	•				•	P4
P19 C Binomial theorem		•		•		•		•							•	•		•	•	•				•	
P20 C Differentiation	•	•	•	•	•	•		m	•	•			m	•	•	•		m	•	•				•	
P21 C Further differentiation	a	•	•	•	•	•		n	•	n		•	•	n	a	•		n	•	n	•	•	dd	•	P5
P22 C Special points	•	•	c	c	c	c		c	•		•		c	•	•	•		•	•	•				•	
P23 C Integration	•	•	•	•	•	•		•		•	•	•	•	•	•	•		•	•	•				•	•
P24 C Methods of integration I		•	g	•	g	•		•		•	•			•		•			•	•			g	•	
P25 Numerical solution of equations	•	•	•	•	•	•	•	p		•	•		v	•	p	•		p	•	•				•	
P26 Polynomials and fractions		•		•			•		•	t	t							•				•		•	P5
P27 Rational functions		•		•			•		•	•	•							•				•		•	P5
P28 More about series																		•	z						P42
P29 Permutations and combinations		†		†		†		†	•	†				†	†				†	†		†		†	†
P30 Binomial series			•		•					•								•				•			
P31 Exponential and logarithmic series		•		e		e								e	x				e	~	cc				
P32 The straight line	k	k	k	k	k	k		k	•	k		k	k		k	q		k		k		k		k	
P33 The circle		•	•	•	•	•				k				w	w									k	
P34 Experimental laws			•	•	•	•		•		•	•														
P35 Sketching unknown curves						•				•	•	•	•	•										•	P4
P36 More trigonometry			•		•			r									y			•	•			•	
P37 Vectors			•		•					•				•	•				•	•	•	•		•	
P38 Vectors and geometry			•		•					•				•	•				•	bb	•	•		•	
P39 Matrices															•										P4
P40 Complex numbers						•									•							•			P4
P41 Complex numbers and graphs						•									•							•			P4
P42 Methods of differentiation	b	•	h		b			h		•		b		•	•							•			P5
P43 Applications of differentiation	•	•	•	•	•	•				•		•			•	•		•	•	•					
P44 Methods of integration II			•		•		•			•		u				•								u	P5
P45 Applications of integration			f	•	f	•		s		s	s			s	•	•		s	s	•		s			
P46 Differential equations		•	•	•		•		•		•	•				•	•		•	•	•	•		•		
P47 Numerical integration			i			•		i			i	i			•						•		i		

Board			NICCEA	WJEC						SEB
			A1/A2			modular	modular	modular	modular	
Level			A	AS/A	A	AS/A	AS/A	A	A	H
Paper			P1/2	P1	P4	P1	P2	P3	P4	P1/2
Notes			#	*				*	*	
P1	C	Rational and irrational numbers	•							
P2	C	Errors and accuracy	•	•		•				
P3	C	Solving simple linear equations	•	•		•		•		
P4	C	Quadratics	•	•	•	•				•
P5	C	Solving equations	•	•		•				
P6	C	Inequations	•	•		•				
P7	C	Polynomials	•	•		j	•			•
P8	C	Indices and logarithms	•	•		jj	•			•
P9	C	Exponential growth and decay		•		•				
P10	C	Coordinates and graphs	•	•		ii	•			•
P11	C	Functions	•	•	•	•		•		•
P12	C	Simple curves	•	•		•		•		•
P13	C	Trigonometrical functions	•	•		•				
P14	C	Plane triangles	•	•			•			•
P15	C	3D figures	•	q		d				•
P16	C	Trigonometrical identities	•	•			•			•
P17	C	Sequences	•	•		•				•
P18	C	Series	•	•		•				
P19	C	Binomial theorem	•	•		•				
P20	C	Differentiation	•	•		•	•			•
P21	C	Further differentiation	a	•			n	•		a
P22	C	Special points	•	•			•	•		•
P23	C	Integration	•	•			•			•
P24	C	Methods of integration I	•	•			•			hh
P25		Numerical solution of equations	P2	•	•	kk	v		•	
P26		Polynomials and fractions	•	u		o	•			ee
P27		Rational functions	•	•			•			
P28		More about series	P2			•			•	
P29		Permutations and combinations	†	†	†	†		†		
P30		Binomial series	•			•		•		
P31		Exponential and logarithmic series								
P32		The straight line		k			•			•
P33		The circle		k				•		•
P34		Experimental laws								•
P35		Sketching unknown curves								•
P36		More trigonometry	•			•			•	y
P37		Vectors	•							•
P38		Vectors and geometry	•							•
P39		Matrices	P2			•		•		
P40		Complex numbers	•			•		•		
P41		Complex numbers and graphs	•			•		•		
P42		Methods of differentiation	h	h	•		h	•		
P43		Applications of differentiation	•			•		•		•
P44		Methods of integration II	u	u	•		u		•	
P45		Applications of integration	s						•	ff
P46		Differential equations	•	•			•			
P47		Numerical integration	•	•						

Notes

C	core topic
mod.	modular
a	excluding inverse functions
b	parametric only
c	excluding points of inflexion
d	excluding planes
e	Maclaurin's series required
f	areas only
g	excluding by parts
h	excluding logarithmic
i	excluding Simpson's rule
j	factor theorem not required
k	equations only
l	excluding sine & cosine rules onwards
m	chain rule not required
n	increasing/decreasing, rates of change only
o	operations only
p	excluding iterative methods
q	3D coordinates only
r	half angle formulae only
s	excluding mean value
t	excluding remainder theorem
u	partial fractions only
v	excluding Newton-Raphson
w	spheres also required
x	Maclaurin & Taylor series required
y	$a\cos\theta + b\sin\theta$ & identities only
z	induction only
aa	quadratic functions only
bb	equation of line only
cc	Taylor series required
dd	excluding trigonometrical functions
ee	remainder theorem only
ff	area between two curves only
gg	3D problems only
hh	excluding by substitution & by parts
ii	excluding parametric equations
jj	excluding logarathims
kk	changes in sign of $f(x)$ only
*	additional material required – outside scope of this book
1	assumes **P1** has been covered
2	assumes **P1** & **P2** have been covered
#	additional content required for **P2** – outside scope of this book
†	parts of this unit may be taught with binomial theorem (**P19**) and/or binomial series (**P30**)

Table Ib Analysis of Examination Syllabuses: Mechanics

Board	AEB	CAMBRIDGE	ULEAC	NEAB	OXFORD	O & C	NICCEA	WJEC

	AEB	CAMBRIDGE					ULEAC		NEAB						OXFORD				O & C					NICCEA		WJEC	
Code	0880	8472 linear	9200 linear	9200 linear	mod.	mod.	mod.			1 SMP 16-19	2 SMP 16-19	3 SMP 16-19	4&5 SMP 16-19	9850/2	9870/41 Nuffield	9870/48 Nuffield			MEI	MEI	MEI		B1	B2			
Level	AS AS/A	AS	A	A	AS AS/A	A	A	AS/A A	AS/A	AS/A A	AS/A AS/A	A	A	A	AS AS/A	A		A A	AS/A A	A	A	A A	A	A	AS/A AS/A AS/A AS/A	mod. mod.
Paper number	op P3	P3	P2	P3	M1 M2	M2	M3	M1 M2	P1						M1 M2		P1,4 P2	P3	M1 M2		M3	P2 P4	P3	P4	P2 P5 M1 M2	
Notes	* *	*			#							#					†*					†*				*

M1 Force diagrams																									
M2 1-D kinematics																									
M3 Graphs in kinematics																									
M4 Relative motion																									
M5 1-D particle dynamics																									
M6 Connected particles																									
M7 Work and energy																									
M8 Power																									
M9 Impulse and momentum																									
M10 Impact																									
M22 Projectiles																									
M12 Motion in a horizontal circle																									
M13 Motion in a vertical circle																									
M14 Variable forces																									
M15 Simple harmonic motion																									
M16 Vectors in dynamics																									
M17 Coplanar concurrent forces																									
M18 Moments and couples																									
M19 Equilibrium																									
M20 Three force problems																									
M21 Friction																									
M22 Bodies in contact																									
M23 Equivalent systems of forces																									
M24 Centre of mass																									
M25 Suspending and toppling																									

* requires **P37** Vectors, **P46** Differential equations
mod. modular
op option
a excluding impulse
b simple pendulum only
c excluding Hooke's Law

d plane figures & laminas only
e direct impact only
f first section only
† requires second order linear differential equations
# requires additional material outside scope of this book

1 Newton's Laws of Motion
2 Modelling with Force and Motion
3 Modelling with Circular Motion
4 Modelling with Differential Equations
5 Modelling with Rigid Bodies

Table Ic Analysis of Examination Syllabuses: Statistics

	Pictorial representation
S1 C	Pictorial representation
S2 C	Frequency distributions
S3 C	Mode & means
S4 C	Median & quantiles
S5 C	Measures of dispersion
S6 C	Comparing frequency distributions
S7 C	Probability
S8	Index numbers & moving averages
S9	Discrete probability distributions
S10	Continuous probability distributions
S11	The Binomial distribution
S12	The Poisson distribution
S13	The Normal distribution
S14	Uses of the Normal distribution
S15	Sampling I
S16	Sampling II
S17	Estimation
S18	Hypothesis testing
S19	The Student t-distribution
S20	Linear regression
S21	Correlation
S22	κ^2
S23	Contingency tables
S24	Special graph papers

Boards (columns): AEB, CAMBRIDGE, ULEAC, NEAB, OXFORD, O & C, NICCEA, WJEC

Legend:

* some of content of S4 beyond the scope of this book
C core
mod. modular
op option
a expectation (mean) & variance only
b bivariate distributions section only
c excluding Fisher's transformation
d Yates' correction not required
e in context of binomial distribution only
g excluding approximations
1 Living with uncertainty (AS option, A compulsory)
2 The Normal Distribution
3 Probability models for data
4 Statistics in action
some content of some other SMP16-19 options also covered by this book
† requires P29 Permutations & Combinations

Table II Analysis of the methods of examination

Board	Syllabus	Level	No. of papers/duration		Style	% marks
AEB MODULAR						
	0880 Mathematics without coursework	AS	1	$2\frac{1}{2}$ hr	*Pure mathematics and applications* Short questions, structured questions and problem solving questions Section A, attempt all questions Section B, attempt all questions from one area of applications of mathematics	100%
	0881 Pure Mathematics without coursework	AS	1	$2\frac{1}{2}$ hr	*Paper 1 Pure Mathematics* Short questions, structured questions and problem solving questions. Attempt all questions	100%
	0882W Mechanics without coursework	AS	1	$2\frac{1}{2}$ hr	*Paper 3 Mechanics* Short questions, structured questions and problem solving questions. Attempt all questions	100%
	0884W Statistics without coursework	AS	1	$2\frac{1}{2}$ hr	*Paper 2 Statistics* Short questions, structured questions and problem solving questions. Attempt all questions	100%
	0882C Mechanics with coursework	AS	1	2hr Cswk	*Paper 3 Mechanics* (as above) Coursework, in-depth study, project or portfolio	80% 20%
	0884C Statistics with coursework	AS	1	2hr Cswk	*Paper 2 Statistics* (as above) Coursework, in-depth study, project or portfolio	80% 20%
AEB MODULAR						
	0680 WS Mathematics without coursework	A	2	$2\frac{1}{2}$ hr $2\frac{1}{2}$ hr	*Paper 1 Pure mathematics* Short questions, structured questions and problem solving questions. Attempt all questions *Paper 2 Statistics* Short questions, structured questions and problem solving questions. Attempt all questions	50% 50%
	0680 WM Mathematics without coursework	A	2	$2\frac{1}{2}$ hr $2\frac{1}{2}$ hr	*Paper 1 Pure mathematics* (as above) *Paper 3 Mechanics* Short questions, structured questions and problem solving questions. Attempt all questions	50% 50%
	0680 WD Mathematics without coursework	A	2	$2\frac{1}{2}$ hr $2\frac{1}{2}$ hr	*Paper 1 Pure mathematics* (as above) *Paper 4 Discrete Mathematics* (not included in this book) Short questions, structured questions and problem solving questions. Attempt all questions	50% 50%
	0680 CS Mathematics with coursework	A	2	2hr 2hr Cswk	*Paper 1 Pure mathematics* (as above) *Paper 2 Statistics* (as above) Coursework, in-depth study, project or portfolio	50% 40% 10%
	0680 CM Mathematics with coursework	A	2	2hr 2hr Cswk	*Paper 1 Pure mathematics* (as above) *Paper 3 Mechanics* (as above) Coursework, in-depth study, project or portfolio	50% 40% 10%
	0680 CD Mathematics with coursework	A	2	2hr 2hr Cswk	*Paper 1 Pure mathematics* (as above) *Paper 4 Discrete mathematics* (not included in this book); (as above) Coursework, in-depth study, project or portfolio	50% 40% 10%
CAMBRIDGE LINEAR						
	8472 Mathematics	AS	3	$1\frac{1}{2}$ hr ea.	All candidates take *Paper 1* and *Paper 2 (Pure mathematics)*, and EITHER *Paper 3 (Mechanics)* OR *Paper 4 (Statistics)* All papers contain questions of various lengths with no restriction on the number of questions which may be attempted	33.3% ea.
	9200	A	2	3hr ea.	*Paper 1 Pure mathematics* and ONE of *Paper 2 Pure mathematics, mechanics and statistics* *Paper 3 Pure mathematics and mechanics* *Paper 4 Pure mathematics and statistics* All papers contain questions of various lengths with no restriction on the number of questions which may be attempted.	50% 50% for ONE
CAMBRIDGE MODULAR						
	8521 Mathematics	AS	3	$1\frac{1}{2}$ hr ea.	All candidates take *Paper 1* and *Paper 2 (Pure mathematics)* and EITHER *M1 (Mechanics)* OR *S1 (Statistics)* All papers contain questions of various lengths with no restriction on the number of questions which may be attempted and are taken in Autumn, Spring and Summer sessions	33.3% ea.
	8522 Pure Mathematics	AS	3	$1\frac{1}{2}$ hr ea.	All candidates take *Paper 1, Paper 2* and *Paper 3 (Pure mathematics)* All papers contain questions of various lengths with no restriction on the number of questions which may be attempted and are taken in Autumn, Spring and Summer sessions	33.3% ea.
	9501 Mathematics	A	6	$1\frac{1}{2}$ hr ea.	All candidates take *Paper 1, Paper 2* and *Paper 3 (Pure mathematics)* and THREE from *Paper 4 (Pure mathematics), M1–M3 (Mechanics), S1–S4 (Statistics)* and *C1* subject to dependency rules	16.7% ea.
					C1 to consist of single project or portfolio All papers contain questions of various lengths with no restriction on the number of questions which may be attempted and are taken in Autumn, Spring and Summer sessions	
	(see next page)					

Table II Analysis of the methods of examination

Board	Syllabus	Level	No. of papers/duration		Style	% marks
CAMB. MOD *cont*	9502 Pure Mathematics	A	6	$1\frac{1}{2}$ hr ea.	All candidates take *Paper 1 – Paper 6** inclusive All papers contain questions of various lengths with no restriction on the number of questions which may be attempted and are taken in Autumn, Spring and Summer sessions * content of *Paper 5 & Paper 6* not included in this book	16.7% ea.
ULEAC	Modular Mathematics			$1\frac{1}{2}$ hr	An A level or AS level may be gained by taking either FOUR or TWO respectively of the modules *P1, P2, M1, M2, T1, T2, D1** in an allowed combination. All papers contain about nine questions with varying mark allocations per question which are stated on the paper. All questions may be attempted A level 9371 *P1 P2 M1 M2* 9384 *P1 P2 M1 T1* 9385 *P1 P2 T1 T2* 9389 *P1 P2 T1 D1** 9393 *P1 P2 M1 D1** AS level 8406 *P1 M1* 8407 *P1 T1* 8397 *P1 D1** Notes *T2* consists of a $1\frac{1}{2}$ hr paper (80%) of about eight questions, plus a project (20%) of 20 hr approx * *D1* not included in this book	
NEAB	3631 Mathematics (Methods and Applied)	AS	1	3hr	*Paper 1 Mathematics (methods and applied)* Short questions and longer structured questions with no restriction on the number of questions which may be attempted	100%
	4631 Mathematics (Methods and Applied)	A	2	3hr 3hr	*Paper 1 Mathematics (methods and applied)* (as above) *Paper 2 Mathematics (methods and applied)* Short questions and longer structured questions with no restriction on the number of questions which may be attempted	50% 50%
	4633 Mathematics (Methods and Mechanics)	A	2	3hr 3hr	*Paper 1 Mathematics (methods and applied)* (as above) *Paper 3 Mechanics* Short questions and longer structured questions with no restriction on the number of questions which may be attempted	50% 50%
	4634 Mathematics (Methods and Statistics)	A	2	3hr 3hr	*Paper 1 Mathematics (methods and applied)* (as above) *Paper 4 Statistics* Short questions and longer structured questions with no restriction on the number of questions which may be attempted	50% 50%
NEAB	3136 Mathematics (SMP16 – 19)	AS	1 2 unit tests	2hr 1hr ea.* Cswk	*Mathematics (Foundations, Introductory Calculus, Functions)* Short questions and longer structured questions with no restriction on the number of questions which may be attempted Unit tests divided into subsections – all questions to be attempted * Problem solving $1\frac{1}{2}$ hr Any comprehension material available at least 48 hours before test 6–8hr each. Half coursework assignments required for each optional unit	60% 24% 16%
	4136 Mathematics (SMP16 – 19)	A	1 5 unit tests	3hr 1hr ea.* Cswk	*Mathematics (Foundations, Introductory Calculus, Functions, Mathematical Methods, Calculus Methods)* Short questions and longer structured questions with no restriction on the number of questions which may be attempted. Unit tests divided into subsections – all questions to be attempted Any comprehension material available at least 48 hours before test * Problem solving $1\frac{1}{2}$ hr 6-8hr each. Half coursework assignments required for each optional unit	50% 30% 20%
OXFORD	9850 Mathematics	AS	3	$1\frac{1}{4}$ hr ea.	An AS level may be gained by taking TWO compulsory modules *Papers 9850/1 & 2 (Pure mathematics with applications)* and ONE of *M1, S1* or *D1** All papers have short questions and longer structured questions All papers carry 50 marks and all questions to be attempted *D1 (Discrete mathematics) not included in this book	33.3% ea.
	9850 Pure Mathematics	AS	3	$1\frac{1}{4}$ hr ea.	An AS level may be gained by taking EITHER the TWO compulsory modules *9850/1 & 2 (Pure mathematics with applications) & P1*, OR *9850/1 (Pure mathematics with applications)*, **P2 (Pure mathematics)* – not included in this book – and ONE other module or option. All papers have short questions and longer structured questions. All papers carry 50 marks and all questions to be attempted	33.3% ea.
	9850 Statistics	AS	3	$1\frac{1}{4}$ hr ea.	An AS level may be gained by taking *S1* and *S2* and ONE other permitted module or option. All papers have short questions and longer structured questions All papers carry 50 marks and all questions to be attempted	33.3% ea.
	9850 Mechanics	AS	3	$1\frac{1}{4}$ hr ea.	An AS level may be gained by taking *M1* and *M2* and ONE other permitted module or option All papers have short questions and longer structured questions All papers carry 50 marks and all questions to be attempted	33.3% ea.
	9850 Mathematics	A	6	$1\frac{1}{4}$ hr ea.	An A level may be gained by taking FOUR Compulsory modules *9850/1–4 (Pure mathematics with applications)* and TWO of the options *P1, M1, M2, S1, S2, D1*, D2** in an allowed combination All papers have short questions and longer structured questions. All papers carry 50 marks and all questions to be attempted *D1, D2 (Discrete mathematics) not included in this book	16.7% ea.
	(see next page)					

(see next page)

Table II Analysis of the methods of examination

Board	Syllabus	Level	No. of papers/duration	Style	% marks
OXFORD *cont*	**9850 Pure Mathematics**	A	6	$1\frac{1}{4}$ hr ea.	An A level may be gained by taking FOUR Compulsory modules and *P1* and *P2** All papers have short questions and longer structured questions All papers carry 50 marks and all questions to be attempted **P2 (Pure), D1, D2 (Discrete mathematics)* not included in this book	16.7% ea.
OXFORD (Nuffield)						
	8770 Mathematics	AS	2	$1\frac{1}{4}$ hr	*Paper 1 Pure mathematics with applications* A number of questions of varying length, all to be attempted	30%
				$2\frac{1}{2}$ hr	*Paper 2 Pure mathematics, statistics and probability* A number of questions of varying length, all to be attempted Includes comprehension question – material provided in advance of examination	50%
				Cswk	*Paper 5.* Up to four pieces between five and ten sides of A4	20%
	9870 Mathematics	A	4	$1\frac{1}{4}$ hr	*Paper 1 Pure mathematics with applications* (as above)	15%
				$2\frac{1}{2}$ hr	*Paper 2 Pure mathematics, statistics and probability* (as above)	25%
				2hr	*Paper 3 Pure mathematics and distributions*	25%

				$1\frac{1}{4}$ hr	Option papers – candidates choose ONE
					    Paper 41 Mechanics 1 *Paper 45 Surfaces**
					    Paper 42 Discrete mathematics* *Paper 46 History of mathematics**
					    Paper 43 Statistics# *Paper 47 Mathematics, Music and Art**
					    Paper 44 Complex numbers and numerical methods# *Paper 48 Mechanics 2 #*
					    * not included in this book # some content included in this book
					 All papers consist of a number of questions of varying length, all to be attempted
						15%

				Cswk	*Paper 5.* Up to four pieces between five and ten sides of A4	20%
OXFORD AND CAMBRIDGE (TIER)						
	Mathematics (Foundation Tier)	AS	1	$2\frac{1}{2}$ hr	*Paper 1 Pure mathematics, statistics and kinematics* Consists of twelve to sixteen short questions, all to be attempted	100%
	Mathematics (Higher Tier)	AS	2	$2\frac{1}{2}$ hr $1\frac{1}{2}$ hr	*Paper 1 Pure mathematics, statistics and kinematics* (as above) *Paper 4 Pure mathematics, statistics and kinematics* Consists of six questions, four to be attempted	60% 40%
	Mathematics (Foundation Tier)	A	2	$2\frac{1}{2}$ hr $2\frac{1}{2}$ hr	*Paper 1 Pure mathematics, statistics and kinematics* (as above) *Paper 2 Pure mathematics, statistics, kinematics and Mechanics* Section A: three short questions, all to be attempted Section B: seven longer questions, four to be attempted	50% 50%
	Mathematics (Higher Tier)	A	3	$2\frac{1}{2}$ hr $2\frac{1}{2}$ hr 2hr	*Paper 1 Pure mathematics, statistics and kinematics* (as above) *Paper 2 Pure mathematics, statistics, kinematics and mechanics* (as above) *Paper 3 Pure mathematics, statistics, kinematics and mechanics* Consists of seven questions, all to be attempted	34.4% 34.4% 31.2%

OXFORD AND CAMBRIDGE (MEI)				$1\frac{1}{2}$ hr ea.	There are 13 papers offered by Oxford & Cambridge. See below for A & AS level choice of papers.
					 P1 Pure mathematics. Five compulsory questions weighted equally
					 P2 Pure mathematics. Five compulsory questions weighted equally, one piece of coursework
					 on the solution of equations by numerical methods (6 – 8 hr)
					 P3 *Pure mathematics.* Four compulsory questions weighted equally and one comprehension
					       question of up to 1 hour
					 P4/5 *Pure mathematics. Four questions, three to be attempted
					 P6 * Pure mathematics. Five questions, one on each option, three to be attempted
					 M1 *Mechanics.* Four compulsory questions weighted equally
					       One assignment involving modelling and experimental work
					 M2 *Mechanics.* Four compulsory questions weighted equally
					       One assignment involving modelling and experimental work
					 M3 *Mechanics.* Four compulsory questions weighted equally
					 S1 *Statistics.* Four compulsory questions. One assignment on data. Exploration of single variable data
					 S2 *Statistics.* Four compulsory questions. One assignment on bivariate data
					 S3 *Statistics.* Four compulsory questions. One assignment involving a hypothesis test
					 DE *Differential equations. Three compulsory questions. One modelling assignment
					 D&D # Decision and discrete mathematics. Four compulsory questions
					       Two projects, each 6 – 8 hours duration, on modelling a realistic problem
					 # some content included in this book
					 # not included in this book	

	9665 Mathematics (MEI)	AS	3	$1\frac{1}{4}$ hr ea.	An AS level may be gained by taking *P1* and *P2* with ONE of *M1, S1* or *D&D* # (see above) Each component equally weighted	
	9665 Mathematics (ME1)	A	6	$1\frac{1}{4}$ hr ea.	An A level may be gained by taking six components, which must include *P1, P2* and *P3* and at least two from *M1, M2, S1, S2* and *D&D* # (see above) All components chosen subject to the constraint of dependency. Each component equally weighted.	

Table II Analysis of the methods of examination

Board	Syllabus	Level	No. of papers/duration		Style	% marks
NICCEA	Pure Mathematics	A	2	3hr	*Paper 1 Pure mathematics A1.* Ten compulsory short questions (approx 50%) and a choice of four from five long questions (approx 50%)	50%
				3hr	*Paper 2 *Pure mathematics A2.* (*some content not included in this book) A choice of eight from ten long questions	50%
	Pure Mathematics and Mechanics	A	3	3hr	*Paper 1 Pure mathematics A1* (as above)	50%
				$1\frac{1}{2}$hr	*Paper 3 Mechanics B1.* Four compulsory short questions (approx 50%) and a choice of two from three long questions (approx 50%)	25%
				$1\frac{1}{2}$hr	*Paper 4 Mechanics B2.* Four compulsory short questions (approx 50%) and a choice of two from three long questions (approx 50%)	25%
	Pure Mathematics and Statistics	A	3	3hr	*Paper 1 Pure mathematics A1* (as above)	50%
				$1\frac{1}{2}$hr	*Paper 5 Statistics C1.* Four compulsory short questions (approx 50%) and a choice of two from three long questions (approx 50%)	25%
				$1\frac{1}{2}$hr	*Paper 6 Statistics C2.* Four compulsory short questions (approx 50%) and a choice of two from three long questions (approx 50%)	25%
	Pure and Applied Mathematics	A	3	–	*Paper 1, Paper 3 & Paper 5* (as above)	
	Further Mathematics	A	3	–	*Paper 2, Paper 4 & Paper 6* (as above)	
WJEC	Mathematics	AS	1	3hr	*Paper 1 Mathematical methods A1*	100%
	Mechanics	AS	1	3hr	*Paper 2 Mechanics A2*	100%
	Statistics	AS	1	3hr	*Paper 3 Statistics A3*	100%
	Applied Mathematics	AS	1	3hr	*Paper 5 Mechanics and Statistics A5* All papers consist of questions of varying mark allocations as indicated on the paper. No restriction on the number of questions that may be attempted	100%
	Mathematics	A	2	3hr ea.	*Paper 1 & either Paper 2 or Paper 3 or Paper 5* (as above)	50% ea.
	Applied Mathematics	A	2	3hr ea.	*Paper 2 & Paper 3* (as above)	50% ea.
	Pure Mathematics	A	2	3hr	*Paper 1* (as above)	50%
				3hr	*Paper 4 Further mathematical methods A4*	50%
WJEC MODULAR				$1\frac{1}{2}$hr ea.	There are eight papers in WJEC Modular. *P1 Mathematical Methods 1 M1 Mechanics 1 S1 Statistics 1* *P2 Mathematical Methods 2 M2 Mechanics 2 S2 Statistics 2* *P3 Mathematical Methods 3* *P4 *Mathematical Methods 4* All Papers have an equal weighting. Questions set in any module require knowledge of the content of previous modules of the set. All papers consist of questions of varying mark allocation, as indicated on the paper. No restriction on the number of questions to be attempted. Module tests are set twice a year, January and June.	
	Pure Mathematics	AS	2	$1\frac{1}{2}$hr ea.	*P1, P2*	50% ea
	Mathematics	AS	2	$1\frac{1}{2}$hr ea.	*P1, M1* OR *P1, S1*	50% ea.
	Mechanics	AS	2	$1\frac{1}{2}$hr ea.	*M1, M2*	50% ea.
	Statistics	AS	2	$1\frac{1}{2}$hr ea.	*S1, S2*	50% ea.
	Applied Mathematics	AS	2	$1\frac{1}{2}$hr ea.	*M1, S1*	50% ea.
	Applied Mathematics	A	4	–	Five combinations of papers are offered for Mathematics at A level. The combinations are : *P1, P2, M1, M2;* OR *P1, P2, S1, S2;* OR *P1, P2, M1, S1;* OR *P1, P2, P3, M1;* OR *P1, P2, P3, S1*	25% ea.
	Applied Mathematics	A	4		*M1, M2, S1, S2*	25% ea.
	Pure Mathematics	A	4		*P1, P2, P3, P4** * some content addressed in this book	25% ea.
SEB	Mathematics	H	2	2hr	*Paper 1,* 20–25 short response questions 25% of marks are on the assessment of problem solving processes	40%
				$2\frac{1}{2}$hr	*Paper 2,* 10 extended response questions	50%
					Investigation, a choice of one from six topics set by the Board.	10%

MATHEMATICAL MODELLING

What is Mathematical Modelling?

Mathematical modelling is used to describe the process of solving a real world problem through the use of mathematics.

The process begins with a problem statement, passes through three main phases, **formulation**, **solution** and **review**, and culminates in a report.

Mathematical models are often revised after the review stage and the formulation, solution, review process is repeated. Each of these three phases is now considered in more detail.

Formulation

Understand the problem

Before embarking on the formulation stage it is important to make sure that you **understand the problem** that has been posed.

List the features

The first part of the formulation stage is to make a **list of all the features** of the problem that could influence the solution you will eventually give.

Some of the features identified may be very important while others are much more trivial.

Simplify the problem

The second stage is to **simplify the problem.** To do this, you state a **set of assumptions** on which to base the problem.

The use of assumptions simplifies the problem considerably and allows a mathematical problem to be stated.

Define a mathematical problem

The assumptions are important because they describe the conditions under which the mathematical solution will be obtained. They allow the problem to be simplified to an extent where it is possible to **define a mathematical problem** that can be solved.

Mathematical solution

The mathematical problem defined in the formulation stage is now solved to give a solution to the problem.

This stage involves many of the mathematical skills and techniques that you will have encountered in your A-level studies.

Review

This stage contains a number of elements which include:

- interpretation
- comparison with reality
- criticism of results
- reformulation

In some cases it will be important for an **interpretation** of the solution to be given.

Comparison of results with real situations can be very useful for determining the validity of a solution.

Criticism of results should show any weaknesses of the solution, which may well be due to the initial assumptions.

In the light of the review of the solution it will very often be desirable to **refine the solution** to the problem. The first stage in this is to **reformulate the problem** to take account of new factors or to revise the assumptions.

The three stages of mathematical modelling are then often repeated until a satisfactory solution is obtained.

The diagram shows how mathematical modelling has a cycle that can be repeated several times.

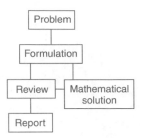

Remember that the review of the original problem will probably lead to a reformulation of the mathematical model and hence to a reworking of the mathematical solution. It may be necessary to go through this loop several times before an acceptable solution is obtained.

We will now consider three examples of mathematical models.

The first example looks at minimising the cost of constructing a cuboid to contain fruit juice and it involves only pure mathematics.

The second example looks at an application of mathematical models to mechanics.

The third example looks at an application of mathematical models to statistics.

Each example follows the stages outlined in this introduction.

An example of mathematical modelling in pure mathematics

Problem statement: *Design a carton to hold* 1 litre *of fruit juice, so that the cost of construction is a minimum.*

Formulation: The list below includes various key features of the problem that could be taken into account in the solution of the problem.

- Amount of material needed.
- The shape of the material to be folded into the carton's final shape. Some shapes require many joins and waste a lot of material.
- The final shape – it should fit on the shelf of a refrigerator and be easy to handle, stack, etc.
- Cost of the materials needed.
- Cost of making joins.

Add to this list any other factors that you think could be taken into account.

In order to formulate a mathematical problem it is necessary to create a list of assumptions or simplifications to allow a solution to be obtained to the problem. The following assumptions allow a mathematical problem to be formulated.

- The carton will be a cuboid, with dimensions as shown below.
- The cost will be proportional to the area of the material used.

Mathematical Modelling

- No material will be used in the joins and there will be no cost for making joins.
- The volume of the carton will be exactly 1000 cm³.
- The carton will be made by folding a sheet of material as shown below to form a cuboid. Note that the shaded areas are folded over and lost.

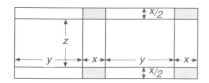

Mathematical problem: Find an expression for the area of the sheet of material in terms of x and y. By considering graphs for different values of y find the minimum area of the sheet and the corresponding dimensions.

Mathematical solution: As the length of the sheet is $2x + 2y$ and the width of the sheet is $x + z$, the area A is given by:

$$A = (x + z)(2x + 2y).$$

This expression is in terms of x, y and z. The variable z can be eliminated by considering the volume of the carton. As its dimensions are x, y and z, and its volume is 1000 cm³,

$$xyz = 1000 \quad \text{or} \quad z = \frac{1000}{xy}.$$

Using this result the area A of the sheet can be expressed as

$$A = \left(x + \frac{1000}{xy} \right)(2x + 2y)$$

In order to find the minimum value of A graphs can be plotted for different values of y. The graph below shows plots for $y = 10$, 12 and 14 cm.

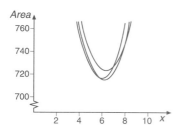

These graphs suggest that the area is close to its minimum when $x = 6$ and $y = 12$. Further graphs or the output of a spreadsheet could be used to give more precise solutions. The output below is from a spreadsheet and gives the area for a range of values of x and y.

	12	12.1	12.2	12.3	12.4	12.5	12.6	12.7	12.8
6	716	715.82	715.67	715.53	715.42	715.33	715.26	715.21	715.18
6.1	715.36	715.20	715.06	714.95	714.86	714.79	714.74	714.71	714.70
6.2	714.93	714.79	714.68	714.58	714.51	714.46	714.43	714.42	714.43
6.3	714.71	714.59	714.49	714.42	714.37	714.34	**714.33**	714.34	714.37
6.4	714.69	714.59	714.51	714.46	714.43	714.42	714.43	714.46	714.51
6.5	714.86	714.78	714.73	714.69	714.68	714.69	714.72	714.77	714.84
6.6	715.22	715.16	715.12	715.11	715.12	715.15	715.20	715.27	715.36
6.7	715.75	715.72	715.70	715.71	715.74	715.79	715.86	715.95	716.06
6.8	716.46	716.45	716.45	716.48	716.53	716.60	716.69	716.80	716.93
6.9	717.34	717.34	717.37	717.42	717.49	717.58	717.69	717.82	717.97
7	718.38	718.40	718.45	718.52	718.60	718.71	718.84	718.99	719.16

y-values (column headers); *x-values* (row labels)

The data suggest that a minimum area of 714 cm² is obtained when $x = 6.3$ cm and $y = 12.6$ cm.

Interpretation: The results indicate that a carton with a base of dimensions 6.3 cm by 12.6 cm should be used. The corresponding height can be calculated using

$$z = \frac{1000}{xy}, \text{ giving } z = \frac{1000}{6.3 \times 12.6} = 12.6 \text{cm}.$$

This carton would fit easily onto the shelf of a refrigerator and be easy to stack and so represents a reasonable outcome.

Compare with reality: Many manufacturers use cartons of a similar design and it is possible to compare these results with typical cartons.

Criticism of the model: The major criticism that could be made concerns the fact that no allowance has been made for the material used in the joins. A revised model could take account of this factor.

Reformulation: In order to take account of the joins an extra 1 cm strip of material is to be added to the sides of the sheet as shown below.

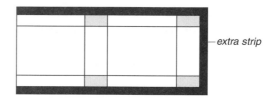

— *extra strip*

The expression for the area now becomes:

$$\text{Area} = (2x + 2y + 1)\left(x + \frac{1000}{xy} + 2 \right).$$

Using similar techniques to those used in the original mathematical solution gives $x = 6.3$ cm, $y = 11.0$ cm and $z = 14.4$ cm.

(See over for examples of mathematical modelling in Mechanics and Statistics.)

Mathematical Modelling

An example of mathematical modelling in mechanics

Problem statement: *A car at an accident skids down a gentle slope leaving a skid mark of* 20 m *before it collides with a stationary vehicle. How fast was the car travelling when it began to skid and was it breaking the* 30 mph *speed limit?*

Formulation: The first step is to draw up a feature list to include all those factors that might affect the solution of the problem. The list below includes a number of important factors.

- The road and tyre conditions.
- The gradient of the slope.
- The speed of impact between the two cars.
- The conditions of the road.
- Were all the wheels locked?

Are there are further factors that you think should be included?

The assumptions below allow a simple model to be formulated so that a mathematical problem can be defined.

- The road is horizontal.
- The speed of impact is zero.
- There is constant friction force and no air resistance.
- The coefficient of friction between the tyres and the road is 0.8.
- The car is to be modelled as a particle.

Mathematical problem: A car skids 20 m to rest on a horizontal road. If the coefficient of friction is 0.8, find the initial speed of the car.

Mathematical solution: As the car is skidding the friction will take its limiting value of μR. So,

$$F = -\mu mg = -0.8 \times 10m = -8m,$$

where m is the mass of the car.

The acceleration a of the car is given by

$$a = \frac{F}{m} = \frac{-8m}{m} = -8 \text{ m s}^{-2}.$$

Now the distance can be found using

$$v^2 = u^2 + 2as$$

to give $\quad 0^2 = u^2 + 2 \times (-8) \times 20$

so that $\quad u^2 = 320$

and $\quad u = 17.9 \text{ m s}^{-1}$.

Interpretation: The initial speed predicted can be converted to give 40 mph. This figure clearly suggests that the car was breaking the speed limit.

Compare with reality: The Highway Code provides a useful source of data that can be used to compare the results with reality. The Highway Code quotes a distance of 80 feet or 24 m as the braking distance for 40 mph. This compares favourably with the prediction made above.

Criticism of the model: The two major criticisms that can be made of this model are that the road is not horizontal and that the speed of impact is not taken into account.

Reformulation: The diagram shows the forces acting when the road is assumed to be at an angle of 5° to the horizontal.

The normal reaction now has the magnitude:

$$R = mg\cos 5°$$

and the resultant force up the slope on the car is

$$F = \mu mg\cos 5° - mg\cos 85°$$
$$= mg(\mu\cos 5° - \cos 85°).$$

So the acceleration is

$$a = -g(\mu\cos 5° - \cos 85°)$$
$$= -6.96 \text{ m s}^{-2}.$$

Using this value for a and with a speed of impact of zero gives

$$0^2 = u^2 + 2 \times (-6.96) \times 20$$
$$\therefore u^2 = 278.4$$

so that $u = 16.7 \text{ m s}^{-1}$ or 37 mph.

Notice that taking account of the hill reduces the initial speed.

As a final refinement to the model an impact speed of 9 m s⁻¹ or approximately 20 mph could be investigated. The condition of the cars after the collision could suggest that such a value is reasonable. Using this gives a revised initial speed

$$9^2 = u^2 + 2 \times (-6.96) \times 20$$
$$\therefore u^2 = 359.4$$

so that $u = 19.0 \text{ m s}^{-1}$ or 42 mph.

It is interesting to note how close the two revised estimates are to the original prediction. The conclusion that the car was breaking the speed limit was confirmed by both revisions.

Mathematical Modelling

An example of mathematical modelling in Statistics

Problem statement: A cereal manufacturer hopes to boost sales by including free model dinosaurs in cereal packets. There are five different models. The manufacturer wants to know how many packets a customer needs to buy before getting a full set of these five dinosaurs.

Formulation: The following factors could influence the problem:

• Are all the dinosaurs put in packets at the same time or are some models withheld initially to make it more difficult to get a set?

• How are the models placed in the packets? For example, is it at random or is one model used on each day of the week?

• How are the packets distributed?

• Are there equal numbers of each model?

A first model can be formulated by assuming that each packet is equally likely to contain any dinosaur.

Mathematical problem: Conduct a simulation to find the number of packets of cereal needed for a complete set of dinosaurs. Use random numbers less than 1 and the table below to decide which model is obtained in each packet.

Random number	Model dinosaur
$0 \leq x < 0.2$	A
$0.2 \leq x < 0.4$	B
$0.4 \leq x < 0.6$	C
$0.6 \leq x < 0.8$	D
$0.8 \leq x < 1.0$	E

Repeat a number of times.

Mathematical solution: The list below shows an actual result of a simulation. It gives the random numbers obtained and the corresponding models that were collected. The list stops when a full set has been obtained.

Random number	Model dinosaur
0.307	B
0.972	E
0.028	A
0.837	E
0.618	D
0.205	B
0.597	C

In this example 7 packets were required for a full set.

This process can be repeated a number of times. The table below gives the results from 200 simulations of this type. These results were obtained with assistance from a simple program.

No. of packets needed	Frequency	No. of packets needed	Frequency
5	9	13	10
6	13	14	5
7	29	15	8
8	19	16	3
9	23	17	7
10	21	18	7
11	15	19	1
12	22	≥20	8

Interpretation: These results suggest that it is unlikely that the full set will be obtained with less than 6 packets as the relative frequency of $\frac{9}{200}$ is very low, less than 0.05. They also suggest that it is unlikely that more than 18 packets would be required. Again the relative frequency is $\frac{9}{200}$.

So in conclusion the simulation suggests that for 90% of the collectors between 6 and 18 packets will be required to obtain a full set of model dinosaurs.

The mean number of packets required for a full set was also calculated from the results as 11 packets.

Criticism of the results: The results assume that it is equally likely to obtain any dinosaur model in any packet. In reality it may be that it is more likely to obtain one model rather than another. A revised model could take account of this type of situation.

As an example assume that the probabilities of obtaining each model are as given in the table below and a revised simulation is to be based on the random numbers also given in the table.

Model	A	B	C	D	E
Probability of being in a packet	0.1	0.3	0.2	0.2	0.2

Running a simulation based on these probabilities gave the results below. As the results cover a wider range some have been grouped as shown.

No. of packets	Frequency
5	6
6 – 10	73
11 – 15	57
16 – 20	25
21 – 25	18
26 – 30	10
31+	11

It is interesting to note that approximately 90% of collectors now require between 6 and 30 packets of cereal for a full set, and that the mean number of packets has increased to 12.5 packets.

Interpretation: Making the changes described has had only a small effect on the solution to the problem. The mean has only increased by 1.5 packets and it is still quite likely to obtain the set with six packets, although more people may now struggle to complete their sets of dinosaurs. In view of this a more effective strategy for the manufacturer may be to increase the number of dinosaurs in the set to 6, which would increase the number of packets needed for a full set without making the manufacturer appear unfair.

COURSEWORK

Coursework at A-level

The nature of coursework – its assessment, the number of pieces required, their length, etc. – varies from syllabus to syllabus. You should first check the requirements for the syllabus that you are following.

(For example, the AEB syllabus allows you to offer coursework in Statistics, Mechanics and Discrete Mathematics, or you may replace one of these by one topic selected from Simulation, Financial Mathematics, the Theory of Numbers or the History of Mathematics.)

There are some common elements for all syllabuses that contain coursework:

• Centre-based assessment (usually coursework and tests) accounts for 20% of the marks available for the examination.

• Students usually choose their coursework task or problem in consultation with their teacher(s) and obtain their approval.

• Students who are sitting the examination a second time are usually allowed to carry forward marks for coursework units for one year, or they can submit new work.

• Each piece of coursework should include evidence for some or all of the following: initiation and the starting assumptions; design; consultation; planning; formulation of hypotheses; collection of data; selection and recording of data; processing data; revision of hypotheses; application of mathematical processes (both familiar and unfamiliar); some extension to the original task; presentation and communication; reflection and evaluation of the work.

• Credits will be given for:

a systematic approach

the use of mathematical knowledge and skills (even if somewhat elementary)

using ideas/techniques covered in the main syllabus.

• Topics should normally be linked to appropriate sections of the syllabus.

• The use of source material is permitted in many tasks if it is identified as such.

Starting coursework

When starting a piece of coursework:

• start by clearly stating what problem you are investigating

• give all your starting assumptions

• include practical work if appropriate

• describe the method of collecting data and other information, with the reasons for your choice

• look up relevant information in books, etc.

• use appropriate methods of analysis – numerical, graphical, algebraic

• interpret your findings with reference to the real world

• validate/justify your findings

• do not always expect to solve the problem completely but make a note in your work of any aspects of the task that you would have liked to explore had you had the time

• finally, you need to write a summary of your conclusions and what you actually achieved – see the Checklist at the end of this chapter.

Some ideas for coursework

Note that the following categories are not exclusive.

Simulation:

A comparison of the efficiency of zebra and pelican crossings, random number generation, simple simulations, e.g. queuing at traffic lights, petrol pumps, check-outs in supermarkets ...

Financial mathematics:

Credit, including APR, i.e. the different ways of obtaining credit: from a shop, an overdraft, credit card, loan from a finance company ... etc. Such a project is usually attempted in a real context, such as buying a car, tax relief, mortality tables, life assurance, savings, resale value of cars, setting up a business, mortgages and their repayment details including the difference between repayment and endowment mortgages, some capital expenditure project e.g. building a new school or leisure centre, ...

Theory of numbers:

Primes, natural numbers, factors, modular arithmetic, residues, Fermat's theorem, cryptology and ciphers, number investigations ...

History of mathematics:

Euclidean geometry and proof, numbers systems, the invention of logarithms, great mathematicians such as Leibnitz and Pythagoras, astronomy, Kepler's laws of planetary motion ...

Statistics:

Weather in holiday resorts, shoe and collar sizes, favourite numbers, pebble populations, journey times, road accidents, extra sensory perception, reading ages, proportional representation, taste testing. Looking for a connection between inflation and unemployment, relationship between foot length and height ...

Mathematical problems/problem solving:

Optimum design of, for example, tins or boxes. An investigation into the graphs of polynomials. Exploration of conics, exploration into fractals ...

Mechanics/Physical structures/Newton's laws:

Experiments to find the centre of mass of various objects. The change in position of the composite centre of gravity of a can of drink as the contents are drunk. Analysis of the loads in a framework – Bow's notation ...

Coding:

Use of check digits in bar coding. Morse code, coding a route through a network of streets ...

Coursework

Some examples of coursework projects

1　A plane is capable of flying at a steady speed in still air. If it takes off from its base with enough fuel for 4 hours flight, how far can it fly and return safely?

What factors are relevant?
*   velocity of the plane
*   velocity and direction of the wind, etc.

What assumptions would you make?
*   velocity of the plane is parallel to the velocity of the wind
*   the actual plane and wind velocities
*   the plane doesn't lose time taking off, landing, climbing or descending, etc.

The solution to the problem could involve vectors, trigonometry, Pythagoras – all appropriate links to the syllabus together with diagrams and graphs – and should include clear diagrams and a clear explanation of the model and assumptions adopted.

2　A comparison between two newspapers

What factors are important?
*   word length
*   sentence length
*   size of page
*   number and size of photographs, etc.

How will you collect the data?
*   size of sample
*   choice of pages – random number generation
*   choice of words – random number generation

How will you show the data and your results?
*   use of average – which one?
*   graphs, box and whisker plots, etc.

Remember to include an explanation of how the data were collected and what factors were considered – e.g., word length and sentence length – and why.

3　Comparing pulse rates

What factors are important?
*   how you choose the subjects for your study – same number of males and females
*   how you collect the measurements
*   under similar conditions
*   before and after exercise
*   consider mean, range, variance, confidence intervals

Remember to include how you collected the data.

4　Design a machine for serving tennis balls.

What factors are important?
*   height of ball as it leaves the machine
*   velocity of ball and direction, i.e. angle of projection

What assumptions will you make?
*   constant speed of projection, i.e. no variation in the machine
*   horizontal full size tennis court
*   ball just clears the net
*   ball just lands in the service court
*   ignore air resistance

Your solution should involve Newton's second law; you may derive, for example, two equations (or inequalities) – one giving the parameters for the ball to clear the net, the other for the ball to land in the court. You must, of course, explain and justify your interpretation and conclusions.

Assessment criteria

Although the wording and criteria vary from syllabus to syllabus, and perhaps from coursework task to coursework task, you will be expected to demonstrate your abilities in some or all of the following:

(a)　Research, select, organise, process and evaluate relevant information, and collect data.

(b)　Analyse problems, design and evaluate mathematical models (if appropriate) and plan solutions to problems.

(c)　Use and demonstrate appropriate techniques including the use of graphics calculators and computers.

(d)　Communicate mathematical ideas, use appropriate mathematical language, organise and present results in a clear and·organised way using tables, graphs and diagrams when and where appropriate.

(e)　Perform calculations, interpret results and outcomes, draw valid conclusions and present clear representations of data.

(f)　Demonstrate a sense of commitment and perseverance.

Writing your final report

Here is a checklist for planning and writing your report:

Model formulation/starting point(s):

I have:
*   defined the problem clearly
*   stated any simplifying assumptions and approaches and discussed their implications
*   chosen the variables and constants.

Data collection and analysis:

I have:
*   collected any data that are needed and set out the calculations and results clearly
*   used relevant theory together with any appropriate numerical, graphical or algebraic analysis.

Interpretation and validation

I have:
*   interpreted my solutions, graphs and diagrams in appropriate mathematical language
*   made predictions and conjectures
*   tested these predictions and conjectures and validated any solutions where possible
*   identified any limitations of the model or the starting assumptions
*   suggested any refinements or implications for further developments
*   indicated any possible errors arising from the practical work, the assumptions made or the choice of constants selected.

Communication:

I have:
*   set out the work clearly and concisely
*   used diagrams and mathematical language effectively and presented results in an organised way
*   given a clear explanation of the results and findings together with their implications.

GRAPHICS CALCULATORS

Graphics calculators at A-level

Students are expected to use graphical programmable calculators in most A-level syllabuses. Such calculators include all the functions of a scientific calculator of the sort used at GCSE, together with the ability to plot graphs and write simple programs.

The style and nature of examination questions is changing to reflect the use of graphics calculators. However, you should find out from your teacher(s) if there are any limitations on the use of calculators. In the examination you should read questions carefully to see if there are any restrictions imposed on calculator usage.

Models of calculator

The models used include the Casio 7000 and 7700 series, the Texas TI-80, TI-81, T1-82 and TI-85 and the Sharp EL-9200/9300. Because the instructions for each model vary slightly we are not giving detailed instructions about how to use your calculator.

It is essential that you are fully competent with the model that you have. While you should consult the handbook for your calculator, if you have any problems the best source of help is usually someone experienced with the same sort of calculator.

Using your calculator

The following notes give a brief description of some ways you can use your calculator .

1.   As a scientific calculator

All models are straightforward to use in this mode.

2.   Drawing graphs

You can use your calculator to display function graphs such as sin, cos, log, etc.

You can also generate your own graphs by following the instructions in your calculator's Handbook. With a little practice it is much quicker than plotting by hand.

More than one graph can be plotted at a time.

Ways to use the graph-plotting function

•   You can use your calculator to solve simultaneous equations. Draw the graphs of $y = x^2$ and $y = 3\sqrt{x}$ on the same screen. Find the coordinates of the point of intersection of the curves by using the ZOOM and TRACE functions.

•   You can use your calculator to solve equations such as $e^x = 5(1 - x)$, or to find the largest root of $x^3 - 5x^2 - 7x + 12 = 0$. Note that for such equations you can draw the normal or the tangent at any point as well as determine the gradient at that point. (See also the questions in P10 and P25.)

•   You can use your calculator for polar plots: for example, find the coordinates of the intersection between the curves $r = 2(1 + \cos \theta)$ and $r = 6 \cos \theta$.

•   It is possible to store data in the calculator (for example, values of distance travelled and time taken for a ball rolling down a slope), and to then plot the points and find the equation of a curve that fits the data. This technique is useful in mechanics.

An examination question where a graphics calculator might be useful to check your answers could be of the form:

1   The figure shows the graph of a function which passes through (2, 7) and (4, 23).

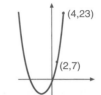

(a) Find a set of values of a, b and c such that the graph of the quadratic function $y = ax^2 + bx + c$ $(a \neq 0)$ passes through (2, 7) and (4, 23).

(b) Describe, with the aid of sketches, the graphs of $y = f(x - 2)$ and $y = f(2x)$.

An examination question that requires the use of a graphics calculator could be:

2   (i) Use your graphics calculator to find the coordinates in the first quadrant of the point of intersection of the graphs of $y = 2x^2$ and $y = x + \dfrac{3}{x}$. Give your answer correct to two decimal places.

(ii) Find the positive solution to the equation $x = 3 \sin x$ where x is in radians. Give your answer correct to two decimal places and explain your method.

3.   Writing programs, performing iterations and repeated calculations

The programming facility is useful for most operations – for example, in association with drawing graphs it is possible to write a program which will display the rate of change for a function. Thus it is possible to draw a velocity curve from a displacement function.

Programs can be written to find approximate solutions to equations using the Newton-Raphson method and for investigating sequences.

The prgramming facility could be useful in the following examples:

3   Investigate the behaviour of the iterative formula

$$x_{n+1} = \frac{3}{x_n + 1}.$$

4   Investigate the growth in a population of bacteria which is given by the relationship

$$p_{n+1} = p_n + ap_n \left(1 - \frac{p_n}{c}\right).$$

5   It can be shown that the infinite series

$1 - \dfrac{1}{2} + \dfrac{1}{3} - \dfrac{1}{4} + \dfrac{1}{5} \ldots$ converges to ln 2 but if the same terms with the same signs are written in a different order, for example, $1 - \dfrac{1}{2} - \dfrac{1}{4} + \dfrac{1}{3} - \dfrac{1}{6} - \dfrac{1}{8} + \dfrac{1}{5} \ldots$, then the total is different. Investigate.

6   A man invests £100 at the beginning of each year for ten years. The rate of compound interest is 9% per annum. Calculate the value of the investment at the end of each year and the total value at the end of the ten full years.

Graphics calculators

Examination questions requiring the use of a graphics calculator could be:

7 Use your graphics calculator to find x_5, the fifth term of the sequence defined by the recurrence relation $x_{n+1} = 3x_n(1 - x_n^2)$ with $x_1 = 0.6$.

8 One sequence of alternating terms of the series $1 + 2 + 3 + 4 + 5 + 8 \ldots$ forms an arithmetic progression, while the other sequence of alternating terms forms a geometric progression. A student has written an algorithm, AP, to calculate the sum of the first 10 terms of the arithmetic progression:

> **Algorithm** AP
> **Input** None
> $1 \rightarrow N$
> $1 \rightarrow Y$
> $1 \rightarrow T$
> **repeat**
> $N+1 \rightarrow N$
> $Y+2 \rightarrow Y$
> $T+Y \rightarrow T$
> display N
> display Y
> display T

(a) Use this algorithm to program your calculator to sum the first 10 terms of the arithmetic progression.

(b) Write down an algorithm to calculate the sum of the first 10 terms of the geometric progression and hence calculate this sum.

(c) Use your answers to (a) and (b) to find the sum of the first 20 terms of the series.

Writing programs to perform repeated calculations is an advantage, for example, in the numerical solution of equations. To illustrate this consider questions 4 and 5 in P25: in the case of question 4, where only the second approximation is required, it may be just as quick to calculate the answer in the usual way. However, if more approximations were required it would probably be easier to express the equation as $x^3 + 2x - 4 = 0$, and write a program such as:

> $:1 \rightarrow N$
> $:1.2 \rightarrow X$
> :Lbl 1
> $:N+1 \rightarrow N$
> $: X - \dfrac{(X^3 + 2X - 4)}{(3X^2 + 2)} \rightarrow X$
> :Disp N
> :Disp X
> :Pause
> :Goto 1

This program, written for the TI-81, is easily adapted for other models.

For question 5, by choosing a suitable range your sketch graph could be verified and if all that was required was the answer (i.e. working not required to be shown), then writing a program similar to that above would enable a quick determination that the root is 0.53. Of course if the questions were written specifically for calculator use then the degree of accuracy or the number of approximations required would be much greater.

4. Performing simulations

For example, modelling queuing, or voting. Such questions or investigations will often arise in coursework tasks. An example could be investigating the flow of traffic through a tunnel where length of vehicle needs to be considered as well as speed and distance between vehicles.

5. Performing matrix manipulation

Including work involving vectors - such as calculating the angle between vectors - and in complex numbers.

For example, evaluate $z_1 z_2$ and $\dfrac{z_1}{z_2}$ in the form $p + iq$ given z_1 and z_2, using the fact that a complex number $z = x + iy$ can be written as a 2×2 matrix in the form:

$$\begin{pmatrix} x & -y \\ y & x \end{pmatrix}$$

An easy example would be:

Express $(6 + 5i)(7 + 2i)$ in the form $a + ib$.

6. Probability and statistics

Graphics calculators will perform all of the statistical functions expected of advanced scientific calculators, i.e., calculation of the mean, median and mode, standard deviation, etc., but will also allow the drawing of scatter graphs and histograms, the investigation of distributions, correlation and regression and hypothesis testing.

For example, question 2 in S20 could be used to demonstrate the functions available. Note that graphics calculators will give a line of regression of y on x. To obtain the line of regression of x on y you will have to re-enter the data exchanging the x and y values. Graphics calculators will also allow you to draw the regression line on a scatter graph.

Glossary of Symbols

LHS	left hand side (of an equation)
RHS	right hand side (of an equation)
$\angle$ or $\wedge$	angle
$\perp$	is perpendicular to
$\parallel$	is parallel to
$\pm$	positive or negative, plus or minus
$=$	is equal to
$\equiv$	is identically equal to
$\approx$	is approximately equal to
$\sim$	approximates to
$\neq$	is not equal to
$<$	is less than
$\leqslant\ \leq$	is less than or equal to
$>$	is greater than
$\geqslant\ \geq$	is greater than or equal to
$\sqrt{}$	the positive square root
$\Rightarrow$	implies that
$\Leftarrow$	is implied by
$\Leftrightarrow$	implies and is implied by (if and only if)
$\{a,\ b,\ c,...\}$	the set with elements a, b, c, ...
$\in$	is an element of
:	such that
n( )	the number of elements in the set ( )
$\varnothing$	the empty set
$\bar{S}$ or S'	the complement of the set S
$\cup$	union
$\cap$	intersection
$\subset$	is a subset of
$\leftrightarrow$	corresponds one-to-one with
$\propto$	varies directly as
$\triangle$	the discriminant of a quadratic equation
$\mid\ \mid$	the modulus of a number
δx or $\triangle x$	a small increment of x
$\dfrac{dy}{dx}$	the derivative of y with respect to x
$\displaystyle\int y\ dx$	the indefinite integral of y with respect to x
$\displaystyle\int_b^a y\ dx$	the definite integral of y with respect to x
f	a function
f^{-1}	the inverse function of f
$f(x)$	the function value for x
$(fg)(x)$ or fg or $f\circ g$	the composition of the functions f and g
$\rightarrow$	is mapped onto (for mappings) approaches, tends to (for limits)
$x\xrightarrow{f}y$	x is mapped into y under the function f

$f:x\rightarrow y$	f is the function under which x is mapped into y
Σ	the sum of (exact limits may be given)
$n!$	n factorial
$\dbinom{n}{r}$	binomial coefficient
$\mathbb{N}$	the set of natural numbers
$\mathbb{Z}$	the set of integers
$\mathbb{Q}$	the set of rational numbers
$\mathbb{R}$	the set of real numbers
$\mathbb{C}$	the set of complex numbers
∞	infinity
$\ln x$ ($\log_e x$)	the natural logarithm of x
$\log x$ ($\log_{10} x$)	the common logarithm of x
$\mathbf{M}^{-1}$	the inverse of the square matrix $\mathbf{M}$
$\det\mathbf{M}$	the determinant of the square matrix $\mathbf{M}$
i	the square root of -1
$|z|$	the modulus of the complex number z
$\arg z$	the argument of the complex number z
z^*	the conjugate of the complex number z
$\dot{x}$	the derivative of x with respect to t
g	the acceleration due to gravity (taken as 10 m/s^2 unless otherwise stated)
$\mathbf{a.b}$	the scalar product of the vectors $\mathbf{a}$ and $\mathbf{b}$
$\hat{\mathbf{r}}$	the unit vector in the direction of the vector $\mathbf{r}$
$|\mathbf{r}|,\ r$	the magnitude of the vector $\mathbf{r}$
$\mathbf{i, j, k}$	unit vectors in the mutually perpendicular directions Ox, Oy, Oz
$E_1,\ E_2$, etc.	events
$E_1\cup E_2$	union of the events E_1 and E_2
$E_1\cap E_2$	intersection of the events E_1 and E_2
$P(E)$	probability of the event E
$\bar{E}$	complement of the event E
$P(E_1|E_2)$	conditional probability of the event E_1 given that the event E_2 has occurred
X, Y, Z, etc.	random variables
x, y, z, etc.	values taken by random variables
p_1, p_2, etc.	probabilities of individual outcomes $x_1, x_2, \ldots$ in the distribution of a discrete random variable X
$f(x)$	probability density function of a continuous random variable X
x_1, x_2, etc.	observations
f_1, f_2, etc.	frequencies with which observations x_1, x_2, etc. occur
n	sample size
$\bar{x}$	sample mean
$F(x)$	distribution function, $P(X<x)$ of the random variable X
$p(x)$	probability density function $P(X=x)$ of the discrete random variable X
$E[X]$	expected value of the random variable X
$\text{Var}[X]$	variance of the random variable X
μ	population mean
σ^2	population variance
σ	population standard deviation

Bin(n, p)	binomial distribution with parameters n and p		π	population proportion
Po(μ)	Poisson distribution with parameter μ		ρ	population product moment correlation coefficient
N(μ, σ^2)	normal distribution with parameters μ and σ^2			
$\varphi(z)$	probability density function of the standardized normal random variable Z (N(0, 1))		$\leftarrow x \rightarrow$	a dimension (x units)
			$- x \rightarrow$	a displacement (x units)
$\Phi(z)$	distribution function for N(0, 1)		$\rightarrow -$	a velocity
s^2	sample variance		$\twoheadrightarrow -$	an acceleration ($a = \dot{v}$)
r	sample proportion		$\longrightarrow\!\!\!\triangleright$	an impulse
r	sample product moment correlation coefficient		$\longrightarrow\!\!\!\blacktriangleright$	a force ($F = \dot{I}$)
r_s	Spearman's rank correlation coefficient for a sample			

The Greek Alphabet

Letters		Name		Letters		Name
A	α	alpha		N	ν	nu
B	β	beta		Ξ	ξ	xi
Γ	γ	gamma		O	o	omicron
Δ	δ	delta		Π	π	pi
E	ε	epsilon		P	ρ	rho
Z	ζ	zeta		Σ	σ	sigma
H	η	eta		T	τ	tau
Θ	θ	theta		Y	υ	upsilon
I	ι	iota		Φ	φ	phi
K	κ	kappa		X	χ	chi
Λ	λ	lambda		Ψ	ψ	psi
M	μ	mu		Ω	ω	omega

ADDRESSES AND CODES FOR EXAM BOARDS

(A)	AEB	Associated Examining Board
		Stag Hill House, Guildford, Surrey GU2 5XJ (telephone: 01483 506506)
(C)	UCLES	University of Cambridge Local Examinations Syndicate
		Syndicate Buildings, 1 Hills Road, Cambridge CB1 2EU (telephone: 01223 553311)
(H)	SEB	Scottish Examination Board (for Higher Grade)
		Ironmills Road, Dalkeith, Midlothian EH22 1LE (telephone: 0131 663 6601)
(J)	NEAB (formerly JMB)	Northern Examinations and Assessment Board
		12 Harter Street, Manchester M1 6HL (telephone: 0161 953 1180)
(L)	ULEAC	University of London Examinations and Assessment Council
		Stewart House 32 Russell Square, London WC1B 5DN (telephone: 0171 331 4000)
(N)	NICCEA	Northern Ireland Council for the Curriculum, Examinations and Assessment
		Beechill House, 42 Beechill Road, Belfast BT8 4RS (telephone: 01232 704666)
(O&C)	OCSEB	Oxford and Cambridge Schools Examination Board
		(1) Purbeck House, Purbeck Road, Cambridge CB2 2PU (telephone: 01223 411211)
		(2) Elsfield Way, Oxford OX2 8EP (telephone: 01865 54421)
(OLE)	UODLE	University of Oxford Delegacy of Local Examinations
		Ewert House, Ewert Place, Summertown, Oxford OX2 7BZ (telephone: 01865 54291)
(W)	WJEC	Welsh Joint Education Committee
		245 Western Avenue, Cardiff CF5 2YX (telephone: 01222 265000)

Part II
Study Units and Questions Banks

Rational and Irrational Numbers
Definitions, Roots, Operations with simple surds, Rationalising denominators.

Definitions

A **rational number** is a number which can be written in the form $\frac{p}{q}$ where p and q are integers and $q \neq 0$. All proper fractions, improper fractions, mixed numbers and integers are rational numbers. So are terminating and recurring decimal fractions.

An **irrational number** is one that is not rational. If an irrational number is written as a decimal fraction, the decimal is infinite and has no repeating pattern.

A **surd** is an expression containing one or more irrational roots of numbers.

i Examples of irrational numbers are:

square and other roots of prime numbers, for example:
$$\sqrt{2} = 1.414\,213\,5...$$
$$\sqrt[3]{7} = 1.191\,293\,5...$$

numbers such as π and e:
$$\pi = 3.141\,592\,653\,589\,793\,238\,462...$$
$$e = 2.718\,281...$$

i $2\sqrt{3}$ and $3\sqrt{5} + 4\sqrt{2}$ are both surds.

Roots

The **square root** of a number may be rational or irrational.

The square root of every square number is **rational**.

The square root of every prime number is **irrational**.

To find out if the root of a number is irrational, simplify it.

To simplify square roots use these rules:
$$\sqrt{ab} = \sqrt{a} \times \sqrt{b} \quad \text{and} \quad \sqrt{\frac{a}{b}} = \frac{\sqrt{a}}{\sqrt{b}}.$$

To simplify other roots use these rules:
$$\sqrt[n]{ab} = \sqrt[n]{a} \times \sqrt[n]{b} \quad \text{and} \quad \sqrt[n]{\frac{a}{b}} = \frac{\sqrt[n]{a}}{\sqrt[n]{b}}.$$

When two irrational numbers are multiplied together, the result may be rational or irrational.

Since $\sqrt{a} \times \sqrt{b} = \sqrt{ab}$, $\sqrt{ab}$ will be rational if and only if ab is a rational square number.

i *Which of these numbers are irrational?*

(a) $\sqrt{35}$ (b) $\sqrt{63}$ (c) $\sqrt{\frac{1}{32}}$ (d) $\sqrt[5]{\frac{1}{32}}$.

(a) $\sqrt{35} = \sqrt{5 \times 7} = \sqrt{5} \times \sqrt{7}$ irrational

(b) $\sqrt{63} = \sqrt{9 \times 7} = \sqrt{9} \times \sqrt{7} = 3\sqrt{7}$ irrational

(c) $\sqrt{\frac{1}{32}} = \frac{\sqrt{1}}{\sqrt{32}} = \frac{1}{\sqrt{16 \times 2}} = \frac{1}{4\sqrt{2}}$ irrational

(d) $\sqrt[5]{\frac{1}{32}} = \frac{\sqrt[5]{1}}{\sqrt[5]{32}} = \frac{1}{\sqrt[5]{2^5}} = \frac{1}{2}$ rational

i *Which of these numbers are rational?*

(a) $\sqrt{2} \times \sqrt{2}$ (b) $\sqrt{\pi} \times \sqrt{\pi}$.

(a) $\sqrt{2} \times \sqrt{2} = \sqrt{2 \times 2} = \sqrt{2^2} = 2$ rational

(b) $\sqrt{\pi} \times \sqrt{\pi} = \sqrt{\pi \times \pi} = \sqrt{\pi^2} = \pi$ irrational

Operations with simple surds

If a, b, c and d are integers then:

multiplication: $a\sqrt{b} \times c\sqrt{d} = ac\sqrt{bd}$

division: $\dfrac{a\sqrt{b}}{c\sqrt{d}} = \dfrac{a}{c}\sqrt{\dfrac{b}{d}} \quad (c, d \neq 0)$

addition: $a\sqrt{b} + c\sqrt{b} = (a+c)\sqrt{b}$

$a\sqrt{b} + c\sqrt{d}$ can only be simplified if $\sqrt{b}$ and $\sqrt{d}$ are multiples of a common root.

subtraction: $a\sqrt{b} - c\sqrt{b} = (a-c)\sqrt{b}$

$a\sqrt{b} - c\sqrt{d}$ can only be simplified if $\sqrt{b}$ and $\sqrt{d}$ are multiples of a common root.

i *Simplify the following leaving your answers in surd form:*

(a) $2\sqrt{3} \times 5\sqrt{7}$ (b) $4\sqrt{15} \div 2\sqrt{5}$

(c) $8\sqrt{2} + 5\sqrt{2}$ (d) $7\sqrt{3} - 2\sqrt{12}$.

(a) $2\sqrt{3} \times 5\sqrt{7} = 2 \times 5\sqrt{3 \times 7} = 10\sqrt{21}$

(b) $4\sqrt{15} \div 2\sqrt{5} = \dfrac{4}{2}\sqrt{\dfrac{15}{5}} = 2\sqrt{3}$

(c) $8\sqrt{2} + 5\sqrt{2} = (8+5)\sqrt{2} = 13\sqrt{2}$

(d) $7\sqrt{3} - 2\sqrt{12} = 7\sqrt{3} - 2\sqrt{4 \times 3}$
$$= 7\sqrt{3} - 2 \times 2\sqrt{3}$$
$$= 7\sqrt{3} - 4\sqrt{3} = 3\sqrt{3}$$

Rationalising denominators

To rationalise the denominator of:

the fraction $\dfrac{a}{\sqrt{b}}$, multiply by $\dfrac{\sqrt{b}}{\sqrt{b}} \quad (=1)$

i.e. $\dfrac{a}{\sqrt{b}} = \dfrac{a}{\sqrt{b}} \times \dfrac{\sqrt{b}}{\sqrt{b}} = \dfrac{a\sqrt{b}}{b}$.

the fraction $\dfrac{a}{b + k\sqrt{c}}$, multiply by $\dfrac{b - k\sqrt{c}}{b - k\sqrt{c}} \quad (=1)$

the fraction $\dfrac{a}{b - k\sqrt{c}}$, multiply by $\dfrac{b + k\sqrt{c}}{b + k\sqrt{c}} \quad (=1)$

since $(b + k\sqrt{c})(b - k\sqrt{c}) = b^2 - bk\sqrt{c} + bk\sqrt{c} - k^2 c$
$$= b^2 - k^2 c.$$

i *Write each of these fractions with a rational denominator.*

(a) $\dfrac{2\sqrt{5}}{\sqrt{7}}$ (b) $\dfrac{4}{\sqrt{3} + 2}$.

(a) $\dfrac{2\sqrt{5}}{\sqrt{7}} = \dfrac{2\sqrt{5}}{\sqrt{7}} \times \dfrac{\sqrt{7}}{\sqrt{7}} = \dfrac{2\sqrt{5} \times \sqrt{7}}{7} = \dfrac{2\sqrt{35}}{7}$

(b) $\dfrac{4}{\sqrt{3} + 2} = \dfrac{4}{2 + \sqrt{3}} = \dfrac{4(2 - \sqrt{3})}{(2 + \sqrt{3})(2 - \sqrt{3})}$
$$= \dfrac{4(2 - \sqrt{3})}{4 - 3}$$
$$= 4(2 - \sqrt{3})$$

Rational and Irrational Numbers

Worked examples, Guided example, Exercise.

 Simplify $\dfrac{1}{(1-\sqrt{2})^2} - \dfrac{1}{(1+\sqrt{2})^2}$.

$$\frac{1}{(1-\sqrt{2})^2} - \frac{1}{(1+\sqrt{2})^2} = \frac{1}{1-2\sqrt{2}+2} - \frac{1}{1+2\sqrt{2}+2}$$

$$= \frac{1}{3-2\sqrt{2}} - \frac{1}{3+2\sqrt{2}}$$

$$= \frac{3+2\sqrt{2}}{(3-2\sqrt{2})(3+2\sqrt{2})} - \frac{3-2\sqrt{2}}{(3+2\sqrt{2})(3-2\sqrt{2})}$$

$$= \frac{3+2\sqrt{2}}{9-8} - \frac{3-2\sqrt{2}}{9-8}$$

$$= 3+2\sqrt{2} - (3-2\sqrt{2})$$

$$= 2\sqrt{2} + 2\sqrt{2}$$

$$= 4\sqrt{2}.$$

 Simplify the expression $\dfrac{3\sqrt{2}+2\sqrt{3}}{3\sqrt{2}-2\sqrt{3}}$.

Leave your answer in the form $a+b\sqrt{c}$ *where a, b and c are rational numbers.*

$$\frac{3\sqrt{2}+2\sqrt{3}}{3\sqrt{2}-2\sqrt{3}} = \frac{(3\sqrt{2}+2\sqrt{3})(3\sqrt{2}+2\sqrt{3})}{(3\sqrt{2}-2\sqrt{3})(3\sqrt{2}+2\sqrt{3})}$$

$$= \frac{(3\sqrt{2})^2 + 6\sqrt{6} + 6\sqrt{6} + (2\sqrt{3})^2}{(3\sqrt{2})^2 - (2\sqrt{3})^2}$$

$$= \frac{18 + 12\sqrt{6} + 12}{18 - 12}$$

$$= \frac{30 + 12\sqrt{6}}{6}$$

$$= 5 + 2\sqrt{6}.$$

 Write the number $2.8\dot{1}\dot{6}$ *in the form* $\dfrac{x}{y}$ *where x and y are integers and* $y \neq 0$.

$$\text{Let } r = 2.8\dot{1}\dot{6}$$

$$\text{then } 1000r = 2\,816.816\ldots$$

$$\text{subtract } 1000r - r = 2\,816.816\ldots - (2.816\,816\ldots)$$

$$\Rightarrow \quad 999r = 2814$$

$$\Rightarrow \quad r = \frac{2814}{999} = \frac{938}{333}.$$

 (*a*) *Write the number* $0.8\dot{3}$ *in the form* $\dfrac{p}{q}$ *where p and q are integers and* $q \neq 0$.
(*b*) *Find an irrational number which lies between 7 and 8. Give your answer in surd form as simply as possible.*

(a) Let $r = 0.8\dot{3}$. Find $10r$ and $100r$ and then find the difference between these two. Express r as a rational number and cancel to a fraction in its lowest terms.
(b) Square the two numbers 7 and 8. Choose a number between the two squares you obtained.
Work out the square root of your chosen number, leaving your answer in surd form. Simplify if possible.

EX 1 Write the following numbers in the form $\dfrac{p}{q}$ where p and q are integers and $q \neq 0$. Give your answers as simply as possible.
  (a) $0.0\dot{9}$ (b) $0.0\dot{1}3\dot{5}$.

2 Simplify the following. Leave your answers in surd form with rational denominators.
  (a) $\sqrt{50}$ (b) $\dfrac{\sqrt{80}}{2}$ (c) $\sqrt{\dfrac{1}{8}}$ (d) $\dfrac{\sqrt{300}}{\sqrt{50}}$.

3 Simplify the following, leaving your answers in surd form:
  (a) $\sqrt{48} + 2\sqrt{3} - \sqrt{75}$ (b) $(2 - 3\sqrt{7})^2$
  (c) $(2\sqrt{5}+1)(3\sqrt{5}-2)$ (d) $(\sqrt{2}-1)^2(3\sqrt{2}+5)$.

4 Simplify these expressions by rationalising their denominators. Write each answer in the form $a+b\sqrt{c}$ where a, b and c are rational numbers.
  (a) $\dfrac{5}{\sqrt{3}-1}$ (b) $\dfrac{\sqrt{3}+1}{\sqrt{3}-1}$ (c) $\dfrac{3\sqrt{5}-4}{2\sqrt{5}+1}$.

5 Simplify these expressions. What do you notice?
  $2\sqrt{63}$, $3\sqrt{28}$, $\sqrt{252}$.

6 Simplify, leaving your answers in surd form:
  (a) $\sqrt[3]{16}$ (b) $\sqrt[3]{24}$ (c) $\sqrt[4]{80}$ (d) $\sqrt[5]{486}$.

7 Find an irrational number which lies between (a) 4 and 5 (b) 17 and 18   (c) –5 and –3.
  Leave your answers in surd form as simply as possible.

8 Given that $p = \sqrt{2}$ and $q = \sqrt{3}$, express $\dfrac{\sqrt{50}-\sqrt{12}}{\sqrt{8}+\sqrt{75}}$ in terms of p and q as simply as possible.

9 Use the diagrams below to find the sine, cosine and tangent of (a) 30° (b) 60° (c) 45°, leaving your answers in surd form where necessary.

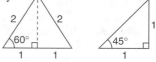

10 Calculate the length of the side marked x in this right-angled triangle.
  Leave your answer in surd form.

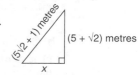

11 Solve the following quadratic equations by using the formula (see Unit P3). Leave your answers in surd form.
  (a) $x^2 - 2x - 5 = 0$ (b) $2x^2 - 6x + 1 = 0$.

12 An equilateral triangular field has sides of length l.

  (a) Find an expression for the area of the field, leaving your answer in surd form.
  (b) Work out the area of the field when
    (i) $l = 250\sqrt{2}$ metres
    (ii) $l = 120(\sqrt{3}-1)$ metres.
  In each case leave your answer in surd form.

P2
core

Errors and Accuracy
Error types, Absolute and relative errors, Error bounds, Absolute and relative errors in calculations.

Error types

There are basically two types of errors which we need to consider in mathematics: **measurement errors** and **round-off errors**. A measurement error is always present whenever a physical quantity is measured. A round-off error is present whenever a number is rounded to a specified number of decimal places (d.p.) or significant figures (s.f.). Round-off errors are also present when a computer chops off (truncates) numbers which it is working with or displaying.

N.B. **By errors we do not mean mistakes.**

| i | 'Sid's height is 182 cm' means his height is 182 cm **to the nearest cm**.

| i | *Round off the number* 6.7955 *to* (*a*) 2 s.f. (*b*) 3 d.p.

(a) 6.7955 = 6.8 rounded to 2 s.f.
(b) 6.7955 = 6.796 rounded to 3 d.p.

| i | *Record the number* 723.864 129 794 *when a computer truncates this to show only* 10 *figures.*

723.864 129 794 is shown as 723.8641297 when truncated to 10 figures.

Absolute and relative errors

If x is an approximation to an exact number X, then:

the **absolute error** in x is e_x where $e_x = x - X$

the **relative error** in x is r_x where $r_x = \dfrac{e_x}{x}$ (or $r_x = \dfrac{e_x}{X}$).

The absolute error e_x can be positive or negative.

N.B. **Check which relative error your Board uses.**

| i | If the 'true length' of a piece of metal is 47 cm and its 'measured length' is 48 cm, then:

absolute error $e_x = 48 - 47 = 1$ cm,

relative error $r_x = \dfrac{e_x}{x} = \dfrac{1}{48} = 0.020\,83... \approx 2.0\%$.

Error bounds

When measuring a physical quantity or rounding off a number it is essential to be able to specify the size of the error which might result from these actions.

The **absolute error bounds** are the limits between which the absolute error lies. So, if $|e_x| \le \varepsilon$, where $\varepsilon > 0$, then ε is called the maximum absolute error bound of x.

Knowing this, we can write $X = x \pm \varepsilon$.

This means that the true value of a number X lies between $x - \varepsilon$ and $x + \varepsilon$, i.e. $X \in [x - \varepsilon,\ x + \varepsilon]$. $x - \varepsilon$ and $x + \varepsilon$ are sometimes called the lower and upper bounds for X respectively.

In general, the maximum absolute error bound when a number has been rounded to n decimal places is

$\frac{1}{2} \times 10^{-n}$, i.e. $0.\underbrace{00...0}_{n \text{ zeros}}5$

| i | A sack contains 50 kg of cement to the nearest kilogram. This means that the absolute error bounds for this mass of cement are ± 0.5 kg. So the true mass of cement in the sack lies between 49.5 kg and 50.5 kg. This is usually given as 50 ± 0.5 kg.

| i | If the irrational number π is taken to be 3.14 (2 d.p.) then the true value of π lies between 3.135 and 3.145. We can say that $\pi = 3.14 \pm 0.005$.

| i | 'The Sun is 93 million miles from the Earth' means that the Sun is 9.3×10^7 miles from Earth, to the nearest million miles.

Here, the absolute error bound is 0.05×10^7 miles.

Absolute and relative errors in calculations

When inexact numbers with known error bounds are used in a calculation, the result of the calculation needs to be given as a value with its calculated error bound. To find such a result, calculate:

• the working value – the answer found by using the given inexact numbers

• the maximum and minimum values – found by using the appropriate upper and lower bounds for the numbers in the calculation

• the mid-value = $\frac{1}{2}$(max. value + min. value)

(The mid-value and working value may differ slightly but both round to the same value.)

• max. absolute error = $\frac{1}{2}$(max. value – min. value)

Then state the result as:

    Result = mid-value   ± error bound.
    or   working value ± error bound

• the error bound is (usually) found by rounding **up** the maximum absolute error to 1 significant figure.
Note: we always round **up** to 1 s.f. when giving the error bound.

The mid-value (or working value) should be rounded **off** to the same *place value* as the significant figure in the error bound.

Relative (or percentage) errors are usually given correct to 2 significant figures.

| i | *If* $x = 3.57$ *and* $y = 4.291$ (*both numbers given correct to the number of decimal places shown*)

(*a*) *write down the absolute errors in x and y*

(*b*) *evaluate xy giving your answer as* $N \pm \varepsilon$, *where* ε *is the absolute error bound*

(*c*) *estimate the approximate maximum relative error in giving the value of xy as N.*

(a) Absolute error in x is ± 0.005.
    Absolute error in y is ± 0.0005.

(b) Working value $= 3.57 \times 4.291 = 15.318\,87$
    maximum value $= 3.575 \times 4.2915 = 15.342\,112\,5$
    minimum value $= 3.565 \times 4.2905 = 15.295\,632\,5$
    mid-value
    $= \frac{1}{2}(15.342\,112\,5 + 15.295\,632\,5) = 15.318\,872\,5$
    maximum absolute error
    $= \frac{1}{2}(15.342\,112\,5 - 15.295\,632\,5) = 0.023\,24$
    error bound $= 0.03$ (i.e. 0.02324 rounded *up* to 1 s.f.)
         $= 3$ *hundredths*

The mid-value (15.318 872 5) and working value (15.318 87) both give 15.32 when rounded *off* to the nearest *hundredth*.
So $xy = 15.32 \pm 0.03$.

(c) Approximate maximum relative error
    $= \dfrac{0.03}{15.32} \approx 0.001\,95... = 0.20\%$ (to 2 s.f.)

Errors and Accuracy
Worked examples, Guided example, Exercises and Exam questions.

 The dimensions of a rectangle are 6.2 cm and 6.4 cm, both measured correct to the nearest millimetre.
Calculate the area of the rectangle, giving absolute error bounds for your answer. State your answer in the form $A \pm \varepsilon$ cm^2, where ε is the absolute error bound.
What is the approximate maximum percentage error in giving the area as A cm^2?

breadth of rectangle: 6.2 ± 0.05 cm

length of rectangle: 6.4 ± 0.05 cm

maximum area $= 6.25 \times 6.45 = 40.3125$

minimum area $= 6.15 \times 6.35 = 39.0525$

maximum absolute error $= \dfrac{\text{max. area} - \text{min. area}}{2} = 0.63$

error bound $= 0.7$ (i.e. 0.63 rounded *up* to 1 s.f.)

$= 7$ *tenths*

area $A \quad = 6.2 \times 6.4 = 39.68$

$= 39.7$ (rounded *off* to the nearest *tenth*)

Result: 39.7 ± 0.7 cm^2

Approximate maximum percentage error is $\dfrac{0.7}{39.7} \approx 1.8\%$.

 A triangular field is surveyed and the following measurements obtained:
AC = 240 m to the nearest metre
angle C = 62° to the nearest degree, and
angle A = 90° exactly.
Calculate the length of the side AB, stating clearly the absolute error bound.

$AC = 240 \pm 0.5$ m

Angle $C = 62 \pm 0.5$ degrees

Using $AB = AC \tan C$,

max. length $AB = 240.5 \times \tan 62.5°$
$ = 461.9962015$

min. length $AB = 239.5 \times \tan 61.5°$
$ = 441.1041272$

max. absolute error $= \dfrac{\text{max.} AB - \text{min.} AB}{2} = 10.44$

error bound $= 20$ (i.e. 10.44 rounded *up* to 1 s.f.) $= 2$ *tens*

$AB = 240 \times \tan 62° = 451.3743517$
$ = 450$ (rounded *off* to the nearest *ten*)

Length $AB = 450 \pm 20$ m.

 A solid right circular cylinder is measured and found to have height 62.6 cm and radius 12.3 cm, each correct to 3 significant figures. Taking π as 3.14,

(a) write down the absolute errors in the measured values for the height and radius of the cylinder and in the given value for π

(b) calculate the surface area of the cylinder, stating clearly the absolute error bound.

(a) Notice that height and radius are each given to 3 s.f. and have 1 d.p. The value for π is given to 3 s.f. and has 2 d.p.

(b) Calculate the maximum and minimum values for the surface area, retaining full calculator display answers.

Use these to find the maximum absolute error, then round this up to 1 significant figure to find the absolute error bound.

Calculate the surface area by finding the mid-value and correcting it to the same number of decimal places as contained in the error bound.

 1 If $x = 2.61$ and $y = 3.57$ (both numbers rounded to 2 d.p.) evaluate the following expressions:

(a) $x + y$ (b) $x - y$ (c) xy (d) $\dfrac{x}{y}$.

Give each answer in the form $N \pm \varepsilon$, where N is the mid-value and ε is the error bound.

2 Three quantities p, q and r are measured and found to be 1.81, 2.43 and 4.86 respectively, correct to two places of decimals.
Find: (a) p^2 (b) $(q - r)^2$ (c) $p^2 - (q - r)^2$
giving each answer correct to two places of decimals. In each case calculate the maximum possible error involved.

3 The formula $T = 2\pi \sqrt{\dfrac{l}{g}}$ is used to calculate the period
T seconds of a pendulum of length l metres.
Estimate the maximum possible percentage error in T when the rounded values for π, l and g are taken to be 3.14, 0.8 and 9.81 respectively.

4 The area of this triangle may be calculated using the formula
$\text{Area} = \frac{1}{2}ab\sin\theta$.
If $a = 5.3$ and $b = 6.2$ (each given correct to 1 d.p.), calculate the area of the triangle when: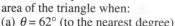
(a) $\theta = 62°$ (to the nearest degree)
(b) $\theta = 127°$ (to the nearest degree).
In each case establish the maximum error in the value obtained. Further, estimate the greatest possible relative error in calculating the area of a triangle in which $a = 6.7$, $b = 4.2$ (each given correct to 1 d.p.) and $\theta = 57°$ (to the nearest degree).

5 When using the formula $A = \pi r^2$, with r measured to within $\frac{1}{4}\%$, give an approximation for the maximum relative error in A if (a) π is taken as 3.142
(b) π is taken as 3.141 59.
What conclusion do you draw about the choice of a numerical value for π?
Find an interval estimate for A when $r = 2.34$ m, correct to the nearest centimetre, and $\pi = 3.142$.

6 Three quantities x, y and z were measured. The results, rounded correct to two significant figures, were
$x = 3.4$, $y = 9.8$, $z = 9.3$.
Find the upper and lower bounds for the values of
(i) $y - z$ (ii) $x / (y - z)$. (O & C)

7 A navigator on a boat at B sights two reference points X and Y which are known to be exactly 1000 m apart, with Y due east of X. The angles θ and ϕ, shown in the diagram, are measured, and the distance x m from B due north to the line XY is calculated from the formula
$$x = \dfrac{1000}{\tan\theta + \tan\phi}.$$
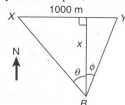
Given that the measured values of the angles are $\theta = 52°$ and $\phi = 15°$, each correct to the nearest degree,
(i) find, correct to 1 decimal place, the greatest and least possible values of x
(ii) estimate the greatest possible relative error in taking
x to be $\dfrac{1000}{\tan 52° + \tan 15°}$. (C)

Solving Equations
Equations in one unknown, Solving linear equations, Solving quadratic equations.

Equations in one unknown

Some algebraic equations contain only **one unknown**. **To solve an equation** in one unknown you have to find the value or values of the unknown for which the equation is true. A **solution** of an equation is said to **satisfy** that equation.

To check a solution, substitute the value in the equation. LHS and RHS should be equal.

> **i** *Check that $x = 2$ and $x = -3$ are solutions of* $x^2 = 6 - x$.
>
> When $x = 2$, LHS : $x^2 = (2)^2 = 4$
>
> RHS : $6 - x = 6 - 2 = 4$ LHS = RHS
>
> When $x = -3$, LHS : $x^2 = (-3)^2 = 9$
>
> RHS : $6 - (-3) = 6 + 3 = 9$ LHS = RHS

Solving linear equations

In a linear equation in x, the only power of x is 1. It can be given in the form $ax + b = 0$, with $a \neq 0$. It has only one solution.

The **balance method** for solving linear equations uses common-sense ideas of balancing and inverses. An equation is like a balanced pair of scales (LHS = RHS). It will still balance if you do exactly the same to each side. To get 'rid of' something, you use an inverse. (*Note*: + and – are 'inverses', × and ÷ are 'inverses'.)

Here is a basic strategy for this method.

• Deal with any brackets and fractions. To clear brackets, multiply them out. To clear fractions, multiply by the lowest common multiple of the denominators.
• Collect x terms on one side of the = sign and number terms on the other. (Use + or –.)
• Obtain 'x = number'. (Use × or ÷.)

The **trial and improvement method** can also be used to solve equations. You try values in the equation in a systematic way until a solution is found.

> **i** $5(2x - 1) = 6x + 11$ is a linear equation in x. It can be given in the form $4x - 16 = 0$. Its solution is $x = 4$.

> **i** *Solve the equation* $\dfrac{2(x-1)}{3} = \dfrac{x}{4} + 1$.
>
> Multiply by 12 $(= 3 \times 4)$: $8(x - 1) = 3x + 12$
>
> Remove brackets: $8x - 8 = 3x + 12$
>
> To get rid of $+3x$, use $-3x$ on both sides.
>
> $5x - 8 = 12$
>
> To get rid of -8, use $+8$ on both sides.
>
> $5x = 20$
>
> To get rid of $\times 5$, divide both sides by 5.
>
> $x = 4$
>
> Check by substituting in the equation.

Solving quadratic equations

A quadratic equation in x contains an x^2 term. It can be given in the form $ax^2 + bx + c = 0$, with $a \neq 0$. In general it has two solutions, but sometimes they are equal. Here are three ways to solve quadratic equations.

1. By factorisation
• Write the equation in the form $ax^2 + bx + c = 0$.
• Factorise the LHS in one of these ways if possible.
Two terms:
Common factor: $ax^2 + bx \equiv x(ax + b)$
Difference of squares: $d^2x^2 - e^2 \equiv (dx + e)(dx - e)$
Three terms:
$a = 1$: Use $x^2 + (m + n)x + mn \equiv (x + m)(x + n)$
$a \neq 1$: Use $prx^2 + (ps + qr)x + qs \equiv (px + q)(rx + s)$
• Since two factors multiply to give zero, one or other or both factors equal zero. Use this to find a value of x from each factor.

2. By completing the square
• Write the equation as: $ax^2 + bx = $ number.
Then divide each term by a (the coefficient of x^2).
• Take half of the new coefficient of x, square it and add this to both sides of the = sign. This completes the square on the LHS. Factorise this perfect square: i.e. $x^2 + px + (\frac{1}{2}p)^2 \equiv (x + \frac{1}{2}p)^2$.
• 'Square root' both sides (remember $\pm\sqrt{}$).
• Find the values of x to the required accuracy.

3. By the formula
• Write the equation in the form: $ax^2 + bx + c = 0$.
• Identify the values of a, b and c. Substitute them in the formula: $x = \dfrac{-b \pm \sqrt{b^2 - 4ac}}{2a}$.
• Find the two values of x to the required accuracy.

Quadratic equations can also be solved by '**trial and improvement**'.

> **i** $2x^2 = 3x + 5$ is a quadratic equation in x. It can be given in the form $2x^2 - 3x - 5 = 0$. Its solutions are $x = 2\frac{1}{2}$ or $x = -1$.

> **i** *Solve*: (a) $3x^2 - 2x = 0$ (b) $x^2 + 6x - 16 = 0$
> (c) $6x^2 - 5x - 4 = 0$.
>
> (a) $3x^2 - 2x = 0 \implies x(3x - 2) = 0$
> $\implies x = 0$ or $(3x - 2) = 0 \implies x = 0$ or $x = \frac{2}{3}$
>
> (b) $x^2 + 6x - 16 = 0 \implies (x + 8)(x - 2) = 0$
> $\implies (x + 8) = 0$ or $(x - 2) = 0 \implies x = -8$ or $x = 2$
>
> (c) $6x^2 - 5x - 4 = 0 \implies (2x + 1)(3x - 4) = 0$
> $\implies (2x + 1) = 0$ or $(3x - 4) = 0 \implies x = -\frac{1}{2}$ or $x = \frac{4}{3}$

> **i** *Solve* $2x^2 - 6x + 1 = 0$ *by completing the square.*
>
> Rearrange the equation: $2x^2 - 6x = -1$
>
> Divide by 2: $x^2 - 3x = -\frac{1}{2}$
>
> Complete the square:
>
> $x^2 - 3x + [\frac{1}{2}(-3)]^2 = -\frac{1}{2} + [\frac{1}{2}(-3)]^2$
>
> Factorise LHS: $[x + \frac{1}{2}(-3)]^2 = 1.75$
>
> Square root: $x + \frac{1}{2}(-3) = \pm\sqrt{1.75}$
>
> Find x : $x = \frac{1}{2}(3) \pm \sqrt{1.75}$
>
> $\therefore x = 2.8$ (to 1 d.p.) or $x = 0.2$ (to 1 d.p.).

> **i** *Solve* $3x^2 = x + 5$ *to 2 decimal places.*
>
> Rearrange $3x^2 = x + 5$ to give $3x^2 - x - 5 = 0$.
>
> Substitute $a = 3$, $b = -1$, $c = -5$ in the formula:
>
> $x = \dfrac{-(-1) \pm \sqrt{(-1)^2 - 4(3)(-5)}}{2(3)} = \dfrac{1 \pm \sqrt{1 + 60}}{6} = \dfrac{1 \pm \sqrt{61}}{6}$
>
> $\therefore x = 1.47$ or $x = -1.14$ (to 2 d.p.).

Solving Equations
Transforming formulae.
Worked examples, Guided example, Exercise.

Transforming formulae

A formula or equation is often given as:

'a letter = an expression not involving that letter'.

The letter on its own on one side of the = sign is called the **subject** of the formula. (It may be on LHS or RHS.)

Transforming (or **transposing**) a formula means rearranging it to change its subject. The method we use is like the balance method for solving equations. Suppose you want to make s the subject of a formula. Here is a step-by-step strategy to follow. (*Remember*: always do the same to both sides.)

• If s is contained in brackets or a root sign or a fraction, deal with anything 'outside' these first.

• Deal with the brackets, root and fractions next. (*Remember*: 'taking the nth root' and 'raising to the power n' are inverses.)

• Collect all 's terms' on one side of the = sign and other terms on the other side. Simplify.

• Factorise each side if possible. (If s occurs more than once, s is a common factor.)

• Get s on its own on its side of the equation. Deal with any multiplier or divisor first. Then deal with powers or roots.

• Write the formula with s on the LHS.

The second $\boxed{\mathbf{i}}$ example uses all the steps. For many formulae you will not need all of them.

$\boxed{\mathbf{i}}$ In the formula $A = lw$, the subject is A. A is expressed in terms of l and w. Either l or w can be made the subject of $A = lw$.

$A = lw$ means $A = l \times w$. So, to make l its subject, use the inverse of '$\times w$', i.e. '$\div w$'. Divide both sides by w.

$$A = l \times w \ \Rightarrow \ \frac{A}{w} = \frac{l \times w}{w} \ \Rightarrow \ \frac{A}{w} = l \ \text{ or } \ l = \frac{A}{w}.$$

To make w the subject of $A = lw$, divide both sides by l.

$\boxed{\mathbf{i}}$ *Make t the subject of* $v = \dfrac{1}{2}\sqrt{\dfrac{gr(u+t)}{1-ut}}$.

Multiply by 2: $\qquad\qquad 2v = \sqrt{\dfrac{gr(u+t)}{1-ut}}$

Square: $\qquad\qquad 4v^2 = \dfrac{gr(u+t)}{1-ut}$

Multiply by $(1-ut)$: $\quad 4v^2(1-ut) = gr(u+t)$

Remove brackets: $\qquad 4v^2 - 4v^2 ut = gru + grt$

Collect 't terms' on RHS, other terms on LHS:

$$4v^2 - gru = 4v^2 ut + grt$$

Factorise: $\qquad\qquad 4v^2 - gru = t(4v^2 u + gr)$

Divide by $(4v^2 u + gr)$: $\dfrac{4v^2 - gru}{4v^2 u + gr} = t$

Write with t on LHS: $\qquad t = \dfrac{4v^2 - gru}{4v^2 u + gr}.$

 Given $A = 180 - \dfrac{360}{n}$, *find n when $A = 162$.*

Substitute $A = 162$: $\qquad 162 = 180 - \dfrac{360}{n}$

Multiply by n: $\qquad 162n = 180n - 360$

Subtract $162n$, add 360: $\qquad 360 = 18n$

Divide by 18: $\qquad 20 = n \ \Rightarrow \ n = 20.$

 Make u the subject of $\dfrac{1}{f} = \dfrac{1}{u} + \dfrac{1}{v}$.

Multiply each term by fuv, LCM of the denominators:

$$\frac{fuv}{f} = \frac{fuv}{u} + \frac{fuv}{v}$$

Cancel: $\qquad\qquad uv = fv + fu$

Collect u terms on LHS: $\quad uv - fu = fv$

Factorise: $\qquad\qquad u(v - f) = fv$

Divide by $(v - f)$: $\qquad u = \dfrac{fv}{v - f}$

$\boxed{\textbf{GE}}$ *For a circle,* $A = \pi r^2$ *and* $C = 2\pi r$.

Express A in terms of C and π.

We must eliminate r from $A = \pi r^2$. Do this as follows. Make r the subject of $C = 2\pi r$. Substitute the expression for r in $A = \pi r^2$. Simplify the result.

$\boxed{\textbf{EX}}$ **1** Solve these linear equations.

(a) $3x - 7 = 32$ (b) $13 - 2(x + 4) = 4(x - 1)$

(c) $\dfrac{4x - 1}{9} = 7$ (d) $\dfrac{x + 2}{3} + \dfrac{2x + 1}{5} = 6$

(e) $5(2x - 3) = 6x + 17$ (f) $5(3x - 1) - 3(1 - 2x) = 76$

(g) $\dfrac{14}{2x + 1} = \dfrac{7}{2}$ (h) $\dfrac{2}{x} = 2 + \dfrac{5}{2x}.$

2 Solve these equations by factorisation.

(a) $8x^2 - x = 0$ (b) $9x^2 - 49 = 0$

(c) $x^2 - 9x + 20 = 0$ (d) $x^2 + 4x - 12 = 0$

(e) $8x^2 + 15 = 22x$ (f) $20x^2 = 9 + 31x.$

3 Solve these equations by completing the square, giving solutions to 1 decimal place.

(a) $x^2 - 8x = 2$ (b) $x^2 = 3 - 5x$

(c) $2x^2 = 8x + 5$ (d) $4x^2 - 3x - 2 = 0.$

4 Solve these equations by formula, giving solutions to 2 decimal places.

(a) $x^2 + 8x + 6 = 0$ (b) $5x^2 = 3 - 3x$

(c) $x^2 - 3x = 5$ (d) $3x^2 + 1 = 5x.$

5 (a) $V = IR$. Find R when $V = 10$, $I = 0.8$.

(b) $y = mx + c$. Find m when $y = 93$, $x = 9$, $c = 66$.

(c) $V = 6rh + 6r^2$. Find h when $V = 48$, $r = 2$.

(d) $C = \dfrac{5}{9}(F - 32)$. Find F when $C = 20$.

(e) $X = a + bt^2$. Find t when $a = 106.3$, $b = 0.03$, $X = 109$.

(f) $N = a + (n - 1)d$. Find n when $a = 3$, $d = 4$, $N = 21$.

6 Rearrange each equation into the given form.

(a) $5y + 2x - 15 = 0$ in the form $y = mx + c$.

(b) $y = 2 - \frac{1}{3}x$ in the form $ay + bx + c = 0$.

(c) $8 - 3x^2 = 9x$ in the form $ax^2 + bx + c = 0$ ($a > 0$).

(d) $6 - 2x^2 = 8x$ in the form $x^2 + px = q$.

7 Make b the subject of each of these formulae.

(a) $V = lbh$ (b) $P = 2(l + b)$

(c) $A = \frac{1}{2}(a + b)h$ (d) $S = 2lb + 2lh + 2bh.$

8 Make r the subject of each of these formulae.

(a) $C = 2\pi r$ (b) $V = \frac{1}{3}\pi r^2 h$

(c) $V = \frac{4}{3}\pi r^3$ (d) $A = \pi(R^2 - r^2)$

(e) $S = \dfrac{r}{1 - r}$ (f) $A = P\left(1 - \dfrac{r}{100}\right)^2.$

Quadratics
Quadratic equations, Quadratic functions.

Quadratic equations

The general **quadratic equation** is of the form

$$ax^2 + bx + c = 0$$

where a, b and c are constants and $a \neq 0$.
The two values of x which make $ax^2 + bx + c$ zero are called the roots of the equation.
The roots are given by

$$x = \frac{1}{2a}\left[-b \pm \sqrt{b^2 - 4ac}\right]$$

$b^2 - 4ac = \Delta$ is the **discriminant** of the equation since it discriminates between the types of roots.
If $\Delta > 0$, the roots are **real** and **different**,
$\quad \Delta = 0$, the roots are **real** and **equal**,
$\quad \Delta < 0$, the roots are **complex**.

Sum and product of roots

If α and β are the roots of $ax^2 + bx + c = 0$, then

$$\alpha + \beta = \frac{-b}{a} \quad \text{and} \quad \alpha\beta = \frac{c}{a}$$

The quadratic equation may be written

$$x^2 - (\text{sum of roots})x + (\text{product of roots}) = 0$$

This can be used to obtain a new quadratic equation whose roots are functions of α and β.
Useful results in such examples are

$$\alpha^2 + \beta^2 = (\alpha + \beta)^2 - 2\alpha\beta$$

$$\alpha^3 + \beta^3 = (\alpha + \beta)^3 - 3\alpha\beta(\alpha + \beta)$$

$$\frac{1}{\alpha} + \frac{1}{\beta} = \frac{\alpha + \beta}{\alpha\beta}$$

$$\frac{1}{\alpha^2} + \frac{1}{\beta^2} = \frac{(\alpha + \beta)^2 - 2\alpha\beta}{(\alpha\beta)^2}$$

ⓘ *Find, to two decimal places, the roots of* $2x^2 - 3x - 4 = 0$.

Use $x = \frac{1}{2a}\left[-b \pm \sqrt{b^2 - 4ac}\right]$ with $a = 2, b = -3, c = -4$.

$$= \tfrac{1}{4}[3 \pm \sqrt{(-3)^2 - 4 \times 2 \times (-4)}]$$
$$= \tfrac{1}{4}[3 \pm \sqrt{41}] = \tfrac{1}{4}[3 \pm 6.403]$$
$$= 2.35 \text{ or } -0.85 \text{ (to 2 d.p.)}$$

ⓘ *Show that* $2x^2 - 3x + 4 = 0$ *has no real roots.*

Use $\Delta = b^2 - 4ac$ with $a = 2, b = -3, c = 4$.
i.e. $\Delta = (-3)^2 - 4 \times 2 \times 4 = 9 - 32 = -23 < 0$.
$\therefore 2x^2 - 3x + 4 = 0$ has no real roots.

ⓘ *If* $3x^2 - 6x + 8 = 0$ *has roots* α *and* β, *find the equation whose roots are* $\frac{1}{\alpha}$ *and* $\frac{1}{\beta}$.

$$\alpha + \beta = -\frac{(-6)}{3} = 2, \quad \alpha\beta = \frac{8}{3}$$

If A *and* B *are the new roots,*

sum of new roots is $A + B = \frac{1}{\alpha} + \frac{1}{\beta} = \frac{\alpha + \beta}{\alpha\beta} = \frac{2}{8/3} = \frac{3}{4}$

product of new roots is $AB = \frac{1}{\alpha} \times \frac{1}{\beta} = \frac{1}{\alpha\beta} = \frac{3}{8}$

The new equation is $x^2 - (A + B)x + (AB) = 0$
i.e. $x^2 - \tfrac{3}{4}x + \tfrac{3}{8} = 0$
or $8x^2 - 6x + 3 = 0$

Quadratic functions

The general **quadratic function** is $f(x) \equiv ax^2 + bx + c$.
By **completing the square** on the RHS.

$$f(x) \equiv a\left[\left(x + \frac{b}{2a}\right)^2 - \left(\frac{b^2 - 4ac}{4a^2}\right)\right]$$

Graph of a quadratic function

The graph of $f(x) \equiv ax^2 + bx + c$ is a **parabola**.

Its **axis of symmetry** is $x = -\frac{b}{2a}$.

If $a > 0$, $f(x)$ has a minimum.
If $a < 0$, $f(x)$ has a maximum.

Its maximum or minimum
value is $-\left(\frac{b^2 - 4ac}{4a}\right)$.

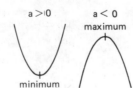

Figure 1

If $f(x) = 0$, the graph
(a) cuts the x-axis twice, if $(b^2 - 4ac) > 0$,
(b) touches the x-axis, if $(b^2 - 4ac) = 0$,
(c) does not cut the x-axis, if $(b^2 - 4ac) < 0$.

Values of a rational quadratic function

To find the range of possible values of a function of
the type $y = \frac{ax^2 + bx + c}{px^2 + qx + r}$, when x is real

(a) rearrange the equation as a quadratic in x,
(b) use the fact that $(b^2 - 4ac) \geq 0$ for real x.

ⓘ *Sketch the graph of* $f(x) \equiv 3x^2 - 7x + 4$.

$f(x)$ is a quadratic function so its graph is a parabola.
Its axis of symmetry is $x = -\frac{(-7)}{2(3)} = \frac{7}{6}$.
Since $a = 3$, i.e. $a > 0$, $f(x)$ has a minimum.

Its value is $-\left[\frac{(-7)^2 - 4(3)(4)}{4(3)}\right] = -\left(\frac{49 - 48}{12}\right) = -\frac{1}{12}$.

Since $\Delta > 0$, $f(x)$ cuts the x-axis twice at

$$x = \frac{-(-7) \pm \sqrt{1}}{2(3)} = \frac{7 \pm 1}{6} = \frac{8}{6} \text{ or } \frac{6}{6}.$$

When $x = 0$, $f(x) = 4$.

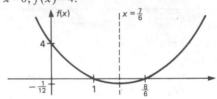

Figure 2

ⓘ *If* x *is real, find the possible range of values of* $y = (x^2 + x + 1)/(x + 1)$.

The given expression is $x^2 + x + 1 - y(x + 1) = 0$
$$x^2 + (1 - y)x + (1 - y) = 0$$

For real x, $b^2 - 4ac \geq 0$
i.e. $(1 - y)^2 - 4.1.(1 - y) \geq 0$
$(1 - y)(1 - y - 4) \geq 0$
$(1 - y)(y + 3) \leq 0$ So $y \geq 1$ or $y \leq -3$.

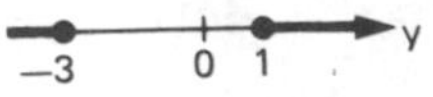

Figure 3

Quadratics
Worked examples, Guided example and Exam questions.

 Show that, for all real x, $0 < \dfrac{1}{x^2+4x+5} \leqslant 1$.

Sketch the curve $y = \dfrac{1}{x^2+4x+5}$.

Completing the square on x^2+4x+5 gives $(x+2)^2+1$.
Since $(x+2)^2 \geqslant 0$, $(x+2)^2+1 \geqslant 1$ and so

$$1 \geqslant \frac{1}{x^2+4x+5}.$$

Since $\dfrac{1}{x^2}$ tends to zero through

positive values for $|x|$ large, $\dfrac{1}{x^2} > 0$.

Similarly $\dfrac{1}{(x+2)^2+1} > 0$

$\therefore \ 0 < \dfrac{1}{x^2+4x+5} \leqslant 1$

To sketch $y = \dfrac{1}{x^2+4x+5}$, consider $y_1 = x^2+4x+5$

$$= (x+2)^2+1$$

which is a parabola, axis of symmetry $x = -2$, vertex down and minimum value $y = 1$.

Clearly for each value of x

$y = \dfrac{1}{y_1}$ and y has axis of

symmetry $x = -2$, vertex up and a maximum value of $y = 1$. The x-axis is an asymptote for y.

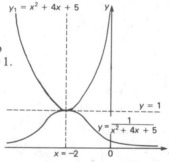

 Given that α and β are the roots of the equation $ax^2+bx+c = 0$, where a, b and c are real and $a \neq 0$, write down the values of $\alpha+\beta$ and $\alpha\beta$ in terms of a, b and c. State the conditions that the roots α and β are equal in magnitude but opposite in sign. Hence find the value of k for which the equation

$$\frac{x^2-2x}{4x-c} = \frac{k-1}{k+1}$$

has roots equal in magnitude but opposite in sign.

If α and β are the roots of $ax^2+bx+c = 0$ then
$\alpha+\beta = -\dfrac{b}{a}$, $\alpha\beta = \dfrac{c}{a}$.

For α and β to be equal in magnitude but opposite in sign, $b = 0$ and a and c have opposite signs.

$\dfrac{x^2-2x}{4x-c} = \dfrac{k-1}{k+1}$

$\Rightarrow (x^2-2x)(k+1) = (4x-c)(k-1)$
$\Rightarrow x^2k - 2xk + x^2 - 2x - 4xk + 4x + ck - c = 0$
i.e. $x^2(k+1) + x(-6k+2) + c(k-1) = 0$
For this equation to have roots equal in magnitude but opposite in sign $-6k+2 = 0$, i.e. $k = \tfrac{1}{3}$.

 Show that $x = 2$ is a root of the equation $x^3+x-10 = 0$. Given that the other roots are α and β, show that $\alpha+\beta = -2$ and find the value of $\alpha\beta$.

Find the equations with numerical coefficients whose roots are
(i) $\alpha+3$ and $\beta+3$; (ii) $5, \alpha+3$ and $\beta+3$.

Let $f(x) = x^3+x-10$.
Show $f(2) = 0$, when $(x-2)$ is a factor of $f(x)$ and $x = 2$ is a root of $f(x) = 0$.
Show $f(x) = (x-2)(ax^2+bx+c)$ i.e. a linear factor times a quadratic factor, when α and β will be the roots of

$ax^2+bx+c = 0$ and $\alpha+\beta = -\dfrac{b}{a}$ and $\alpha\beta = \dfrac{c}{a}$

(i) Let $A = \alpha+3$, $B = \beta+3$
Find $A+B$ and AB when required equation is
$x^2-(A+B)x+AB = 0$

(ii) The required equation will be
$(x-5)[x^2-(A+B)x+AB] = 0$

---

 1 Find the range of values of q for which the roots of the equation $x^2+6x+q^2-7 = 0$ are real. If q is a positive integer, list the values of q for which the roots of the equation are real and of the same sign, giving reasons for your answer. *(A)*

2 (a) Given that the roots of $x^2+px+q = 0$ are α and β, form an equation whose roots are $\dfrac{1}{\alpha}$ and $\dfrac{1}{\beta}$.

(b) Given that α is a root of the equation $x^2 = 2x-3$ show that (i) $\alpha^3 = \alpha-6$, (ii) $\alpha^2-2\alpha^3 = 9$. *(C)*

3 (a) Find the set of values of k for which the equation $x^2+kx+2k-3 = 0$ has no real roots.
When $k = 7$, the roots of the equation $x^2+kx+2k-3 = 0$ are α and β, where $\alpha > \beta$.
(b) Write down the values of $(\alpha+\beta)$ and $\alpha\beta$.
(c) Form an equation with integral coefficients whose roots are $\dfrac{\alpha}{\beta}$ and $\dfrac{\beta}{\alpha}$.
(d) Prove that $\alpha-\beta = \sqrt{5}$. *(L)*

4 (a) If α^2 and β^2 are the roots of $x^2-21x+4 = 0$ and α and β are both positive, find:
(i) $\alpha\beta$; (ii) $\alpha+\beta$; (iii) the equation with roots $\dfrac{1}{\alpha^2}$ and $\dfrac{1}{\beta^2}$
(b) If $\alpha+\beta = 5$ and $\alpha\beta = 2$, calculate $\dfrac{1}{\alpha}+\dfrac{1}{\beta}$ and hence determine the values of m and n such that $x^2+mx+n = 0$ has roots $\dfrac{1}{\alpha}$ and $\dfrac{1}{\beta}$. *(S)*

5 Prove that the equation $x(x-2p) = q(x-p)$ has real roots for all real values of p and q. If $q = 3$, find a non-zero value for p so that the roots are rational. *(H)*

6 Given that α and β are the roots of the equation $3x^2+x+2 = 0$,
(i) evaluate $\dfrac{1}{\alpha^2}+\dfrac{1}{\beta^2}$;
(ii) find an equation whose roots are $\dfrac{1}{\alpha^2}$ and $\dfrac{1}{\beta^2}$;
(iii) show that $27\alpha^4 = 11\alpha+10$. *(A)*

7 (a) Find the set of real values of x for which $x^2-9x+20$ is negative.
(b) Find the set of values of k for which x^2+kx+9 is positive for all real values of x. *(A)*

8 The real roots of the equation $x^2+6x+c = 0$ differ by $2n$, where n is real and non-zero. Show that $n^2 = 9-c$. Given that the roots also have opposite signs, find the set of possible values of n. *(J)*

P5
core

Solving Simultaneous Equations
Simultaneous equations in two unknowns, Solving simultaneous linear equations,
One linear and one quadratic equation.

Simultaneous equations in two unknowns

Only pairs of **simultaneous equations in two unknowns**, x and y say, are solved in this Unit. They are called simultaneous equations because the two letters stand for the **same two numbers** in each equation. A solution is made up of **two numbers** (a value of x and a value of y) that satisfy **both** equations **at the same time**, i.e. simultaneously.

To check a solution, substitute both values in each equation. In each case, LHS should equal RHS.

[i] $x - y = 5$ and $y = 3x - 9$ are simultaneous equations in x and y. The solution is $x = 2$, $y = -3$.

Check this solution by substituting $x = 2$, $y = -3$ in each equation.

In $x - y = 5$: LHS $= x - y = 2 - (-3) = 2 + 3 = 5$
                    RHS $= 5$
In $y = 3x - 9$: LHS $= y = -3$
                     RHS $= 3x - 9 = 3(2) - 9 = -3$
In each case, LHS = RHS.

Solving simultaneous linear equations

In a linear equation the highest power of each unknown is 1.

Some methods of solving a pair of simultaneous **linear equations** in two unknowns (x and y) are given below.

Graphical method

Draw the graph of each equation on the same axes. The (x, y) coordinates of the point where the two graphs cross solve the equations simultaneously. Read off these values as accurately as you can. Check them by substituting in **both** equations. *Remember*: the solution may be only approximate. See **WE** opposite.

Substitution method

This method is easiest to use when one equation contains a simple x or $-x$ or y or $-y$.

(a) Make x or y the subject of one equation, i.e.
    $x =$ expression in terms of y only, or
    $y =$ expression in terms of x only.

(b) Substitute this expression for the unknown in the other equation. The result is an equation in only one unknown. Solve this equation.

(c) Substitute the value found into the simpler **original** equation and find the value of the other unknown.

(d) Check the solution by substituting the x- and y-values in the other **original** equation.

Elimination method

(a) Write x's, y's and numbers in the same order in both equations. Rearrange the terms if necessary.

(b) Compare x's and y's in the two equations. Decide which unknown is easier to eliminate. Make sure the 'number' of this unknown is the same in both equations. This may involve multiplying one or both equations by a number or numbers.

(c) Eliminate the 'equal terms' by adding or subtracting equations. If the 'equal terms' have the same signs ($+ +$ or $- -$), subtract. If they have different signs ($+ -$ or $- +$), add.

(d) Solve the resulting equation. This gives the value of one unknown. Substitute it in the simpler **original** equation and find the value of the other unknown.

(e) Check the solution by substituting it in the other **original** equation.

Simultaneous equations can also be solved by tria**l and improvement.**

[i] $2x + 5y = 3$ is a linear equation in x and y. The highest powers of x and y in it are x^1 and y^1.

[i] The graph of each linear equation is a straight line. Two straight-line graphs may:

(a) cross at one point (giving one solution), or

(b) be parallel (giving no solution), or

(c) be identical (giving an infinite number of solutions).

[i] *Solve* $x + 2y = 8$, $3y - 4x = 1$ *simultaneously*.

Rearrange $x + 2y = 8$ to give x in terms of y:
$$x + 2y = 8 \Rightarrow x = 8 - 2y$$

Substitute $(8 - 2y)$ for x in $3y - 4x = 1$ and solve this equation to find the value of y:
$$3y - 4(8 - 2y) = 1$$
$$\Rightarrow 3y - 32 + 8y = 1 \Rightarrow 11y = 33 \Rightarrow y = 3$$

Substitute $y = 3$ in $x + 2y = 8$: $x + 2(3) = 8$
Find the value of x: $x = 8 - 6 = 2$

So the solution is $x = 2$, $y = 3$.

Check whether $x = 2$, $y = 3$ satisfy $3y - 4x = 1$.

[i] *Solve* $7y = 6 - 4x$, $3x = 2y + 19$ *simultaneously*.
$$7y = 6 - 4x \quad \Rightarrow 4x + 7y = 6 \quad\quad [1]$$
$$3x = 2y + 19 \quad \Rightarrow 3x - 2y = 19 \quad\quad [2]$$

We choose to eliminate y.

Multiply [1] by 2: $8x + 14y = 12$
Multiply [2] by 7: $21x - 14y = 133$
Add these equations: $29x \quad\quad = 145$

Find the value of x: $x = \dfrac{145}{29} = 5$

Substitute $x = 5$ into $7y = 6 - 4x$: $7y = 6 - 4(5)$
Find the value of y: $7y = -14$
                                 $\Rightarrow y = -2$

So the solution is $x = 5$, $y = -2$.

Check whether $x = 5$, $y = -2$ satisfy $3x = 2y + 19$.

One linear and one quadratic equation

In a **quadratic equation** the highest power of each unknown is 2.

A linear and a quadratic equation in the same two unknowns can be solved simultaneously by **trial and improvement**, **graphically** or **by substitution.**

These equations have, in general, *two solutions*. Always state clearly which two values make up each solution.

[i] A linear equation gives a straight-line graph and a quadratic gives a curve. These two graphs may:

(a) cross at two points (giving two solutions), or

(b) touch at one point (giving one solution), or

(c) not cross or meet (giving no solutions).

Solving Simultaneous Equations

Worked examples, Guided example, Exercises and Exam questions.

 Use the graph below to solve these simultaneous equations:

(a) $y = 3 + x$ and
     $x + y = 3$

(b) $y = 3 + x$ and
     $y = x^2 - x - 2$

(c) $x + y = 3$ and
     $y = x^2 - x - 2$.

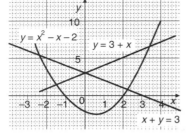

From the points of intersection of the graphs, the solutions are:

(a) $x = 0$, $y = 3$.

(b) $x \approx -1.4$, $y \approx 1.5$ and $x \approx 3.4$, $y \approx 6.5$.

(c) $x \approx -2.2$, $y \approx 5$ and $x \approx 2.2$, $y \approx 0.5$.

 Solve the simultaneous equations: $y - 2x = 1$, $y^2 = 2x^2 + x$.

We choose to use the linear equation to give y in terms of x;

$$y - 2x = 1 \Rightarrow y = 1 + 2x.$$

Substitute $(1 + 2x)$ for y in $y^2 = 2x^2 + x$:

$$(1 + 2x)^2 = 2x^2 + x$$

This gives a quadratic equation:

$$1 + 4x + 4x^2 = 2x^2 + x$$
$$2x^2 + 3x + 1 = 0$$

Solve this equation to find the values of x:

$$(2x + 1)(x + 1) = 0 \Rightarrow x = -\tfrac{1}{2} \text{ or } -1.$$

Substitute these values in $y - 2x = 1$ to find the values of y.

When $x = -\tfrac{1}{2}$, $y - 2(-\tfrac{1}{2}) = 1 \Rightarrow y = 0$

When $x = -1$, $y - 2(-1) = 1 \Rightarrow y = -1$

The solutions are $x = -\tfrac{1}{2}$, $y = 0$ and $x = -1$, $y = -1$.

(Check these solutions satisfy $y^2 = 2x^2 + x$.)

 Solve simultaneously:

$$\log_2(x + y) = 0 \text{ and } \log_2 x - 2\log_2 y = 1.$$

Use the basic rules of logarithms (see Unit P8) to rewrite each equation.

$$\log_2(x + y) = 0 \Rightarrow x + y = 2^0 \Rightarrow x + y = 1 \qquad [1]$$

$$\log_2 x - 2\log_2 y = 1 \Rightarrow \log_2\left(\frac{x}{y^2}\right) = 1 \Rightarrow \frac{x}{y^2} = 2^1$$
$$\Rightarrow x = 2y^2 \qquad [2]$$

Solve equations [1] and [2] simultaneously in the usual way.

1 (a) Find the gradient of the line $2y = x + 4$.
   (b) On a grid, draw and label the lines $2y = x + 4$ and $y = 4 - x$.
   (c) Obtain the solution of the simultaneous equations $2y = x + 4$, $y = 4 - x$ giving the value of x and the value of y correct to 1 decimal place.   *(MEG)*

2 Find the coordinates of the point of intersection of $y = 2x - 3$ and $x + 2y = 7$ by a graphical method and by an algebraic method.

3 Solve these linear equations simultaneously:
   (a) $x = 9 - 3y$ and $4x - 2y = 1$
   (b) $2a - 3b = 11$ and $3a - 2b = 6\tfrac{1}{2}$
   (c) $3p - 4q = 10$ and $5p + 2q = 8$
   (d) $3x = 11 + 2y$ and $5x - 3y = 18$.

4 Solve these equations simultaneously:
   (a) $x^2 + y^2 = 1$ and $2x + y = 2$
   (b) $3x + 2y = 25$ and $xy = 4$
   (c) $2x - y + 1 = 0$ and $x^2 - 2xy + y^2 = 1$
   (d) $y = 3x - 2$, $y^2 = x$.

5 Try to solve these equations simultaneously:
   (a) $y = 3x - 1$ and $2y = 6x + 1$
   (b) $x + 4y = 1$ and $3x = 3 - 12y$
   (c) $y = x^2 + 5$ and $y + x + 3 = 0$
   (d) $y + 3 = 2x$ and $y = x^2 - 2x + 1$
   Comment on what you find.

6 The points $A(q, p)$ and $B(q + 1, 2p - 2)$ both lie on the line whose equation is $y = 5x + 1$. Find the values of p and q and the coordinates of A and B.

7 The sides of a triangle are the lines $y = 0$, $x = 3y - 5$ and $2x + y - 7 = 0$. Find the coordinates of the vertices of the triangle.

8 The graph of $y = mx + c$ passes through the points $(1, -1)$ and $(3, 5)$. Find the values of m and c.

9 Find the coordinates of the points of intersection of $x - 2y = 1$ and $x^2 - 2xy + 2y^2 = 25$.

10 Solve these equations simultaneously:

$$2y - 3x = 2 \text{ and } 4y^2 - 4xy - 18x^2 = 5.$$

11 Solve the simultaneous equations: $y = x - 2$, $y^2 = x$.   *(C)*

12 Solve the simultaneous equations:
   $x + y = 2$, $x^2 + 2y^2 = 11$.   *(C)*

13 Solve the simultaneous equations:

$$y = 6x + 4, \quad y = \frac{2}{x + 1} - 1.$$ *(O & C)*

14 Solve the simultaneous equations:

$$4x^2 + y^2 = 25$$
$$xy = 6$$

giving all possible pairs of values of x and y.   *(W)*

15 Solve the simultaneous equations:

$$\log_2 xy = 7$$
$$\log_2 \frac{x^2}{y} = 5.$$ *(A)*

16 Find the values of x and y such that $y = 2x$ and $\log_2 y + \log_2 x = 3$.

17 Show that $\log_9(xy^2) = \tfrac{1}{2}\log_3 x + \log_3 y$.
   Hence or otherwise, solve the simultaneous equations:
   $$\log_9(xy^2) = \tfrac{1}{2}$$
   $$(\log_3 x)(\log_3 y) = -3.$$ *(A)*

P6

core

Inequations
Rules for manipulating inequations, Solving inequations, Modulus.

Rules for manipulating inequations

If a, b, c, d and k are numbers such that $a>b$ and $c>d$, then:

(a) $a\pm k>b\pm k$

(b) $ak>bk$ for $k>0$

      $ak<bk$ for $k<0$.

(c) $a+c>b+d$

A similar set of results arise for $<$.

Note: We cannot make any deductions about:
$a-c$ and $b-d$ or ac and bd or $a\div c$ and $b\div d$.

ℹ️ $5>-2$ and $5+1>-2+1$ i.e. $6>-1$
$4>2$ and $4-7>2-7$ i.e. $-3>-5$

$4>-6$ and $2\times4>2\times-6$ i.e. $8>-12$
$3>-1$ and $-1\times3<-1\times-1$ i.e. $-3<1$

$4>2$ and $3>-1$, so $4+3>2+-1$ i.e. $7>1$

Solving inequations

The **solution of an inequation** is a range (or ranges) of values of the variable.

1. Linear inequations in one unknown
These can be solved using the rules of inequations. The solution set can be illustrated on a number line. Note the symbols used:

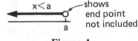

Figure 1 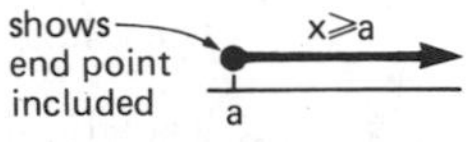   Figure 2

2. Linear inequations in two unknowns
These are best solved graphically.
The corresponding equality gives the boundary line. This is drawn as:

(a) a continuous line if the inequation is $\geqslant$ or $\leqslant$,
(b) a dotted line if the inequation is $>$ or $<$.

A convenient point is chosen to identify on which side of the line the inequation applies. The solution set of the inequation is usually left unshaded.

3. Quadratic inequations

(a) solution using a number line
If the inequation is written as $f(x)>0$ or $f(x)<0$, then the end points of the inequation can be found by solving the corresponding quadratic equation. A convenient point is tested to identify the range.

(b) graphical solution
The graph of the corresponding quadratic equality (a parabola) is sketched. By inspection the range corresponding to the inequation can be seen.

4. Other inequations
These are usually solved graphically.

ℹ️   Find the solution of $8-x\geqslant5x-4$.

$8-x\geqslant5x-4\Rightarrow8+4\geqslant5x+x\Rightarrow12\geqslant6x$
$\Rightarrow\ 2\geqslant x$

This is illustrated as:

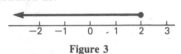

Figure 3

ℹ️   *Solve $y\geqslant0$, $x+y\leqslant2$ and $y-2x<2$.*

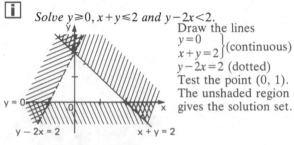

Draw the lines
$\left.\begin{array}{l}y=0\\x+y=2\end{array}\right\}$(continuous)
$y-2x=2$ (dotted)
Test the point $(0, 1)$.
The unshaded region gives the solution set.

Figure 4

ℹ️   Find the solution of $x^2-2x-8\leqslant0$.

(a) $x^2-2x-8\leqslant0\Rightarrow(x-4)(x+2)\leqslant0$
End points are $x=4$, $x=-2$.
Test $x=0$: $(-4)(2)=-8\leqslant0$ (true)
So $-2\leqslant x\leqslant4$.

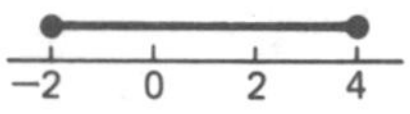

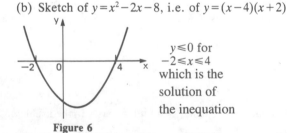

Figure 5

(b) Sketch of $y=x^2-2x-8$, i.e. of $y=(x-4)(x+2)$

$y\leqslant0$ for
$-2\leqslant x\leqslant4$
which is the
solution of
the inequation

Figure 6

Modulus

The **modulus function** $f(x)=|x|$ is defined as

$$|x|=x\ \text{for}\ x\geqslant0,$$
$$|x|=-x\ \text{for}\ x<0.$$

So $|x|$ is the numerical value of x.
$|x|$ is read as 'mod x'.
The graphs of $y=x$ and $y=|x|$ are:

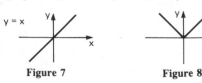

Figure 7   Figure 8

For $x<0$, $y=|x|$ is the reflection of $y=x$ in x-axis.

ℹ️ $\left.\begin{array}{l}|x-4|\leqslant2\ \text{means}\ x-4\leqslant\ \ 2\Rightarrow x\leqslant6\\ \text{or}\ -(x-4)\leqslant2\ \text{ i.e. }x-4\geqslant-2\Rightarrow x\geqslant2\end{array}\right\}$ So $2\leqslant x\leqslant6$.

ℹ️   *Solve $|x|>|2-x|$.*

$$|x|>|2-x|$$
$$\Rightarrow\ \ \ \ x>2-x\ \text{or}\ -x>2-x$$
$$\Rightarrow\ \ \ 2x>2\ \ \ \ \text{or}\ \ \ 0>2\ (\text{impossible})$$

Hence $2x>2$
$$\Rightarrow\ \ \ \ x>1$$

Inequations
Worked example, Guided example and Exam questions.

 Obtain the three sets of values of x for which

(a) $2x > \dfrac{1}{x}$

(b) $\dfrac{1}{x-1} > \dfrac{x}{3-x}$

(c) $2|x-1| > |x+1|$

(a) To preserve the order of the inequality, multiply both sides by x^2 to give $2x^3 > x$

i.e. $2x^3 - x > 0$

or $x(2x^2 - 1) > 0$

giving $x(\sqrt{2}x - 1)(\sqrt{2}x + 1) > 0$

The values $x = -\dfrac{1}{\sqrt{2}}$, $x = 0$ and $x = \dfrac{1}{\sqrt{2}}$ divide the domain

into four parts. The sign of the factors in each part is best investigated using a tabular display.

	$x < -\dfrac{1}{\sqrt{2}}$	$-\dfrac{1}{\sqrt{2}} < x < 0$	$0 < x < \dfrac{1}{\sqrt{2}}$	$\dfrac{1}{\sqrt{2}} < x$
x	$-$	$-$	$+$	$+$
$(\sqrt{2}x - 1)$	$-$	$-$	$-$	$+$
$(\sqrt{2}x + 1)$	$-$	$+$	$+$	$+$
$x(\sqrt{2}x - 1)(\sqrt{2}x + 1)$	$-$	$+$	$-$	$+$
		$-\dfrac{1}{\sqrt{2}} < x < 0$		$\dfrac{1}{\sqrt{2}} < x$

$\therefore$ Solution set is $\left\{ x: -\dfrac{1}{\sqrt{2}} < x < 0 \text{ or } \dfrac{1}{\sqrt{2}} < x \right\}$

(b) $\dfrac{1}{x-1} > \dfrac{x}{3-x}$

To preserve the order of the inequality multiply both sides by $(x-1)^2$ and $(3-x)^2$, giving $(x-1)(3-x)^2 > x(3-x)(x-1)^2$

i.e. $(x-1)(3-x)[(3-x) - x(x-1)] > 0$

$\qquad (x-1)(3-x)(3-x^2) > 0$

or $\qquad (x-1)(3-x)(\sqrt{3}-x)(\sqrt{3}+x) > 0$

The four values $x = -\sqrt{3}, x = 1, x = \sqrt{3}, x = 3$ divide the domain into five parts, the sign of each factor in each part is best investigated in a tabular form.

	$x < -\sqrt{3}$	$-\sqrt{3} < x < 1$	$1 < x < \sqrt{3}$	$\sqrt{3} < x < 3$	$3 < x$
$(\sqrt{3}+x)$	$-$	$+$	$+$	$+$	$+$
$(x-1)$	$-$	$-$	$+$	$+$	$+$
$(\sqrt{3}-x)$	$+$	$+$	$+$	$-$	$-$
$(3-x)$	$+$	$+$	$+$	$+$	$-$
Product	$+$	$-$	$+$	$-$	$+$
	$x < -\sqrt{3}$		$1 < x < \sqrt{3}$		$3 < x$

$\therefore$ the solution set is

$\{x: x < -\sqrt{3} \text{ or } 1 < x < \sqrt{3} \text{ or } 3 < x\}$

(c) $2|x-1| > |x+1|$

$2(x-1) > (x+1)$ or $-2(x-1) > (x+1)$

$\quad 2x - 2 > x + 1$ or $\quad -2x + 2 > x + 1$

$\qquad x > 3$ or $\qquad\qquad 1 > 3x$

$\qquad\qquad\qquad\qquad\qquad\qquad \tfrac{1}{3} > x$

$\therefore$ the solution set is $\{x: x < \tfrac{1}{3} \text{ or } 3 < x\}$

Find the set of values of x for which

(a) $x^2 - 5x + 6 \geqslant 2$

(b) $\dfrac{1}{x^2 - 5x + 6} \leqslant \dfrac{1}{2}$

(a) Rearrange the inequality to give $x^2 - 5x + 4 \geqslant 0$ and solve directly.

(b) A sketch of $y = x^2 - 5x + 6$ is helpful.

Write $y = (x-3)(x-2) = \left(x - \dfrac{5}{2}\right)^2 - \dfrac{1}{4}$

from which we deduce that the graph has zeros at $x = 2$, $x = 3$, is vertex down with axis of symmetry $x = \dfrac{5}{2}$ and minimum value $-\dfrac{1}{4}$. The graph indicates that there are three sets of values of x to be considered, two where y is positive and one where y is negative.

Now consider $\dfrac{1}{y} \leqslant \dfrac{1}{2}$ for each of these sets of values of x,

taking care with the direction of the inequality when rearranging, deduce the values of x within these ranges for which the inequality holds.

1 (a) Find the range of values of x for which $4x^2 - 12x + 5 < 0$.

   (b) Find the ranges of values of x such that $x > \dfrac{2}{x-1}$. *(A)*

2 Find in each case the set of real values of x for which:

   (i) $3(x+1) \geqslant x - 1$;

   (ii) $\dfrac{3}{x-1} \geqslant \dfrac{1}{x+1}$. *(A)*

3 For what real values of x is $\left|\dfrac{1}{1+2x}\right| = 1$?

   Solve the inequality $\left|\dfrac{1}{1+2x}\right| < 1$. *(O & C)*

4 Find the sets of real values of x for which:

   (i) $(2-3x)(1+x) < 0$;

   (ii) $\dfrac{x}{(2-3x)(1+x)} > 0$;

   (iii) $\dfrac{2}{x} - 3x < 1$. *(A)*

5 Solve the inequality $x^2 - |x| - 12 < 0$. *(J)*

6 Find the set of values of x for which $\dfrac{x(x+2)}{x-3} < x + 1$. *(C)*

7 Sketch the region in the xy plane within which all three of the following inequalities are satisfied:
   (i) $y < x+1$; (ii) $y > (x-1)^2$; (iii) $xy < 2$.
   Determine the area of this region. *(J)*

P7 Polynomials
core
Definitions, Operations, Factorising, Factor theorem.

Definitions

A **polynomial** in x, a variable, is an expression of the form

$$c_0 x^n + c_1 x^{n-1} + c_2 x^{n-2} + \ldots + c_{n-1} x + c_n$$

where n is a positive integer
and $c_0, c_1, c_2, \ldots, c_{n-1}, c_n$ are constants.

The **degree** of the polynomial is n, the highest power of x.

The **constant** term is c_n.

For brevity we often write $f(x)$ for

$$c_0 x^n + c_1 x^{n-1} + c_2 x^{n-2} + \ldots + c_{n-1} x + c_n.$$

| i |

$$2x^7 + 3x^5 - x^4 + 6x + 4$$

is a polynomial of degree 7, with constant term 4.

$4x^2 + \dfrac{5}{x^3}$ is *not* a polynomial. It contains $\dfrac{5}{x^3}$ $(= 5x^{-3})$ i.e. a negative power of x.

Polynomials of low degree have special names.

Degree	Name	Example
1	linear	$3x - 2$
2	quadratic	$4x^2 + 3x + 8$
3	cubic	$8x^3 - 7x + 2$

Operations

Addition and subtraction

Add or subtract *like terms* (i.e. with the same power of x). *Remember*: the sign in front of a term 'belongs' to it. The working can be set out like an ordinary 'sum'. Put one polynomial underneath the other. Put terms in order with the highest power of x first. Write like terms in the same column. Leave gaps for missing terms.

Multiplication

Multiply each term in one polynomial by each term in the other. Collect like terms together. The working can be set out like a long multiplication. Write one polynomial underneath the other with like terms in the same column. Leave gaps for missing terms. Multiply by each term on the second line in turn. Record the result of each of these steps on a separate line. Put each term in its correct column. Finally add like terms.

| i |

$$f(x) \equiv 3x^4 - 5x^3 \qquad\quad + x - 4$$
$$g(x) \equiv \qquad\quad 4x^3 - 3x^2 + 4x + 3$$
$$\overline{f(x) + g(x) \equiv 3x^4 - x^3 - 3x^2 + 5x - 1}$$

| i |

$$f(x) \equiv 3x^4 - 5x^3 \qquad\quad + x - 4$$
$$g(x) \equiv \qquad\quad 4x^3 - 3x^2 + 4x + 3$$
$$\overline{f(x) - g(x) \equiv 3x^4 - 9x^3 + 3x^2 - 3x - 7}$$

| i |

$$f(x) \qquad\quad 3x^3 \quad -2x + 4$$
$$g(x) \qquad\qquad\quad x^2 \quad\; - 3$$
$$f(x) \times x^2 \quad 3x^5 - 2x^3 + 4x^2$$
$$f(x) \times -3 \qquad\quad - 9x^3 \qquad + 6x - 12$$
$$\overline{f(x) \times g(x) \;\; 3x^5 - 11x^3 + 4x^2 + 6x - 12}$$

Factorising

Factorising a polynomial changes it from a sum of terms into a **product of factors**. Multiplying the factors together gives the polynomial as a sum of terms again. (This is a useful check of a factorisation.)

A **common factor** is a factor of each term in the polynomial. When factorising, always take out a common factor first if you can.

The factors of the following polynomials are useful to know or recognise.

Difference of two squares: $x^2 - a^2 = (x - a)(x + a)$

Perfect square trinomials: $x^2 \pm 2ax + a^2 = (x \pm a)^2$

Quadratic trinomials:

$$x^2 + (m + n)x + mn = (x + m)(x + n)$$
$$prx^2 + (ps + qr)x + qs = (px + q)(rx + s)$$

Sum and difference of two cubes:
$$x^3 \pm a^3 = (x \pm a)(x^2 \mp ax + a^2)$$

| i | $x^4 + x^3 - 3x^2 - 4x - 4$ factorises into

$(x + 2)(x - 2)(x^2 + x + 1)$, i.e. two linear factors,

$(x + 2)$ and $(x - 2)$, and a quadratic factor, $(x^2 + x + 1)$.

$$8x^6 + 4x^3 - 6x = (2x \times 4x^5) + (2x \times 2x^2) - (2x \times 3)$$
$$= 2x(4x^5 + 2x^3 - 3)$$

| i | $9x^2 - 4 = (3x)^2 - (2)^2 = (3x - 2)(3x + 2)$

$$x^2 + 6x + 9 = (x + 3)^2, \quad x^2 - 2x + 1 = (x - 1)^2$$

$$x^2 + 2x - 15 = (x - 3)(x + 5)$$
$$3x^2 - 17x + 10 = (3x - 2)(x - 5)$$

$$x^{12} + 125 = (x^4)^3 + 5^3 = (x^4 + 5)(x^8 - 5x^4 - 25)$$
$$8x^3 - 1 = (2x)^3 - 1^3 = (2x - 1)(4x^2 + 2x + 1)$$

Factor theorem

If $(x - a)$ is a **factor** of $f(x)$, then $f(a) = 0$. Conversely if $f(a) = 0$, then $(x - a)$ is a factor of $f(x)$.

This may be used to find the factors of a polynomial. Factors of the constant term are usually tested first.

If it is suspected that $(x - a)$ is a repeated factor:
(a) 'take out' the factor, either by inspection or long division to give
$$f(x) \equiv (x - a)g(x),$$
(b) test $(x - a)$ as a factor of $g(x)$.

| i | *Find the factors of $f(x) = x^3 - 5x^2 + 2x + 8$.*

Try the factors of 8, i.e. $\pm 1, \pm 2, \pm 4, \pm 8$.

Try $a = 1$. $f(1) = (1)^3 - 5(1)^2 + 2(1) + 8 = 6 \neq 0$.
So $(x - 1)$ is not a factor.
Try $a = -1$. $f(-1) = (-1)^3 - 5(-1)^2 + 2(-1) + 8 = 0$.
So $(x + 1)$ is a factor.
Try $a = 2$. $f(2) = (2)^3 - 5(2)^2 + 2(2) + 8 = 0$.
So $(x - 2)$ is a factor.
Try $a = 4$. $f(4) = (4)^3 - 5(4)^2 + 2(4) + 8 = 0$.
So $(x - 4)$ is a factor.

Polynomials
Worked examples, Guided example, Exercises and Exam questions.

 The expression $x^3 + 8x^2 + kx + 10$ has a factor $(x+2)$.
(a) Find the value of k.
(b) Factorise the expression completely.

(a) Let $f(x) = x^3 + 8x^2 + kx + 10$.
Since $(x + 2)$ is a factor of $f(x)$, $f(-2) = 0$.
$$f(-2) = (-2)^3 + 8(-2)^2 + k(-2) + 10 = 0$$
$$\Rightarrow \quad -8 + 32 - 2k + 10 = 0$$
$$\Rightarrow k = 17$$

(b) Since $(x + 2)$ is a factor of $f(x)$,
$$f(x) = (x + 2)(ax^2 + bx + 5).$$
The factors of 5 are ± 1, ± 5.
Try $x = 1$: $f(1) = 1 + 8 + 17 + 10 \neq 0$
So $(x - 1)$ is not a factor.
Try $x = -1$: $f(-1) = (-1)^3 + 8(-1)^2 + 17(-1) + 10 = 0$
So $(x + 1)$ is a factor.
Try $x = -5$: $f(-5) = (-5)^3 + 8(-5)^2 + 17(-5) + 10 = 0$
So $(x + 5)$ is a factor.
Hence, $f(x) = (x + 1)(x + 2)(x + 5)$.

 The function f is given by $f(x) = 2x^3 - x^2 - 18x + 9$.
(a) Show that $(x - 3)$ is a factor of $f(x)$.
(b) Write $f(x)$ in the form $(x - 3)(ax^2 + bx + c)$ and find the values of a, b and c.
(c) Solve the equation $f(x) = 0$.

(a) If $(x - 3)$ is a factor of $f(x)$ then $f(3) = 0$.
$$f(3) = 2(3)^3 - (3)^2 - 18(3) + 9$$
$$= 54 - 9 - 54 + 9 = 0.$$
Hence, $(x - 3)$ is a factor of $f(x)$.

(b) Let $f(x) \equiv (x - 3)(ax^2 + bx + c)$,
then $2x^3 - x^2 - 18x + 9 \equiv (x - 3)(ax^2 + bx + c)$.

Since this identity is true for all values of x, putting x equal to chosen, simple values of x will enable us to find a, b and c.
Let $x = 0$: $9 \equiv -3c \Rightarrow c = -3$.
Let $x = 1$: $2 - 1 - 18 + 9 \equiv (-2)(a + b - 3)$
$$\Rightarrow a + b = 7.$$
Let $x = -1$: $-2 - 1 + 18 + 9 \equiv (-4)(a - b - 3)$
$$\Rightarrow a - b = -3.$$

Solving the two equations in a and b gives $a = 2$, $b = 5$.

(c) $f(x) = (x - 3)(2x^2 + 5x - 3)$
$$= (x - 3)(2x - 1)(x + 3).$$
$f(x) = 0$
$$\Rightarrow (x - 3)(2x - 1)(x + 3) = 0$$
$$\Rightarrow x = 3 \text{ or } \tfrac{1}{2} \text{ or } -3.$$
Hence, the solutions of $f(x) = 0$ are $x = -3$, $x = \tfrac{1}{2}$, $x = 3$.

 The polynomial $f(x)$ is given by
$$f(x) \equiv x^4 + x^3 - 7x^2 + 3x + 2$$

If, also, $f(x) \equiv (x - 1)(x - 2)(x + 3)(x + c) + Px + Q$, find the values of P, Q and c.

First, establish an identity using the two given expressions for $f(x)$.

Put $x = 1$ in the identity to find an equation involving P and Q.

Put $x = 2$ in the identity to find a second equation involving P and Q.

Putting $x = 0$ in the identity, together with the calculated values of P and Q, will enable c to be found.

EX

1 Add $5x^6 + 2x^4 + 3x$ and $6x^6 + 2x^5 + 3x^4 + 7$.

2 Subtract $3x^7 - 2x^5 + 9$ from $5x^7 + 11x - 3$.

3 Multiply $4x^3 - 3x - 5$ by $2x^2 - 3x + 5$.

4 Simplify $(5x^3 - 7x^2 + 9) - (3x^3 - 2x + 5)$.

5 Simplify $(2x^4 - 5x + 4)(x^3 - 2x^2 + 3x - 1)$.

6 Simplify $(-3x^5 + 2x^3 - 7)(-6x^4 - 2x^3 + 3)$.

7 Factorise the following polynomials:
(a) $6x^5 + 9x^3 - 15x^2$ (b) $25 - 4x^6$
(c) $x^2 + 8x + 16$ (d) $x^2 - 10x + 25$
(e) $5x^2 + 10x + 5$ (f) $3x^3 - 6x^2 + 3x$
(g) $x^2 + 3x - 4$ (h) $2x^2 - 7x + 3$
(i) $1000 - 27x^6$ (j) $x^9 + 64$.

8 (a) Given that $x + 1$ and $x - 2$ are factors of $6x^4 - x^3 + ax^2 - 6x + b$, find the value of a and b.
(b) Given that
$x^3 - 3x^2 - 4x + 16 \equiv (x - 2)(x + 3)(x - c) + Px + Q$,
find the value of P, of Q, and of c.   *(C)

9 Given that $2x - 1$ is a factor of $8x^3 + 4x^2 + kx + 15$, find the value of k and then factorise the expression fully when k has this value.   (H)

10 Given that $f(x) \equiv 3 - 7x + 5x^2 - x^3$, show that $3 - x$ is a factor of $f(x)$. Factorise $f(x)$ completely and hence state the set of values of x for which $f(x) \leq 0$.   (L)

11 Three of the factors of $x^4 + ax^3 + bx^2 + x + c$ are x, $x + 1$ and $x - 1$. Find a, b and c.   (O & C)

12 The function f is given by $f(x) = x^3 - 3x^2 - 2x + 6$.
(a) Use the factor theorem to show that $(x - 3)$ is a factor of $f(x)$.
(b) Write $f(x)$ in the form $(x - 3)(ax^2 + bx + c)$, giving the values of a, b and c.
(c) Hence solve $f(x) = 0$.
(d) Using your solutions to $f(x) = 0$, write down the solutions of the equation $f(x + 1) = 0$.   (J)

13 (a) Show that $(x + 2)$ is a factor of the polynomial $f(x)$ given by $f(x) = 2x^3 - 3x^2 - 11x + 6$.
(b) Express $f(x)$ as the product of three linear factors.
(c) By considering the graph of $y = f(x)$, or otherwise, solve the inequality $f(x) \leq 0$.   (J)

14 Show that $(x - 2)$ is a factor of $x^3 - 9x^2 + 26x - 24$. Find the set of values for x for which
$x^3 - 9x^2 + 26x - 24 < 0$.   (A)

15 Given that the expression $ax^3 + 8x^2 + bx + 6$ is exactly divisible by $x^2 - 2x - 3$, find the values of a and b.   (OLE)

16 Show that $x + 3$ is a factor of $x^3 + 2x^2 + x + 12$.   (C)

P8
core

Indices and Logarithms

Index notation, Basic rules of indices, Logarithms, Basic rules of logarithms, Solving exponential equations.

Index notation

a^n means $\underbrace{a \times a \times a \times a \times \ldots \times a}_{n \text{ factors}}$

n is the **index** (plural **indices**). a is the **base**.
An index is also called a **power** or an **exponent**.

$\boxed{i}$ $8^5 = \underbrace{8 \times 8 \times 8 \times 8 \times 8}_{5 \text{ factors}}$

5 is the index. 8 is the base.
8^5 is read as '8 to the power 5'.

Basic rules of indices

When m and n are positive rational numbers:

multiplication: $a^m \times a^n = a^{m+n}$

division: $a^m \div a^n = a^{m-n}$

raising to a power: $(a^m)^n = a^{mn}$

zero index: $a^0 = 1$

negative index: $a^{-m} = \dfrac{1}{a^m}$

fractional indices: $a^{\frac{1}{n}} = \sqrt[n]{a}$

$a^{\frac{m}{n}} = (\sqrt[n]{a})^m$

$\boxed{i}$ The basic laws of indices can be illustrated as follows:

$a^3 \times a^2 = a^{3+2} = a^5$

$a^7 \div a^3 = a^{7-3} = a^4$

$(a^3)^2 = a^{3 \times 2} = a^6$

$7^0 = 1$

$5^{-2} = \dfrac{1}{5^2} = \dfrac{1}{25}$

$8^{\frac{1}{3}} = \sqrt[3]{8} = 2$

$\sqrt[3]{a^6} = a^{\frac{6}{3}} = a^2$

Logarithms

If $N = a^x$, then we define x as the **logarithm of N to the base a**,
i.e. if $N = a^x$, then $x = \log_a N$.
This can be used to convert from 'index form' to 'logarithmic form' and vice versa.
Logarithms to the **base e**, written **ln x** or **$\log_e x$**, are called **natural** or **Naperian** logarithms.
Logarithms to the base 10, written **log x** or **$\log_{10} x$**, are called **common** logarithms.

$\boxed{i}$ If $8 = 2^3$, then 3 is the logarithm of 8 to the base 2.

i.e. $8 = 2^3 \Rightarrow \log_2 8 = 3$

If $7 = e^x$, then $x = \log_e 7$.

$100 = 10^2$, so $\log_{10} 100 = 2$.

Basic rules of logarithms

multiplication: $\log_a(p \times q) = \log_a p + \log_a q$

division: $\log_a(p \div q) = \log_a p - \log_a q$

raising to a power: $\log_a p^n = n \log_a p$

logarithm of unity: $\log_a 1 = 0$

logarithm of the base: $\log_a a = 1$

To change a logarithm from one base to another use

$$\log_b N = \frac{\log_a N}{\log_a b}$$

In particular, $\log_e N = \dfrac{\log_{10} N}{\log_{10} e}$ and $\log_b a = \dfrac{1}{\log_a b}$.

$\boxed{i}$

$\log 3 + \log 2 = \log (3 \times 2) = \log 6$

$\log 8 - \log 4 = \log (8 \div 4) = \log 2$

$\log_a 8 = \log_a (2^3) = 3 \log_a 2$

$\log_{10} 1 = 0$

$\log_e e = 1$

$\log_2 10 = \dfrac{\log_{10} 10}{\log_{10} 2} = \dfrac{1}{\log_{10} 2}$

Solving exponential equations

Exponential equations, i.e. equations in which the variable is an index, can often be solved by

either (a) taking logs of both sides of the equation and using the basic rules of logarithms,

or (b) using a substitution of the form $y = a^x$ to obtain an equation in y (usually quadratic) which can then be solved.

$\boxed{i}$ *Solve (a)* $5^x = 4$ *(b)* $2^{2x+1} - 5(2^x) + 2 = 0$.

(a) Taking logs gives $\log 5^x = \log 4$
$x \log 5 = \log 4$
$x = \log 4 \div \log 5 = 0.8614$

(b) The equation is $2(2^x)^2 - 5(2^x) + 2 = 0$
Using $y = 2^x$, this is $2y^2 - 5y + 2 = 0$
$(2y - 1)(y - 2) = 0$
$y = \frac{1}{2}$ or $y = 2$
So $2^x = \frac{1}{2} = 2^{-1} \Leftrightarrow x = -1$ or $2^x = 2^1 \Leftrightarrow x = 1$

Indices and Logarithms
Graphs.
Worked examples and Exam questions.

Graphs

Exponential functions are functions in which the variable is in the index, or exponent, e.g. a^x.
e^x is called **the exponential function**.
e is the number such that the gradient of $y = e^x$ at $(0, 1)$ is 1.

The **logarithmic function** $y = \log_e x$ is the inverse of the exponential function $y = e^x$.

The graph shows the typical exponential and logarithmic curve shapes.

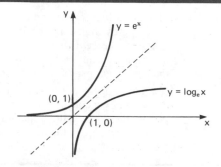

WE (a) *Evaluate:* (i) $\left(\dfrac{81}{256}\right)^{\frac{3}{4}}$, (ii) $\left(\dfrac{25}{49}\right)^{-\frac{1}{2}}$,

(b) *Simplify:* $\dfrac{27^{n+2} - 6.3^{3n+3}}{3^n.9^{n+2}}$,

(c) *Simplify:* $\dfrac{x}{y^{\frac{1}{2}} + x^{\frac{1}{2}}} + \dfrac{x}{y^{\frac{1}{2}} - x^{\frac{1}{2}}}$.

(a)
(i) $\left(\dfrac{81}{256}\right)^{\frac{3}{4}} = \dfrac{(81)^{\frac{3}{4}}}{(256)^{\frac{3}{4}}} = \dfrac{(81^{\frac{1}{4}})^3}{(256^{\frac{1}{4}})^3} = \dfrac{(3)^3}{(4)^3} = \dfrac{27}{64}.$

(ii) $\left(\dfrac{25}{49}\right)^{-\frac{1}{2}} = \left(\dfrac{49}{25}\right)^{\frac{1}{2}} = \dfrac{(49)^{\frac{1}{2}}}{(25)^{\frac{1}{2}}} = \dfrac{7}{5} = 1\frac{2}{5}.$

(b) $\dfrac{27^{n+2} - 6.3^{3n+3}}{3^n.9^{n+2}} = \dfrac{(3^3)^{n+2} - 2.3^1.3^{3n+3}}{3^n.(3^2)^{n+2}}$

$= \dfrac{3^{3(n+2)} - 2.3^{3n+4}}{3^n.3^{2(n+2)}} = \dfrac{3^{3n}.3^6 - 2.3^{3n}.3^4}{3^{3n}.3^4}$

$= \dfrac{3^{3n}(3^6 - 2.3^4)}{3^{3n}.3^4} = \dfrac{3^4(3^2 - 2)}{3^4} = 7.$

(c) $\dfrac{x}{y^{\frac{1}{2}} + x^{\frac{1}{2}}} + \dfrac{x}{y^{\frac{1}{2}} - x^{\frac{1}{2}}} = \dfrac{x(y^{\frac{1}{2}} - x^{\frac{1}{2}}) + x(y^{\frac{1}{2}} + x^{\frac{1}{2}})}{(y^{\frac{1}{2}} + x^{\frac{1}{2}})(y^{\frac{1}{2}} - x^{\frac{1}{2}})}$

$= \dfrac{xy^{\frac{1}{2}} - x^{\frac{3}{2}} + xy^{\frac{1}{2}} + x^{\frac{3}{2}}}{y - x}$

$= \dfrac{2x\sqrt{y}}{y - x}.$

WE *Solve the following equations:*
(a) $\log_x 3 + \log_x 27 = 2$;   (b) $\log_3 x + 3\log_x 3 = 4$.

(a) $\log_x 3 + \log_x 27 = 2$
$\therefore \log_x (3 \times 27) = 2$
    i.e. $\log_x 81 = 2$
so, $81 = x^2$
$\Rightarrow$ $x = 9$

(b) $\log_3 x + 3\log_x 3 = 4$,   can be rewritten as

$\log_3 x + 3 \dfrac{1}{\log_3 x} = 4$

    i.e. $(\log_3 x)^2 - 4\log_3 x + 3 = 0$.
Let $\log_3 x = y$, then we need to solve,
       $y^2 - 4y + 3 = 0$,
    i.e. $(y-3)(y-1) = 0$
$\Rightarrow y = 3$ or 1.
Hence, $\log_3 x = 3 \Rightarrow x = 3^3 = 27$,
or, $\log_3 x = 1 \Rightarrow x = 3^1 = 3$.
So, the solutions of the equations are 3 and 27.

EX 1 (a) Given that $x^y = z$, find:
   (i) z when $x = 9$ and $y = \frac{1}{2}$;
   (ii) z when $x = 64$ and $y = -\frac{1}{3}$;
   (iii) x when $y = -\frac{1}{2}$ and $z = 4$;
   (iv) y when $z = 2$ and $x = \frac{1}{2}$.

(b) Express $3^{2y} - 3^{y+1} - 3^y + 3$ in terms of z, where $z = 3^y$.
Hence solve the equation $3^{2y} - 3^{y+1} - 3^y + 3 = 0$.

(c) Without using tables evaluate
$\log 6 + \log 4 + \log 20 - \log 3 - \log 16$, where all logarithms are to the base 10.   *(W)*

2 (a) Simplify: $\dfrac{(x^{\frac{3}{2}} + x^{\frac{1}{2}})(x^{\frac{1}{2}} - x^{-\frac{1}{2}})}{(x^{\frac{3}{2}} - x^{\frac{1}{2}})^2}$

(b) Without using a calculator find the logarithm of 8 to the base a: (i) when $a = 64$; (ii) when $a = \frac{1}{4}$.   *(A)*

3 Without the use of tables, slide rules or calculators:
   (i) evaluate $8^{\frac{1}{3}} + 81^{\frac{1}{4}}$
   (ii) find the value of x given that $\log_5 x + \log_2 8 = 0$.   *(L)*

4 (a) Express in its simplest form, $\log_2 64 - \log_2 16$.
(b) Given that $\log_x u + \log_x v = p$ and $\log_x u - \log_x v = q$, prove that $u = x^{\frac{1}{2}(p+q)}$ and find a similar expression for v.   *(H)*

5 (a) Solve the equation $\log_5 x = 16 \log_x 5$.
(b) Find the values of y which satisfy the equation:

$$(8^y)^y . \dfrac{1}{32^y} = 4.$$
    (S)

6 (i) If $2^{2x} = 51 \times 3^{3x}$, prove that $x \log \dfrac{4}{27} = \log 51$ and hence find x.
(ii) If y varies directly as $x^{-\frac{3}{2}}$ and $x = 4$ when $y = 64$, find the value of y when $x = 16$.   *(O & C)*

7 (a) Given that $\log_9 x = p$ and $\log_{\sqrt 3} y = q$, express xy and $\dfrac{x^2}{y}$ as powers of 3.
(b) Solve for x the equation $e^{2x} + e^x - 6 = 0$.   *(A)*

8 (a) Simplify (i) $20 \times 8^{2n} - 5 \times 4^{3n+1}$; (ii) $(\log_2 5) \times (\log_5 8)$.
(b) Find x and y given that $e^x + 3e^y = 3$ and $e^{2x} - 9e^{2y} = 6$, expressing each answer as a logarithm to base e.   *(A)*

9 If $2 \log_y x + 2 \log_x y = 5$, show that $\log_y x$ is either $\frac{1}{2}$ or 2. Hence find all pairs of values of x and y which satisfy simultaneously the equation above and the equation $xy = 27$.   *(J)*

10 (a) Find the real value of k such that $10^x = e^{kx}$ for all x.
(b) Find $g(x)$ such that $x^x = e^{xg(x)}$ for all x.
Hence, or otherwise, find the derivatives of 10^x and of x^x with respect to x.   *(A)*

Exponential Growth and Decay

Growth and decay, Finding simple models, Using models, Graphs.

Growth and decay

Many real-life growth and decay rates are exponential. In such growth patterns, an initial amount increases by a constant percentage in a fixed time period, then the new total amount increases by the same percentage in the next equal period of time and so on ...

If a rate of decay is exponential, an initial amount decreases by a constant percentage in a fixed time period, then the resulting quantity decreases by the same percentage in the next equal time period and so on ...

i Suppose that the human population of the world is growing at about 3% per annum. This would mean that at the end of each year, the world's population would be 3% greater than it was at the beginning of that year.

i The radioactive element radium has a half-life of 1600 years. This means that the number of atoms in a sample of radium will have halved in 1600 years. After a further 1600 years the number of atoms will halve again and so on.

Finding simple models

If a quantity is increasing at a constant rate of x% per unit interval of time, then the model which describes this process can be represented by the equation

$$P = P_0[(100 + x)\%]^t$$

$$\text{or } P = P_0\left[1 + \tfrac{x}{100}\right]^t$$

where P is the size of the quantity at the end of the time interval t and P_0 is the size of the quantity at time $t = 0$.

If a quantity is decreasing at a constant rate of x% per unit interval of time, then the model which describes this process can be represented by the equation

$$P = P_0[(100 - x)\%]^t$$

$$\text{or } P = P_0\left[1 - \tfrac{x}{100}\right]^t$$

where P, P_0 and t have the same meaning as before.

i *Every day a biologist measures the area of an organism growing in her laboratory. Her results for the first three days of the experiment are shown in this table:*

Day	0	1	2
Area (cm²)	4	4.4	4.84

Assuming the rate of growth remains the same, find a model for the area A cm² of the organism, t days after the start of the experiment.

Day to day percentage increase in area

$$= \frac{0.4}{4} = \frac{0.44}{4.4} = 0.1 = 10\%, \text{ i.e. constant.}$$

Initial size of organism is 4 cm².

A suitable model for this situation is given by
$$A = 4(1.1)^t.$$

Using models

When using a given model of a situation involving growth or decay, you may need to:

(a) find the values of the constants contained in the equation, then

(b) use the resulting equation to determine new values.

To find the values of the constants:

(i) substitute any given values into the equation,

(ii) solve the resulting exponential equation by trial and improvement or by using the methods given in P6.

i *The radioactivity, R becquerels per gram, of a substance can be modelled using the equation $R = A \times 2^{-Bt}$, where t is the time in hours and A and B are constants.*
A substance is found initially to have a radioactivity of 28 becquerels; one hour later it is 26 becquerels. Find the values of A and B and the half life of the substance.

When $t = 0$, $R = 28 \Rightarrow A = 28$

When $t = 1$, $R = 26 \Rightarrow 26 = 28 \times 2^{-B} \Rightarrow 2^{-B} = \dfrac{26}{28}$

$$\Rightarrow -B\ln 2 = \ln\left(\frac{26}{28}\right) \Rightarrow B = 0.107 \text{ (3 d.p.)}$$

To find the half life, use $R = \tfrac{1}{2} \times 28 = 14$.

So, $14 = 28 \times 2^{-0.107t} \Rightarrow 2^{0.107t} = 2 \Rightarrow 0.107t = 1$

$$\Rightarrow t = \frac{1}{0.107} = 9.35 \text{ hours (2 d.p.)}$$

Graphs

A mathematical model for an exponential growth pattern may take the form

$$y = ka^t \text{ or } y = ka^{bt} \text{ or } y = c + ka^{bt} \text{ or } y = c - ka^{-bt}$$

where k, a, b, and c are positive constants, t is time and y is the resulting quantity.

These may be represented graphically:

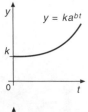
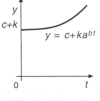
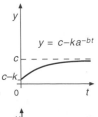

Similar models for exponential decay may be represented graphically too:

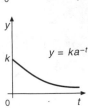

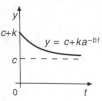
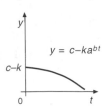

Exponential Growth and Decay
Worked examples and Exam questions.

 The population of a certain town has been falling at a constant rate each year. At the end of 1956 *the population was* 60 000 *and after one year it had fallen to* 57 000.

(*a*) *Find a model for the population size of the town, during the nth year after* 1956.

(*b*) *In which year did the population fall below* 10 000?

(a)   In the first year after 1956 the fall in population was 3000.

$$\text{Percentage fall } = \frac{3000}{60\,000} = 5\%$$

The population P during the nth year after the end of 1956 is given by the model

$$P = 60\,000(0.95)^n.$$

(b)   We need to find n such that

$$60\,000(0.95)^n < 10\,000$$
$$\Rightarrow \ (0.95)^n < \frac{1}{6} \quad (= 1.666\ldots).$$

Using trial and improvement,

$$(0.95)^{34} = 0.1748\ldots \quad > \tfrac{1}{6}$$
$$(0.95)^{35} = 0.16608\ldots \quad < \tfrac{1}{6}.$$

So, the population fell below 10 000 during the 35th year after 1956, i.e. during 1991.

 The value £H of a particular house in a certain part of East Anglia during the period 1988 *to* 1994 *can be modelled by the equation* $H = Ae^{-pt}$.

The value of the house in 1988 *was £65 000 and its value in* 1989 *was £61 100.*

State the value of A and calculate the value of p correct to 2 *significant figures.*

What was the value of the house in 1993? *Give your answer to the nearest £100.*

Using $H = Ae^{-pt}$
$$65\,000 = Ae^{-p \times 0}$$
$$\Rightarrow \ A = 65\,000.$$

When $t = 1$, $H = 61\,100$.

So, $61\,100 = 65\,000e^{-p}$
$$\Rightarrow \ e^{-p} = 0.94$$
$$\Rightarrow \ -p = \ln(0.94)$$
$$\Rightarrow \ p = 0.062 \ (2\text{ s.f.}).$$

To find the value in 1993, let $t = 5$.

So $H = 65\,000e^{-0.062 \times 5}$
$$\Rightarrow H = 47\,700 \ (\text{to nearest } 100).$$

Hence the value in 1993 is £47 700 (to nearest £100).

---

 1 An athlete plans a training schedule which involves running 20 km in the first week of training; in each subsequent week the distance is to be increased by 10% over the previous week. Write down an expression for the distance to be covered in the nth week according to this schedule, and find in which week the athlete would first cover more than 100 km. (*C*)

2 The value, £V, of a particular car can be modelled by the equation
$$V = ke^{-\lambda t}$$
where t years is the age of the car.
The car's original price was £7499, and after one year it is valued at £6000.
State the value of k and calculate λ giving your answer to 2 decimal places. Hence obtain the value of the car when it is three years old. (*J*)

3 Medical researchers studying the growth of a strain of bacteria observe that the number of bacteria, present after t hours, is given by the formula

$$N(t) = 40e^{1.5t}$$

(a) State the number of bacteria present at the start of the experiment.
(b) How many minutes will the bacteria take to double in number? (*H*)

4 A forest fire spreads so that the number of hectares burnt after t hours is given by

$$h = 30(1.65)^t.$$

(i)   By what constant factor is the burnt area multiplied from time $t = N$ to time $t = N + 1$? Express this as a percentage increase.
(ii) 1.65 can be written as e^K. Find the value of K.
(iii) Hence show that $dh/dt = 15e^{Kt}$.
(iv) This shows that dh/dt is proportional to h. Find the constant of proportionality. (*O & C*)

5 A microbiologist measures the population of a certain type of bacterium. He starts the experiment at time $t = 0$. The population, n, at time t hours is given by the formula

$$n = A(1 - e^{-Bt})$$

where A and B are positive constants.
(a) State a graph of n against t.

When $t = 2$, $n = 10\,000$ and when $t = 4$, $n = 15\,000$.
(b) Show that $2e^{-4B} - 3e^{-2B} + 1 = 0$.
(c) Use the substitution $y = e^{-2B}$ to show that

$$2y^2 - 3y + 1 = 0.$$

(d) Solve this equation for y and hence show that $B = 0.347$ to 3 significant figures.
(e) Determine, to the nearest 100, the maximum population size. (*O*)

P10
core

Coordinates and Graphs
Rectangular cartesian coordinates, Definitions, Drawing graphs, Solutions of equations.

Rectangular cartesian coordinates

Rectangular cartesian coordinates determine the position of a point in the plane by reference to:
- a fixed point O (**the origin**),
- a pair of perpendicular lines (**axes**) through O.

Any point P can be described by an ordered pair of numbers (x, y). The **x-coordinate** (or **abscissa**) is given first, the **y-coordinate** (or **ordinate**) second.

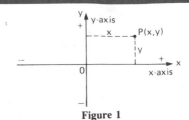

Figure 1

Definitions

Let A, B, C be (x_1, y_1), (x_2, y_2), (x_3, y_3) respectively.

The **length** of AB is $\sqrt{(x_1-x_2)^2+(y_1-y_2)^2}$.

The **gradient** of AB is $\dfrac{y_2-y_1}{x_2-x_1}$.

The **midpoint** of AB is $(\tfrac{1}{2}[x_1+x_2], \tfrac{1}{2}[y_1+y_2])$

The point P which divides AB in the ratio $\lambda:\mu$ is
$$\left(\frac{\lambda x_2+\mu x_1}{\lambda+\mu}, \frac{\lambda y_2+\mu y_1}{\lambda+\mu}\right).$$
Area of $\triangle ABC$ is
$$\tfrac{1}{2}[x_1(y_2-y_3)+x_2(y_3-y_1)+x_3(y_1-y_2)]$$

ℹ️ A, B, C are $(2, 3)$, $(4, 7)$, $(7, 3)$ respectively.

The length of AB is $\sqrt{(2-4)^2+(3-7)^2}=\sqrt{20}=2\sqrt{5}$

The gradient of BC is $\dfrac{7-4}{3-7}=\dfrac{3}{-4}=-\dfrac{3}{4}$

The midpoint of AC is $(\tfrac{1}{2}[2+7], \tfrac{1}{2}[3+3])=(4\tfrac{1}{2}, 3)$

The point P which divides BC in the ratio $1:2$ is
$$\left(\frac{1\times7+2\times4}{1+2}, \frac{1\times3+2\times7}{1+2}\right)=(5, 5\tfrac{2}{3})$$

Area of ABC is
$$\tfrac{1}{2}[2(7-3)+4(3-3)+7(3-7)]=10 \text{ units}^2$$

Drawing graphs

To draw the graph of $y=f(x)$

(a) Ascertain the range of values of x and calculate, to two decimal places, the corresponding values of y. The results are usually displayed in a table.

(b) Draw axes Ox and Oy intersecting at right angles on graph paper. The position of the axes on the paper is determined by the ranges of values of x and y.

(c) Choose suitable scales and sensible units (and sub-units) for the axes. The graph should use as much of the graph paper as possible. Different scales may be used on the axes but they distort familiar shapes.

(d) Mark the ordered pairs with $\odot$ or $\times$.

(e) Draw the curve faintly first to obtain a general impression and then use a heavier line.

When points are required from the graph:

(a) if the point(s) lie between calculated, or given, values, the process is known as interpolation,

(b) if the graph has to be extended to find the point(s), the process is known as extrapolation.

ℹ️ *Draw the graph of $y=4x^3-4x^2-11x+6$, plotting points for values of $x=-2, -1.5, -1, -0.5, \ldots, +2$.*

A table of values gives

x	-2	-1.5	-1	-0.5	0	$+0.5$	$+1$	$+1.5$	$+2$
y	-20	0	$+9$	$+10$	$+6$	0	-5	-6	0

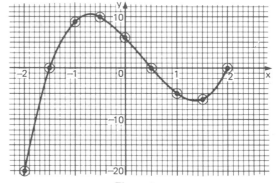

Figure 2

Solutions of equations

1. To solve $f(x)=0$

(a) Draw the graph of $y=f(x)$.

(b) Find the point(s) where the curve cuts the x-axis ($y=0$).

2. To solve $f(x)=a$

(a) Draw the curve $y=f(x)$ and the line $y=a$.

(b) Find the point(s) where the curve cuts the line.

3. To solve $f(x)=0$, rewritten as $F(x)=G(x)$

(a) Draw the curves $y=F(x)$ and $y=G(x)$ on the same graph paper using the same axes and scales.

(b) Find any point(s) of intersection of the curves.

This 'two graph method' is often used when $F(x)$ is an algebraic function and $G(x)$ is non-algebraic. Non-algebraic functions, e.g. $\sin x$, $\log x$, are called transcendental functions.

ℹ️ The solution of $4x^3-4x^2-11x+6=0$ can be found at the points where the curve $y=4x^3-4x^2-11x+6$ cuts the x-axis ($y=0$). From the above graph these are where $x=-1.5$, $x=+0.5$, $x=+2$.

The solution of $4x^3-4x^2-11x+10=0$
i.e. $4x^3-4x^2-11x+6=-4$
is found from the graph of $y=4x^3-4x^2-11x+6$ by drawing the line $y=-4$. This line cuts the curve where $x\approx-1.65$, $x\approx+0.9$, $x\approx+1.75$.

The solution of $4x^3-4x^2-8x+6=0$
rewritten as $4x^3-4x^2-11x+6=-3x$
is found from the graphs of $y=4x^3-4x^2-11x+6$ and $y=-3x$.
If $y=-3x$ is drawn on the above graph, it cuts the curve where $x\approx-1.35$, $x\approx+0.7$, $x\approx+1.65$.

Coordinates and Graphs
Parametric equations.
Worked example, Guided example and Exam questions.

Parametric equations

The equation of a curve, $y = f(x)$, may be given by two equations, $x = f(t)$ and $y = f(t)$, called **parametric equations**. These give the coordinates (x and y) of any point on the curve in terms of a third independent variable, t, called a **parameter**.

Each value of the parameter gives the coordinates of only one point on the curve. Every point on the curve has a unique value of the parameter.

To draw a graph from parametric equations, find values of x and y for a succession of values of the parameter and then plot x against y.

To find the Cartesian equation, $y = f(x)$, from parametric equations, eliminate the parameter from them.

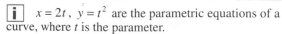 $x = 2t$, $y = t^2$ are the parametric equations of a curve, where t is the parameter.

Some points on the curve are given in this table.

t	-2	-1	0	1	2
x	-4	-2	0	2	4
y	4	1	0	1	4

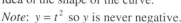

Plotting the points (x, y) gives an idea of the shape of the curve.

Note: $y = t^2$ so y is never negative.

Finding the Cartesian equation shows it is a parabola.

$x = 2t \Rightarrow t = \tfrac{1}{2}x$

Substitute $t = \tfrac{1}{2}x$ in $y = t^2 \Rightarrow y = (\tfrac{1}{2}x)^2$ or $y = \tfrac{1}{4}x^2$.

 Find the Cartesian equations of the curves with these parametric equations.

(a) $x = 3 - 2t$, $y = 3t - 2$

(b) $x = 4\cos\theta$, $y = 5\sin\theta$ $(0 \le \theta \le 2\pi)$

(a) $x = 3 - 2t \Rightarrow t = \tfrac{1}{2}(3 - x)$

$y = 3t - 2 \Rightarrow t = \tfrac{1}{3}(y + 2)$

Eliminating t: $\tfrac{1}{2}(3 - x) = \tfrac{1}{3}(y + 2)$

$\Rightarrow 3(3 - x) = 2(y + 2)$

$\Rightarrow 3x + 2y = 5$ (i.e. a straight line)

(b) To eliminate angle θ, use $\cos^2\theta + \sin^2\theta = 1$.

$x = 4\cos\theta \Rightarrow \cos\theta = \dfrac{x}{4} \Rightarrow \cos^2\theta = \dfrac{x^2}{16}$

$y = 5\sin\theta \Rightarrow \sin\theta = \dfrac{y}{5} \Rightarrow \sin^2\theta = \dfrac{y^2}{25}$

$\cos^2\theta + \sin^2\theta = 1$ gives $\dfrac{x^2}{16} + \dfrac{y^2}{25} = 1$ (an ellipse).

 Draw the graph of $y = \dfrac{2}{x}$, plotting values of x at $\tfrac{1}{2}$-unit intervals from $x = \tfrac{1}{2}$ to $x = 4$, using the same scale on both axes. With the same scales and axes draw the graph of $y = x(3 - x)$ from $x = 0$ to $x = 4$ for $\tfrac{1}{2}$-unit intervals. Read off the values of x at their intersections. Of what equation in x are they the roots?

Table of values for $y = \dfrac{2}{x}$

x	$\tfrac{1}{2}$	1	$1\tfrac{1}{2}$	2	$2\tfrac{1}{2}$	3	$3\tfrac{1}{2}$	4
y	4	2	1.33	1	0.80	0.67	0.57	0.50

Table of values for $y = x(3 - x)$

x	0	$\tfrac{1}{2}$	1	$1\tfrac{1}{2}$	2	$2\tfrac{1}{2}$	3	$3\tfrac{1}{2}$	4
y	0	1.25	2	2.25	2	1.25	0	-1.75	-4

Draw a graph of these two functions.
The values of x at the points of intersection are approximately 1 and 2.75.

They are the roots of the equation $\dfrac{2}{x} = x(3 - x)$,

i.e. $x^3 - 3x^2 + 2 = 0$

EX

1 Three points have coordinates $P(-2, -3)$, $Q(2, 0)$, $R(8, -8)$: (i) Prove that $P\hat{Q}R = 90°$; (ii) Calculate the area of $\triangle PQR$; (iii) Calculate the length of PR and hence, or otherwise, find the perpendicular distance of Q from PR.

(C)

2 Draw the graph $y = \dfrac{4}{x}$, plotting values of x at $\tfrac{1}{2}$-unit intervals from $x = \tfrac{1}{2}$ to $x = 4$, taking 2 cm to represent a unit on both axes. With the same scales and axes, again plotting values of x at $\tfrac{1}{2}$-unit intervals, draw the graph $y = x(4 - x)$ from $x = 0$ to $x = 4$. Read off the values of x at their intersections. Of what equation in x are they roots?

(O & C)

3 Three points have coordinates $A(-2, -1)$, $B(6, 9)$ and $C(2 - 3)$. The line through the midpoint of AB parallel to AC meet the x-axis at X and the y-axis at Y. Calculate the coordinates of X and Y. Hence deduce the area of $\triangle XOY$, where O is the origin.

(C)

4 The points A and B have coordinates $(-3, -1)$ and $(7, 4)$ respectively. Find the coordinates of the point C which divides AB internally in the ratio $2:3$. Find also the equation of the line through B perpendicular to AB.

(L)

5 Given the three points $A(4, 0)$, $B(0, 2)$ and $C(-2, -2)$, show that: (i) $AB = BC$; (ii) AB is perpendicular to BC. A square $ABCD$ is formed. Calculate the coordinates of D. [A diagram will be found helpful, but a solution using measurements from an accurate drawing is not acceptable.]

(C)

6 Find the Cartesian equations of the curves whose parametric equations are given below.
(a) $x = 2t - 1$, $y = 5t + 3$
(b) $x = 4t - 1$, $y = 3t^2 + 2$

(c) $x = 2t$, $y = \dfrac{1}{t}$

(d) $x = t^2$, $y = t^3$
(e) $x = 1 + 4\cos\theta$, $y = 3 + 4\sin\theta$
(f) $x = 2 + r\cos30°$, $y = -1 + r\cos30°$
(g) $x = a(1 + \cos\theta)$, $y = a\sin\theta$
(h) $x = e^\theta + e^{-\theta}$, $y = e^\theta - e^{-\theta}$ for $\theta \ge 0$.

P11
core

Functions
Definitions, Graphs, Inverse function, Composite function, Even and odd functions.

Definitions

A **function** f from set A to set B, written $f: A \rightarrow B$, is a rule which associates with each element $x \in A$, one and only one element in B. This element of B is usually denoted by $f(x)$.

$f(x)$ is called the **image** of x, under f, or, more commonly, **the value of f at x**.

Set A is called the **domain** of the function and set B the **image set** of the function. It is not necessary for all the elements of B to be the image of some $x \in A$ under f.

The **range** of the function is that subset of the image set B which consists of all the possible images under f of all the elements of the domain A. It is denoted by $f(A)$.

The function f is called **one-one** if the images of distinct points of A, under f, are distinct points of B. Functions can be **many-one** or **one-one relations**.

ℹ $x^2 + 1$ is the function value at x of the function which 'squares x and adds 1'.
We sometimes write 'the function $f(x) = x^2 + 1$'.
Strictly $f(x)$ is not the function but the value of the function at x. However this $f(x)$ notation is the most common way of identifying a function.

ℹ
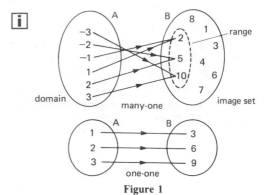
Figure 1

Graphs

The **graph of a function** is usually represented by using rectangular cartesian coordinates and plotting $f(x)$ against x.

To find the range for a given domain and function, it is safer to sketch the cartesian graph of the function over its domain.

Note: The end points of the domain do not necessarily give the end points of the range.

ℹ The graph of the function $f(x) = x^2 - 2x + 3$, x real, $0 \leqslant x \leqslant 3$, is shown.

From the graph it is clear that the range of $f(x)$ is $\{y : 2 \leqslant x \leqslant 6\}$

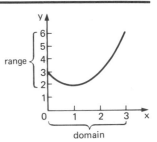
Figure 2

Inverse function

If a function f is one-one and maps an element x in the domain to an element y in the range, then the function that maps y back to x is the **inverse** of f, f^{-1}.

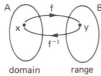
Figure 3

It can be seen from the graph of a function whether its inverse function exists, since one and only one value of x must correspond to any one value of y.

The graph of $f^{-1}(x)$ is the reflection of the graph of $f(x)$ in the line $y = x$. So if the graph of $f(x)$ is known, then the graph of $f^{-1}(x)$ can be sketched easily.

ℹ Let $f(x) = x^3$ i.e. $y = x^3$ so $x = y^{\frac{1}{3}}$. Then the inverse function is $f^{-1}(y) = y^{\frac{1}{3}}$.

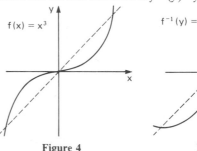

Figure 4   Figure 5

Composite function (or 'function of a function')

To find the **composite function**, $fg(x)$, of two functions f and g acting on suitably defined sets:
first find the image of x under g, i.e. $g(x)$, then find the image of $g(x)$ under f.
Note: The order of a composite function is important.
Alternative notation for $fg(x)$ is fg or $f \circ g$.

The inverse of fg is $(fg)^{-1} = g^{-1}f^{-1}$.

ℹ If $f(x) = x^3$ and $g(x) = x^{\frac{1}{3}}$, find $gf(x)$.

$gf(x) = g(x^3) = x$ This is expected since $g = f^{-1}$ and so maps y back to x.

ℹ $f(x) = 5x + 4$ and $g(x) = 3x - 2$, find $f \circ g$ and $g \circ f$

$f \circ g = 5(3x - 2) + 4 = 15x - 6$ ⎫ Note:
$g \circ f = 3(5x + 4) - 2 = 15x + 10$ ⎭ $f \circ g \neq g \circ f$

Even and odd functions

An **even function** f is one for which $f(-x) = f(x)$, for all values of x.

The graph of an even function has the y-axis as a line of symmetry.

An **odd function** f is one for which $f(-x) = -f(x)$, for all values of x.

The graph of an odd function has rotational symmetry of order 2 about $(0, 0)$.

ℹ

$y = x^2$ an even function $y = x^3$ an odd function

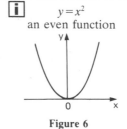
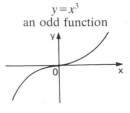

Figure 6   Figure 7

Functions
Worked example and Exam questions.

 The functions f and g are defined by
$$f:x\to 5x+4,$$
$$g:x\to 6x-k,$$
where $x \in \mathbb{R}$ and k is a constant.
(a) Find the value of k for which $fg=gf$
(b) Prove that $fff:x\to 125x+124$

(a) $fg:x\to 5(6x-k)+4=30x-5k+4$

$\quad gf:x\to 6(5x+4)-k=30x+24-k$

$\quad$ If $fg=gf$ then $30x-5k+4=30x+24-k$
$$k=-5$$

(b) $f:x\to 5x+4$

$\quad ff:x\to 5(5x+4)+4=25x+24$

$\quad fff:x\to 5(25x+24)+4=125x+124,$

$\quad$ as required.

 Let $f(x)=\dfrac{px+q}{x+r}$ where x, p, q, r are real and $x\neq \pm r$.

Find the condition for f to be an even function. Deduce that if f is an even function then $f(x)$ must reduce to the form $f(x)=k$, where k is constant.

If $f(x)$ is an even function then $f(-x)=f(x)$

$\quad$ i.e. $\dfrac{p(-x)+q}{(-x)+r}=\dfrac{px+q}{x+r}$

$\quad (x+r)(-px+q)=(r-x)(px+q)$

$-px^2+qx-rpx+rq=rpx+rq-px^2-qx$

$\qquad 2qx-2rpx=0$

$\quad$ i.e. $\quad 2x(q-rp)=0$

$\quad$ i.e. $q=rp$, since x is generally non-zero.

If $q=rp$,
$$f(x)=\frac{px+rp}{x+r}=\frac{p(x+r)}{(x+r)}=p,$$
which is of the form $f(x)=k$, k a constant.

 A function f is defined by $f(x)=4x^2+5$ where $x \in \mathbb{R}^+$ and g is the inverse function of f.
Obtain a formula for $g(x)$.
Show $[(g'\circ f)(1)]\times[f'(1)]=1$

Let $y=4x^2+5$, then $x=\sqrt{\dfrac{y-5}{4}}=\dfrac{\sqrt{y-5}}{2}$

$\quad$ i.e. $g:y\to\dfrac{\sqrt{y-5}}{2}$

$\therefore$ the inverse function of f is g where $g(x)=\dfrac{\sqrt{x-5}}{2}$

$g'(x)=\tfrac{1}{4}(x-5)^{-\frac{1}{2}}=\dfrac{1}{4\sqrt{x-5}}$

$f'(x)=8x$

$(g'\circ f)(x)=\dfrac{1}{4\sqrt{4x^2+5-5}}=\dfrac{1}{8x}$

$\therefore (g'\circ f)(1)=\dfrac{1}{8}$ and $f'(1)=8$

$\therefore [(g'\circ f)(1)]\times[f'(1)]=\dfrac{1}{8}\times8=1$, as required.

---

 1 The function f is defined by $f:x\to 4-2x-x^2$, where $x \in \mathbb{R}$.
(a) Find the maximum value of $f(x)$.
(b) State the range of f. $\qquad$ *(L)

2 Express in terms of the functions $f:x\to\sqrt{x}$ and $g:x\to x+5$:
(i) $x\to\sqrt{x+5}$; $\qquad$ (iv) $x\to\sqrt{x}+10$;
(ii) $x\to x-5$; $\qquad$ (v) $x\to x^2+5$.
(iii) $x\to x+10$; $\qquad\qquad\qquad$ *(C)

3 The function f is defined by
$$f:x\to\frac{1}{2-x},$$
where $x \in \mathbb{R}$ and $x\neq 2$.
(a) Define in a similar way the inverse function f^{-1} and state its domain;
(b) Evaluate (i) $ff(3)$; (ii) $f^{-1}(3)$. $\qquad$ *(L)

4 Sketch:
(i) $y=|x|$ for the domain $-5\leqslant x\leqslant5$;
(ii) $y^2=x+1$ for the domain $-1\leqslant x\leqslant3$;
(iii) $y=[x]$ for the domain $0<x\leqslant5$, where $[x]$ denotes the greatest integer less than x. $\qquad$ *(C)

5 Let $f(n)=9^{2n}-5^{2n}$, where n is a non-negative integer.
(a) Evaluate $f(0)$ and $f(1)$.
(b) Write down the value of $f(n+1)$.
(c) Prove that $f(n+1)-25f(n)=56(9^{2n})$.
(d) Hence, using induction, prove that $f(n)$ is always divisible by 7. $\qquad$ (O & C)

6 Functions f and g are defined by
$$f:x\to\log_a x,\quad (x \in \mathbb{R}_+, a>1),$$
$$g:x\to\frac{1}{x},\quad (x \in \mathbb{R}_+).$$
State the ranges of f and g, and show that if h denotes the composite function $f\circ g$, then $h(x)+f(x)=0$.
Explain briefly why the composite function $g\circ f$ cannot be properly defined unless the domain is restricted to a subset of $\mathbb{R}_+$, and state a possible subset which would be suitable.
Define fully the inverses of f and g, and determine whether or not $h^{-1}(x)+f^{-1}(x)=0$. $\qquad$ (C)

7 The function φ is defined by $\varphi(x)=x^3+2x-1$, and the inverse function φ^{-1} is denoted by ψ. Find the values of $\psi(2)$ and $\psi'(2)$. $\qquad$ (W)

8 The functions f and g are defined by:
$f:x\to\sin 2x;\quad x \in \mathbb{R}$;
$g:x\to\cot x;\quad x \in \mathbb{R}, x\neq k\pi\ (k \in \mathbb{Z})$.
State the periods of f and g. Find the period of the function $f\circ g$. On separate axes, sketch the graphs of f, g and $f.g$ for the interval $\{x:-\pi<x<\pi, x\neq0\}$. Find the range of the function $f.g$. $\qquad$ (J)

9 The functions f, g are defined for $x>0$ by;
$f:x\to x^2$; $\qquad g:x\to\log_e x$.
Sketch and label the graphs of g, $f\circ g$ and g^{-1} on the same axes, using the same scale. $\qquad$ (A)

10 A function f is defined on the set S, where
$$S=\{x:x \in R, x\neq3\}, \text{ by } f:x\to\frac{3x+b}{x-3},\quad (b\neq-9).$$
(i) Show that the inverse of f is f;
(ii) Determine the range of values of b for which there are two invariant values of x and find these values of x when $b=55$.
A function g is defined on the set T, where $T=\{x:x \in R\}$, by $g:x\to x+2$. Determine whether the functions f and g are commutative under composition of functions on the set V, where $V=\{x:x \in S \cap T, x\neq1\}$. $\qquad$ (A)

11 The functions f and g, each with domain D, where $D=\{x:x \in \mathbb{R} \text{ and } 0\leqslant x\leqslant\pi\}$, are defined by $f:x\to\cos x$ and $g:x\to x-\tfrac{1}{2}\pi$. Write down and simplify an expression for $f[g(x)]$, giving its domain of definition. Sketch the graph of $y=f[g(x)]$. $\qquad$ (L)

P12 Simple Curves

core

Shapes of graphs, Transforming graphs, Modulus function.

Shapes of graphs

A sketch graph shows the basic shape of the graph and any special points on it, such as where it crosses the axes and any turning points. The basic shape may be predicted from the equation of the graph. For example:

$y = mx + c$: linear function → straight-line

$y = ax^2 + bx + c$: quadratic function → parabola

$y = \dfrac{a}{bx + c}$: reciprocal function → rectangular hyperbola

Sketch graphs of $y = f(x)$ for some simple standard functions.

Straight line   Parabola   Rectangular parabola

Transforming graphs

The graph of $y = f(x)$ may be transformed into the graphs of some related functions as follows.

Graphs of more complicated functions may be drawn by combining transformations.

Translations

$y = f(x) + a$: Translate the graph of $y = f(x)$ by a units, parallel to the y-axis.

Note the effect of the sign of a:

$a > 0$: If a is positive, then the translation is 'up', i.e. in the positive y-direction.

$a < 0$: If a is negative, then the translation is 'down', i.e. in the negative y-direction.

$y = f(x + a)$: Translate the graph of $y = f(x)$ by a units, parallel to the x-axis.

Note the effect of the sign of a:

$a > 0$: If a is positive, then the translation is to the left, i.e. in the negative x-direction.

$a < 0$: If a is negative, then the translation is to the right, i.e. in the positive x-direction.

Reflections

$y = -f(x)$: Reflect the graph of $y = f(x)$ in the x-axis.

$y = f(-x)$: Reflect the graph of $y = f(x)$ in the y-axis.

One-way stretches

$y = af(x)$: Stretch the graph of $y = f(x)$ by factor a, parallel to the y-axis.

Note the effect of the size of factor a.

$a > 1$: Multiplying by a number greater than 1 increases the 'y-values'. So the stretch is an increase in the y-direction.

$0 < a < 1$: Multiplying by a proper fraction decreases the 'y-values'. This gives a decrease or 'shrink' in the y-direction.

$y = f(ax)$: Stretch the graph of $y = f(x)$ by factor $\dfrac{1}{a}$, parallel to the x-axis.

Note the effect of the size of factor a.

$a > 1$: Multiplying by a proper fraction, $\dfrac{1}{a}$, decreases the 'x-values'. This gives a decrease or 'shrink' in the x-direction.

$0 < a < 1$: $\dfrac{1}{a}$ is greater than 1. Multiplying by this increases the 'x-values'. So the stretch is an increase in the x-direction.

The sketches below are transformations of this sketch graph of $y = \sin x$ i.e. $f(x) = \sin x$.

$y = (\sin x) + 1 = f(x) + 1$ $y = (\sin x) - 1 = f(x) - 1$

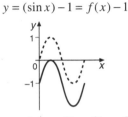

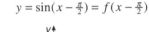

$y = \sin(x + \frac{\pi}{2}) = f(x + \frac{\pi}{2})$ $y = \sin(x - \frac{\pi}{2}) = f(x - \frac{\pi}{2})$

$y = -\sin x = -f(x)$ $y = \sin(-x) = f(-x)$

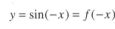

     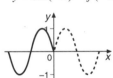

$y = 2\sin x = 2f(x)$ $y = \frac{1}{2}\sin x = \frac{1}{2}f(x)$

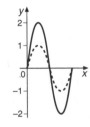   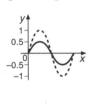

$y = \sin 2x = f(2x)$ $y = \sin\frac{1}{2}x = f(\frac{1}{2}x)$

     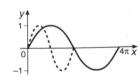

Modulus function

To sketch the graph of $y = |f(x)|$:

(1) Start with the sketch graph of $y = f(x)$.

(2) Reflect in the x-axis all points on $y = f(x)$ that are below the x-axis, i.e. where $f(x) < 0$.

(3) Leave the rest of the graph unchanged.

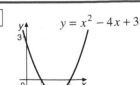

$y = x^2 - 4x + 3$

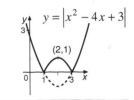

$y = |x^2 - 4x + 3|$

Simple Curves
Worked example, Guided example, Exam questions.

WE *A sketch graph of* $y = f(x)$, *where* $f(x) = x^2 + 4x$, *is given.*

(i) *Explain how this graph can be used to sketch graphs of the following.*

(a) $y = f(2x)$ (b) $y = f(\frac{1}{2}x)$

(c) $y = 2f(x)$ (d) $y = \frac{1}{2}f(x)$.

(ii) *Make separate sketches showing the graph of* $y = f(x)$ *and each of the graphs in part (i).*

Give the coordinates of the lowest point on each graph.

(i) (a) For the graph of $y = f(2x)$, 'stretch' the graph by factor $\frac{1}{2}$ parallel to the x-axis, i.e. 'shrink' it in this direction. (To do this, choose a few points on the graph of $y = f(x)$. Multiply the x-coordinates by $\frac{1}{2}$, leave the y-coordinates unchanged.)

(b) For the graph of $y = f(\frac{1}{2}x)$, stretch the graph by factor 2, parallel to the x-axis. (To do this, multiply the x-coordinates by 2.)

(c) For the graph of $y = 2f(x)$, stretch the graph of $y = f(x)$ by factor 2, parallel to the y-axis. (To do this, choose a few points on the graph of $y = f(x)$. Multiply the y-coordinates by 2, leave the x-coordinates unchanged.)

(d) For the graph of $y = \frac{1}{2}f(x)$, stretch the graph of $y = f(x)$ by factor $\frac{1}{2}$, parallel to the y-axis, i.e. 'shrink' it in this direction. (To do this multiply the y-coordinates by $\frac{1}{2}$.)

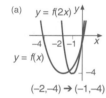
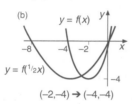

(-2,-4) ➜ (-1,-4)   (-2,-4) ➜ (-4,-4)

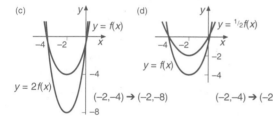

(-2,-4) ➜ (-2,-8)   (-2,-4) ➜ (-2,-2)

GE (a) *Sketch the graph of* $y = x^2$.

(b) *Use this graph to sketch the graphs of these equations:*

(i) $y = x^2 + 3$ (ii) $y = (x-2)^2$

(iii) $y = (x+3)^2 - 2$ (iv) $y = -x^2$.

Give the coordinates of the turning point of each graph.

(c) *Rewrite* $x^2 - 8x + 3$ *as* $(x+a)^2 + b$. *Hence find the coordinates of its turning point. Sketch the graph of* $y = x^2 - 8x + 3$.

(a) See first opposite.

(b) Rewrite each function in terms of $f(x)$, where $f(x) = x^2$. Then transform the graph of $y = x^2$ as indicated by each expression.

(i) $y = x^2 + 3 = f(x) + 3$ (ii) $y = (x-2)^2 = f(x-2)$

(iii) $y = f(x+3) - 2$ (iv) $y = -f(x)$.

Turning points are (0, 3), (2, 0), (-3, -2), (0, 0).

(c) Use the technique 'completing the square':

$x^2 - 8x + 3 = [x^2 - 8x] + 3 = [(x-4)^2 - 16] + 3 = \dots$

The turning point has coordinates $(-a, b)$.
Sketch the graph by using two translations.

EX **1** The diagram shows the curve with the equation $y = f(x)$ where $f(x) = 0$ when $x < 0$ or $x > 4$.

Sketch, on separate axes, showing clearly the scales on each axis, the graphs of:

(a) $y = f(x) - 1$ (b) $y = f(-x)$

(c) $y = \frac{1}{2}f(x)$ (d) $y = f(x+1)$

(e) $y = f(2x)$

(OLE)

2 The function f has domain the set of all non-zero real numbers, and is given by $f(x) = \dfrac{1}{x}$ for all x in this set. Sketch each of the following graphs, and indicate the geometrical relationships between them.

(i) $y = f(x)$ (ii) $y = f(x+1)$ (iii) $y = f(x+1) + 2$.

Deduce, explaining your reasoning, the coordinates of the point about which the graph of $y = \dfrac{2x+3}{x+1}$ is symmetrical.

(C)

3 The function $f(x)$ is defined for all values of x except $x = 0$ and is an odd function, i.e. $f(-x) = -f(x)$.

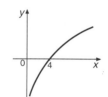

(a) Part of the graph of $y = f(x)$ is given here. Copy and complete the sketch.

(b) Draw a separate sketch to illustrate the graph of $y = f(x+3)$ showing clearly where the graph will intercept the x-axis.

(J)

4 A function $f(x) = (x+a)^2 + b$ has zeros at $x = 1.36$ and $x = 4.64$ precisely.

(a) Sketch the graph of $y = f(x)$, marking the points where the graph crosses the x-axis.

(b) Hence write down the x-coordinate of the vertex of the graph, and state the value of a.

(c) Calculate the exact value of b.

(J)

5 (a) For the graph with equation $y = 10\sin 2x$ state
(i) the period
(ii) the amplitude
(iii) the equation of a line of symmetry.

(b) This graph can be produced from the graph of $y = \sin x$ by means of two simple transformations. Identify these transformations. Does it matter in which order they are carried out?

(O & C)

6 The graph of $y = 2e^{-x} - 3$ intersects the x-axis at A and the y-axis at B. Find the coordinates of A and of B.

Sketch, on the same scales and axes, the graphs of $y = e^x$ and $y = 2e^{-x} - 3$. The graph of $y = 2e^{-x} - 3$ may be obtained from the graph of $y = e^x$ by means of three separate transformations. Describe three such transformations in detail and list the order in which they should be applied.

(J)

Trigonometrical Functions

Angle measure, Arcs and sectors, Trig ratios for angles of any size, Features and graphs.

Angle measure

Degrees (°): 1 full turn = 360°
$\frac{1}{4}$ turn = 90° = 1 right angle
1° = 60 minutes (60′), 1 minute = 60 seconds (60″)

Radians (also called **circular measure**):
One radian (1^c or 1 rad) is the size
of the angle subtended at the centre
of a circle by an arc equal in length
to the radius of the circle.

To change radians to degrees and vice versa, use:
1 full turn = 2π radians = 360° $\Rightarrow$ π radians = 180°.

 Angles that are simple fractions or multiples of
180° are often given in radians in terms of π. The
radian symbol or word is usually omitted.

30°	45°	60°	90°	120°	135°	180°	360°
$\frac{1}{6}\pi$	$\frac{1}{4}\pi$	$\frac{1}{3}\pi$	$\frac{1}{2}\pi$	$\frac{2}{3}\pi$	$\frac{3}{4}\pi$	π	2π

 Change: (a) 1^c *to degrees (b)* 1° *to radians.*
(a) $\pi = 180°$ $\Rightarrow$ 1^c = $(180 \div \pi)° = 57.3°$ (to 1 d.p.)
(b) $180° = \pi \Rightarrow 1° = (\pi \div 180)$rad = 0.0175^c (to 3 s.f.)

Arcs and sectors

An arc *AB* subtends an angle θ at the centre, *O*, of a
circle, radius *r*. If θ is in radians:

length of arc $AB = r\theta$

area of sector $AOB = \frac{1}{2}r^2\theta$

Note: answers are often given
in terms of π.

 Find the length of minor arc AB
and the area of major sector AOB.

Minor arc: $AB = r\theta = 4 \times \frac{1}{3}\pi = \frac{4}{3}\pi$ cm

Major sector *AOB*:

Angle at centre $\alpha = 2\pi - \frac{1}{3}\pi = \frac{5}{3}\pi$

Area $= \frac{1}{2}r^2\alpha = \frac{1}{2} \times 4^2 \times \frac{5}{3}\pi = \frac{40}{3}\pi$ cm^2.

Trig ratios for angles of any size

To define trig ratios for angles of any size, we use
coordinates. Think of *OP* on axes as shown.

P is the point (*x*, *y*). $OP = r$ (always positive).
OP is fixed at origin, *O*. As *OP* rotates about *O*, it
makes angle θ with the positive *x*-axis.
(anticlockwise $\rightarrow$ + angle,
clockwise $\rightarrow$ − angle)

The basic trig functions are
defined as follows:

$$\sin\theta = \frac{y}{r}, \quad \cos\theta = \frac{x}{r}, \quad \tan\theta = \frac{y}{x}$$

$\sin\theta$, $\cos\theta$, and $\tan\theta$ may be
positive or negative. The sign
depends on which quadrant θ is
in. This diagram shows which
ratios are positive in each quadrant.

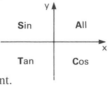

Trig ratios of any angle θ can be written as trig ratios of
a positive acute angle α. Decide which quadrant angle
θ is in. (Draw a diagram to help.) Find the sign of the
wanted trig ratio for an angle in that quadrant. Work out
the size of α, the acute angle made with the *x*-axis.

 Find, without a calculator, the values of $\cos\theta$ *and*
$\tan\theta$, *if* $\sin\theta = \frac{5}{13}$.

$\sin\theta$ is positive. So θ may be in 1st or 2nd quadrant.

$\sin\theta = \frac{y}{r} = \frac{5}{13} \Rightarrow y = 5, r = 13$
$\Rightarrow x = \pm\sqrt{13^2 - 5^2} = \pm 12$

1st quadrant: *x* is positive   2nd quadrant: *x* is negative

$\therefore \cos\theta = \frac{x}{r} = \frac{12}{13}$ $\therefore \cos\theta = \frac{x}{r} = \frac{-12}{13} = -\frac{12}{13}$

$\tan\theta = \frac{y}{x} = \frac{5}{12}$ $\tan\theta = \frac{y}{r} = \frac{5}{-12} = -\frac{5}{12}$.

 Find the exact value of $\tan(-240°)$.
−240° is in the 2nd quadrant.
So $\tan(-240°)$ is negative.
$\alpha = 240° - 180° = 60°$
$\tan(-240°) = -\tan 60° = -\sqrt{3}$.

Features and graphs

1. Features of $y = \sin\theta$ **and** $y = \cos\theta$

• Continuous. Defined for all values of θ.

• Periodic with period 360° (repeats every 360°).

• $-1 \leq \sin\theta \leq 1$ and $-1 \leq \cos\theta \leq 1$, i.e. they lie entirely
in the range −1 to 1. Amplitude is 1.

• Graph of $\cos\theta$ is the sine curve translated 90° to the
left, i.e. a phase shift of 90°.

• For $y = \sin\theta$, $\theta = 90°$ is a line of symmetry,
O is a centre of rotational symmetry, order 2.

For $y = \cos\theta$, $\theta = 0$ is a line of symmetry,
(90°, 0) is a centre of rotational symmetry, order 2.

• $\sin\theta$ is an odd function: $\sin(-\alpha) = -\sin\alpha$.
$\cos\theta$ is an even function: $\cos(-\alpha) = \cos\alpha$.

2. Features of $y = \tan\theta$

• Not continuous. Undefined for $\theta = \pm 90°$, $\pm 270°$,...

• Periodic with period 180°.

• Unlimited range of values, i.e. $-\infty \leq \tan\theta \leq \infty$.

• *O* is a centre of rotational symmetry, order 2.

• An odd function: $\tan(-\alpha) = -\tan\alpha$.

Graphs of $y = \sin\theta$ **and** $y = \cos\theta$ for $-360° \leq \theta \leq 360°$
—— $y = \sin\theta$ - - - $y = \cos\theta$

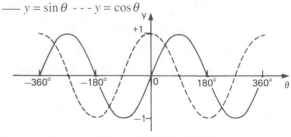

Graph of $y = \tan\theta$ for $-360° \leq \theta \leq 360°$.

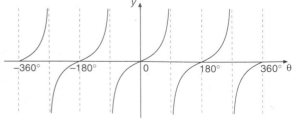

Transformations of these graphs give the graphs of
other trig functions (see P12).

Trigonometrical Functions

Inverse trig functions, Solving simple trig equations, Trig ratios of 30°, 60° and 45°.
Worked example, Guided example, Exercise.

Inverse trig functions

Arcsin, **arccos**, **arctan** and **sin⁻¹**, **cos⁻¹**, **tan⁻¹** are names of the *inverse* functions of sin, cos, tan.

arcsin x (or sin⁻¹x) means 'the angle in the range $-90° \le \theta \le 90°$ whose sine is x'.

arccos x (or cos⁻¹x) means 'the angle in the range $0° \le \theta \le 180°$ whose cosine is x'.

arctan x (or tan⁻¹x) means 'the angle in the range $-90° \le \theta \le 90°$ whose tangent is x'.

ℹ Values of inverse trig functions are angles. Use known trig ratios or a calculator to find them.

arcsin $\frac{1}{2}$ = 30° or $\frac{1}{6}\pi$

arccos(0.6) = 53.1° or 0.927 rad

arctan(−2) = −63.4° or −1.12 rad

Solving simple trig equations

To solve $\sin\theta = a$ for values of θ in a stated range, sketch the graph of $y = \sin\theta$ for this range of θ and mark $\theta = \arcsin a$. Work out all wanted solutions from the sketch by symmetry. Use a calculator to check each solution. *(Note:* we usually give solutions in the same unit as in the stated range of θ. Make sure the calculator is set to this mode.)

To solve $\sin k\theta = a$ (or $\sin(\theta + k) = a$), find values of $k\theta$ (or $\theta + k$) that fit the equation first. Then find the values of θ from these. *(Note:* if θ is wanted in the range $\alpha \le \theta \le \beta$, find $k\theta$ in the range $k\alpha \le k\theta \le k\beta$ (or find $\theta + k$ in the range $\alpha + k \le \theta + k \le \beta + k$).)

Solve other simple trig equations in a similar way.

Graphical method: to solve $f(\theta) = g(\theta)$, draw the curves $y = f(\theta)$ and $y = g(\theta)$ on the same axes. The values of θ at points of intersection give the solutions. *(Note:* rearranging the given equation first may give simpler graphs to draw.)

Small angles: when θ is small and in radians,
$$\sin\theta \approx \theta, \quad \tan\theta \approx \theta, \quad \cos\theta \approx 1 - \tfrac{1}{2}\theta^2$$

Trig equations with small angle solutions may be solved approximately using these.

ℹ *Solve* $\sin x = 0.4$ *for* $0° \le \theta \le 360°$.

$\sin x = 0.4$ has two solutions, a and b, in this range.
$a = \arcsin 0.4 = 23.6°$
$b = 180° - 23.6° = 156.4°$
Therefore
$x = 23.6°, \ 156.4°$ (1 d.p.)

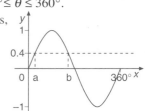

ℹ *Solve* $\cos\frac{1}{2}\theta = 0.59$ *for* $-2\pi \le \theta \le 2\pi$.

For this range of θ, find $\frac{1}{2}\theta$ such that $-\pi \le \frac{1}{2}\theta \le \pi$.
$\cos\frac{1}{2}\theta$ has two solutions, $\pm a$, in this range.
$a = \arccos 0.59 = 0.940$ rad
$\Rightarrow \frac{1}{2}\theta = \pm 0.940$ rad (to 3 s.f.)
$\Rightarrow \theta = \pm 1.88$ rad (to 3 s.f.)

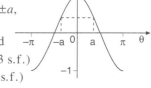

ℹ *Find an approximate solution for* $\cos\theta = 0.999$.

$\cos\theta$ is nearly 1, so θ is small and $\cos\theta \approx 1 - \frac{1}{2}\theta^2$
$1 - \frac{1}{2}\theta^2 \approx 0.999 \Rightarrow \theta^2 \approx 0.002$
$\Rightarrow \theta = \pm 0.0477^c$ (to 3 s.f.)

Trig ratios of 30°, 60° and 45°

Exact values for these trig ratios are often used. Learn them or work them out from these triangles.

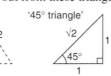
'30°–60° triangle'   '45° triangle'

ℹ
$\sin 30° = \frac{1}{2}$ $\cos 30° = \frac{\sqrt{3}}{2}$ $\tan 30° = \frac{1}{\sqrt{3}}$

$\sin 60° = \frac{\sqrt{3}}{2}$ $\cos 60° = \frac{1}{2}$ $\tan 60° = \sqrt{3}$

$\sin 45° = \frac{1}{\sqrt{2}}$ $\cos 45° = \frac{1}{\sqrt{2}}$ $\tan 45° = 1$

WE *Without using tables or a calculator, find the exact value of*
(a) sin 210° (b) cos 675°.

(a)

210° is in the 3rd quadrant.
So sin 210° is negative.
The marked angle $= 210° - 180° = 30°$.
$\therefore \sin 210° = -\sin 30° = -\frac{1}{2}$.

(b)
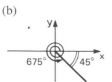
$675° = 360° + 315°$
315° and 675° are in the 4th quadrant.
So cos 675° is positive.
The marked angle $= 360° - 315° = 45°$.
$\therefore \cos 675° = \cos 45° = \frac{1}{\sqrt{2}}$.

GE *C is the centre of a circle, radius 10 cm and AB is a chord.*
$A\hat{C}B = 2.5$ radians. *Calculate the perimeter and area of the minor segment cut off by AB.*
Sketch diagram. Draw $CX \perp AB$..
Perimeter: minor arc AB + chord AB.
For arc, use $r\theta$. For chord, use sin ratio in triangle ACX.
Area: minor sector ACB − triangle ACB.
Use $\frac{1}{2}r\theta^2$ for sector and $\frac{1}{2}ab\sin c$ for triangle.

EX

1 An arc AB, 6 cm long, subtends an angle AOB at the centre, O, of a circle, radius 3 cm. Find the size of angle AOB and the area of minor sector AOB.

2 Find, without using a calculator, the value of:
(a) $\sin\theta$ and $\cos\theta$, if $\tan\theta = \frac{3}{4}$
(b) $\tan\theta$ and $\sin\theta$, if $\cos\theta = \frac{4}{5}$
(c) $\cos\theta$ and $\tan\theta$, if $\sin\theta = \frac{24}{25}$.

3 Solve these equations:
(a) $2\sin x = 1, \ 0 \le x \le 2\pi$
(b) $\tan x = -0.75, \ -180° \le x \le 180°$
(c) $\cos x = \sin 57°, \ 0° \le x \le 360°$
(d) $\cos 2x = 0.63, \ 0 \le x \le 2\pi$
(e) $\sin 4x = -0.5, \ -180° \le x \le 180°$
(f) $\tan 3x = 3.7583, \ -90° \le x \le 90°$
(g) $\sin(x - 15°) = 0.2, \ 0° \le x \le 180°$
(h) $3\cos(x + 30°) = -0.6, \ 0° \le x \le 360°$
(i) $\tan(\pi + 2x) = 3.681, \ -\pi \le x \le \pi$

4 Find an approximation in radians to the positive solution of $\cos\theta - \theta\sin\theta = 0.9976$, when θ is small.

P14

core

Plane Triangles

Standard notation, Solving triangles, Special triangles, Sine and cosine rules,
Applications of the sine and cosine rules, Other formulae, Area of a triangle.

Standard notation

In a triangle ABC,
$\left.\begin{array}{l}\text{the angles are } A, B, C\\ \text{the sides are } a, b, c\end{array}\right\}$ side a is opposite angle A, etc

angles

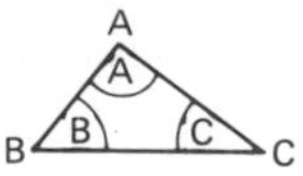

sides

Figure 1   **Figure 2**

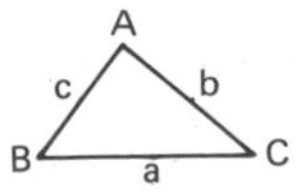

Solving triangles

Solving a triangle means finding all the unknown sides and angles in that triangle.
To solve a triangle:
(a) Sketch the triangle and mark in the given data.
(b) Use the appropriate formula(e).

Useful geometric facts about a triangle:
(a) The angle sum of a triangle is 180°, i.e. $A + B + C = 180°$.
(b) The greatest side is opposite the greatest angle, the smallest side is opposite the smallest angle.

Special triangles

Right angled and **isosceles** triangles can be solved using **Pythagoras' Theorem** and/or the basic trigonometrical ratios.

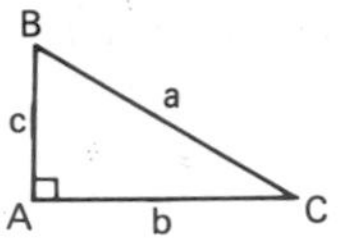

Figure 3

$a^2 = b^2 + c^2$ Pythagoras' Theorem

$\sin B = \dfrac{b}{a}, \cos B = \dfrac{c}{a}, \tan B = \dfrac{b}{c}$, etc.

Sine and cosine rules

Triangles without right angles can be solved using the sine and/or cosine rules.

Sine rule: $\dfrac{a}{\sin A} = \dfrac{b}{\sin B} = \dfrac{c}{\sin C} = 2R$

where R is the radius of the circumcircle of the triangle.

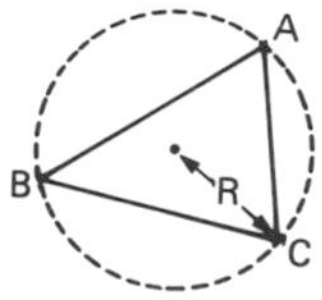

Figure 4

Cosine rule: $a^2 = b^2 + c^2 - 2bc \cos A$ $b^2 = a^2 + c^2 - 2ac \cos B$ $c^2 = a^2 + b^2 - 2ab \cos C$

or $\cos A = \dfrac{b^2 + c^2 - a^2}{2bc}$ or $\cos B = \dfrac{a^2 + c^2 - b^2}{2ac}$ or $\cos C = \dfrac{a^2 + b^2 - c^2}{2ab}$

Applications of the sine and cosine rules

(a) **Given three sides**, find:
the largest angle by the cosine rule,
the second angle by the cosine or sine rule,
the third angle by the 'angle sum'.

(b) **Given two sides and the included angle**, find:
the third side by the cosine rule,
the smaller angle by the sine rule,
the third angle by the 'angle sum'.

(c) **Given two sides and a non-included angle** (the ambiguous case):
try to find an angle using the sine rule (this can give two, one or no possible solutions),
find the third angle by the 'angle sum',
the third side by the sine rule.

(d) **Given one side and two angles**, find:
the third angle by the 'angle sum'
the other sides by the sine rule.

(e) **Given two or three angles only:**
The sides cannot be found.
The sine rule gives the ratios between sides.

$\boxed{i}$ *Solve the triangle with sides* 6, 14, 16 *units.*

The largest angle is opposite to the '16 unit' side.

$\cos A = \dfrac{14^2 + 6^2 - 16^2}{2 \times 14 \times 6}$

Figure 5

$= -0.1429 \Rightarrow A = 98.2°$

$\cos C = \dfrac{16^2 + 6^2 - 14^2}{2 \times 16 \times 6} = 0.5 \Rightarrow \hat{C} = 60°$

So $\hat{B} = 21.8°$ (angle sum)

$\boxed{i}$ *Solve the triangle illustrated.*

Sine rule: $\dfrac{9}{\sin 50°} = \dfrac{10}{\sin A}$

Figure 6

$\sin A = 0.8512$, so $\hat{A} = 58°20'$ or $121°40'$
So there are two possible triangles.
If $\hat{A} = 58°20'$, $\hat{C} = 71°40'$ (angle sum).
Sine rule gives $c = 11.15$ (2 d.p.)
If $\hat{A} = 121°40'$, $\hat{C} = 8°20'$ (angle sum)
Sine rule gives $c = 1.70$ (2 d.p.)

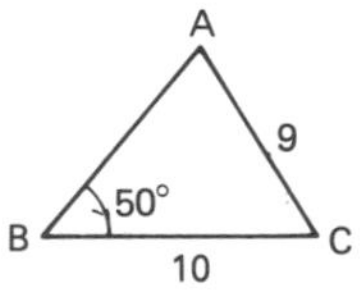

Other formulae

Half angle formulae (used when three sides are known)

$\sin \tfrac{1}{2}A = \sqrt{\dfrac{(s-b)(s-c)}{bc}}$ $\cos \tfrac{1}{2}A = \sqrt{\dfrac{s(s-a)}{bc}}$

$\tan \tfrac{1}{2}A = \sqrt{\dfrac{(s-b)(s-c)}{s(s-a)}}$ where $s = \tfrac{1}{2}(a+b+c)$

Included angle formulae (used when two sides and an included angle are known)

$\tan \tfrac{1}{2}(B-C) = \left(\dfrac{b-c}{b+c}\right) \cot \tfrac{1}{2}A$

etc.

Area of a triangle

The **area of a triangle** is often denoted by $\triangle$.

$\triangle = \tfrac{1}{2}ab \sin C$ or $\tfrac{1}{2}ac \sin B$ or $\tfrac{1}{2}bc \sin A$

Hero's (or Heron's) formula

$\triangle = \sqrt{s(s-a)(s-b)(s-c)}$ where $s = \tfrac{1}{2}(a+b+c)$

Plane Triangles
Worked examples and Exam questions.

 A triangle ABC has area 20 cm². *Given that AC = 10 cm, BC = 6 cm and that ∠ACB is obtuse, calculate (i) ∠ACB, (ii) the length of AB.*

(i) Area $\triangle ABC = 20$ cm².
   With standard notation

   $\frac{1}{2}ab \sin C = 20$

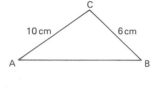

   i.e. $\frac{1}{2} \times 10 \times 6 \times \sin C = 20$

   giving $\sin C = \frac{2}{3}$

   and $\angle ACB = 138.2°$

(ii) The cosine rule for AB gives,
   $AB^2 = 10^2 + 6^2 - 2 \times 10 \times 6 \times \cos 138.2°$
   $= 100 + 36 + 120 \times 0.7455$
   $= 225.46$
   $\therefore AB = 15.02$ cm

CHECK $a = 6$ $s = 15.51$
         $b = 10$ $s - a = 9.51$
         $c = 15.02$ $s - b = 5.51$
         $2s = 31.02$ $s - c = 0.49$
         $s = 15.51$ cm

   $\triangle = \sqrt{s(s-a)(s-b)(s-c)}$
   $= \sqrt{15.51 \times 9.51 \times 5.51 \times 0.49}$
   $= 19.96$ cm²

 The perimeter of a triangle is 42 cm, *one side is of length* 14 cm *and the area is* $21\sqrt{15}$ cm². *Find the lengths of the other two sides and show that the cosine of the largest angle is* $\frac{1}{4}$.

With the standard notation
$2s = a + b + c = 42$, i.e. $s = 21$
Let $a = 14$, then $b + c = 28$

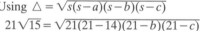
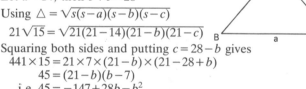

Using $\triangle = \sqrt{s(s-a)(s-b)(s-c)}$
$21\sqrt{15} = \sqrt{21(21-14)(21-b)(21-c)}$
Squaring both sides and putting $c = 28 - b$ gives
$441 \times 15 = 21 \times 7 \times (21-b) \times (21-28+b)$
$45 = (21-b)(b-7)$
i.e. $45 = -147 + 28b - b^2$
i.e. $b^2 - 28b + 192 = 0$
$(b-16)(b-12) = 0$, so $b = 16$ or 12.
If $b = 16$ then $c = 12$ or if $b = 12$ then $c = 16$.
$\therefore$ the lengths of the other two sides are 12 cm and 16 cm.
Let $a = 14$, $b = 16$ and $c = 12$, when B will be the largest angle,

and $\cos B = \dfrac{a^2 + c^2 - b^2}{2ac} = \dfrac{196 + 144 - 256}{2 \times 14 \times 12}$

$= \dfrac{84}{2 \times 14 \times 12} = \dfrac{1}{4}$, as required.

---

 1 In $\triangle ABC$, $BC = 8$ cm, $AC = 5$cm and $\angle ABC = 30°$.
(a) Calculate the two possible values of $\angle BAC$, giving your answers in degrees to one decimal place.
(b) Draw a diagram to illustrate your answers.
   (L)

2 In $\triangle ABC$, $AB = 12$ cm, $BC = 6\sqrt{3}$ cm and $A\hat{B}C = 150°$.
Calculate (i) AC, (ii) $A\hat{C}B$.
   (C)

3 (i) The sides of a triangle are 3, 7 and 8 units respectively. Prove that one of the angles is 60° and calculate the other two angles to the nearest degree. (ii) Solve the equation $\sqrt{3} \cos \theta - \sin \theta = 1$ for $0° < \theta < 360°$.
   (O & C)

4 In the triangle ABC, $AB = 12$ cm, $BC = 10$ cm and angle $CAB = 45°$. Find, to the nearest degree, the two possible values of angle BCA. Find also the corresponding lengths of the side AC.
   (A)

5 In $\triangle ABC$, $BC = 12$ cm, $AB = 4$ cm and angle C is acute with $\sin C = \frac{1}{6}$. Find, in radians, the two possible values of the angle A, leaving your answer in terms of π.
   (L)

6 In triangle ABC, angle $C = \dfrac{\pi}{3}$.
(a) Prove that $\sin A = \frac{1}{2}(\sqrt{3} \cos B + \sin B)$.
(b) Given that $b = 2a$, where the usual notation for triangle ABC applies, find, by using the sine rule or otherwise, the size of angle B.
   (H)

7 In any triangle ABC, prove, by using the sine rule or
otherwise, that $\tan \frac{1}{2}(B - C) = \dfrac{b-c}{b+c} \tan \frac{1}{2}(B+C)$.

In a particular triangle the angle A is 51° and $b = 3c$. Find the angle B in degrees and minutes. The area of this triangle is 0.47 m². Find a to 3 significant figures.
   (A)

8 In the triangle ABC, angle $CAB = \alpha°$, D is a point on AB such that $AD = 3DB$, and angle ACD = angle $BCD = 15°$. Prove that $\cot \alpha = 6 - \sqrt{3}$.
   (J)

9 A man walks due north. When he is at a point A he sees a pole on a bearing of 40°. After walking 200 m he is at the point B from which the bearing of the pole is 70°. Find, to the nearest metre, the distance of the pole from:
(i) the man's path, (ii) the midpoint of AB.
   (A)

10 An isosceles triangle ABC, in which $AB = AC$ and $\angle A = 2\theta$, is inscribed in a circle of radius 5 cm. Prove that the two equal altitudes of the triangle have length $10 \cos \theta \sin 2\theta$ cm. If the sum of the lengths of the three altitudes is 10 cm, find the three angles of the triangle to the nearest degree.
   (O & C)

11 ABC is a triangle, with sides of lengths a, b, c opposite A, B, C respectively. The point P is on the opposite side of BC to A, as shown in the diagram, and the triangle BCP is equilateral. Write down an expression for AP^2 in terms of a, c and the angle ABC. If the area of the triangle ABC is S, deduce that $AP^2 = \lambda(a^2 + b^2 + c^2) + \mu S$, where λ and μ are numerical constants, and find λ and μ.
   (J)

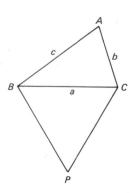

P15
core
3-D Figures
3-D problems, 3-D coordinates, Problems involving planes.

3-D problems

3-D problems are usually solved by finding lengths and/or angles in triangles. These triangles may be in the same plane or in different planes.

This strategy is useful when solving 3-D problems:

(a) Sketch a '3-D diagram' of the situation. Mark in the known facts. Identify any right angles.

(b) Pick out the triangle containing the wanted length or angle. Draw it separately with the known facts.

(c) Decide which relationship(s) you need to use to find what you want, e.g. trig ratios, Pythagoras' Theorem, cosine rule, sine rule. Identify any other lengths and/or angles you need to find to use them.

(d) Pick out the relevant triangle for each length and/or angle you have to find. Draw each one separately.

Questions often involve angles of elevation and depression. These angles are measured from the horizontal:
elevation → upwards, depression → downwards.

> **i** *An observer notes that the angle of elevation of the top of a tower is $\alpha°$ from a point A, while at a point B, x metres nearer to the tower, the angle of elevation is $\beta°$.*

A, B and the base of the tower lie in a straight line in the same horizontal plane. Find the height of the tower in terms of α, β and x.

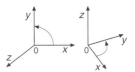

The diagram shows the situation.

PQ represents the tower of height h metres. $\triangle APQ$ and $\triangle BPQ$ are in the same vertical plane.

In $\triangle APQ$, $h = (x + BQ)\tan\alpha$ [1]

In $\triangle BPQ$, $h = BQ\tan\beta$ [2]

[2] gives: $BQ = \dfrac{h}{\tan\beta}$. Substituting in [1] gives:

$$h = \left(x + \frac{h}{\tan\beta}\right)\tan\alpha \implies h = \frac{x\tan\beta\tan\alpha}{\tan\beta - \tan\alpha}$$

3-D coordinates

For 3-D coordinates we use 3 axes: x-, y- and z-axes.

The axes are at right angles to each other and cross at O, the origin. They obey the 'RH corkscrew rule', i.e. if you turn a corkscrew from the ^+x-axis to the ^+y-axis it moves in the ^+z-direction.

To locate a point P in 3-D we give 3 coordinates: the x-coordinate, the y-coordinate and the z-coordinate in that order, written as (x, y, z). These coordinates give the distances of P from O, the origin, in the directions of the x-, y- and z-axes. The origin, O, is $(0, 0, 0)$.

To find the distance from A (x_1, y_1, z_1) to B (x_2, y_2, z_2) think of AB as the diagonal of a cuboid as shown here.

Its edges are $AP = (x_2 - x_1)$,

$PQ = (y_2 - y_1)$, $QB = (z_2 - z_1)$.

By Pythagoras' Theorem:

$$AB^2 = AQ^2 + QB^2$$
$$= AP^2 + PQ^2 + QB^2$$
$$\implies AB = \sqrt{(x_2 - x_1)^2 + (y_2 - y_1)^2 + (z_2 - z_1)^2}$$

> **i** There are many ways to draw x-, y- and z-axes. Two are shown here. See how they obey the 'RH corkscrew rule'.

> **i** In this diagram P is $(4, 3, 2)$.
> From origin O, P is:
> 4 units in the ^+x-direction,
> 3 units in the ^+y-direction,
> 2 units in the ^+z-direction.

> **i** *Given O $(0, 0, 0)$, A $(3, 1, 2)$ and B $(-5, 0, 1)$, calculate the lengths of OA, OB and AB.*

By Pythagoras' Theorem:

$OA = \sqrt{3^2 + 1^2 + 2^2} = \sqrt{14} = 3.7$ (to 1 d.p.)

$OB = \sqrt{(-5)^2 + 0^2 + 1^2} = \sqrt{26} = 5.1$ (to 1 d.p.)

$AB = \sqrt{(-5-3)^2 + (0-1)^2 + (1-2)^2}$
$\quad = \sqrt{(-8)^2 + (-1)^2 + (-1)^2} = \sqrt{66}$
$\quad = 8.1$ (to 1 d.p.)

Problems involving planes

The solution of some three-dimensional problems requires the use of one or more of the following facts about angles and planes.

A line perpendicular to a plane is perpendicular to every line in that plane.

The angle between a line and a plane is the angle between the line and its projection in the plane.

The angle between two planes is the angle between two lines, one in each plane, both perpendicular to the line common to the two planes.

The line of greatest slope in a plane is a line perpendicular to the line of intersection of the plane and the horizontal plane.

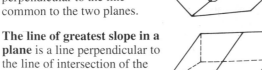

> **i** *Find the angle between two faces of a regular tetrahedron VABC.*

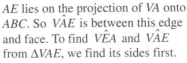

In $VABC$, E is the mid-point of BC. $VE \perp BC$ and $AE \perp BC$. So $V\hat{E}A$ is between faces VBC and ABC.

AE lies on the projection of VA onto ABC. So $V\hat{A}E$ is between this edge and face. To find $V\hat{E}A$ and $V\hat{A}E$ from $\triangle VAE$, we find its sides first.

Let each edge of $VABC$ be $2l$. In $\triangle VBE$, $VA = 2l$, $BE = l$ and, by Pythagoras' Theorem,
$VE = \sqrt{4l^2 - l^2} = \sqrt{3}\,l$.
$AE = VE$ (altitudes of congruent triangles).

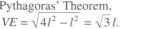
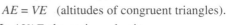

In $\triangle VAE$, the cosine rule gives:

$$\cos E = \frac{3l^2 + 3l^2 - 4l^2}{2 \times \sqrt{3}\,l \times \sqrt{3}\,l} = \frac{2l^2}{2 \times 3l^2} = \frac{1}{3}$$

$\therefore \hat{E} = 70.5°$ (to 1 d.p.)

$\hat{A} = \hat{V} = \frac{1}{2}(180° - \hat{E}) = 54.8°$ (to 1 d.p.)

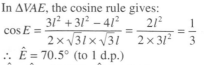

Therefore the angle between two faces is 70.5° and the angle between an edge and a face is 54.8°.

3-D Figures

Worked example, Guided example and Exam questions.

 ABCD is a horizontal rectangle with AB = 4 cm, AD = 3 cm. PA is a vertical line of length 9 cm.
Calculate: (a) *the angle between PC and the plane ABCD,*
(b) *the angle between the planes PBD and ABCD.*

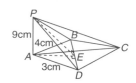

In rectangle *ABCD*,
DC = AB = 4 cm
and *BC = AD* = 3 cm,
$\hat{A} = \hat{B} = \hat{C} = \hat{D} = 90°$.

ABCD is a horizontal plane
and *PA* is a vertical line.
So *PA* is perpendicular to any line in plane *ABCD*.

(a) The required angle is between *PC* and its projection onto the plane *ABCD*, i.e. $P\hat{C}A$.

We can use a trig. ratio to find its size from $\triangle PCA$ if we can find *AC* or *PC*.

AC is a diagonal of *ABCD*.

Pythagoras' Theorem in $\triangle ADC$ gives *AC* = 5 cm (3, 4, 5 triangle).

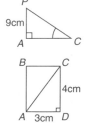

In $\triangle PCA$, $\tan P\hat{C}A = \dfrac{AP}{AC} = \dfrac{9}{5} = 1.8$

$P\hat{C}A = \tan^{-1} 1.8 = 60.9°$ (to 1 d.p.)

(b) *BD* is the line common to planes *PBD* and *ABCD*. *E* is on *BD* so that *PE* (in plane *PBD*) and *AE* (in plane *ABCD*) are both perpendicular to *BD*. So the required angle is between *PE* and *AE*, i.e. $P\hat{E}A$.

$P\hat{E}A$ is in right-angled $\triangle PEA$.
We can use a trig ratio to find its size if we can find *AE* or *AP*.

To find *AE*, use triangles in this diagram. .

In $\triangle ADE$, $AE = AD\sin A\hat{D}E = 3\sin A\hat{D}E$.
In $\triangle ADB$,

$\sin A\hat{D}B = \dfrac{AB}{BD} = \dfrac{4}{5} \Rightarrow \sin A\hat{D}E = \dfrac{4}{5}$.

So $AE = 3\sin A\hat{D}E = 3 \times \dfrac{4}{5} = 2.4$ cm

In $\triangle PEA$, $\tan P\hat{E}A = \dfrac{AP}{AE} = \dfrac{9}{2.4} = 3.75$

$P\hat{E}A = \tan^{-1} 3.75 = 75.1°$ (to 1 d.p.)

 Three observers stand at points A, B and C on a flat horizontal marsh. A is due West of B and C is on a bearing of 135° from A.

A hot-air balloon H is 500 m vertically above A. The angle of depression from H to B is 50° and from H to C is 30°. Calculate the distance BC.

3-D sketch of the situation:

Vertical line *HA* is perpendicular to any line in horizontal plane *ABC*.
So $H\hat{A}B = 90°$ and $H\hat{A}C = 90°$.

To find *BC*, use the 'horizontal' triangle *ABC*.

In $\triangle ABC$, $\hat{A} = 135° - 90° = 45°$.

By the cosine rule:
$BC^2 = AB^2 + AC^2 - 2 \times AB \times AC \times \cos A$

To use this you need to find *AB* and *AC*, which are sides of the 'vertical' triangles *HAB* and *HAC*. Use the tan ratio to find *AB* and *AC*.

Then use *AB* and *AC* to find *BC* by the cosine rule.

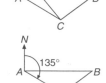

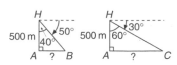

 1 A (1, 0, 0), B (6, 0, 0), C (6, 3, 0) and D (1, 0, 2) are four vertices of a cuboid.
(a) Label these four vertices on the diagram.
(b) Write down the coordinates of the other vertices of the cuboid.
(c) Write down the coordinates of the centre of the cuboid.
(L)

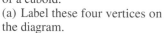

2 (a) The distance between the point P (3, 4, 0) and the point Q (3, 4, 12) is 12 units.
(i) Write down the coordinates of three other points which are 12 units from Q.
(ii) Describe fully the geometrical figure formed by the set of points which are 12 units from Q.
(b) (i) Calculate the length of the line from the origin O (0, 0, 0) to the point Q (3, 4, 12).
(ii) Write down the coordinates of the point R on the positive z-axis such that RQ = OQ
(iii) Calculate the size of angle OQR. (M)

3 C is (2, 3, –2) and D is (1, 4, 2). Calculate:
(a) the distances from the origin, O, to C and D,
(b) the length of CD,
(c) the angles of triangle OCD.

4 Given P (5, 2, 3), Q (6, 3, 7) and R (2, 5, 3),
(a) calculate the lengths of PQ, QR and RP,
(b) show that angle QPR is a right angle.

5 An eagle, 200 metres above ground level, is observed from two points x metres apart at ground level. From one point, which is due South of the eagle, the angle of elevation is 30° and from the other point, which is due East of the eagle, the angle of elevation is 40°. Calculate the value of x.
(C)

6 PA is a straight horizontal path; ABC is a straight path uphill so that PABC is a vertical plane; PAB = 150°, AB = 50 m and the angle of depression of P from B is 10°. What must be the length of BC (to the nearest metre) if the angle of depression of P from C is 16°? *(O & C)*

7 A vertical tower AB of height 40 metres is observed from two points C and D in the same horizontal plane as B, the foot of the tower. The points B, C and D lie in a straight line and BC = CD. Given that the angle of elevation of A from D is 60°, calculate:
(i) the distance of C from the foot of the tower; and
(ii) the angle of elevation of A from C. *(W)*

8 To find the height of a pylon a surveyor sets up his theodolite some distance from the pylon and finds the angle of elevation of the top of the pylon to be 30°. He then moves 50 m nearer to the pylon and finds the angle of elevation to be 45°. Find the height of the pylon given that the ground is horizontal and that the instrument is 1.5 m above ground level. *(W)*

9 A vertical mast, OM, of height 80 m, is built in a horizontal field. The angles of elevation of the top, M, of the mast from two points in the field, A and B, are 20° and 30°, respectively. A is due South of the mast, whilst B is on a bearing of N50°E (050°) from the mast. Calculate the distances OA, OB and AB. Find the area of the triangle AOB. *(S)*

10 ABCD is a tetrahedron in which ∠BAC = ∠CAD = ∠DAB = 60°, AB = AD = BD = 9 cm, BC = 10 cm. Calculate ∠ACB, the length of the perpendicular from B to AC, and the angle between the planes ABC and ADC. (O & C)

Trigonometrical Identities
Reciprocal trig functions, Using standard trig identities, Solving trig equations.

Reciprocal trig functions

Cosecant, secant and **cotangent** are the reciprocals of the sine, cosine and tangent functions.

$$\csc\theta = \frac{1}{\sin\theta} = \frac{r}{y}$$

$$\sec\theta = \frac{1}{\cos\theta} = \frac{r}{x}$$

$$\cot\theta = \frac{1}{\tan\theta} = \frac{x}{y}$$

Their properties and graphs can be found from those of sin, cos and tan (see P13).

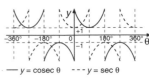 $y = \csc\theta$ and $y = \sec\theta$ for $-360° \le \theta \le 360°$.
Period 360° (2π).
Not continuous:
$\csc\theta$ undefined for $\theta = 0°, \pm180°, \ldots$;
$\sec\theta$ undefined for $\theta = \pm90°, \pm270°, \ldots$

— $y = \csc\theta$ - - - $y = \sec\theta$

$y = \cot\theta$ for $-360° \le \theta \le 360°$.
Period 180° (π)
Not continuous:
undefined for $\theta = 0°, \pm180°, \pm360°\ldots$
Unlimited range.

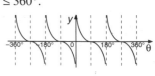

Using standard trig identities

An **identity** is a relationship which is true for *all* values of the variable.

The **standard trig identities** needed at this stage are listed opposite. Examples of their main uses follow:

1.   To find values of trig ratios
(a)   Some angles are the sum or difference of special angles such as 30°, 45°, 60°, 90°,... To find exact values for trig ratios of these angles use compound angle formulae. Simplify the result.
(b)   Trig ratios of the sum or difference of two unknown angles may be found if a trig ratio of each angle is known. State the compound angle formula to be used. Work out the unknown 'single angle' trig ratios from 'quadrant diagrams'. Substitute values in the formula. Simplify. (See Worked Example.)

2.   To eliminate trig terms from a pair of equations
Rearrange each equation to give the trig ratio in terms of the other variables. Substitute these expressions in the Pythagorean identity that links the two trig ratios. Simplify.

3.   To simplify trig expressions
This may involve reducing the number of terms, giving the expression in terms of one ratio only, rewriting it without compound angles, eliminating fractions, ...

4.   To establish other trig identities
Start with one side of the identity (usually the more complicated expression). Using standard identities change it, a step at a time, into the form on the other side. Do not work with both sides of the given identity at the same time.

Sometimes LHS and RHS of an identity must be worked on separately. Simplify LHS. Simplify RHS to the same expression. So LHS ≡ RHS (see Guided example).

$\boxed{i}$ $1 + \cot^2 A \equiv \csc^2 A$ is a standard trig identity.
It is true for all values of A.
($\equiv$ means 'is identical to'. This is the 'correct' symbol to use in an identity, but we usually use =.)

$\boxed{i}$ *Find the exact value for* cos 75°.

$$\cos 75° = \cos(30° + 45°) = \cos 30° \cos 45° - \sin 30° \sin 45°$$

$$= \left(\frac{\sqrt{3}}{2}\right)\left(\frac{1}{\sqrt{2}}\right) - \left(\frac{1}{2}\right)\left(\frac{1}{\sqrt{2}}\right)$$

$$= \frac{1}{2\sqrt{2}}(\sqrt{3} - 1) = \frac{\sqrt{2}}{4}(\sqrt{3} - 1)$$

$\boxed{i}$ *Eliminate* θ *from* $x = 2 + \tan\theta$, $y = 2\cos\theta$.

$$x = 2 + \tan\theta \implies \tan\theta = x - 2$$

$$y = 2\cos\theta \implies \cos\theta = \frac{y}{2} \implies \sec\theta = \frac{2}{y}$$

Using $1 + \tan^2\theta = \sec^2\theta$ gives $1 + (x-2)^2 = \left(\frac{2}{y}\right)^2$

$$\implies y^2(x^2 - 4x + 5) = 4$$

$\boxed{i}$ *Simplify* $\sin(x + y) - \sin(x - y)$.

$$\sin(x + y) - \sin(x - y)$$

$$= [\sin x \cos y + \cos x \sin y] - [\sin x \cos y - \cos x \sin y]$$

$$= \sin x \cos y - \sin x \cos y + \cos x \sin y + \cos x \sin y$$

$$= 2\cos x \sin y$$

$\boxed{i}$ *Show that* $\cot\theta + \tan\theta \equiv \csc\theta\sec\theta$.

$$\cot\theta + \tan\theta \equiv \frac{\cos\theta}{\sin\theta} + \frac{\sin\theta}{\cos\theta} \equiv \frac{\cos^2\theta + \sin^2\theta}{\sin\theta\cos\theta}$$

$$\equiv \frac{1}{\sin\theta\cos\theta} \equiv \csc\theta\sec\theta$$

Solving trig equations

The main steps in **solving trig equations** are:
(a)   finding value(s) for trig ratios (by solving a trig equation like an algebraic equation)
(b)   finding the angles (in the required range) that give each of these values. (*Note*: Do not cancel a trig ratio from an equation or part of the solution will be lost.)

Some trig equations must be simplified using trig identities before they can be solved. For example:

1.   Equations containing two or more trig ratios
Express in terms of one ratio by using standard identities. Solve the resulting equation as usual.

2.   Equations containing multiples of one angle
Express the equation in terms of the 'single angle' by using multiple angle formula. Collect terms on LHS to give 'trig expression' = 0. Factorise if possible. Solve the resulting equation as usual.

$\boxed{i}$ *Solve* $\cos\theta = 2\sin^2\theta - 1$ *for* $0° \le \theta \le 360°$.
$$\cos\theta = 2\sin^2\theta - 1$$
$$\implies \cos\theta = 2(1 - \cos^2\theta) - 1$$
$$\implies 2\cos^2\theta + \cos\theta - 1 = 0$$
$$\implies (2\cos\theta - 1)(\cos\theta + 1) = 0 \implies \cos\theta = \tfrac{1}{2} \text{ or } \cos\theta = -1$$
In the given range, $\cos\theta = \tfrac{1}{2} \implies \theta = 60°, 300°$
$$\cos\theta = -1 \implies \theta = 180°.$$

$\boxed{i}$ *Solve* $\sin 2x + \cos x = 0$ *for* $-180° < x < 180°$.
$$\sin 2x + \cos x = 0$$
$$\implies 2\sin x \cos x + \cos x = 0$$
$$\implies \cos x(2\sin x + 1) = 0 \implies \cos x = 0 \text{ or } \sin x = -\tfrac{1}{2}$$
In the given range, $\cos x = 0 \implies x = 90°, -90°$
$$\sin x = -\tfrac{1}{2} \implies x = -30°.$$

Trigonometrical Identities

Standard trig identities
Worked examples, Guided example and Exam questions.

Standard trig identities

The standard trig identities used at this stage are given below.

$$\tan A = \frac{\sin A}{\cos A}$$

$$\cot A = \frac{\cos A}{\sin A}$$

Pythagorean identities:

$$\sin^2 A + \cos^2 A = 1$$

$$1 + \tan^2 A = \sec^2 A$$

$$1 + \cot^2 A = \operatorname{cosec}^2 A$$

Double angle formulae:

$$\sin 2A = 2 \sin A \cos A$$

$$\cos 2A = \cos^2 A - \sin^2 A$$
$$= 1 - 2 \sin^2 A$$
$$= 2 \cos^2 A - 1$$

$$\tan 2A = \frac{2 \tan A}{1 - \tan^2 A}$$

Compound angle formulae (also called sum and difference formulae):

$$\sin(A + B) = \sin A \cos B + \cos A \sin B$$
$$\sin(A - B) = \sin A \cos B - \cos A \sin B$$
$$\cos(A + B) = \cos A \cos B - \sin A \sin B$$
$$\cos(A - B) = \cos A \cos B + \sin A \sin B$$

$$\tan(A + B) = \frac{\tan A + \tan B}{1 - \tan A \tan B}$$

$$\tan(A - B) = \frac{\tan A - \tan B}{1 + \tan A \tan B}$$

WE *a and b are acute angles such that*:

$$\sin a = \frac{1}{\sqrt{10}} \quad \text{and} \quad \sin b = \frac{1}{\sqrt{5}}$$

Find, without using tables or calculator, the exact value of $\sin(a + b)$.

Use: $\sin(a + b) = \sin a \cos b + \cos a \sin b$.

a and *b* are acute angles, i.e. in the first quadrant.

Quadrant diagrams:

$$\sin a = \frac{1}{\sqrt{10}} \qquad\qquad \sin b = \frac{1}{\sqrt{5}}$$

$$\Rightarrow y = 1, \ r = \sqrt{10} \qquad \Rightarrow y = 1, \ r = \sqrt{5}$$

$$\Rightarrow x = 3 \text{ and } \cos a = \frac{3}{\sqrt{10}} \qquad \Rightarrow x = 2 \text{ and } \cos b = \frac{2}{\sqrt{5}}$$

$$\sin(a + b) = \sin a \cos b + \cos a \sin b$$

$$= \frac{1}{\sqrt{10}} \times \frac{2}{\sqrt{5}} + \frac{3}{\sqrt{10}} \times \frac{1}{\sqrt{5}}$$

$$= \frac{1}{\sqrt{50}}(2 + 3) = \frac{5}{\sqrt{50}} = \frac{5}{5\sqrt{2}} = \frac{1}{\sqrt{2}}$$

WE (a) *Find* $\cos 3A$ *in terms of* $\cos A$ *only*.
(b) *Hence find all values of A, for* $-180° \le A \le 180°$, *which satisfy the equation* $\cos 3A + 2\cos A = 0$.

(a) $\cos 3A = \cos(2A + A)$

$$= \cos 2A \cos A - \sin 2A \sin A$$
$$= (2 \cos^2 A - 1) \cos A - (2 \sin A \cos A) \sin A$$
$$= 2 \cos^3 A - \cos A - 2 \sin^2 A \cos A$$
$$= 2 \cos^3 A - \cos A - 2(1 - \cos^2 A) \cos A$$
$$= 2 \cos^3 A - \cos A - 2 \cos A + 2 \cos^3 A$$
$$= 4 \cos^3 A - 3 \cos A$$

(b) $\cos 3A + 2 \cos A = 0 \ \Rightarrow \ (4 \cos^3 A - 3 \cos A) + 2 \cos A = 0$

$$\Rightarrow \ 4 \cos^3 A - \cos A = 0$$
$$\Rightarrow \ \cos A(4 \cos^2 A - 1) = 0$$
$$\Rightarrow \ \cos A = 0 \text{ or } \cos A = \pm \tfrac{1}{2}$$

In the given range: $\cos A = 0 \ \Rightarrow \ A = 90° \text{ or } -90°$

$$\cos A = \tfrac{1}{2} \ \Rightarrow \ A = 60° \text{ or } -60°$$

$$\cos A = -\tfrac{1}{2} \ \Rightarrow \ A = 120° \text{ or } -120°$$

GE *Show that* $\dfrac{\sec \theta + \operatorname{cosec} \theta}{\tan \theta + \cot \theta} = \dfrac{\tan \theta - \cot \theta}{\sec \theta - \operatorname{cosec} \theta}$.

Start with LHS. Simplify numerator and denominator separately at first. Write each trig ratio in terms of $\sin \theta$ and $\cos \theta$. This gives fractions in both numerator and denominator.
Write them over a common denominator. (Remember: $\sin^2 \theta + \cos^2 \theta = 1$.) Simplify 'numerator' ÷ 'denominator'.
The result is $\text{LHS} = \sin \theta + \cos \theta$.
Now start with the RHS. Again, write it in terms of $\sin \theta$ and $\cos \theta$ and simplify. Show that $\text{RHS} = \sin \theta + \cos \theta$.
∴ LHS = RHS.

EX 1 Prove the identity $\sec^2 A + \operatorname{cosec}^2 A = 4 \operatorname{cosec}^2 2A$. Find all the values of A between $0°$ and $360°$ such that $4 \operatorname{cosec}^2 2A - \operatorname{cosec}^2 A = 3$. For which range of values of the constant k has the equation $4 \operatorname{cosec}^2 2A - \operatorname{cosec}^2 A = k$ no solutions? *(OLE)*

2 Find all possible values of x from $0°$ to $360°$ when:
   (i) $\sin^2 x = 0.75$;   (ii) $5 \sin x = 3 \cos x$;
   (iii) $\sec 2x = 2$;   (iv) $3 \sin^2 x + 2 \cos x = 2$.
   (O & C)

3 Given that $\sin x = \frac{12}{13}$ and that $\frac{1}{2}\pi < x < \pi$, show that $\cos x = -\frac{5}{13}$. Without using tables or a calculator, evaluate:
   (a) $\sin(x + \pi)$; (b) $\tan(x + 2\pi)$;
   (c) $\cot(\pi - x)$; (d) $\sec(x + \frac{1}{2}\pi)$.
   (A)

4 Find the values of x between $0°$ and $360°$ which satisfy:
   (i) $\cos(3x - 75°) = 0.5$; (ii) $2 - \sin x = \cos^2 x + 7 \sin^2 x$.
   (C)

5 Solve the equation $4 \tan^2 x + 12 \sec x + 1 = 0$, giving all solutions in degrees, to the nearest degree, in the interval $-180° < x < 180°$.
   (A)

6 (a) Find the values of $\cos x$ for which $6 \sin^2 x = 5 + \cos x$.
   (b) Find all the values of x in the interval $180° < x < 540°$ for which $6 \sin^2 x = 5 + \cos x$.

7 Show that $\tan \theta + \cot \theta = \dfrac{2}{\sin 2\theta}$. Hence, or otherwise, solve the equation $\tan \theta + \cot \theta = 4$, giving all the values of θ between $0°$ and $360°$.
   (C)

8 Prove the identity $\operatorname{cosec} x - \sin x \equiv \cos x \cot x$. *(OLE)*

9 Prove that $\sin 3\theta = 3 \sin \theta - 4 \sin^3 \theta$.
   Hence find all values of θ, for $0° \le \theta \le 360°$, which satisfy the equation $\sin 3\theta = 2 \sin \theta$.
   (C)

P17
core

Sequences
Definitions, Finite sequences, Recurrence relations, Infinite sequences, Graphs, Behaviour of sequences.

Definitions

A **sequence** is a set of terms in a definite order with a rule for obtaining each term. The terms are sometimes called **elements**. A sequence may be finite or infinite.

> **i** 2, 4, 6, 8, 10 is a finite sequence of five terms.

> **i** 1, 2, 3, 4, 5, … is the infinite sequence of positive integers.

Finite sequences

A **finite sequence** can be specified by:
• a complete or incomplete list of its elements, or
• a function with domain a subset of the natural numbers.

The kth term of a sequence specified by a function f can be written $f(k)$. The terms of a sequence are often written as $u_1, u_2, u_3, \ldots$ and the general, kth, term as u_k.
(The general term of a sequence may be called: the rth term (u_r) or the nth term (u_n) or any similar letter pair, e.g. t_n.)

> **i** The finite sequence $1, \frac{1}{2}, \frac{1}{3}, \frac{1}{4}, \frac{1}{5}, \frac{1}{6}$ can also be specified by the function
> $$f: k \mapsto \frac{1}{k} \quad (k \in \{1, 2, 3, 4, 5, 6\}).$$
> For this sequence, $f(k) = \frac{1}{k}$. The terms can be written
> $$u_1 = 1, \ u_2 = \frac{1}{2}, \ u_3 = \frac{1}{3}, \ u_4 = \frac{1}{4}, \ u_5 = \frac{1}{5}, \ u_6 = \frac{1}{6}$$
> and the kth term, $u_k = \frac{1}{k}$.

Recurrence relations

A **recurrence relation** expresses the kth element of a sequence in terms of one or more of its predecessors. In order to know where the sequence begins, it is necessary to state the value of the first term of the sequence, called u_1 (or u_0), or possibly the first two terms. Sometimes a recurrence relation gives, say, the $(n+1)$th term in terms of the nth.

> **i** The finite sequence $1, \frac{1}{3}, \frac{1}{12}, \frac{1}{60}$ can be specified by the recurrence relation
> $$u_k = \frac{u_{k-1}}{k+1} \quad (u_1 = 1; \ k = 2, 3, 4)$$
> since $u_1 = 1, \quad u_2 = \frac{u_{2-1}}{2+1} = \frac{u_1}{3} = \frac{1}{3}, \ldots$

Infinite sequences

An infinite sequence can be specified by:
• an incomplete list of its elements, or
• a function with domain the natural numbers, or
• a recurrence relation.

If the sequence is specified by an incomplete list of elements, there should be no ambiguity about the way the sequence continues.

> **i** The sequence of powers of 2 can be given as:
> • an incomplete list : 1, 2, 4, 8, 16, …
> • a function: $f: k \mapsto 2^{k-1} \ (k \in N)$
> • a recurrence relation: $u_1 = 1$
> $$u_k = 2u_{k-1} \quad (k = 2, 3, 4, \ldots)$$
> (Alternatively, the recurrence relation may be stated as:
> $u_1 = 1, \ u_{n+1} = 2u_n \ (n = 1, 2, 3, 4, \ldots).)$

Graphs

A graph of a sequence helps you to see how it behaves.

It may be possible to draw the complete graph of a finite sequence.

Plotting the first few points for an infinite sequence should give a good indication of its behaviour.

To draw the graph of a sequence:
(a) draw two axes and label the horizontal axis k (or n or …), and the vertical axis u_k (or u_n or …),
(b) plot the points $(1, u_1), (2, u_2), (3, u_3), \ldots (k, u_k)$,
(c) join the plotted points with dotted lines.

Since a sequence is defined on the natural numbers only, a graph will consist of a set of discrete points. Joining the points with dotted lines will indicate the behaviour of the sequence. Intermediate 'points' have no meaning.

> **i** *Sketch the graphs of the sequences:*
> (a) 1, 2, 4, 8, 16, … (b) $u_k = (-1)^k \ (k \in N)$.
> (a)
>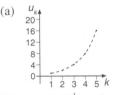
> (b) $u_1 = (-1)^1 = -1, \ u_2 = (-1)^2 = 1, \ u_3 = (-1)^3 = -1,$
>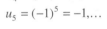
> $u_4 = (-1)^4 = 1,$
> $u_5 = (-1)^5 = -1, \ldots$
>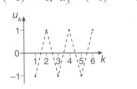

Behaviour of sequences

If the terms of a sequence get closer and closer to a fixed number as k increases, the sequence is said to **converge**. The fixed number is called the **limit** of the sequence.

A sequence which does not converge is called **non-convergent**. It may:
• be divergent (the difference between successive terms gets larger and larger),
• be periodic (regularly repeating),
• oscillate between fixed values.

The **period** of a periodic sequence is the smallest interval for a complete cycle of values after which the sequence repeats.

> **i** In the two examples above:
> (a) the sequence 1, 2, 4, 8, 16, … is divergent, the elements of the sequence get larger and larger;
> (b) the sequence $u_k = (-1)^k \ (k \in N)$ oscillates between -1 and 1. It is also periodic since the graph of the sequence for $k = 1$, $k = 2$ and $k = 3$ is repeated for $k = 3$, $k = 4$ and $k = 5$ and so on forever. The graph is repeated from $k = 3$ onwards so the period of the sequence is $3 - 1 = 2$.

Sequences
Worked examples, Exercise and Exam questions.

 (a) *Find the general term u_r $(r \in N)$ for each of the following sequences:*

(i) $0, \dfrac{1}{2}, \dfrac{2}{3}, \dfrac{3}{4}, \dfrac{4}{5}, \ldots$ (ii) $1, -2, 3, -4, 5, \ldots$

(iii) $5, 20, 45, 80, 125, \ldots$

(b) *Sketch each sequence.*

(c) *Describe the behaviour of each sequence.*

(a) (i) The sequence can be written as

$\dfrac{0}{1}, \dfrac{1}{2}, \dfrac{2}{3}, \dfrac{3}{4}, \ldots$ or $\dfrac{1-1}{1}, \dfrac{2-1}{2}, \dfrac{3-1}{3}, \dfrac{4-1}{4}, \dfrac{5-1}{5}, \ldots$

So, the general term $u_r = \dfrac{r-1}{r}$.

(ii) The sequence can be written as
$(-1)^{1+1}1, \; -(1)^{2+1}2, \; (-1)^{3+1}3, \; (-1)^{4+1}4, \; (-1)^{5+1}5, \ldots$

So, the general term $u_r = (-1)^{r+1}r$.

(iii) 5 is a factor of each term, so the sequence can be written
as $5 \times 1, \; 5 \times 4, \; 5 \times 9, \; 5 \times 16, \; 5 \times 25, \ldots$
or $5 \times 1^2, \; 5 \times 2^2, \; 5 \times 3^2, \; 5 \times 4^2, \; 5 \times 5^2, \ldots$

So, the general term $u_r = 5r^2$.

(b) (i) 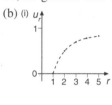   (ii) 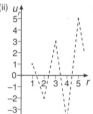   (iii)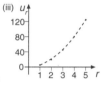

(c) Sequence (i) is convergent with limit 1.

Sequence (ii) is divergent. The difference between successive pairs of values increases as r gets larger.

Sequence (iii) is divergent too.

 Three sequences are defined as follows:

(i) $u_n = n(n+1)(n+2)$ $(n \in N)$

(ii) $u_{n+1} = 1 - \dfrac{1}{1+u_n}$ where $u_1 = 1$ $(n \in N)$

(iii) $f : n \mapsto \cos(60n°)$ $(n \in N)$.

(a) *Find the first four terms of each sequence.*

(b) *Describe the behaviour of each sequence.*

(a) (i) $u_1 = 1(1+1)(1+2) = 6$, $u_2 = 2(2+1)(2+2) = 24$,

$u_3 = 3(3+1)(3+2) = 60$, $u_4 = 4(4+1)(4+2) = 120$.

(ii) $u_1 = 1$, $u_2 = 1 - \dfrac{1}{1+u_1} = 1 - \dfrac{1}{1+1} = \dfrac{1}{2}$

$u_3 = 1 - \dfrac{1}{1+u_2} = 1 - \dfrac{1}{1+\frac{1}{2}} = 1 - \dfrac{2}{3} = \dfrac{1}{3}$

$u_4 = 1 - \dfrac{1}{1+u_3} = 1 - \dfrac{1}{1+\frac{1}{3}} = 1 - \dfrac{3}{4} = \dfrac{1}{4}$.

(iii) $f(1) = \cos 60° = \tfrac{1}{2}$, $f(2) = \cos 120° = -\tfrac{1}{2}$,

$f(3) = \cos 180° = -1$, $f(4) = \cos 240° = -\tfrac{1}{2}$.

(b) (i) The sequence is divergent. The terms of the sequence get larger and larger.

(ii) The sequence is convergent with limit equal to zero.

(iii) Finding the value of a few more terms of the sequence shows that this sequence is periodic. The terms $f(1)$ to $f(6)$ are repeated from $f(7)$ to $f(13)$ and so on. So the period of this sequence is six.

 1 Write down the first five terms of the sequences specified by these nth terms (in each case $n \in N$):

(a) $u_n = 4n$ (b) $u_n = 3n - 2$ (c) $t_n = 2n^2 + 1$

(d) $r_n = 2^{n-1}$ (e) $u_n = (-1)^n \dfrac{n^2}{n+1}$.

2 Write down the first five terms of the sequences specified by these recurrence relations:

(a) $u_1 = 2$, $u_k = 3 + 2u_{k-1}$ $(k = 2, 3, \ldots)$

(b) $u_1 = 5$, $u_k = 1 + \dfrac{u_{k-1}}{10}$ $(k = 2, 3, \ldots)$

(c) $u_1 = 0$, $u_n = \dfrac{1}{5 - u_{n-1}}$ $(n \geq 2)$

(d) $u_1 = 0$, $u_2 = 1$, $u_r = 2u_{r-1} - u_{r-2}$ $(r \geq 3)$

(e) $u_1 = 1$, $u_2 = 3$, $u_n = 3u_{n-1} - 2u_{n-2}$ $(n \geq 3)$.

3 Write down functions which specify the following sequences:

(a) $\tfrac{1}{2}, \tfrac{1}{3}, \tfrac{1}{4}, \tfrac{1}{5}, \ldots$ (b) $1, 3, 5, 7, 9, \ldots$

(c) $\tfrac{1}{2}, \tfrac{1}{4}, \tfrac{1}{8}, \tfrac{1}{16}, \ldots$ (d) $1, -2, 3, -4, 5, \ldots$

(e) $-1, \tfrac{1}{4}, -\tfrac{1}{9}, \tfrac{1}{16}, -\tfrac{1}{25}, \ldots$.

4 Write down recurrence relations which specify the following sequences:

(a) $2, 4, 6, 8, 10, \ldots$ (b) $2, 6, 18, 54, 162, \ldots$

(c) $1, 3, 7, 15, 31, \ldots$ (d) $1, 2, 5, 14, 41, \ldots$

5 Sketch the graph of the sequence

$0.3, 0.33, 0.333, 0.3333, \ldots$

Is this sequence convergent, divergent, oscillating or periodic? Give as full a description of the behaviour of the sequence as you can.

6 The sequence $u_1, u_2, u_3, \ldots$ where u_1 is a given real number, is defined by

$$u_{n+1} = \frac{1}{2}\left(u_n + \frac{10}{u_n}\right)$$

Describe the behaviour of the sequence when $u_1 = 3$.

Use the results of your investigation to give $\sqrt{10}$ correct to six decimal places. Show all steps in your working.

7 (a) Write down the first five terms of the sequence given by the recurrence relation $u_{r+1} = ku_r$ $(r \geq 0)$ when $u_0 = 3$ and k is a constant.

(b) Hence give the general formula for u_n.   (H)

8 A sequence $\{u_r : r \in Z\}$ is given by the rule
$u_{r+1} = mu_r + c$, for constants m, c.
If $u_0 = 0$, $u_1 = 1$ and $u_2 = 3$, find
(a) the constants m, c (b) u_3.   (H)

9 The sequence $u_1, u_2, u_3, \ldots$, where u_1 is a given real number, is defined by $u_{n+1} = u_n^2 - 1$.
(i) Describe the behaviour of the sequence for each of the cases $u_1 = 0$, $u_1 = 1$ and $u_1 = 2$.
(ii) Given that $u_2 = u_1$, find exactly the two possible values of u_1.
(iii) Given that $u_3 = u_1$, show that $u_1^4 - 2u_1^2 - u_1 = 0$.
      (C)

10 The nth terms of two sequences are defined as follows:

(a) $t_n = 1 - \dfrac{1}{n}$ (b) $u_n = 1 - \dfrac{1}{u_{n-1}}$, where $u_1 = 2$.

Decide in each case whether the sequence is convergent, divergent or oscillating or periodic, giving reasons for your answers.   (OLE)

Definitions

A **series** is formed when the terms of a sequence are added. The series formed from

$$u_1, u_2, u_3, \ldots, u_n, \ldots \text{ is}$$

$$u_1 + u_2 + u_3 + \ldots + u_n + \ldots$$

S_n is the **sum** of the **first n terms** of a series.
S_∞ is the **sum to infinity** of a series.

$\displaystyle\sum_{r=a}^{b} u_r$ means the sum of all terms such as u_r, where r takes all integral values from a to b inclusive.
It is read as 'sigma from $r=a$ to b of u_r'.

ⓘ $6, 24, 60\ 120, \ldots$ is an infinite sequence with $u_r = r(r+1)(r+2)$.

The series formed from $6, 24, 60, 120, \ldots$ is

$$6 + 24 + 60 + 120 + \ldots$$

$$S_\infty = \sum_{r=1}^{\infty} r(r+1)(r+2)$$

ⓘ $\displaystyle\sum_{r=1}^{n} r = 1 + 2 + 3 + \ldots + n$

$$\sum_{r=3}^{7} r^2 = 3^2 + 4^2 + 5^2 + 6^2 + 7^2$$

Arithmetic series

An **arithmetic series** is of the form

$$a + (a+d) + (a+2d) + (a+3d) + \ldots$$

a is the **first term**, d is the **common difference**.
To find d, subtract any term from the next term.

$$u_n = [a + (n-1)d] \quad S_n = \sum_{r=1}^{n}[a + (n-1)d]$$
$$= \tfrac{1}{2}n[2a + (n-1)d]$$
$$= \tfrac{1}{2}n(a + l)$$
where l is the last term.

The 'sum formula' for an arithmetic series can be used to find a formula for its nth term, $u_n = S_n - S_{n-1}$.

Problems involving arithmetic series are often solved by solving simultaneous equations in a and d. These equations may be obtained from a 'standard form' of the series using a and d or the standard formulae for its nth term and sum.

ⓘ *Find the sum to 21 terms of the series*

$$(-20) + (-18) + (-16) + \ldots$$

This is an arithmetic series with $a = -20$ and $d = 2$.
Use $S_n = \tfrac{1}{2}n[2a + (n-1)d]$
$$S_{21} = \tfrac{1}{2} \times 21[2 \times (-20) + (21-1)(2)]$$
$$= \tfrac{1}{2} \times 21[-40 + 40]$$
$$= 0$$

ⓘ *Three consecutive terms of an arithmetic series have sum 21 and product 315. Find the numbers.*

Here it is easier to let the three terms be

$$(a-d), a, (a+d).$$

Sum of terms: $(a-d) + a + (a+d) = 21$
$$3a = 21 \Rightarrow a = 7.$$
Product of terms: $(a-d)a(a+d) = 315$
$$a(a^2 - d^2) = 315$$
But $a = 7$, so $7(7^2 - d^2) = 315 \Rightarrow d = \pm 2$.
So the numbers are $5, 7, 9$.

Geometric series

A **geometric series** is of the form

$$a + aR + aR^2 + aR^3 + \ldots$$

a is the **first term**, R is the **common ratio**.
To find R, divide any term into the next term.

$$u_n = aR^{n-1} \qquad S_n = \sum_{r=1}^{n} aR^{n-1}$$

For $R \neq 1$, $S_n = \dfrac{a(1 - R^n)}{(1 - R)}$. For $R = 1$, $S_n = na$.

If $|R| < 1$, a geometric series may be **summed to infinity**, and $S_\infty = \dfrac{a}{1 - R}$.

To solve problems involving geometric series, we often have to solve simultaneous equations in a and R. To obtain these equations you may use a 'standard form' of the terms of the series using a and R or the standard formulae for its nth term and sum.

ⓘ *Find the sum to infinity of the series*

$$1 + \tfrac{1}{2} + \tfrac{1}{4} + \ldots$$

This is a geometric series with $a = 1$ and $R = \tfrac{1}{2}$.
Since $-1 < R < 1$,

use $S_\infty = \dfrac{a}{1 - R} = \dfrac{1}{1 - \frac{1}{2}} = 2$.

ⓘ *Three consecutive terms of a geometric series have product 343 and sum $\dfrac{49}{2}$. Find the numbers.*

Here it is easier to let the terms be $\dfrac{a}{R}, a, aR$.

Product of terms: $\dfrac{a}{R} \cdot a \cdot aR = 343$
$$a^3 = 343 \Rightarrow a = 7.$$
Sum of terms: $\dfrac{a}{R} + a + aR = \dfrac{49}{2}$
i.e. $\dfrac{a}{R}(1 + R + R^2) = \dfrac{49}{2}$
But $a = 7$, so $2 + 2R + 2R^2 = 7R$
i.e. $2R^2 - 5R + 2 = 0 \Rightarrow R = \tfrac{1}{2}$ or 2.

So the numbers are $\dfrac{7}{2}, 7, 14$.

Series

Worked examples, Guided example and Exam questions.

 The first three terms of a geometric progression are $k-3$, $2k-4$, $4k-3$, in that order. Find the value of k and the sum of the first eight terms of the progression.

Since $k-3$, $2k-4$, $4k-3$ are three consecutive terms of a geometric progression

$$\frac{2k-4}{k-3}=\frac{4k-3}{2k-4}$$

i.e. $(2k-4)^2=(k-3)(4k-3)$
$4k^2-16k+16=4k^2-15k+9$
$k=7$

The first three terms of the progression are 4, 10, 25

i.e. $a=4$, $r=\dfrac{5}{2}$

$\therefore$ the sum to.eight terms is $S_8=\dfrac{4\left(1-\left(\dfrac{5}{2}\right)^8\right)}{\left(1-\dfrac{5}{2}\right)}$

$$=4066.3438$$

 In a certain arithmetic progresssion, the sum of the first and fifth terms is 18 and the fifth term is 6 more than the third term. Show that the sum of the first ten terms of the progression is 165.

Let the first six terms of the arithmetic progression be
a, $a+d$, $a+2d$, $a+3d$, $a+4d$, $a+5d$
Given $a+(a+4d)=18$
$\qquad(a+4d)=(a+2d)+6$
i.e. $\qquad 2a+4d=18$
and $\qquad 2d=6$
$\therefore d=3$ and $a=3$
$\therefore$ the arithmetic progression .has first term 3 and common difference 3.

So the sum of the first ten terms is

$$S_{10}=\frac{10}{2}\times(2\times3+9\times3)$$

$$=165 \text{ as required}$$

 The three real, distinct and non-zero numbers a, b, c are such that a, b, c are in arithmetic progression and a, c, b are in geometric progression. Find the numerical value of the common ratio of the geometric progression.
Hence find an expression, in terms of a, for the sum to infinity of the geometric series whose first terms are a, c, b.

Since a, b, c are in arithmetic progression

$b-a=c-b$ [1]

Since a, c, b are in geometric progression

$\dfrac{c}{a}=\dfrac{b}{c}$ [2]

Eliminate b between [1] and [2] and solve the resulting quadratic in c (c will be found in terms of a). Using these values of c in [2] the common ratio of the corresponding geometric progression can be found. One value of r is less than 1, hence the sum to infinity of the geometric progression can be found.

 1 Three consecutive terms in a geometric progression are c, $c+4$ and $c+6$, in that order. Determine the value of c and the value of the common ratio of the progression. *(S)*

2 Show that there are 18 integers which are multiples of 17 and which lie between 200 and 500. Find the sum of all these integers. *(L)*

3 The nth term of an arithmetic progression is denoted by u_n, and the sum of the first n terms is denoted by S_n.
(a) In a certain arithmetic progression, $u_5+u_{16}=44$ and $S_{18}=3S_{10}$. Calculate the value of the first term and of the common difference.
(b) In another arithmetic progression, $u_1=1$. Given that u_7, u_{11} and u_{17} are in geometric progression, find the value of each. *(C)*

4 (i) A man invests £100 at the beginning of each year for ten years. The rate of compound interest is 9% per annum. Calculate the total value of the investment at the end of the ten full years.
(ii) Write down the sum of the arithmetic progression, $1+2+3+\ldots+n$. Let

$$S_n=\frac{1+2+3+\ldots+n}{n^2}.$$

Find a value of n such that $S_n-\tfrac{1}{2}<10^{-6}$. *(OLE)*

5 Find the common ratio of the geometric sequence
$\sin 2\alpha$, $-\sin 2\alpha\cos 2\alpha$, $\sin 2\alpha\cos^2 2\alpha$, $\ldots$.
Prove that for $0<\alpha<\dfrac{\pi}{2}$ the series
$\sin 2\alpha-\sin 2\alpha\cos 2\alpha+\sin 2\alpha\cos^2 2\alpha+\ldots$.
has a sum to infinity and show that the sum to infinity is $\tan\alpha$. *(H)*

6 Find the sum to infinity of the geometrical progression
$$1+x/(x+1)+x^2/(x+1)^2+\ldots$$
and determine the set of values of x for which the result holds. *(O & C)*

7 Find the set of values of θ, $(-\pi<\theta\leqslant\pi)$, for which the series
$$1+2\cos^2\theta+4\cos^4\theta+8\cos^6\theta+\ldots+2^r\cos^{2r}\theta+\ldots$$
has a sum to infinity.
Show that, for this set of values of θ, the sum to infinity of the series is $-\sec 2\theta$. *(J)*

8 It is given that $\dfrac{1}{b+c}$, $\dfrac{1}{c+a}$, $\dfrac{1}{a+b}$ are three consecutive terms of an arithmetic series. Show that a^2, b^2 and c^2 are also three consecutive terms of an arithmetic series. *(J)*

9 The sum of the first twenty terms of an arithmetic progression is 45, and the sum of the first forty terms is 290. Find the first term and the common difference.
Find the number of terms in the progression which are less than 100. *(J)*

10 One sequence of alternating terms of the series
$$1+2+3+4+5+8+\ldots$$
forms an arithmetic progression, while the other sequence of alternating terms forms a geometric progression. Sum the first 10 terms of each progression and hence find the sum of the first 20 terms of the series. *(L)*

11 The first term of an arithmetic series is $(3p+5)$ where p is a positive integer. The last term is $(17p+17)$ and the common difference is 2.
Find, in terms of p (i) the number of terms; (ii) the sum of the series. Show that the sum of the series is divisible by 14, only when p is odd. *(A)*

P19 Binomial Theorem

core

Binomial expansions, Binomial theorem, Powers of numbers.

Binomial expansions

A **binomial** is a polynomial having *two* terms.

A power of a binomial of the form $(a + x)^n$, where *n is a positive integer*, may be expanded by multiplying out the brackets.

$$(a + x)^n = \underbrace{(a + x)(a + x)(a + x)...(a + x)}_{n \text{ brackets multiplied together}}$$

The result is the **binomial expansion** of $(a + x)^n$. The coefficients of the terms in '*ax*' in this expansion form a pattern. It is seen in the rows of **Pascal's triangle**. This is useful when *n* is small.

n			Pascal's triangle				expansion
1			1	1			$(a + x)^1 = 1a + 1x$
2		1	2	1			$(a + x)^2 = 1a^2 + 2ax + 1x^2$
3		1	3	3	1		$(a + x)^3 = 1a^3 + 3a^2x + 3ax^2 + 1x^3$
4	1	4	6	4	1		$(a + x)^4 = 1a^4 + 4a^3x + 6a^2x^2 + 4ax^3 + 1x^4$
5	1	5	10	10	5	1	$(a + x)^5 = 1a^5 + 5a^4x + 10a^3x^2 + 10a^2x^3 + 5ax^4 + 1x^5$

Note: each row starts and ends with a 1. Every other number is the sum of the two numbers immediately above it in the preceding row.

$\boxed{i}$ $a + b, 2x - 1, x^2 + y, 3ab + c$ and $\dfrac{2}{x} + \dfrac{y}{x^2}$ are examples of binomials.

$\boxed{i}$
$$(2x - 1)^2 = (2x - 1)(2x - 1) = 4x^2 - 4x + 1$$
$$(2x - 1)^3 = (2x - 1)(2x - 1)(2x - 1)$$
$$= (2x - 1)(4x^2 - 4x + 1)$$
$$= 8x^3 - 12x^2 + 6x - 1$$
$$(2x - 1)^4 = (2x - 1)(2x - 1)(2x - 1)(2x - 1)$$
$$= (2x - 1)(8x^3 - 12x^2 + 6x - 1)$$
$$= 16x^4 - 32x^3 + 24x^2 - 8x + 1$$

Row $n = 5$ 1   5   10   10   5   1

Row $n = 6$ 1   6   15   20   15   6   1

Binomial theorem

The **binomial theorem** gives this formula for binomial expansions, when *n is a positive integer*.

$$(a + x)^n = a^n + na^{n-1}x + \frac{n(n-1)}{2!}a^{n-2}x^2 + ...$$
$$... + \frac{n(n-1)(n-2)...(n-r+1)}{r!}a^{n-r}x^r + ... + x^n$$

Note these features of the expansion:
• It is a *finite* expression with $(n + 1)$ terms.
• In each term, the indices of *a* and *x* add up to *n*.
• The general term, i.e., the term in x^r, is the $(r + 1)$th term.

• Binomial coefficients may be given as $\binom{n}{r}$ or ^nC_r.

$$\binom{n}{r} = {}^nC_r = \frac{(n-1)(n-2)...(n-r+1)}{r!} \leftarrow r \text{ factors}$$

In the expansion of $(a + x)^n$, *a* and *x* may be replaced by other terms or groups of terms. Use brackets to write the given expression in the form $[(a) + (x)]$ first. Give the expansion of $(a + x)^n$ for the wanted value of *n*. Then replace *a* and/or *x* by the required term or terms.

$\boxed{i}$ *Give the first four terms of* $(a + x)^{15}$ *in ascending powers of x.*

$(a + x)^{15}$
$$= a^{15} + 15a^{14}x + \frac{15 \times 14}{2!}a^{13}x^2 + \frac{15 \times 14 \times 13}{3!}a^{12}x^3 + ...$$
$$= a^{15} + 15a^{14}x + 105a^{13}x^2 + 455a^{12}x^3 + ...$$

$\boxed{i}$ *Find the term in* x^7 *in the expansion of* $(1 + x)^{10}$.

Put $a = 1, r = 7, n = 10$ in the general term of $(a + x)^n$.

This gives: $\dfrac{10 \times 9 \times 8 \times 7 \times 6 \times 5 \times 4}{7!}(1)^{10-7}x^7 = 120x^7$.

$\boxed{i}$ *Find the first three terms of* $(2x - y)^6$.

Treat $(2x - y)^6$ as $[(2x) + (-y)]^6$. Replace *a* by $(2x)$ and *x* by $(-y)$ in the expansion of $(a + x)^6$.

$$(a + x)^6 = a^6 + 6a^5x + \frac{6 \times 5}{2!}a^4x^2 + ...$$
$$(2x - y)^6 = (2x)^6 + 6(2x)^5(-y) + \frac{6 \times 5}{2!}(2x)^4(-y)^2 + ...$$
$$= 64x^6 - 192x^5y + 240x^4y^2 + ...$$

Powers of numbers

The binomial theorem given above may be used to calculate the **exact or approximate value of (number)^n**, where *n* is a positive integer. Write the 'number' as the sum or difference of two values, i.e. in the form $(a + x)$ or $(a - x)$. (Questions often give the values to use. In general, *x* should be small and powers of *a* and *x* should be easy to work out without a calculator.) Use the binomial theorem to expand $(a + x)^n$ or $(a - x)^n$ for the required power of *n*. Replace *a* and *x* in this expansion by the chosen values. Then calculate the result.

For the *exact value* of (number)^n, write down and use *all* the terms in the expansion. (*Remember*: it is a finite expression when *n* is a positive integer.)

For an *approximate value* of (number)^n, you may need *only the first few terms* of the expansion. (*Remember*: if *x* is small, successive powers of *x* in the expansion quickly become negligible in value.) Always make sure that you take sufficient terms to give the accuracy required (see $\boxed{WE}$).

$\boxed{i}$ *Find the exact value of* $(1.001)^5$.

Write $1.001 = 1 + 0.001$.

So treat $(1.001)^5$ as $(1 + 0.001)^5$.

$$(a + x)^5 = a^5 + 5a^4x + 10a^3x^2 + 10a^2x^3 + 5ax^4 + x^5$$

Replacing *a* by 1 and *x* by 0.001 gives:

$$(1 + 0.001)^5 = 1^5 + 5(1)^4(0.001) + 10(1)^3(0.001)^2$$
$$+ 10(1)^2(0.001)^3 + 5(1)(0.001)^4 + (0.001)^5$$

Here is the working for the sum of terms:

$$1^5 = 1$$
$$5(1)^4(0.001) = 0.005$$
$$10(1)^3(0.001)^2 = 0.000010$$
$$10(1)^2(0.001)^3 = 0.000000010$$
$$5(1)(0.001)^4 = 0.000000000005$$
$$\underline{(0.001)^5 = 0.000000000000001}$$
$$(1 + 0.001)^5 = 1.005010010005001$$

$\therefore (1.001)^5 = 1.005010010005001$

Binomial Theorem
Worked examples, Guided Example, Exercises and Exam questions.

 Expand $(2+3x+x^2)^4$ *in ascending powers of x up to and including the term in* x^2.

Treat $(2+3x+x^2)^4$ as $[2+(3x+x^2)]^4$.

Use the binomial expansion of $(a+x)^4$, replacing a by 2 and x by $(3x+x^2)$. Record only terms up to and including x^2.

$(2+3x+x^2)^4 = [2+(3x+x^2)]^4$

$= 2^4 + 4(2)^3(3x+x^2) + \dfrac{4\times3}{2\times1}(2)^2(3x+x^2)^2 + \text{ terms} > x^2$

$= 16 + 32(3x+x^2) + 24(3x+x^2)^2 + \text{ terms} > x^2$

$= 16 + 96x + 32x^2 + 24(9x^2+\ldots) + \text{ terms} > x^2$

$= 16 + 96x + 32x^2 + 216x^2 + \text{ terms} > x^2$

$= 16 + 96x + 248x^2 + \text{ terms} > x^2$

 (a) *Find the first four terms of the expansion of* $\left(1-\dfrac{x}{2}\right)^6$ *in ascending powers of x.*
(b) *Use these terms to find the value of* $(0.99)^6$ *correct to four decimal places.*

(a) Treat $\left(1-\dfrac{x}{2}\right)^6$ as $\left[1+\left(\dfrac{-x}{2}\right)\right]^6$.

Use the first four terms of the binomial expansion of $(a+x)^6$, replacing a by 1 and x by $\left(\dfrac{-x}{2}\right)$.

$\left(1-\dfrac{x}{2}\right)^6 = \left[1+\left(\dfrac{-x}{2}\right)\right]^6$

$= 1^6 + 6(1)^5\left(\dfrac{-x}{2}\right) + \dfrac{6\times5}{2\times1}(1)^4\left(\dfrac{-x}{2}\right)^2 + \dfrac{6\times5\times4}{3\times2\times1}(1)^3\left(\dfrac{-x}{2}\right)^3$

$= 1 - 3x + \dfrac{15}{4}x^2 - \dfrac{5}{2}x^3 + \ldots$

(b) Let $\left(1-\dfrac{x}{2}\right) = 0.99$

$\Rightarrow \dfrac{x}{2} = 1 - 0.99 \Rightarrow x = 2(0.01) \Rightarrow x = 0.02$

$\therefore (0.99)^6 = \left(1-\dfrac{0.02}{2}\right)^6$

Substituting $x = 0.02$ in the expansion from (a) gives:

$(0.99)^6 \approx 1 - 3\times(0.02) + \dfrac{15}{4}\times(0.02)^2 - \dfrac{5}{2}\times(0.02)^3$

$= 1 - 0.06 + \dfrac{15}{4}\times0.0004 - \dfrac{5}{2}\times0.00008$

$= 0.94 + 0.0015 - 0.00002$

$= 0.9415 - 0.00002$

$= 0.9415 \text{ (to four decimal places)}$

Note: other terms in the expansion are too small to affect the result given.

 Calculate the value of the term independent of x in the expansion of $\left(x-\dfrac{3}{x^2}\right)^{15}$.

Treat $\left(x-\dfrac{3}{x^2}\right)^{15}$ as $\left[x+\left(\dfrac{-3}{x^2}\right)\right]^{15}$.

The general term of $(a+x)^{15}$ is $^{15}C_r\, a^{15-r}x^r$.

So the general term of this expansion is: $^{15}C_r\, x^{15-r}\left(\dfrac{-3}{x^2}\right)^r$.

For the term independent of x, the index of x must be zero, since $x^0 = 1$.

The power of x in the general term is given by:

$x^{15-r}\left(\dfrac{1}{x^2}\right)^r = x^{15-r}(x^{-2})^r = x^{15-r}x^{-2r} = x^{15-3r}$

If this is x^0, then $15 - 3r = 0 \Rightarrow r = 5$.
Substituting r = 5 in the general term gives:

$^{15}C_5\, x^{10}\left(\dfrac{-3}{x^2}\right)^5 = \,^{15}C_5(-3)^5$

$= \dfrac{15\times14\times13\times12\times11}{5\times4\times3\times2\times1}\times(-3)^5$

$= -729729$

$\therefore$ the term independent of x is $-729\,729$.

Note: since $r = 5$, this term is the $(5 + 1)$th term, i.e., the 6th term.

 Find the first four terms in the expansion of $(1-x)^4(1+2x)^7$ *in ascending powers of x.*

The expansion will be in the form $1 + ax + bx^2 + cx^3$. Expand each binomial separately as far as the term in x^3. Then multiply the two polynomials (set out the working like a long multiplication if it helps.). Keep only terms up to and including x^3.

---

 1 Expand: (a) $(1-3x)^4$ (b) $\left(1+\dfrac{x^2}{2}\right)^5$.

2 Expand fully: (a) $(2x+3y)^3$ (b) $\left(\dfrac{2p}{5}-\dfrac{3}{2q}\right)^4$.

3 Find the coefficient of:
(a) x^3 in $(3-x)^{10}$ (b) y^4 in $(2-3y)^7$.

4 By putting $a+a^2 = b$, expand $(1+a+a^2)^3$.

5 Find the coefficient of p^3 in the expansion of $(1-p)^3(1+p+p^2)^4$.
(*Hint*: $1-p^3 = (1-p)(1+p+p^2)$.)

6 Expand $\left(2-\dfrac{x}{2}\right)^5$ in ascending powers of x. Use the first four terms of the expansion to find an approximate value for $(1.99)^5$. *(C)*

7 Using the binomial theorem, or otherwise, find an expression, in descending powers of x and with whole number coefficients, for $(2x-3)^4 - (2x+3)^4$. *(L)*

8 Find, in ascending powers of x, the first three terms in the expansion of $(2-3x)^8$. Use the expansion to find the value of $(1.997)^8$ correct to the nearest whole number. *(C)*

9 Expand $(2+x)^5$ in ascending powers of x up to and including the term in x^2. Use these terms to find the value of 2.01^5, giving your answer to 3 d.p. *(S)*

10 Determine the coefficient of x^3 in the binomial expansion of $(1-2x)^7$. *(A)*

11 The coefficient of x^5 in the expansion of $(1+5x)^8$ is equal to the coefficient of x^4 in the expansion of $(a+5x)^7$. Find the value of a. *(O)*

12 Write down the expansion of $(1+x)^5$. Hence, by letting $x = z+z^2$, find the coefficient of z^3 in the expansion of $(1+z+z^2)^5$ in powers of z. *(C)*

13 Find the term independent of x in the expansion of $\left(x^2-\dfrac{2}{x}\right)^6$. *(C)*

39

P20
core

Differentiation
Notation, Standard results, Rules, Chain rule.

Notation

Differentiation is the process of finding the **derivative** of a function.
The derivative of a function is also called its **derived function** and also its **differential coefficient**.

The derivative of y with respect to x is usually written as $\dfrac{dy}{dx}$ or y' or $\dot{y}$.

The derivative of $f(x)$ with respect to x is usually written as $f'(x)$ or $\dfrac{d}{dx}[f(x)]$.

Standard results

	function	derivative
algebraic	constant	0
	x^n	nx^{n-1}
trigonometrical (x in radians)	$\sin x$	$\cos x$
	$\cos x$	$-\sin x$
	$\tan x$	$\sec^2 x$

	function	derivative
logarithmic and exponential	$\ln x$	$\dfrac{1}{x}$
	e^x	e^x

Rules

1. Sum and difference
A sum of terms can be differentiated term by term.

ℹ️ If $y = x^3 + \cos x - \ln x + 4$
$$\frac{dy}{dx} = 3x^2 - \sin x - \frac{1}{x}$$

2. Product
(a) If $y = au$, where a is a constant and u is a function of x,

then $\dfrac{dy}{dx} = a\dfrac{du}{dx}$

ℹ️ If $y = 7x^4$
$$\frac{dy}{dx} = 7(4x^3)$$
$$= 28x^3$$

(b) If $y = uv$, where u and v are functions of x.

then $\dfrac{dy}{dx} = v.\dfrac{du}{dx} + u.\dfrac{dv}{dx}$

ℹ️ If $y = xe^x$

let $u = x$ and $v = e^x$

then $\dfrac{du}{dx} = 1$ and $\dfrac{dv}{dx} = e^x$

Using $\dfrac{dy}{dx} = v\dfrac{du}{dx} + u\dfrac{dv}{dx}$
$$= e^x.1 + x.e^x$$
$$= e^x(1+x)$$

3. Quotient
If $y = \dfrac{u}{v}$, where u and v are functions of x,

then $\dfrac{dy}{dx} = \dfrac{v.\dfrac{du}{dx} - u.\dfrac{dv}{dx}}{v^2}$

ℹ️ If $y = \dfrac{\sin x}{x^2}$

let $u = \sin x$ and $v = x^2$

then $\dfrac{du}{dx} = \cos x$ and $\dfrac{dv}{dx} = 2x$

Using $\dfrac{dy}{dx} = \dfrac{v.\dfrac{du}{dx} - u.\dfrac{dv}{dx}}{v^2}$
$$= \frac{x^2.\cos x - \sin x.2x}{x^4}$$
$$= \frac{x.\cos x - 2\sin x}{x^3}$$

Chain rule

If y is a function of u and u is a function of x, then y is called a **function of a function** of x.

This can be differentiated using the **chain rule**
$$\frac{dy}{dx} = \frac{dy}{du}.\frac{du}{dx}$$

It is useful to remember that, by the chain rule,
$$\frac{d}{dx}(y^2) = 2y.\frac{dy}{dx}$$
$$\frac{d}{dx}(y^3) = 3y^2.\frac{dy}{dx} \text{ and so on.}$$

ℹ️ *Differentiate x^{2x} with respect to x.*

y is a function (i.e. the 7th power) of $(3x^4 - 5)$, which is a function of x.
So y is a function of a function of x.

Let $y = u^7$ where $u = (3x^4 - 5)$

so $\dfrac{dy}{du} = 7u^6$ and $\dfrac{du}{dx} = 12x^3$

Using $\dfrac{dy}{dx} = \dfrac{dy}{du}.\dfrac{du}{dx}$
$$= 7u^6.12x^3$$
$$= 84x^3(3x^4 - 5)^6$$

Differentiation
Limits.
Worked example, Guided Example and Exam questions.

Limits

$y = f(x)$. As x changes from a to $a + h$, y changes from $f(a)$ to $f(a + h)$.

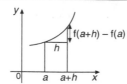

The ratio $\dfrac{f(a+h)-f(a)}{h}$ is the average rate of change over the interval a to $a + h$. As h tends to zero, the limit of the ratio is the actual rate of change of the function when $x = a$. This is written

$$f'(a) = \lim_{h \to 0} \frac{f(a+h)-f(a)}{h}$$

Alternative notation

The ratio is sometimes written using δx for h and δy for $f(a+h) - f(a)$.

Then $\displaystyle\lim_{\delta x \to 0} \dfrac{\delta y}{\delta x}$ is written as $\dfrac{dy}{dx}$.

In terms of the graph $y = f(x)$, the average rate of change is the gradient of the chord and the limit of this is the gradient of the tangent, i.e. $f'(a)$ is the gradient of the tangent to $y = f(x)$ at $x = a$.

Differentiate with respect to x:

(a) $(2x^3 - 1)\sin x$ (b) $\dfrac{\ln(5x)}{x^2}$.

(a) Let $y = (2x^3 - 1)\sin x$, a product,
so let $u = 2x^3 - 1$ and $v = \sin x$.

Now $\dfrac{du}{dx} = 6x^2$ and $\dfrac{dv}{dx} = \cos x$.

Using $\dfrac{d}{dx}(uv) = v\dfrac{du}{dx} + u\dfrac{dv}{dx}$,

$$\frac{dy}{dx} = \sin x.6x^2 + (2x^3 - 1).\cos x$$
$$= 2x^3 \cos x + 6x^2 \sin x - \cos x.$$

(b) Let $y = \dfrac{\ln(5x)}{x^2}$, a quotient,

so let $u = \ln(5x)$ and $v = x^2$.

Now $\dfrac{du}{dx} = 5.\dfrac{1}{5x}$ (chain rule) and $\dfrac{dv}{dx} = 2x$.

Using $\dfrac{d}{dx}\left(\dfrac{u}{v}\right) = \dfrac{v\dfrac{du}{dx} - u\dfrac{dv}{dx}}{v^2}$

$$\frac{dy}{dx} = \frac{x^2\dfrac{1}{x} - \ln(5x).2x}{x^4}$$
$$= \frac{1 - 2\ln(5x)}{x^3}.$$

(a) Differentiate $e^x \sin x$ with respect to x.

(b) Given that $y = x^5 \ln x + \cos x$, find $\dfrac{dy}{dx}$.

(a) A product, so use product rule with $u = e^x$ and $v = \sin x$.

(b) $x^5 \ln x$ is a product, so use product rule with $u = x^5$ and $v = \ln x$. Then differentiate $\cos x$. Add the derivatives together to get the final result.

EX

1 Differentiate with respect to x: (a) $(2x-1)(3x+2)$;

(b) $x^4 - 2x + \dfrac{1}{x^2}$; (c) $\dfrac{(2x-3)}{\sqrt[4]{x}}$.

(A)

2 Prove that $\dfrac{d}{dx}(\tan x - x) = \tan^2 x$.

(L)

3 Differentiate with respect to x: (a) $x^{-\frac{3}{2}}$; (b) $2x^2(x+1) + 2$;

(c) $\dfrac{3x^4 - x}{x^3}$.

(O & C)

4 Differentiate with respect to x: (a) $x^3 \ln x$. (b) $\dfrac{1 + \cos x}{x}$.

(L)

5 Given that $y = \dfrac{x^2 - 1}{2x^2 + 1}$, find $\dfrac{dy}{dx}$ and state the set of values of x for which $\dfrac{dy}{dx}$ is positive.

Find the greatest and least values of y for $0 \leqslant x \leqslant 1$.

(L)

6 Given that $y = \dfrac{x^2 - 2x - 4}{x^2 - 4}$, find and simplify $\dfrac{dy}{dx}$. Find also the greatest and least values of y for $-1 \leqslant x \leqslant 1$.

(A)

7 (i) Differentiate with respect to x:
(a) $(x^2 + 1)^3$; (b) $\sin^4 3x$; (c) $x(2x+1)^{\frac{1}{4}}$.

(ii) If $y = \dfrac{x \cos x + \sin x}{x^2}$, find $\dfrac{dy}{dx}$ and simplify your answer as much as possible.

(OLE)

8 Differentiate the following expressions with respect to x, giving your answers in as simple a form as possible:

(i) $x^2 \cos 3x$; (ii) $e^x \log_e x$; (iii) $(x^2 + 2)^3$; (iv) $\dfrac{3x-1}{\sqrt{(x^2+1)}}$.

(W)

9 Differentiate with respect to x: (i) $\tan^4 2x$; (ii) $\dfrac{x-1}{2x-3}$;
(iii) $x^2 \log_e x$.

(S)

41

P21
core

Further Differentiation
Inverse functions, Standard results, Higher derivatives, Increasing and decreasing functions, Rates of change.

Inverse functions

If $f:x \mapsto f(x)$ is a function and $f^{-1}:x \mapsto f^{-1}(x)$ is its inverse, then the gradient of the curve $y = f^{-1}(x)$ (where it exists) is given by $\dfrac{dy}{dx} = \dfrac{1}{\frac{dx}{dy}}$.

i *A curve has equation* $y = \sin^{-1} x$. *Find* $\dfrac{dy}{dx}$.

$y = \sin^{-1} x \implies x = \sin y$.

So, $\dfrac{dx}{dy} = \cos y = \sqrt{1 - \sin^2 y} = \sqrt{1 - x^2}$.

Hence, $\dfrac{dy}{dx} = \dfrac{1}{\frac{dx}{dy}} = \dfrac{1}{\sqrt{1 - x^2}}$.

Standard results

function	derivative
cosec x	$-\operatorname{cosec} x \cot x$
sec x	$\sec x \tan x$
cot x	$-\operatorname{cosec}^2 x$
$\sin^{-1} x$	$\dfrac{1}{\sqrt{1 - x^2}}$
$\cos^{-1} x$	$\dfrac{-1}{\sqrt{1 - x^2}}$
$\tan^{-1} x$	$\dfrac{1}{1 + x^2}$

trigonometrical (*x* in radians)

inverse trigonometrical

i *Given* $y = \sec x$, *find* $\dfrac{dy}{dx}$.

$y = \sec x = \dfrac{1}{\cos x}$

Using the quotient rule (see P20),

$\dfrac{dy}{dx} = \dfrac{\cos x .0 - 1.(-\sin x)}{\cos^2 x}$

$= \dfrac{\sin x}{\cos^2 x}$

$= \dfrac{1}{\cos x}.\tan x$

$= \sec x \tan x.$

Higher derivatives

If the derivative of a function of x is differentiated with respect to x, the 2nd derivative of the function is obtained. If the 2nd derivative is differentiated, the 3rd derivative is obtained, and so on.

The 2nd, 3rd, ..., nth derivatives of y with respect to x are usually written as $\dfrac{d^2 y}{dx^2}, \dfrac{d^3 y}{dx^3}, ..., \dfrac{d^n y}{dx^n}$.

The usual function notation for these derivations is $f''(x), f'''(x), ..., f^n(x)$.

i If $y = x^6 + 4x^2 - \dfrac{3}{x}$

$\dfrac{dy}{dx} = 6x^5 + 8x + \dfrac{3}{x^2}$ first derivative

$\dfrac{d^2 y}{dx^2} = 30x^4 + 8 - \dfrac{6}{x^3}$ second derivative

$\dfrac{d^3 y}{dx^3} = 120x^3 + \dfrac{18}{x^4}$ third derivative.

Increasing and decreasing functions

An increasing function f increases as x increases on an interval $a < x < b$.
On this interval, $f'(x) > 0$.

i On the interval $0 < x < 4$, $y = x^2$ is an increasing function; $\dfrac{dy}{dx} = 2x > 0$.

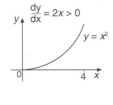

A decreasing function f decreases as x increases on an interval $a < x < b$.
On this interval, $f'(x) < 0$.

i On the interval $-3 < x < 0$, $y = x^2$ is a decreasing function; $\dfrac{dy}{dx} = 2x < 0$.

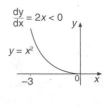

Rates of change

Rates of change can be expressed using **differentials**.
Rates of **increase** are **positive**.
Rates of **decrease** are **negative**.
They are often, but not always, rates of change 'with respect to time'.
However, by convention
'the rate of change of a quantity Q' means
'the rate of change of Q with respect to time' i.e. $\dfrac{dQ}{dt}$.
This use of differentials has important applications in science.

i *The radius, r cm, of a circular pool of oil, t seconds after it begins to form, is given by $r = 3t^2$. What is the rate of increase of r when $t = 2$?*

$r = 3t^2$.

So, $\dfrac{dr}{dt} = 6t$ is the rate of increase.

When $t = 2$, rate of increase of $r = 6 \times 2 = 12$ cm s^{-1}.

Further Differentiation

Worked examples, Guided example, Exam questions.

Given that $y = x^4 - x^3 + 4x - 1$, *find* $\dfrac{d^2y}{dx^2}$ *and state the set of values of x for which* $\dfrac{d^2y}{dx^2}$ *is zero.*

$$y = x^4 - x^3 + 4x - 1$$
$$\frac{dy}{dx} = 4x^3 - 3x^2 + 4$$
$$\frac{d^2y}{dx^2} = 12x^2 - 6x = 6x(2x-1)$$

When $\dfrac{d^2y}{dx^2} = 0$, $6x(2x-1) = 0 \Rightarrow x = 0$ or $\tfrac{1}{2}$.

An inverted right circular cone of semi-vertical angle 45° is collecting water from a tap at a steady rate of $18\pi \text{ cm}^3 \text{ s}^{-1}$. *Find the rate at which the depth h of water is rising when* $h = 3$ *cm.*

Given h and the rate of increase of water volume V, we must write V as a function of h and find the rate of increase of h.

Volume of a cone $V = \tfrac{1}{3}\pi r^2 h$.

Since the semi-vertical angle is 45°, $r = h$.

So $V = \tfrac{1}{3}\pi h^3$ and $\dfrac{dV}{dh} = \pi h^2$.

Using $\dfrac{dV}{dt} = \dfrac{dV}{dh} \cdot \dfrac{dh}{dt}$
$$= \pi h^2 \cdot \frac{dh}{dt}.$$

So $\dfrac{dh}{dt} = \dfrac{1}{\pi h^2} \cdot \dfrac{dV}{dt}.$

When $h = 3$ cm and $\dfrac{dV}{dt} = 18\pi \text{ cm}^3 \text{ s}^{-1}$,

$\dfrac{dh}{dt} = \dfrac{1}{\pi 3^2} \cdot 18\pi \text{ cm s}^{-1} = 2 \text{ cm s}^{-1}.$

So the depth of water is rising at a rate of 2 cm s⁻¹.

Show that $y = \tan x$ *is an increasing function on the interval*
$$-\frac{\pi}{2} < x < \frac{\pi}{2}.$$

Calculate $\dfrac{dy}{dx}$ and show that this is positive on the given interval.

EX

1 Given that $y = \dfrac{\sin x - \cos x}{\sin x + \cos x}$, show that $\dfrac{dy}{dx} = 1 + y^2$.

Prove that $\dfrac{d^2y}{dx^2}$ is zero only when $y = 0$. *(J)*

2 Given that $x = 3 + 2e^{-t}$, express $\dfrac{dx}{dt}$ (i) in terms of t
(ii) in terms of x. *(J)*

3 The radius of a circular oil slick is increasing at 1.5 m/s. Taking π to be 3.14, find, to 2 significant figures, the rate at which the area of the slick is increasing when its radius is 300 m. *(L)*

4 (a) The radius of a circular disc is increasing at a constant rate of 0.003 cm/s. Find the rate at which the area is increasing when the radius is 20 cm.
(b) The area of another circular disc increases from 100π to 101π cm². Use calculus to find the corresponding increase in the radius. *(C)*

5 The volume of a sphere is given by $V = \tfrac{4}{3}\pi r^3$. An elastic spherical balloon is being blown up so that the radius is increasing at the rate of 1 cm per second. Calculate the rate at which the volume of the balloon is increasing when the radius is 5 cm. *(W)*

6 You are given that $x = y^2 + 4$.
(i) Find $\dfrac{dx}{dy}$ and hence write down $\dfrac{dy}{dx}$ in terms of y.
(ii) Rearrange $x = y^2 + 4$ in the form $y = g(x)$, and hence find $\dfrac{dy}{dx}$ in terms of x (by substituting for y in your answer to part (i)).
(iii) Differentiate $y = g(x)$, and comment on your answer.
(iv) For what values of x are your answers valid? *(O & C)*

7 Show that the function $f(x) = x^3 - x^2 + x - 1$ is never decreasing. *(H)*

8 A spherical balloon is inflated by gas being pumped in at the constant rate of 200 cm³ per second. What is the rate of increase of the surface area of the balloon when its radius is 100 cm? (Surface area of sphere $= 4\pi r^2$, volume of sphere $= \dfrac{4}{3}\pi r^3$.) *(S)*

9 The area of the region enclosed between two concentric circles of radii x and y $(x > y)$ is denoted by A. Given that x is increasing at the rate of 2 m s⁻¹, y is increasing at the rate of 3 m s⁻¹ and, when $t = 0$, $x = 4$ metres and $y = 1$ metre, find:
(i) the rate of increase of A when $t = 0$
(ii) the ratio of x to y when A begins to decrease
(iii) the time at which A is zero. *(J)*

10 Fluid enters a leaky vessel through a valve. The valve admits fluid at a rate proportional to the volume of fluid already in the vessel, and the rate of leakage is proportional to the square of the volume already in the vessel. There is a balance between inflow and outflow when the volume in the vessel is V_0. Initially there is a volume $\tfrac{1}{4}V_0$ in the vessel, and the volume increases to $\tfrac{1}{2}V_0$ in time T. Find the time taken for the volume to increase from $\tfrac{1}{4}V_0$ to $\tfrac{3}{4}V_0$. *(O)*

11 The radius r cm of a circular ink spot, t seconds after it first appears, is given by
$$r = \frac{1 + 4t}{2 + t}.$$
Calculate
(a) the time taken for the radius to double its initial value
(b) the rate of increase of the radius in cm s⁻¹ when $t = 3$
(c) the value to which r tends as t tends to infinity. *(A)*

12 In a medical treatment 500 milligrams of a drug are administered to a patient. At time t hours after the drug is administered X milligrams of the drug remain in the patient. The doctor has a mathematical model which states that $X = 500e^{-\frac{1}{5}t}$.
(a) Find the value of t correct to 2 d.p., when $X = 200$.
(b) (i) Express $\dfrac{dX}{dt}$ in terms of t.
(ii) Hence show that when $X = 200$ the rate of decrease of the amount of the drug remaining in the patient is 40 milligrams per hour. *(J)*

Special Points
Local maxima and minima, Points of inflexion, Tests for points, Applications.

Local maxima and minima

At a point of **local maximum** a function has a greater value than at points immediately on either side of it.
At a point of **local minimum** a function has a smaller value than at points immediately on either side of it.

Local maxima and minima are also called **turning points**.
A function may have more than one turning point.
The local maxima and minima are not necessarily the greatest or least values of a function in a given range.

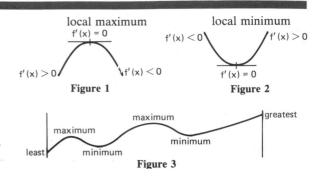

Figure 1 **Figure 2**

Figure 3

Points of inflexion

At a **point of inflexion**, the graph of a function changes the direction in which it is curving.

horizontal points of inflexion

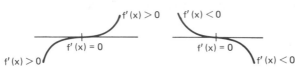

Figure 4

general points of inflexion

Figure 5

Tests for points

A **stationary point** is a point at which $f'(x) = 0$.
Local maxima, minima and horizontal points of inflexion are stationary points.
To test for stationary points
(a) Find $f'(x)$ and $f''(x)$.
(b) Put $f'(x) = 0$ and solve the resulting equation to find the x-coordinate(s) of the point(s).
(c) Find $f''(x)$ at the stationary point(s).
  (i) If $f''(x) < 0$, the point is a local maximum.
  (ii) If $f''(x) > 0$, the point is a local minimum.
  (iii) If $f''(x) = 0$, find the sign of $f'(x)$ for a value of x just to the left and just to the right of the point.

Sign to left	sign to right	type of point
+	−	maximum
−	+	minimum
+	+	} point of
−	−	} inflexion

To test for general points of inflexion
(a) Find $f''(x)$.
(b) Put $f''(x) = 0$ and solve the resulting equation to find the possible x-coordinate(s).
(c) Find the sign of $f''(x)$ for a value of x just to the left and just to the right of the point. If $f''(x)$ changes sign, the point is a point of inflexion.

ℹ️ *Find the stationary points of $f(x) = \frac{1}{3}x^3 - 2x^2 + 3x$ and identify their nature.*

$$f(x) = \tfrac{1}{3}x^3 - 2x^2 + 3x$$
$$f'(x) = x^2 - 4x + 3$$
$$f''(x) = 2x - 4$$

At stationary points $f'(x) = 0$,
i.e. $x^2 - 4x + 3 = 0$
$(x-3)(x-1) = 0$
$x = 3$ and $x = 1$.

When $x = 3$, $f''(x) = 2(3) - 4 > 0$, i.e. a minimum.
$$f(x) = \tfrac{1}{3}(3)^3 - 2(3)^2 + 3(3) = 0.$$
Therefore $(3, 0)$ is a local minimum.

When $x = 1$, $f''(x) = 2(1) - 4 < 0$, i.e. a maximum.
$$f(x) = \tfrac{1}{3}(1)^3 - 2(1)^2 + 3(1) = \tfrac{4}{3}.$$
Therefore $(1, \tfrac{4}{3})$ is a local maximum.

ℹ️ *Find any points of inflexion of $f(x) = \frac{1}{3}x^3 - 2x^2 + 3$.*

From ℹ️ above: $f''(x) = 2x - 4$
At a general point of inflexion $f''(x) = 0$,
i.e. $2x - 4 = 0 \Rightarrow x = 2$.
For $x = 2^+$, $f''(x) > 0$ } i.e. $f''(x)$ changes
For $x = 2^-$, $f''(x) < 0$ } sign
So $(2, -\tfrac{7}{3})$ is a general point of inflexion.

Applications

The above methods can be applied to practical problems in which the **maximum** or **minimum value** of a quantity is required. The procedure is
(a) write an expression for the required quantity,
(b) use the given conditions to rewrite it in terms of a single variable,
(c) find the turning point(s) and their type(s). It is often obvious from the problem itself whether a maximum or minimum has been obtained.

ℹ️ *A rectangle has perimeter 28m. What is its maximum area?*

Let x and y metres be the sides of the rectangle.
Its perimeter $= 2x + 2y = 28 \Leftrightarrow y = 14 - x$.
Its area $A = xy = x(14 - x)$.

$$\frac{dA}{dx} = 14 - 2x.$$

When A is a maximum, $\dfrac{dA}{dx} = 0$, i.e. $14 - 2x = 0 \Leftrightarrow x = 7$
When $x = 7$, $y = 14 - x = 7$.
So the maximum area xy is 7^2 m^2 = 49 m^2.

Special Points
Worked example, Guided example and Exam questions.

 The lengths of the sides of a rectangular sheet of metal are 8 cm and 3 cm. A square of side x cm is cut from each corner of the sheet and the remaining piece is folded to make an open box.

(a) Show that the volume V of the box is given by $V = 4x^3 - 22x^2 + 24x$ cm³.

(b) Find the value of x for which the volume of the box is a maximum. Calculate the maximum volume.

(a)

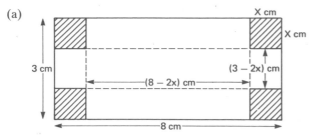

The volume of the box $V = (8-2x)(3-2x)x$ cm³
i.e. $V = 4x^3 - 22x^2 + 24x$ cm³. (1)

(b) Differentiating (1) with respect to x gives

$$\frac{dV}{dx} = 12x^2 - 44x + 24$$

For a maximum (or minimum) value of V, $\frac{dV}{dx} = 0$,

i.e. $12x^2 - 44x + 24 = 0$
$\Rightarrow \quad (3x-2)(x-3) = 0$
i.e. $x = \frac{2}{3}$ or 3.

Clearly x cannot be 3 cm since the width of the sheet initially is only 3 cm. So $x = \frac{2}{3}$ cm.

Differentiating again gives,

$$\frac{d^2V}{dx^2} = 24x - 44.$$

When $x = \frac{2}{3}$, $\frac{d^2V}{dx^2} < 0$ i.e. V is a maximum.

So the maximum volume is given by substituting $x = \frac{2}{3}$ in (1) giving

$$V_{\max} = \frac{200}{27} = 7\frac{11}{27} \text{ cm}^3.$$

 Find the coordinates of the stationary points on the curve $y = x^4 - 4x^3$. Show that the curve has a point of inflexion at $x = 2$.

Calculate $\frac{dy}{dx}$. Equate this to zero to find the two values of x

where these stationary points occur.

Next calculate $\frac{d^2y}{dx^2}$ and use it to find the nature of the

stationary points. (This check fails for one value of x so it is necessary to find the type of stationary point by considering

the gradient $\frac{dy}{dx}$ on each side of this point.)

To show the curve has a point of inflexion at $x = 2$, show that

$\frac{d^2y}{dx^2}$ is zero at $x = 2$ and the sign of the gradient of the curve on

each side of the point is the same.

---

 1 The curve for which $\frac{dy}{dx} = a(x-p)(x-q)$, where a, p and q

are constants, has turning-points at (2, 0) and (1, 1).
(i) State the value of p and q.
(ii) Using these values, determine the value of a.
(C)

2 The curve $y = x^2 + ax + b$ has a turning point at (1, 3). Find a and b.
(S)

3 An open rectangular box is made of very thin sheet metal. Its volume is 128 cm³, its width is x cm, and its length is 4x cm. Obtain an expression for its depth in terms of x. Show that the total surface area of its base, its ends and its

sides is equal to $\left(4x^2 + \frac{320}{x}\right)$ cm². Calculate the dimensions

of the box for which the surface area is a minimum; explain why your answer gives a minimum rather than a maximum.
(W)

4 Differentiate the function $\frac{x+3}{\sqrt{(1+x^2)}}$ with respect to x. Find

the value of x at which the function has a stationary value and determine the nature of the stationary value.

5 (a) The function f is defined by: $f(x) = \frac{4}{x-2} - \frac{1}{x+1}$.

Show that $f'(x) = -\frac{3x(x+4)}{(x-2)^2(x+1)^2}$.

Find the local maxima and minima of f, and sketch its graph.
(b) Show that the expression $\sin\theta + 2\cos\theta$, where $0 \le \theta \le \frac{1}{2}\pi$, has a maximum value equal to $\sqrt{5}$.
(W)

6 The parametric equations of a curve are $x = \log_e(1+t)$,

$y = e^t$ for $t > -1$. Find $\frac{dy}{dx}$ and $\frac{d^2y}{dx^2}$ in terms of t. Prove that

the curve has only one turning point and that it must be a minimum.
(A)

7 Find the maximum point on the curve $y = \frac{1}{x^2 + 2x + 4}$

and show that there are points of inflexion at $(0, \frac{1}{4})$ and $(-2, \frac{1}{4})$.
(S)

8 Investigate the nature of the turning points of the curve $y = (x-1)(x-a)^2$ in the cases of (i) $a > 1$, (ii) $a < 1$. Sketch on separate diagrams the curves $y = (x-1)(x-a)^2$ when $a > 1$ and when $0 < a < 1$.
(L)

9 State the derivatives of $\sin x$ and $\cos x$, and use these results to show that the derivative of $\tan x$ is $\sec^2 x$.
Show further that

$$\frac{d}{dx}(\tan^{-1}x) = \frac{1}{1+x^2}.$$

A vertical rod AB of length 3 units is held with its lower end B at a distance 1 unit vertically above a point O. The angle subtended by AB at a variable point P on the horizontal

plane through O is θ. Show that $\theta = \tan^{-1}x - \tan^{-1}\frac{x}{4}$, where

$x = OP$. Prove that, as x varies, θ is a maximum when $x = 2$, and that the maximum value of θ can be expressed as

$\tan^{-1}\frac{3}{4}$.
(J)

10 A right circular cone with semivertical angle θ is inscribed in a sphere of radius a, with its vertex and the rim of its base on the surface of the sphere. Prove that its volume is $\frac{8}{3}\pi a^3 \cos^4\theta \sin^2\theta$. If a is fixed and θ varies, find the limits within which this volume must lie.
(O & C)

P23
core

Integration
Definition, Using standard integrals, Definite integral, Area under a curve.

Definition

Integration is the **inverse of differentiation**.

It is the process of finding a function given its derivative.

If $f'(x)$ is the derivative of $f(x)$ with respect to x, then the **indefinite integral** of $f'(x)$ with respect to x is:

$$\int f'(x)dx = f(x) + c$$

where c is a **constant of integration**.

The constant c is necessary because not only is

$$\frac{d}{dx}(f(x)) = f'(x), \text{ but also } \frac{d}{dx}(f(x) + c) = f'(x).$$

i *Differentiate each of these functions:*

(a) $\dfrac{x^4}{4}$ *(b)* $\dfrac{x^4}{4} + 1$ *(c)* $\dfrac{x^4}{4} - 3$ *(d)* $\dfrac{x^4}{4} + 17$.

What can you conclude about $\int x^3 dx$?

The derivative of each function is x^3.

So, $\int x^3 dx = \dfrac{x^4}{4} + c$ where c is a constant.

Using standard integrals

Standard integrals may be used directly.

In some cases the function may need to be rewritten in the given form first.

Remember: $\sqrt{x} = x^{\frac{1}{2}}, \quad \sqrt[n]{x^m} = x^{\frac{m}{n}}, \quad \dfrac{1}{x^n} = x^{-n}$.

A standard integral may also be used to integrate other related functions as follows:

1. Function multiplied by a constant

Multiply the integral of the function by the constant. If a is a constant,

$$\int a f(x)dx = a\int f(x)dx.$$

2. Sum or difference of functions

Integrate each function separately:

$$\int [f(x) \pm g(x)]dx = \int f(x)dx \pm \int g(x)dx.$$

3. Function with x replaced by $(ax + b)$, a and b constants

Replace x in integral by $(ax + b)$ and divide by a.

If $\int f(x)dx = F(x)$, then $\int f(ax+b)dx = \dfrac{1}{a}F(ax+b)$.

i $\displaystyle\int \frac{1}{\sqrt{x}}dx = \int x^{-\frac{1}{2}}dx$

$$= 2x^{\frac{1}{2}} + c$$
$$= 2\sqrt{x} + c.$$

i $\displaystyle\int 3\cos x\, dx = 3\int \cos x\, dx$
$$= 3\sin x + c.$$

i $\displaystyle\int (\sqrt{x} - \sin x)dx = \int \sqrt{x}\, dx - \int \sin x\, dx$
$$= \int x^{\frac{1}{2}}dx - \int \sin x\, dx$$
$$= \tfrac{2}{3}x^{\frac{3}{2}} + \cos x + c.$$

i $\displaystyle\int e^{2x-5}dx = \tfrac{1}{2}e^{2x-5} + c$

since $\int e^x dx = e^x + c$.

Definite integral

The **definite integral from a to b of $f(x)$** is:

$$\int_a^b f(x)dx = \left[F(x)\right]_a^b \text{ where } F(x) = \int f(x)dx$$
$$= F(b) - F(a).$$

a and b are called the **limits of integration**.

Note: the constant c is eliminated in the subtraction. Square brackets are always used as shown.

i $\displaystyle\int_2^4 \frac{5}{x}dx = \left[5\ln x\right]_2^4$

$$= [5\ln 4] - [5\ln 2]$$
$$= 5\ln\left(\frac{4}{2}\right)$$
$$= 5\ln 2.$$

Area under a curve

Integration can be used to find an **area under a curve**.

Before calculating areas, sketch the curve.

The area bounded by the curve $y = f(x)$, the x-axis and the lines $x = a$, $x = b$ is given by

$$\int_a^b y\, dx.$$

This is positive if the area is above the x-axis and negative if below.

If the curve cuts the x-axis between the given limits

(a) find areas above and below the x-axis separately,

(b) add their numerical values.

i *Find the area enclosed by* $y = x^3 - 4x^2 + 3x$ *and the x-axis between* $x = 0$ *and* $x = 3$.

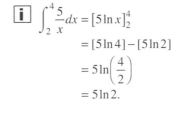

Area $A = \displaystyle\int_0^1 (x^3 - 4x^2 + 3x)dx$

$$= \left[\frac{x^4}{4} - \frac{4x^3}{3} + \frac{3x^2}{2}\right]_0^1$$

$$= \left[\frac{1}{4} - \frac{4}{3} + \frac{3}{2}\right] - \left[\frac{0}{4} - \frac{0}{3} + \frac{0}{2}\right] = \frac{5}{12} \text{ square units.}$$

Area $B = \displaystyle\int_1^3 (x^3 - 4x^2 + 3x)dx = \left[\frac{x^4}{4} - \frac{4x^3}{3} + \frac{3x^2}{2}\right]_1^3$

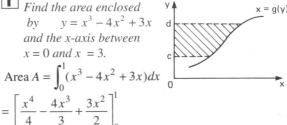

$$= \left[\frac{81}{4} - \frac{108}{3} + \frac{27}{2}\right] - \left[\frac{1}{4} - \frac{4}{3} + \frac{3}{2}\right] = -\frac{32}{12} \text{ square units.}$$

Total area $= \dfrac{5}{12} + \dfrac{32}{12} = \dfrac{37}{12}$ square units.

Integration
Standard integrals.
Worked example, Exam questions.

Standard integrals

At this stage you should know these standard integrals. In each case, c is the constant of integration.

algebraic		logarithmic and exponential		trigonometrical (x in radians)	
function	integral	function	integral	function	integral
constant k	$kx + c$	$\dfrac{1}{x}$	$\ln|x| + c$	$\sin x$	$-\cos x + c$
$x^n\ (n \neq -1)$	$\dfrac{x^{n+1}}{n+1} + c$	e^x	$e^x + c$	$\cos x$	$\sin x + c$

Evaluate each of the following integrals:

(a) $\displaystyle\int_0^1 (3 + e^x)(2 + e^{-x})dx$ (b) $\displaystyle\int_1^4 \left(\frac{3}{x} - \sqrt{x}\right)^2 dx$

(c) $\displaystyle\int_0^{\frac{\pi}{6}} \sin 3x\, dx$ (d) $\displaystyle\int_1^3 \frac{dx}{2x-1}\,dx.$

(a) $\displaystyle\int_0^1 (3 + e^x)(2 + e^{-x})dx = \int_0^1 (6 + 3e^{-x} + 2e^x + 1)dx$

$= \left[7x + (-1)3e^{-x} + 2e^x\right]_0^1$

$= [7 - 3e^{-1} + 2e] - [-3 + 2]$

$= 8 - \dfrac{3}{e} + 2e.$

(b) $\displaystyle\int_1^4 \left(\frac{3}{x} - \sqrt{x}\right)^2 dx = \int_1^4 \left(\frac{9}{x^2} - \frac{6}{\sqrt{x}} + x\right)dx$

$= \displaystyle\int_1^4 (9x^{-2} - 6x^{-\frac{1}{2}} + x)dx$

$= \left[\dfrac{9x^{-1}}{-1} - \dfrac{6x^{\frac{1}{2}}}{\frac{1}{2}} + \dfrac{x^2}{2}\right]_1^4$

$= \left[-\dfrac{9}{4} - 24 + 8\right] - \left[-9 - 12 + \dfrac{1}{2}\right]$

$= 2\tfrac{1}{4}.$

(c) $\displaystyle\int_0^{\frac{\pi}{6}} \sin 3x\, dx = \left[-\frac{1}{3}\cos 3x\right]_0^{\frac{\pi}{6}}$

$= \left[-\dfrac{1}{3}\cos\dfrac{\pi}{2}\right] - \left[-\dfrac{1}{3}\cos 0\right] = \dfrac{1}{3}.$

(d) $\displaystyle\int_1^3 \frac{dx}{2x-1}\,dx = \frac{1}{2}\left[\ln(2x-1)\right]_1^3$

$= \tfrac{1}{2}\left([\ln 5] - [\ln 1]\right) = \tfrac{1}{2}\ln 5.$

EX

1 Evaluate: $\displaystyle\int_1^2 \frac{x^4 - 1}{x^3}dx.$ *(S)

2 (a) Given that $f(x) = \left(2x - \dfrac{1}{x^2}\right)^2$, $(x \neq 0)$, find $f'(x)$.

(b) Evaluate $\displaystyle\int_1^8 \left(\sqrt[3]{x} + \frac{1}{2\sqrt[3]{x}}\right)dx.$ *(H)

3 (a) Integrate with respect to x:
(i) $(2 - x^2)^2$
(ii) $(x+1)x^{-\frac{1}{2}}$

(b) Evaluate $\displaystyle\int_0^2 x(x-2)(x+1)dx.$ *(A)

4 Given that $a > 1$ and $\displaystyle\int_1^a (3x^2 - 2x - 4)dx = 10$, find a.

(H)

5 The sketch shows the graph of $y = x(3 - x)$.

(a) Find $\displaystyle\int x(3 - x)dx.$

(b) Hence calculate the area enclosed between the curve and the x-axis.   (J)

6 The figure shows a sketch of the graph of $y = |3x - 2|$.

(i) State the coordinates of the points labelled A and B.
(ii) Make a copy of the figure, and shade in the area represented by

$$\int_0^2 |3x - 2|\, dx.$$

(iii) Evaluate this area.   (O & C)

7 The curve with equation $y = \sqrt{x} + \dfrac{1}{\sqrt{x}}$ is sketched for $x > 0$.

The region R, shaded in the diagram, is bounded by the curve, the x-axis and the lines $x = 1$ and $x = 4$. Use integration to determine R.   (O)

8 The diagram shows a sketch of the graph of $y = e^{-x}$. The points A and B have coordinates $(n, 0)$ and $(n + 1, 0)$ respectively, and the points C and D on the curve are such that AD and BC are parallel to the y-axis.

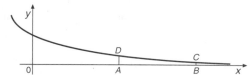

(i) Show that B lies on the tangent to the curve at D.
(ii) Find the area of the region $ABCD$ under the curve, and show that the line BD divides this region into two parts whose areas are in the ratio $e : e - 2$.   (C)

Methods of Integration I
Recognition, Substitution, Parts.

Recognition

When a function of $f(x)$ is differentiated, the result may be a product with $f(x)$ and $f'(x)$ (the derivative of $f(x)$) in its factors. The integral of such a product must be a function of $f(x)$.

$$\int f'(x)f(x)dx = g[f(x)] + c$$

By recognising $f(x)$ and $f'(x)$ in a product, you can often guess which function of $f(x)$ is its integral. (To check the guess, differentiate it by the chain rule. Adjust any numerical factor.)

Products of the form $f'(x)[f(x)]^n$ can often be integrated in this way. Since differentiating $[f(x)]^{n+1}$ gives $(n+1)f'(x)]^n$, we have:

$$\int f'(x)[f(x)]^n dx = \frac{1}{n+1}[f(x)]^{n+1} + c$$

$f(x)$ is usually a polynomial or trig function here.

Any product of the form $f'(x)e^{f(x)}$ can also be integrated by recognition. Since differentiating $e^{f(x)}$ gives $f'(x)e^{f(x)}$, we have:

$$\int f'(x)e^{f(x)}dx = e^{f(x)} + c$$

---

[i] *Integrate* $\sec^2 x \tan^2 x$ *with respect to x.*

If $f(x) = \tan x$, then $f'(x) = \sec^2 x$

$$\therefore \int \sec^2 x \tan^2 x\, dx = \tfrac{1}{3}\tan^3 x + c$$

[i] *Integrate* $x^2(8+x^3)^5$ *with respect to x.*

If $f(x) = (8+x^3)$, then $f'(x) = 3x^2 \Rightarrow x^2 = \tfrac{1}{3}f'(x)$.

$$\therefore \int x^2(8+x^3)^5 dx = \tfrac{1}{3}\int 3x^2(8+x^3)^5 dx$$
$$= \tfrac{1}{3}\cdot\tfrac{1}{6}(8+x^3)^6 + c$$
$$= \tfrac{1}{18}(8+x^3)^6 + c$$

[i] *Integrate* $xe^{(1+x^2)}$ *with respect to x.*

If $f(x) = (1+x^2)$, $f'(x) = 2x \Rightarrow x = \tfrac{1}{2}f'(x)$.

$$\therefore \int xe^{(1+x^2)}dx = \tfrac{1}{2}\int 2xe^{(1+x^2)}dx = \tfrac{1}{2}e^{(1+x^2)} + c.$$

Substitution

It is sometimes easier to find an integral by using a substitution to change the variable. The substitutions may be algebraic or trig functions (for trig substitutions, see p.).

To integrate $f(x)$ by substitution, take these steps:

(a) Write down a suitable substitution, $u = g(x)$ say. (A question often gives this.) Use it to give x in terms of u if necessary.

(b) Find $\frac{dx}{du}$ either directly or by working out $\frac{du}{dx}$ and then using its reciprocal. If necessary you can give it in terms of u.

(c) Use $\int f(x)dx = \int F(u)\frac{dx}{du}du$.

When finding an indefinite integral of $f(x)$ in this way, change the result obtained in terms of u back into a function of x for the answer (see Worked example).

When evaluating a definite integral of $f(x)$ in this way, change the limits of integration from x values to u values. Use these new limits to calculate the answer from the result obtained in terms of u.

---

[i] *Using the substitution* $u = \sqrt{5x+1}$, *evaluate*

$$\int_0^3 2x\sqrt{5x+1}\,dx$$

If $u = \sqrt{5x+1}$, then $x = \frac{u^2-1}{5}$ and $\frac{dx}{du} = \frac{2u}{5}$.

Change limits:

x	u
3	4
0	1

$$\therefore \int_0^3 2x\sqrt{5x+1}\,dx = \int_1^4 2.\frac{(u^2-1)}{5}.u.\frac{2u}{5}du$$
$$= \frac{4}{25}\int_1^4 (u^4 - u^2)du$$
$$= \frac{4}{25}\left[\frac{u^5}{5} - \frac{u^3}{3}\right]_1^4$$
$$= \frac{4}{25}\left[\left(\frac{4^5}{5} - \frac{4^3}{3}\right) - \left(\frac{1}{5} - \frac{1}{3}\right)\right]$$
$$= 29.376$$

Parts

To integrate by parts we use the formula

$$\int u\frac{dv}{dx}dx = uv - \int v\frac{du}{dx}dx$$

It is often used to integrate a product of a 'power of x' and a log or trig or exponential function.

To find the functions and derivatives to substitute in the formula, split the product to be integrated into 2 'parts', i.e. factors. Identify one part as u and the other as $\frac{dv}{dx}$.

Differentiate u to find $\frac{du}{dx}$, integrate $\frac{dv}{dx}$ to find v.

Note: take care over this choice of 'parts'. Compare differentiating and integrating each part.

If one 'part' is easier to integrate, try it as $\frac{dv}{dx}$.

u usually differentiates to a simpler function.

If $v\frac{du}{dx}$ is not simpler to integrate than $u\frac{dv}{dx}$, make the other 'part' u.

---

[i] *Find* (a) $\int x\sin x\, dx$ (b) $\int \ln x\, dx$.

(a) Choosing $u = x$ and $\frac{dv}{dx} = \sin x$

gives $\frac{du}{dx} = 1$ and $v = -\cos x$.

$$\int x\sin x\, dx = x.(-\cos x) - \int(-\cos x).1.dx$$
$$= -x\cos x + \int \cos x\, dx$$
$$= -x\cos x + \sin x + c$$

(b) Rewrite $\ln x$ as $(\ln x) \times 1$. Choosing $u = \ln x$ and $\frac{dv}{dx} = 1$ gives $\frac{du}{dx} = \frac{1}{x}$ and $v = x$.

$$\int \ln x\, dx = (\ln x)x - \int x.\frac{1}{x}dx$$
$$= x\ln x - \int dx$$
$$= x\ln x - x + c.$$

Methods of Integration I
Worked example, Guided example, Exam questions.

 By using the substitution $u = x^2 - 3$, *find*

$$\int x(x^2 - 3)^5 \, dx.$$

If $u = x^2 - 3$, then $\dfrac{du}{dx} = 2x$ and $\dfrac{dx}{du} = \dfrac{1}{2x}$.

We do not need to give x in terms of u, since $x \times \dfrac{1}{2x}$ will now appear in the integral and x will cancel.

$$\therefore \int x(x^2 - 3)^5 \, dx = \int x.u^5.\frac{1}{2x} \, du$$
$$= \tfrac{1}{2} \int u^5 \, du$$
$$= \tfrac{1}{2}.\tfrac{1}{6} u^6 + c$$
$$= \tfrac{1}{12}(x^2 - 3)^6 + c.$$

Note: it is also possible to find this integral 'by recognition' since the product is of the form $f'(x)[f(x)]^n$. However the equation states clearly that the substitution $u = x^2 - 3$ is to be used. So any other method, even if it is correct, will not gain marks.

 Find $\int x^2 \cos x \, dx$.

Choosing $u = x^2$ and $\dfrac{dv}{dx} = \cos x$

gives $\dfrac{du}{dx} = 2x$ and $v = \sin x$.

Integrating by parts:

$$I = \int x^2 \cos x \, dx = x^2 \sin x - \int (\sin x) 2x \, dx$$
$$= x^2 \sin x - 2 \int x \sin x \, dx$$

The integral of $x \sin x$ has to be found by integrating by parts. The working in [i] opposite gives

$$\int x \sin x \, dx = -x \cos x + \sin x + c$$

Substituting in the expression above gives:

$$I = x^2 \sin x - 2(-x \cos x + \sin x + c)$$
$$= x^2 \sin x + 2x \cos x - 2 \sin x + k$$

 Integrate $e^{2x} \cos 3x$ *with respect to x.*

Let $I = \int e^{2x} \cos 3x \, dx$.

Integrate by parts, choosing $u = \cos 3x$ and $\dfrac{dv}{dx} = e^{2x}$.

This gives an equation $I = ...$, with the integral of $e^{2x} \sin 3x$ on the RHS. Call this equation [1].

Integrate this second integral by parts, choosing $\dfrac{dv}{dx} = e^{2x}$ again and $u = \sin 3x$. The expression obtained for this integral contains the original integral, I. Substitute this expression in equation [1].

Collect I terms on the LHS and the other terms on the RHS. Simplify and find the expression for I. Don't forget the constant of integration in the answer.

 1 Evaluate $\int_1^2 x(2 - x)^7 \, dx$. *(L)*

2 Evaluate, correct to two decimal places, $\int_0^1 (1 - x) \sin x \, dx$. *(J)*

3 (a) Evaluate (i) $\int_0^{\frac{\pi}{6}} \tan 2x \, dx$. (ii) $\int_1^e x^2 \ln x \, dx$.

    (b) Find $\int \dfrac{e^{-\sqrt{x}}}{\sqrt{x}} \, dx$. *(C)*

4 (a) Calculate the value of each of the following definite integrals: (i) $\int_{-1}^2 (x + 1)(2x - 3) \, dx$ (ii) $\int_3^{27} \sqrt{3x} \, dx$ (iii) $\int_1^2 \sin(3\pi x) \, dx..$

    (b) Draw a sketch of the part of the curve $y = \sqrt{x^2 - 9}$ between $x = 3$ and $x = 6$. Without attempting to evaluate the integral, deduce that $4 < \int_5^6 \sqrt{(x^2 - 9)} \, dx < 3\sqrt{3}$, explaining your reasoning. *(OLE)*

5 Integrate the following with respect to x:

    (i) $x^3(x^4 - 3)^5$ (ii) $\tan x$ (iii) xe^{x^2}. *(S)*

6 Find $\int \sin x(1 + \cos^2 x) \, dx$. *(C)*

7 Find $\int x \sin 2x \, dx$. *(J)*

8 (a) Differentiate $(1 + x^3)^{\frac{1}{2}}$ with respect to x.
    (b) Use the result from (a), or an appropriate substitution, to find the value of

$$\int_0^2 \frac{x^2}{\sqrt{1 + x^3}} \, dx. \qquad (A)$$

9 (i) Use the chain rule to differentiate $(3 + 2x)^4$ with respect to x.
    (ii) Hence evaluate $\int_0^1 (3 + 2x)^3 \, dx$.

    (iii) Expand $(3 + 2x)^3$ in powers of x, and use your answer to check the value of the integral in (ii). *(O & C)*

10 (i) Using the substitution $u = x^2 + 4$ or otherwise, find the indefinite integral

$$\int \frac{x}{x^2 + 4} \, dx.$$

    (ii) You are given that $f(x) = \dfrac{2}{2x + 1} - \dfrac{x}{x^2 + 4}$.

The figure shows the graph of $y = f(x)$ between $x = 0$ and $x = 8$. Show that the area of the shaded region between this graph and the axes is equal to **exactly** $\tfrac{1}{2} \ln 17$.
(iii) Find an expression for $f'(x)$. Use this to calculate the gradient of the graph at $x = 0$ and $x = 8$.
(iv) Write $f(x)$ as a single fraction in its simplest form. *(O & C)*

P25 Numerical Solution of Equations
Introduction, Initial values, Interval bisection, Iterative methods.

Introduction

Many equations cannot be solved exactly, but various methods of finding approximate numerical solutions exist. The most commonly used methods have two main parts:
(a) finding an initial approximate value   (b) improving this value by an iterative process.

Initial values

The roots of $f(x)=0$ can be located approximately by either a graphical or an algebraic method.

Graphical method
Either (a) Plot (or sketch) the graph of $y=f(x)$. The real roots are at the points where the curve cuts the x-axis.
or   (b) Rewrite $f(x)=0$ in the form $F(x)=G(x)$. Plot (or sketch) $y=F(x)$ and $y=G(x)$. The real roots are at the points where these graphs intersect.

$\boxed{i}$ *Locate an approximate value for the root of*
$$f(x)=x+e^x=0.$$

Graphical method
Rewrite $f(x)=0$ as $e^x=-x$.
Let $F(x)=-x$ and $G(x)=e^x$.
Sketch $F(x)$ and $G(x)$

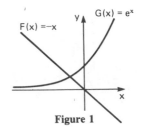

Figure 1

When $x=0$, $G(x)>F(x)$
$\quad\quad\quad x=-1$, $G(x)<F(x)$
$\therefore f(x)=0$ has a root
between -1 and 0.

Algebraic method
Find two values a and b such that $f(a)$ and $f(b)$ have different signs. At least one root must lie between a and b if $f(x)$ is continuous.
If more than one root is suspected between a and b, sketch a graph of $y=f(x)$.

Algebraic method
$f(x)=x+e^x$
$f(1)=1+e^1=3.72$
$\left.\begin{array}{l}f(0)=0+e^0=1\\f(-1)=-1+e^{-1}=-0.63\end{array}\right\}$ different signs
$\therefore f(x)=0$ has a root between -1 and 0.

Interval bisection

When a root, α, of $f(x)=0$ has been located between x_1 and x_2, bisect the interval (x_1, x_2) to find the mid-interval value x_3.

Calculate $f(x_3)$ and compare its sign with those of $f(x_1)$ and $f(x_2)$ to determine whether α lies in the interval (x_1, x_3) or (x_3, x_2).

Repeat this process until α has been located within a narrow enough interval to give its value to the required degree of accuracy.

$\boxed{i}$ *The equation $x^3-3x-4=0$ has a root between $x=2$ and $x=3$. Find the root correct to 2 decimal places.*

$f(x)=x^3-3x-4$
$f(2)<0$ and $f(3)>0 \Rightarrow 2<\alpha<3$
$f(2.5)>0 \Rightarrow 2<\alpha<2.5$
$f(2.25)>0 \Rightarrow 2<\alpha<2.25$
$f(2.125)<0 \Rightarrow 2.125<\alpha<2.5$
$f(2.1875)<0 \Rightarrow 2.1875<\alpha<2.25$
So, $\alpha=2.2$ (to 2 d.p.).

Iterative methods

All iterative methods follow the same basic pattern.

A sequence of approximations $x_1, x_2, x_3, x_4, \ldots$ is found, each one closer to the root α of $f(x)=0$.

Each approximation is found from the one before it using a specified method.

The process is continued until the required accuracy is reached.

General iteration method
Rewrite the equation $f(x)=0$ in the form $x=g(x)$.
If the initial approximation is x_1
then calculate $x_2=g(x_1)$
$\quad\quad\quad\quad\quad x_3=g(x_2)$
$\quad\quad\quad\quad\quad x_4=g(x_3)$
$\quad\quad\quad\quad\quad$ and so on . . .

This method fails if $|g'(x)|>1$ near the root.

Newton–Raphson method
If x_1 is an approximation to a root α of $f(x)=0$, then a better approximation x_2 is given by
$$x_2=x_1-\frac{f(x_1)}{f'(x_1)}$$
Repeat this process as required.

This method fails if (a) $f'(\alpha)$ is near to zero,
or (b) $f''(\alpha)$ is very large.

(See worked example.)

$\boxed{i}$ *Find the solution of $x+e^x=0$ near $x=-1$ correct to three decimal places.*

General iteration method
Write the given equation as $x=-e^x$.

$x_1=-1$
$x_2=-e^{-1}=-0.368$
$x_3=-e^{-0.368}=-0.692$
$x_4=-e^{-0.692}=-0.500$
$x_5=-e^{-0.500}=-0.607$
$x_6=-e^{-0.607}=-0.545$
$x_7=-e^{-0.545}=-0.580$
$x_8=-e^{-0.580}=-0.560$
$x_9=-e^{-0.560}=-0.571$
$x_{10}=-e^{-0.571}=-0.565$
$x_{11}=-e^{-0.565}=-0.568$
$x_{12}=-e^{-0.568}=-0.567$
$x_{13}=-e^{-0.567}=-0.567$ is the required solution.

Numerical Solution of Equations
Worked examples and Exam questions.

 Show that the equation $x^3+x-6=0$ has a root between 1 and 2. Using Newton's approximation with starting point 1.6 determine, by means of two iterations, an approximation to this root, giving your answer to two decimal places.

Let $f(x)=x^3+x-6$

$f(1)=1+1-6=-4<0$

$f(2)=8+2-6=\ \ 4>0$

$\therefore\ f(x)=0$ between $x=1$ and $x=2$

i.e. $x^3+x-6=0$ between $x=1$ and $x=2$

$\therefore\ x^3+x-6=0$ has a root between $x=1$ and $x=2$.

Let $x_2=x_1-\dfrac{f(x_1)}{f'(x_1)}$ where $f'(x)=3x^2+1$

$x_2=1.6-\dfrac{(1.6^3+1.6-6)}{3\times1.6^2+1}$, using $x_1=1.6$

$=1.6-(-0.0350)=1.6350$

$x_3=1.6350-\dfrac{(1.6350^3+1.6350-6)}{3\times1.6350^2+1}$

$=1.6350-(0.0006)=1.6344$

$\therefore$ to two decimal places the root is 1.63.

 Show that $x^3+3x-12=0$ has only one real root α, and that $1<\alpha<2$. Use linear interpolation to determine the number k, expressed to one decimal place, such that $k<\alpha<k+0.1$.

Given that α is a root of $x^3+3x-12=0$

Then $(x-\alpha)$ is a factor of $x^3+3x-12$

Dividing $(x-\alpha)$ into $x^3+3x-12$ gives the quadratic factor
$x^2+\alpha x+(3+\alpha^2)$

$\therefore\ x^3+3x-12=(x-\alpha)[x^2+\alpha x+(3+\alpha^2)]=0$

The factor $x^2+\alpha x+(3+\alpha^2)$ does not give rise to real roots because its discriminant is negative.

$\therefore\ x=\alpha$ is the only real root of $x^3+3x-12=0$

$f(1)=1+3-12=-8<0$

$f(2)=8+6-12=\ \ 2>0$

$\therefore\ 1<\alpha<2$

From the similar triangles shown in the diagram

$\dfrac{8}{x}=\dfrac{2}{1-x}$, i.e. $8-8x=2x$

$\therefore\ x=0.8$

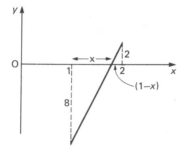

Let $k=1.8$, $f(1.8)=-0.768<0$

$f(1.9)=\ \ 0.559>0$

$\therefore$ if $k=1.8$ then $1.8<\alpha<1.8+0.1=1.9$

---

 1 Show graphically, or otherwise, that the equation $\ln x=4-x$ has only one real root and prove that this root lies between 2.9 and 3. By taking 2.9 as a first approximation to this root and applying the Newton–Raphson process once to the equation $\ln x-4+x=0$, or otherwise, find a second approximation, giving your answer to 3 significant figures.

(L)

2 Give, on the same diagram, a sketch of the graph of $y=3e^{\frac12 x}$ and of the graph $y=4x+6$. State the number of roots of the equation $3e^{\frac12 x}=4x+6$. Taking 4 as a first approximation to one root α of this equation, find a second approximation to α, giving three significant figures in your answer and showing clearly how this answer has been

obtained. Using a suitable integer as first approximation to another root β of the equation, find a second approximation to β, again giving three significant figures in your answer and showing clearly how this answer has been determined.

(C)

3 Use Newton's method once, starting with the approximation $x=2$, to obtain a second approximation x_1 for a root of the equation $x^5=x^3+25$. What does it mean to claim that x_1 is correct to two decimal places? State briefly how you would prove this (no detailed working is expected).

(O & C)

4 Show that the equation $x(x^2+2)-4=0$ has only one real root, and that this root lies between 1 and 1.5. Taking 1.2 as a first approximation to this root, use Newton's method to obtain a second approximation, giving your result to two places of decimals (or to six places if you use a machine).

(J)

5 Show, by means of a sketch graph, or otherwise, that the equation $e^{2x}+4x-5=0$ has only one real root, and that this root lies between 0 and 1. Starting with the value 0.5 as a first approximation to this root, use the Newton–Raphson method to evaluate successive approximations, showing the stages of your work and ending when two successive approximations give answers which, when rounded to two decimal places, agree.

(C)

6 Find, by *any* method, the solution of the equation $x^2+20\ln x=400$, giving your answer correct to 3 significant figures.

(O & C)

7 The sequence given by the iteration formula
$x_{n+1}=2(1+e^{-x_n})$ with $x_1=0$, converges to α. Find α correct to 3 decimal places, and state an equation of which α is a root. *(C)*

8 Show that the equation $x^3-x^2-2=0$ has a root α which lies between 1 and 2.
(a) Using 1.5 as a first approximation for α, use the Newton-Raphson method once to obtain a second approximation for α, giving your answer to 3 decimal places.
(b) Show that the equation $x^3-x^2-2=0$ can be arranged in the form
$$x=\sqrt[3]{f(x)}$$
where $f(x)$ is a quadratic function.
Use an iteration of the form $x_{n+1}=g(x_n)$ based on this rearrangement and with $x_1=1.5$, to find x_2 and x_3, giving your answers to 3 decimal places.

(A)

Division

When dividing one polynomial in x by another the working can be set out like a long division:

$$\frac{quotient}{divisor)\,dividend}$$

Write the terms in both polynomials in order, with the highest power of x first. Leave gaps for 'missing' terms. Divide the first term in the dividend (the polynomial being divided) by the first term in the divisor (the polynomial you are dividing by). Write the result in the 'correct column' over the division line, i.e. in the quotient. Multiply all the terms in the divisor by this result and subtract the answer from the dividend. A 'new dividend' is now left. Repeat this process until the dividend that is left is of a lower degree than the divisor.

If a polynomial can be *divided exactly* by another, i.e. without remainder, then the divisor is a **factor** of that polynomial. The quotient is also a factor. The polynomial can be written as a *product* of these two factors.

$$polynomial \div divisor = quotient$$
$$\Rightarrow \qquad polynomial = (divisor)(quotient)$$

The result of dividing one polynomial by another may be a *quotient and a remainder*. The relationship between the polynomial, divisor, quotient and remainder may be given in several ways.

$$polynomial \div divisor = quotient \text{ and remainder}$$

or $\quad \dfrac{polynomial}{divisor} = quotient + \dfrac{remainder}{divisor}$

or $\quad polynomial = (divisor)(quotient) + remainder$

$\boxed{\mathbf{i}}$ *Divide* $(x^3 - x^2 - 5x + 2)$ *by* $(x + 2)$.

$$
\begin{array}{r}
x^2 - 3x + 1 \quad \leftarrow quotient \\
divisor \rightarrow x+2\,)\,\overline{x^3 - x^2 - 5x + 2} \quad \leftarrow dividend \\
\underline{x^3 + 2x^2} \qquad\qquad\quad \\
-3x^2 - 5x \qquad\quad \\
\underline{-3x^2 - 6x} \qquad\quad \\
x + 2 \\
\underline{x + 2} \\
\leftarrow no\ remainder
\end{array}
$$

$\therefore (x^3 - x^2 - 5x + 2) \div (x + 2) = x^2 - 3x + 1$

So $(x + 2)$ and $(x^2 - 3x + 1)$ are factors of $(x^3 - x^2 - 5x + 2)$.

And $(x^3 - x^2 - 5x + 2) = (x + 2)(x^2 - 3x + 1)$.

$\boxed{\mathbf{i}}$ *Find the quotient and remainder for:*
$$\frac{x^4 - 2x^2 + 3x - 6}{x^2 - 4x + 3}$$

$$
\begin{array}{r}
x^2 + 4x + 11 \qquad\qquad \\
x^2 - 4x + 3\,)\,\overline{x^4 \qquad - 2x^2 + 3x - 6} \\
\underline{x^4 - 4x^3 + 3x^2} \qquad\qquad \\
4x^3 - 5x^2 + 3x \qquad \\
\underline{4x^3 - 16x^2 + 12x} \qquad \\
11x^2 - 9x - 6 \\
\underline{11x^2 - 44x + 33} \\
35x - 39
\end{array}
$$

The quotient is $x^2 + 4x + 11$.

The remainder is $35x - 39$.

$\therefore \dfrac{x^4 - 2x^2 + 3x - 6}{x^2 - 4x + 3} = x^2 + 4x + 11 + \dfrac{35x - 39}{x^2 - 4x + 3}$.

Remainder theorem

If a polynomial $f(x)$ is divided by $(x - a)$, then the remainder is $f(a)$.

$f(a)$ is the value of $f(x)$ when $x = a$.

The *Factor theorem* (see P7) is a special case of the Remainder theorem in which $f(a) = 0$, i.e. there is *no* remainder, and $(x - a)$ is a *factor* of $f(x)$.

$\boxed{\mathbf{i}}$ *Find the remainder when* $3x^5 - x^2 + 1$ *is divided by* $(x + 2)$.

$$f(x) = 3x^5 - x^2 + 1$$
$$f(-2) = 3(-2)^5 - (-2)^2 + 1 = -96 - 4 + 1 = -99$$

Partial fractions

If the *denominator* of a fraction *factorises*, then the fraction can be split into **partial fractions**. The fraction can be expressed as the sum of two or more of these partial fractions.

Each *linear factor* $(ax + b)$ in the denominator of such a fraction gives a partial fraction of the form $\dfrac{A}{ax + b}$.

The **cover-up rule** is a simple method of finding A. 'Cover-up' the factor $(ax + b)$ in the denominator of the original fraction. Then substitute the value of x given by $(ax + b) = 0$ into what is left 'uncovered'. The result is the value of A.

Note: this method can be used *only* for linear factors. Methods used for other types of factor are given in P27.

After expressing a fraction in partial fractions, always *check* your answer by reversing the process. Write the partial fractions with a common denominator and combine the numerators. Simplify to give a single fraction.

$\boxed{\mathbf{i}}$ *Express* $\dfrac{5x + 3}{(x - 1)(2x + 1)}$ *in partial fractions.*

Each linear factor in the denominator gives a partial fraction.

Let $\dfrac{5x + 3}{(x - 1)(2x + 1)} \equiv \dfrac{A}{x - 1} + \dfrac{B}{2x + 1}$

Use the cover-up rule to find A and B.

To find A, cover up $(x - 1) \rightarrow \dfrac{5x + 3}{(\quad)(2x + 1)}$

$(x - 1) = 0 \Rightarrow x = 1$. So put $x = 1$ in this expression.

$A = \dfrac{5(1) + 3}{(\quad)(2(1) + 1)} = \dfrac{8}{3}$

To find B, cover up $(2x + 1)$: $\rightarrow \dfrac{5x + 3}{(x - 1)(\quad)}$

$(2x + 1) = 0 \Rightarrow x = -\frac{1}{2}$. So put $x = -\frac{1}{2}$ in this expression.

$B = \dfrac{5(-\frac{1}{2}) + 3}{(-\frac{1}{2} - 1)(\quad)} = \dfrac{-\frac{1}{2}}{-1\frac{1}{2}} = -\dfrac{1}{3}$

$\therefore \dfrac{5x + 3}{(x - 1)(2x + 1)} = \dfrac{8}{3(x - 1)} - \dfrac{1}{3(2x + 1)}$

Polynomials and fractions
Worked examples, Guided example and Exam questions.

 The expression $2x^3 + ax^2 + bx + 2$ is exactly divisible by $(x+2)$ and leaves a remainder of 12 on division by $(x-2)$. Calculate the values of a and b and factorise the expression completely.

Let $f(x) = 2x^3 + ax^2 + bx + 2$
$(x+2)$ is a factor of $f(x)$, so $f(-2) = 0$
$f(-2) = 2(-2)^3 + a(-2)^2 + b(-2) + 2 = -16 + 4a - 2b + 2 = 0$

　i.e. $4a - 2b = 14$ ⟶ [1]

Division by $(x-2)$ leaves a remainder of 12, so $f(2) = 12$
$f(2) = 2(2)^3 + a(2)^2 + b(2) + 2 = 16 + 4a + 2b + 2 = 12$

　i.e. $4a + 2b = -6$ ⟶ [2]

$[1] + [2]$ gives $8a = 8$, $a = 1$ and $[2] - [1]$ gives $4b = -20$, $b = -5$
$\therefore f(x) = 2x^3 + x^2 - 5x + 2$
Since $(x+2)$ is a factor of $f(x)$
divide $f(x)$ by $(x+2)$ to obtain a quotient $2x^2 - 3x + 1$
$\therefore f(x) = (x+2)(2x^2 - 3x + 1)$
　　　$= (x+2)(2x-1)(x-1)$, by factorisation
$\therefore f(x) = (x+2)(2x-1)(x-1)$

 When the polynomial $P(x)$ is divided by $(x-1)$ the remainder is 7, and when divided by $(x-3)$ the remainder is 13. Find, by writing
$$P(x) \equiv (x-1)(x-3)Q(x) + ax + b$$
the remainder when $P(x)$ is divided by $(x-1)(x-3)$. If also $P(x)$ is a cubic in which the coefficient of x^3 is unity and $P(2) = 6$, determine $Q(x)$.

Division by $(x-1)$ leaves a remainder of 7, so $P(1) = 7$

　i.e. $a + b = 7$ ⟶ [1]

Division by $(x-3)$ leaves a remainder of 13, so $P(3) = 13$

　i.e. $3a + b = 13$ ⟶ [2]

$[2] - [1]$ gives $2a = 6$, $a = 3$ and from [1] $b = 4$
$\therefore P(x) \equiv (x-1)(x-3)Q(x) + 3x + 4$

$$\frac{P(x)}{(x-1)(x-3)} \equiv Q(x) + \frac{3x+4}{(x-1)(x-3)}$$

Thus the remainder on division by $(x-1)(x-3)$ is $3x+4$
If $P(x)$ is a cubic with the coefficient of x^3 unity then
$Q(x) \equiv (x+c)$

　i.e. $P(x) = (x-1)(x-3)(x+c) + 3x + 4$
and $P(2) = 6$, $(2-1)(2-3)(2+c) + 3(2) + 4 = 6$
　　　　　　　　　　　$-(2+c) + 10 = 6$
　　　　　　　i.e.　　$c = 2$
$\therefore Q(x) = x + 2$

 The quadratic polynomial $P(x)$ leaves a remainder of 3 on division by $(x-1)$, a remainder of 12 on division by $(x-2)$ and no remainder on division by $(x+2)$. Find $P(x)$ and solve $P(x) = 0$.

Let $P(x) \equiv ax^2 + bx + c$ ⟶ [1]
Let $P(1) = 3$, $P(2) = 12$, $P(-2) = 0$, obtaining three equations in a, b and c.
The found values of a, b and c are substituted in [1] which may then be factorised and $P(x) = 0$ easily solved.

EX   **1** Use long division to find the missing factor in each statement.
　(a) $x^5 + x^4 + 3x^3 + 5x^2 + 2x + 8 = (x^2 - x + 2)(\ldots)$
　(b) $6x^5 + x^4 - x^3 - 15x + 5 = (3x - 1)(\ldots)$
　(c) $x^6 + 2x^5 - 3x^3 + 12x = (x^2 + 2x)(\ldots)$
　(d) $8 + 10x^5 - 16x^2 - x^8 - x^3 = (8 - x^3)(\ldots)$.

2 Find the quotient and remainder for each division.
　(a) $(x^4 - 3x^2 + 7) \div (x+3)$
　(b) $(3x^5 - 5x^4 + x^2 + 1) \div (x^3 + 1)$

3 Express these as a quotient and a fraction.
　(a) $\dfrac{x^3 - x^2 - 4}{x^2 - 1}$ 　　(b) $\dfrac{2x^5 - 3x^2 + 1}{x^2 + 2x}$

4 The expression $2x^3 + ax^2 + bx + 6$ is exactly divisible by $(x-2)$ and on division by $(x+1)$ gives a remainder of -12. Calculate the values of a and b and factorise the expression completely. 　*(A)*

5 　　　　　　$f(x) \equiv x^2 + ax + b$
When $f(x)$ is divided by $(x-2)$, the remainder is 8. When $f(x)$ is divided by $(x+3)$, the remainder is 18. Find the values of the constants a and b. 　*(L)*

6 If $f(x)$ denotes the polynomial $2x^3 - 3x^2 - 8x - 3$, find the remainders when $f(x)$ is divided by (i) $x-1$, (ii) $x+3$, and (iii) $2x+1$. Deduce which of $(x-1)$, $(x+3)$, and $(2x+1)$ is a factor of $f(x)$, and find its remaining factors. 　*(O & C)*

7 State the Remainder Theorem.
When the cubic polynomial $x^3 + ax^2 - 3x + 4$ is divided by $x-3$, the remainder obtained is twice the remainder obtained when the polynomial is divided by $x-2$. Calculate a. 　*(S)*

8 When $f(x)$, where $f(x) \equiv x^4 - 2x^3 + ax^2 + bx + c$, is divided by $x-2$ the remainder is -24. When $f(x)$ is divided by $x+4$ the remainder is 240. Given that $x+1$ is a factor of $f(x)$, show that $x-1$ is also a factor. 　*(A)*

9 (a) Given that $f(x) = x^3 + kx^2 - 2x + 1$ and that when $f(x)$ is divided by $(x-k)$ the remainder is k, find the possible values of k.
(b) When the polynomial $p(x)$ is divided by $(x-1)$ the remainder is 5 and when $p(x)$ is divided by $(x-2)$ the remainder is 7. Given that $p(x)$ may be written in the form $(x-1)(x-2)q(x) + Ax + B$, where $q(x)$ is a polynomial and A and B are numbers, find the remainder when $p(x)$ is divided by $(x-1)(x-2)$. 　*(C)*

10 When the polynomial $P(x)$ is divided by $x-2$ the remainder is 4, and when $P(x)$ is divided by $x-3$ the remainder is 7. Find, by writing $P(x) \equiv (x-2)(x-3)Q(x) + ax + b$, the remainder when $P(x)$ is divided by $(x-2)(x-3)$. If also $P(x)$ is a cubic in which the coefficient of x^3 is unity, and $P(1) = 1$, determine $Q(x)$. 　*(J)*

11 Find the constants A and B in the following identity:
$$\frac{x+2}{x^2-1} \equiv \frac{A}{x-1} + \frac{B}{x+1} \qquad (L)$$

12 Express the following in partial fractions.
　(a) $\dfrac{4-3x}{(1-2x)(2+x)}$ 　　(b) $\dfrac{1}{(1-2x)(1-3x)}$
　(c) $\dfrac{2}{(x+7)(x+9)}$ 　　(d) $\dfrac{2x+5}{(x+2)(x+3)}$

13 Express the following as a quotient and a fraction. Then express each fraction in partial fractions.
　(a) $\dfrac{x^2 + 10x + 6}{x^2 + 2x - 8}$ 　　(b) $\dfrac{x^3}{(x+1)(x+2)}$

P27 Rational functions

Definitions, More partial fractions, Using partial fractions.

Definitions

A **rational function** of x is a function of the form $\dfrac{P(x)}{Q(x)}$, where $P(x)$ and $Q(x)$ are polynomials in x.

If the degree of $P(x) <$ the degree of $Q(x)$, then $\dfrac{P(x)}{Q(x)}$ is a **proper fraction.**

If the degree of $P(x) \leq$ the degree of $Q(x)$, then $\dfrac{P(x)}{Q(x)}$ is an **improper fraction.**

A rational function that is an improper fraction can be written as a polynomial or constant together with a proper fraction. To do this you can divide the numerator by the denominator (see P26).

$\boxed{i}$ $\dfrac{x+1}{x^2-1}$, $\dfrac{2x^5-x^2+1}{x^3+x-1}$ and $\dfrac{3x^2+5}{x^2-x-1}$ are rational functions of x.

degree $1 \to$ $\dfrac{x+1}{x^2-1}$ is a proper fraction.
degree $2 \to$

degree $5 \to$ $\dfrac{2x^5-x^2+1}{x^3+x-1}$ is an improper fraction.
degree $3 \to$

degree $2 \to$ $\dfrac{3x^2+5}{x^2-x-1}$ is an improper fraction.
degree $2 \to$

$\boxed{i}$ $\dfrac{2x^5-x^2+1}{x^3+x-1} = 2x^2-2+\dfrac{x^2+2x-1}{x^3+x-1}$

More partial fractions

If a rational function, $\dfrac{P(x)}{Q(x)}$, is a proper fraction and its denominator, $Q(x)$, will *factorise*, then the fraction can be given as a sum of **partial fractions**. The method used depends on the type(s) of factors in the denominator.

If the denominator has *unrepeated linear factors only*, then the '*cover-up rule*' may be used (see P26). In this Unit the fractions we deal with may have *linear factors* and/or *repeated linear factors* and/or *quadratic factors* in their denominators.

The basic method used is outlined below.

1. Identify the form(s) of the partial fractions

(a) For every **linear factor** $(ax+b)$ of the denominator there will be a corresponding partial fraction $\dfrac{A}{(ax+b)}$.

(b) For every **repeated linear factor** $(cx+d)^2$ of the denominator there will be two corresponding partial fractions $\dfrac{B}{(cx+d)} + \dfrac{C}{(cx+d)^2}$.

(c) For every **quadratic factor** (ex^2+fx+g) of the denominator there will be a corresponding fraction $\dfrac{Dx+E}{(ex^2+fx+g)}$.

2. To find the constants A, B, C,...

(a) Form an identity between the original fraction and the sum of the partial fractions.

(b) Write all the fractions using a common denominator.

(c) Compare the two numerators by
  (i) comparing 'convenient coefficients' on each side of the identity
and/or (ii) substituting values of x which reduce individual factors to zero.

Always check your answer by reversing the process, i.e., by combining the partial fractions to form a single fraction.

If an improper fraction has to be expressed in partial fractions, divide numerator by denominator first to obtain a quotient and a proper fraction. Then find the partial fractions for the proper fraction as before (see $\boxed{\text{WE}}$).

$\boxed{i}$ $\dfrac{9x+9}{(x+2)^2(x-1)} \equiv \dfrac{3}{(x+2)^2} - \dfrac{2}{(x+2)} + \dfrac{2}{(x-1)}$
  rational function   partial fractions

$\boxed{i}$ *Express* $\dfrac{x+1}{x(x-1)^2}$ *in partial fractions.*

Linear factor $x \to$ partial fraction $\dfrac{A}{x}$.

Repeated linear factor $(x-1)^2$

$\to$ partial fractions $\dfrac{B}{(x-1)} + \dfrac{C}{(x-1)^2}$.

Let $\dfrac{x+1}{x(x-1)^2} \equiv \dfrac{A}{x} + \dfrac{B}{(x-1)} + \dfrac{C}{(x-1)^2}$

$\Rightarrow \dfrac{x+1}{x(x-1)^2} \equiv \dfrac{A(x-1)^2+Bx(x-1)+Cx}{x(x-1)^2}$

$\Rightarrow x+1 \equiv A(x-1)^2+Bx(x-1)+Cx$

Substituting $x=1 \Rightarrow 1+1=C \Rightarrow C=2$

Substituting $x=0 \Rightarrow 0+1=A(-1)^2 \Rightarrow A=1$.

Comparing coefficients of x^2:

$0 = A+B \Rightarrow 0 = 1+B \Rightarrow B=-1$.

So $\dfrac{x+1}{x(x-1)^2} = \dfrac{1}{x} - \dfrac{1}{(x-1)} + \dfrac{2}{(x-1)^2}$.

$\boxed{i}$ *Express* $\dfrac{9x+9}{(x-3)(x^2+9)}$ *in partial fractions.*

Linear factor $(x-3) \to$ partial fraction $\dfrac{A}{(x-3)}$.

Quadratic factor $(x^2+9) \to$ partial fraction $\dfrac{Bx+C}{(x^2+9)}$.

Let $\dfrac{9x+9}{(x-3)(x^2+9)} \equiv \dfrac{A}{(x-3)} + \dfrac{Bx+C}{(x^2+9)}$

$\Rightarrow \dfrac{9x+9}{(x-3)(x^2+9)} \equiv \dfrac{A(x^2+9)+(Bx+C)(x-3)}{(x-3)(x^2+9)}$

$\Rightarrow 9x+9 \equiv A(x^2+9)+(Bx+C)(x-3)$

Substituting $x=3 \Rightarrow 9(3)+9 \Rightarrow A(3^2+9) \Rightarrow A=2$.

Comparing coefficients:

$[x^2]$: $0 = A+B \Rightarrow 0 = 2+B \Rightarrow B=-2$
$[\text{constant}]$: $9 = 9A-3C \Rightarrow 9 = 9(2)-3C \Rightarrow C=3$

So $\dfrac{9x+9}{(x-3)(x^2+9)} = \dfrac{2}{(x-3)} + \dfrac{3-2x}{(x^2+9)}$.

Using partial fractions

Expressing an algebraic fraction in terms of partial fractions is rarely used on its own. It is however often an important first stop in problem-solving. Some exam questions identify this step clearly for you in their first part.

$\boxed{i}$ You may need to use partial fractions to solve problems in Integration, Differentiation, Summation of Series and Binomial Series. Four typical examples are given in the $\boxed{\text{GE}}$ s opposite.

Rational Functions
Worked example, Guided examples, Exercises and Exam questions.

 WE Express $\dfrac{4x^3+16x^2-15x+13}{(x+2)(2x-1)^2}$ in partial fractions.

Both numerator and denominator are of degree 3. So this fraction is improper. It must be divided out to obtain a quotient and a proper fraction. Expand the denominator first. Then do the division.

$(x+2)(2x-1)^2=(x+2)(4x^2-4x+1)=4x^3+4x^2-7x+2$

$$4x^3+4x^2-7x+2 \overline{)4x^3+16x^2-15x+13} \quad 1$$
$$\underline{4x^3+\ 4x^2-\ 7x+\ 2}$$
$$12x^2-\ 8x+11$$

$\therefore \dfrac{4x^3+16x^2-15x+13}{(x+2)(2x-1)^2}=1+\dfrac{12x^2-8x+11}{(x+2)(2x-1)^2}$

Let

$\dfrac{12x^2-8x+11}{(x+2)(2x-1)^2}\equiv\dfrac{A}{(x+2)}+\dfrac{B}{(2x-1)}+\dfrac{C}{(2x-1)^2}$

i.e. $12x^2-8x+11\equiv A(2x-1)^2+B(x+2)(2x-1)+C(x+2)$

Substituting:

$x=-2\ \Rightarrow 48+16+11=25A\ \Rightarrow A=3$

$x=\frac{1}{2}\ \Rightarrow 3-4+11=\frac{5}{2}C\Rightarrow C=4$

$x=0\ \Rightarrow 11=A-2B+2C\Rightarrow 11=3-2B+8\ \Rightarrow B=0$

$\therefore \dfrac{12x^2-8x+11}{(x+2)(2x-1)^2}\equiv\dfrac{3}{(x+2)}+\dfrac{4}{(2x-1)^2}$

and $\dfrac{4x^3+16x^2-15x+13}{(x+2)(2x-1)^2}\equiv 1+\dfrac{3}{(x+2)}+\dfrac{4}{(2x-1)^2}$

 GE Express $\dfrac{1}{x(x+2)}$ in partial fractions, and hence find the sum to n terms of the series

$$\frac{1}{1.3}+\frac{1}{2.4}+\frac{1}{3.5}+\dots$$

Write $\dfrac{1}{x(x+2)}\equiv\dfrac{A}{x}+\dfrac{B}{(x+2)}$.

Use the 'cover-up rule' (see page 52) with $x=0$ and $x=-2$ to find the values of A and B.

This gives $\dfrac{1}{x(x+2)}\equiv\dfrac{1}{2x}-\dfrac{1}{2(x+2)}$.

Use these partial fractions to write the 1st, 2nd, 3rd and 4th terms and the $(n-2)$th, $(n-1)$th and nth terms of the series. Set them out in columns to show the pattern.

1st term: $\quad\dfrac{1}{1\times3}\quad=\dfrac{1}{2\times1}-\dfrac{1}{2\times3}$

....

nth term: $\quad\dfrac{1}{n(n+2)}\quad=\dfrac{1}{2n}-\dfrac{1}{2(n+2)}$

To find the sum of the series, imagine adding terms. Pick out terms on the RHS that give zero when added together, e.g. $-\frac{1}{2\times3}+\frac{1}{2\times3}=0$. Work out which terms will be left at the 'beginning' and at the 'end'. These give the required sum.

 GE Express $\dfrac{2+x^2}{(2-x)^2(4+x)}$ as partial fractions, and hence expand the function in a series of ascending powers of x as far as the term in x^3.

Write $\dfrac{2+x^2}{(2-x)^2(4+x)}\equiv\dfrac{A}{(2-x)}+\dfrac{B}{(2-x)^2}+\dfrac{C}{(4+x)}$ and find the values of A, B and C.

Write each partial fraction in the form: $a^n\left(1+\dfrac{x}{a}\right)^n$.

Use the binomial theorem to expand each of these as a series in ascending powers of x as far as the term in x^3. Collect like terms from the three expansions.

GE Express $\dfrac{1}{(x+1)(x+2)}$ as partial fractions and hence evaluate

$$\int_2^3\frac{1}{(x+1)(x+2)}dx.$$

Write $\dfrac{1}{(x+1)(x+2)}\equiv\dfrac{A}{(x+1)}+\dfrac{B}{(x+2)}$.

Find the values of A and B by the 'cover-up rule' (see page 52), using $x=-1$ and $x=-2$. Rewrite the given integral using the partial fractions. Integrate each fraction in turn. Evaluate using the limits of integration. Use the basic rules of logarithms to simplify the result.

GE Express $f(x)=\dfrac{2x-1}{(x-2)^2}$ as partial fractions and hence find the first and second derivatives of $f(x)$.

Write $\dfrac{2x-1}{(x-2)^2}\equiv\dfrac{A}{(x-2)}+\dfrac{B}{(x-2)^2}$ and find the values of A and B. Write each partial fraction using a negative power of $(x-2)$. Differentiate w.r.t. x to find $f'(x)$. Then differentiate $f'(x)$ w.r.t. x to find $f''(x)$. Give each result using positive powers of $(x-2)$.

 EX Express these functions in partial fractions:

1 $\dfrac{2x^2-x}{(2+x)(1+x^2)}$ **2** $\dfrac{5x^2+6x+7}{(x-1)(x+2)^2}$

3 $\dfrac{1+2x}{(1+x)(1-2x^2)}$ **4** $\dfrac{9}{(1+2x)(1-x)^2}$

5 $\dfrac{3x+1}{(x+1)^2}$ **6** $\dfrac{2x-2}{(x+1)(x-2)^2}$

7 $\dfrac{3x^2-x-2}{(1+2x)(x+2)^2}$ **8** $\dfrac{x-1}{(x+1)(x^2+1)}$

9 $\dfrac{x^2}{(x-1)(x^2+1)}$

10 (i) Write $\dfrac{1}{y(3-y)}$ in partial fractions.

(ii) Find $\displaystyle\int\frac{1}{y(3-y)}dy$.

(iii) Solve the differential equation $x\dfrac{dy}{dx}=y(3-y)$ where $x=2$ when $y=2$, giving y as a function of x.　　(O&C)

11 (a) Express $\dfrac{1-x-x^2}{(1-2x)(1-x)^2}$ as a sum of three partial fractions.

(b) Hence, or otherwise, expand this expression in ascending powers of x up to and including the term in x^3.

(c) State the range of values of x for which the expansion is valid.　　(J)

12 (a) Express $f(x)=\dfrac{x^2+7x+2}{(1+x^2)(2-x)}$ in terms of partial fractions.

(b) Hence prove that $\displaystyle\int_0^1 f(x)dx=\frac{11}{2}\ln 2-\frac{\pi}{4}$　　(OLE)

P28 More about series
Mathematical induction, Arithmetic and geometric means, Some special results.

Mathematical induction

Mathematical induction is a method of proving a given (or suspected) result for positive integers.

This method is often used to prove the formula for the sum to n terms of a series.

To prove by induction

(a) Assume that the stated result is true for some positive integral value of n, say k, and show that it is true for the next integral value, i.e. $k+1$.

(b) Show that the result is true for the first value, i.e. for $k=1$.

(c) Conclude that, by the principle of mathematical induction, the result holds for all positive integers k.

This concludes the proof because:
since the result is true for $k=1$,
then by (a) it has been shown to be true for $k=2$,
since it is true for $k=2$,
then by (a) it is true for $k=3$, ... and so on.
So it is true for all positive integers k.

i *Show by induction that*

$$S_n = \sum_{r=1}^{n}[a+(r-1)d] = \tfrac{1}{2}n[2a+(n-1)d]$$

i.e. the sum to n terms of an arithmetic series.

Assume the result is true when $n=k$,
i.e. $S_k = \tfrac{1}{2}k[2a+(k-1)d]$
Add the next term, the $(k+1)$th, giving

$$\begin{aligned}S_{k+1} &= \tfrac{1}{2}k[2a+(k-1)d]+[a+(k+1-1)d] \\ &= \tfrac{1}{2}[2ak+k^2d-kd+2a+2kd] \\ &= \tfrac{1}{2}[2a(k+1)+kd(k+1)] \\ &= \tfrac{1}{2}(k+1)[2a+kd]\end{aligned}$$

But this is S_n with n replaced by $(k+1)$.
∴ if the result is true for k, it is true for $(k+1)$.
Put $k=1$, $S_1 = \tfrac{1}{2}[2a+(1-1)d]=a$,
i.e. the first term is a, which is true.

∴ by the principle of mathematical induction the formula is true for all n.

Arithmetic and geometric means

a, b, c form an arithmetic series if $b=\tfrac{1}{2}(a+c)$.
b is the **arithmetic mean** of a and c.
x, y, z form a geometric series if $y=\sqrt{(xz)}$.
y is the **geometric mean** of x and z.
For the n values $x_1, x_2, x_3, \ldots, x_n$,

the arithmetic mean is $\dfrac{1}{n}(x_1+x_2+x_3+\ldots+x_n)$,

the geometric mean is $\sqrt[n]{(x_1. x_2. x_3 \ldots x_n)}$.

Given any two numbers it is possible to insert any number of arithmetic (or geometric) means between the two numbers to make the resulting terms form an arithmetic (or geometric) series.

i *Insert*
(a) five arithmetic means between 6 and 30,
(b) four geometric means between 243 and 1.

(a) 6, the five arithmetic means and 30 form an arithmetic series.

1st term: $6=a$; 7th term: $30=a+6d \Rightarrow d=4$.
So the arithmetic means are 10, 14, 18, 22, 26 hence 6, 10, 14, 18, 22, 26, 30 form an arithmetic series.

(b) 243, the four geometric means and 1 form a geometric series.

1st term: $243=a$; 6th term: $1=aR^5 \Rightarrow R=\tfrac{1}{3}$.
So the geometric means are 81, 27, 9, 3 hence 243, 81, 27, 9, 3, 1 form a geometric series.

Some special results

The following special results can be useful when summing series.

1. Distributive property of Σ
i.e. $\Sigma[af(x)+bg(x)+ch(x)+\ldots]$
$= a\Sigma f(x)+b\Sigma g(x)+c\Sigma h(x)+\ldots$

2. Natural number series

(a) $1+2+3+4+\ldots+n = \sum_{r=1}^{n}r = \tfrac{1}{2}n(n+1)$

(b) $1^2+2^2+3^2+4^2+\ldots+n^2 = \sum_{r=1}^{n}r^2 = \tfrac{1}{6}n(n+1)(2n+1)$

(c) $1^3+2^3+3^3+4^3+\ldots+n^3 = \sum_{r=1}^{n}r^3 = \tfrac{1}{4}n^2(n+1)^2$

Note: $\sum_{r=1}^{n}r^3 = \left(\sum_{r=1}^{n}r\right)^2$.

3. Sum of a constant

$$\sum_{r=1}^{n}a = \frac{\overbrace{a+a+a+\ldots}^{n \text{ times}}}{} = an$$

i *Find the sum to n terms of a series whose general term is $4r^2+3r+1$.*

We require $S_n = \sum_{r=1}^{n}(4r^2+3r+1)$

$$= \sum_{r=1}^{n}4r^2 + \sum_{r=1}^{n}3r + \sum_{r=1}^{n}1$$

$$= 4\sum_{r=1}^{n}r^2 + 3\sum_{r=1}^{n}r + \sum_{r=1}^{n}1$$

$$= 4[\tfrac{1}{6}n(n+1)(2n+1)]+3[\tfrac{1}{2}n(n+1)]+n$$

$$= \tfrac{1}{6}n(8n^2+21n+19)$$

More about series
Worked example, Guided example and Exam questions.

(a) *Prove by mathematical induction that*

$$\frac{1}{1.2}+\frac{1}{2.3}+\ldots+\frac{1}{n(n+1)}=\frac{n}{n+1}$$

for all positive integers n.

(b) *Obtain, and simplify, an expression for the sum of each of the following series:*

$$1.2+3.4+5.6+\ldots+(2n-1).2n$$
$$2-3+4-5+6-7+\ldots+2n-(2n+1)$$

(a) Assume

$$S_k=\frac{1}{1.2}+\frac{1}{2.3}+\ldots+\frac{1}{k(k+1)}=\frac{k}{k+1}$$

Then

$$S_{k+1}=\left[\frac{1}{1.2}+\frac{1}{2.3}+\ldots+\frac{1}{k(k+1)}\right]+\frac{1}{(k+1)(k+2)}$$

$$=\frac{k}{(k+1)}+\frac{1}{(k+1)(k+2)}$$

$$=\frac{k(k+2)+1}{(k+1)(k+2)}=\frac{(k+1)^2}{(k+1)(k+2)}=\frac{k+1}{k+2}$$

(N.B. The result for S_{k+1} is that for S_k with k replaced by $k+1$.)

$\therefore$ assuming S_k is true, S_{k+1} is true.

$$S_1=\frac{1}{1.2}=\frac{1}{1+1}=\frac{1}{2},\text{ which is true.}$$

$\therefore$ by mathematical induction the result is true for all positive integral n.

(b) Let $S_n=1.2+3.4+5.6\ldots+(2n-1)\times 2n$

Let the rth term be $u_r=(2r-1)\times 2r$

We require

$$\sum_{r=1}^{n}u_r=\sum_{r=1}^{n}(2r-1)\times 2r$$

$$=4\sum_{r=1}^{n}r^2-2\sum_{r=1}^{n}r$$

$$=4\times\frac{n}{6}(n+1)(2n+1)-2\times\frac{n}{2}(n+1)$$

$$=n(n+1)\left[\frac{2}{3}(2n+1)-1\right]$$

$$=\frac{n(n+1)}{3}[4n+2-3]=\frac{n(n+1)(4n-1)}{3}$$

Let $S=(2-3)+(4-5)+\ldots+[2n-(2n+1)]$
This series contains $2n$ terms which taken in n pairs, each pair having sum -1, has sum $(-1)\times n=-n$.

Use induction to prove that the sum to n terms of the series

$$\frac{5}{2\times 3\times 4}+\frac{7}{3\times 4\times 5}+\frac{9}{4\times 5\times 6}+\ldots$$

is $\frac{(2n+3)(2n+5)}{2(n+2)(n+3)}-\frac{5}{4}$. *Find the sum to infinity of the series.*

Assume

$$S_k=\frac{5}{2\times 3\times 4}+\frac{7}{3\times 4\times 5}+\ldots+\frac{(2k+3)}{(k+1)(k+2)(k+3)}$$

$$=\frac{(2k+3)(2k+5)}{2(k+2)(k+3)}-\frac{5}{4}$$

Then show

$$S_{k+1}=\frac{(2k+5)(2k+7)}{2(k+3)(k+4)}-\frac{5}{4}.$$

$\therefore$ assuming S_k is true, S_{k+1} is true.

$$S_1=\frac{5}{2\times 3\times 4}=\frac{5\times 7}{2\times 3\times 4}-\frac{5}{4}=\frac{5\times 7-2\times 15}{2\times 3\times 4}$$

which is true.

$\therefore$ by mathematical induction the result is true for all positive integral n

write S_n as $\dfrac{\left(2+\dfrac{3}{n}\right)\left(2+\dfrac{5}{n}\right)}{2\left(1+\dfrac{2}{n}\right)\left(1+\dfrac{3}{n}\right)}-\dfrac{5}{4}$

Show $\displaystyle\lim_{n\to\infty}S_n=\frac{3}{4}$

---

1 (a) Find the sum of n terms of the following series:
(i) $1.1+2.3+3.5+\ldots$; (ii) $2x+4x^2+8x^3+\ldots$, $x<\frac{1}{2}$.
In each case give your answer in as simple a form as possible.
(b) Show that the nth term of the series
$1+(1+2)+(1+2+2^2)+(1+2+2^2+2^3)+\ldots$ is 2^n-1.
Hence find (i) the sum of n terms of the series; (ii) the value of n if $T_{n+1}-T_n=64$, where T_n denotes the nth term.
*(W)

2 Prove by induction, or otherwise, that
(a) $\displaystyle\sum_{r=1}^{n}r(r+1)=\frac{n}{3}(n+1)(n+2)$,

(b) $\displaystyle\sum_{r=1}^{n}r(r+1)(r+2)=\frac{n}{4}(n+1)(n+2)(n+3)$.

Show that $r^3\equiv r(r+1)(r+2)-3r(r+1)+r$ and hence prove that

$$\sum_{r=1}^{n}r^3=\frac{n^2}{4}(n+1)^2.$$

Evaluate $\displaystyle\sum_{r=1}^{20}r(r+3)(r+6)$

(L)

3 Prove by induction that, for all positive integers n,
$1^3+2^3+\ldots+n^3=\frac{1}{4}n^2(n+1)^2$.
Deduce that
$(n+1)^3+(n+2)^3+\ldots+(2n)^3=\frac{1}{4}n^2(3n+1)(5n+3)$.
(J)

4 Prove by induction that, for every positive integer n,
$(1\times 4)+(2\times 5)+(3\times 6)+\ldots+n(n+3)=\frac{1}{3}n(n+1)(n+5)$.
(J)

5 By induction, or otherwise, prove the following results:
(i) $\displaystyle\sum_{r=1}^{n}\cos(2r-1)x=\frac{\sin 2nx}{2\sin x}$;

(ii) $\displaystyle\sum_{r=1}^{n}\frac{(r+4)}{2^r r(r+1)(r+2)}=\frac{1}{2}-\frac{1}{2^n(n+1)(n+2)}$.
(O & C)

6 *Use induction* to prove that the sum of the first $2n$ terms of the series $1^2-3^2+5^2-7^2+\ldots$ is $-8n^2$.
Write down the sum to $(2n+1)$ terms.
(O & C)

7 If $x^3=x+1$, prove, by induction or otherwise, that
$x^{3n}=a_nx+b_n+c_nx^{-1}$, where $a_1=1$, $b_1=1$, $c_1=0$, and
$a_n=a_{n-1}+b_{n-1}$, $b_n=a_{n-1}+b_{n-1}+c_{n-1}$, $c_n=a_{n-1}+c_{n-1}$,
for $n=2, 3,\ldots$.
(OLE)

P29 Permutations and Combinations

Factorial notation, Permutations, Permutations with identical items, Combinations.

Factorial notation

$n! = n(n-1)(n-2)(n-3)\ldots 2.1$
i.e. the product of all integers from n to 1 inclusive.
$n!$ is read as '**factorial n**' or '**n factorial**'.
We define $0! = 1$.

ℹ️ $5! = 5 \times 4 \times 3 \times 2 \times 1$
$\quad = 120$

Permutations

A **permutation** is an arrangement of items.

ℹ️ The permutations of A, B, C
ABC, ACB, BAC, BCA, CAB, CBA.

The number of permutations of n different items taken r at a time is written as ^nP_r or $_nP_r$.

$$^nP_r = \frac{n!}{(n-r)!}$$

ℹ️ *Find the number of permutations of the letters A, B, C taken two at a time.*

$$^3P_2 = \frac{3!}{(3-2)!} = 3 \times 2 = 6$$

If $r = n$, i.e. n items are taken n at a time,

$$^nP_n = \frac{n!}{0!} = n! \text{ since } 0! = 1.$$

ℹ️ *In how many ways can the letters of MATHS be arranged?*

$$^5P_5 = 5! = 120 \text{ ways}$$

Permutations with identical items

(a) **One set of identical items**
The number of permutations of n items taken n at a time, when p of the items are identical and the rest are all different, is

$$\frac{n!}{p!}$$

ℹ️ *In how many ways can the letters of MIME be arranged?*

There are 4 letters, so $n = 4$,
$\quad$ 2 Ms, so $p = 2$.

Number of permutations $= \dfrac{4!}{2!} = 4 \times 3 = 12$.

(b) **Two sets of identical items**
The number of permutations of n items taken n at a time,
when p items are identical and of one kind,
$\quad q$ items are identical and of a second kind,
the rest are all different, is

$$\frac{n!}{p!\,q!}$$

ℹ️ *Find the number of permutations of the letters of PARALLEL.*

There are 8 letters, so $n = 8$,
$\quad$ 2 As, so $p = 2$; 3 Ls, so $q = 3$.

Number of permutations $= \dfrac{8!}{2!\,3!} = 3360$.

(c) **Repeated items**
The number of permutations of n different items taken r at a time, when each item may be used repeatedly, is n^r.

ℹ️ *Find the number of three-letter codes.*

The number of permutations, with repetition, is $26^3 = 17576$.

Combinations

A **combination** is a selection of items when arrangement is not important. Different permutations of the same items count as one combination.

ℹ️ There is only one combination of the letters ABC.

The number of combinations of n different items taken r at a time is written as $\binom{n}{r}$ or ^nC_r.

$$\binom{n}{r} = {}^nC_r = \frac{n!}{r!\,(n-r)!}$$

Some useful results are:

$$\binom{n}{r} = {}^nC_r = \frac{n(n-1)(n-2)\ldots \leftarrow r \text{ factors starting at } n}{r(r-1)(r-2)\ldots \leftarrow r \text{ factors starting at } r}$$

$$^nC_r = {}^nC_{n-r}$$

The total number of selections from n items when each can be either included or excluded is $2^n - 1$, if at least one item is to be taken.

ℹ️ *A sub-committee of six, including a chairperson, is to be chosen from a main committee of twelve. If the chairperson is to be a specified member of the main committee, in how many ways can the sub-committee be chosen?*

As the specified member of the main committee has to be included, we require the number of combinations of 5 from 11, i.e.

$$\binom{11}{5} = \frac{11 \times 10 \times 9 \times 8 \times 7}{5 \times 4 \times 3 \times 2 \times 1} = 462.$$

Permutations and Combinations
Worked examples, Guided example and Exam questions.

 A committee of four is chosen from five teachers and three sixth-formers. In how many ways can this be done so that the committee contains:

(a) at least one teacher; (b) at least one teacher and one sixth-former?

(a) Tabulating the possibilities for the committee gives

No. of teachers	No. of ways	No. of sixth-formers	No. of ways
1	$^5C_1$	3	$^3C_3$
2	$^5C_2$	2	$^3C_2$
3	$^5C_3$	1	$^3C_1$
4	$^5C_4$	0	$^3C_0$

$\therefore$ No. of committees
$= {}^5C_1 \times {}^3C_3 + {}^5C_2 \times {}^3C_2 + {}^5C_3 \times {}^3C_1 + {}^5C_4 \times {}^3C_0$

$= 5 \times 1 + \dfrac{5 \times 4}{1 \times 2} \times 3 + \dfrac{5 \times 4}{1 \times 2} \times 3 + 5 \times 1$

$= 5 + 30 + 30 + 5 = 70$

(b) Tabulating the possibilities for the committee would give the first three rows of the table above.

$\therefore$ No. of committees $= 5 + 30 + 30 = 65$.

 How many different arrangements of letters can be made by using all the letters of the word MINIMUM? In how many of these are the vowels separated?

There are 7 letters, including 3 Ms and 2 Is.

$\therefore$ the number of possible arrangements $= \dfrac{7!}{3!2!} = 420$

Treat the three vowels I, I, U as one letter, then the number of arrangements with the vowels together is $3 \times \dfrac{5!}{3!} = 60$

The factor 3 is introduced to allow for the three possible arrangements of the vowels among themselves. Thus the number of arrangements with the vowels separated is $420 - 60 = 360$.

 A batch code on the side of a food container is composed of six dots, one blue, two white and three black. Find the number of different codes possible.
It is decided to use only five dots chosen from six where one is blue, two are white and three are black. Find the number of different codes possible in this case.

The number of codes possible is equal to the number of permutations of six objects of which two are alike and of one kind and three are alike and of another kind. In the second case, consider the possible selection of five dots, which is best presented in a tabular fashion.

Blue	White	Black
1	2	2
1	1	3
0	2	3

For each selection find the possible number of permutations of five objects, e.g. the first selection gives $\dfrac{5!}{2!2!}$

Hence the total number of codes that can be formed with five dots can be found.

EX **1** At an athletics meeting, eight lanes are marked on the running track. Find the number of ways in which the runners in a heat can be allocated to these lanes when there are:
(i) 8 competitors in a heat;
(ii) 5 competitors in a heat and no restriction on which lanes are used;
(iii) 10 competitors in a heat, so that two competitors have to share lane 3 and two have to share lane 8, but no account is taken of the way in which these lanes are shared;
(iv) two teams, each of four competitors, on the starting line, and members of the same team may not be in adjacent lanes.
(A)

2 A concert pianist has prepared seven different pieces of music for a recital, three of which are modern and four are classical. Calculate the number of different orders in which she can play the seven pieces when:
(a) there are no restrictions;
(b) the recital must start and end with classical pieces;
(c) classical and modern pieces must alternate throughout the recital.
(A)

3 Calculate the number of different 7-letter arrangements which can be made with the letters of the word MAXIMUM. In how many of these do the 4 consonants all appear next to one another?
(C)

4 Four visitors Dan, May, Nan and Tom arrive in a town which has five hotels. In how many ways can they disperse themselves among the five hotels
(a) if four hotels are used to accommodate them,
(b) if three hotels are used to accommodate them in such a way that May and Nan stay in the same hotel?
(L)

5 The result (home-win, score-draw, goalless-draw or away-win) is forecast for each of ten football matches. In how many different ways can the results of these ten matches be forecast to give exactly seven correct results?
(L)

6 From eight persons, including Mr and Mrs Smith, a committee of four persons is to be chosen. Mr Smith will not join the committee without his wife, but his wife will join the committee without her husband. In how many ways can the committee be formed?
(L)

7 Find the number of different permutations of the 8 letters of the word *SYLLABUS*. Find the number of different selections of 5 letters which can be made from the letters of the word *SYLLABUS*.
(L)

8 Five people, of whom three are women and two are men, are to form a queue. Find how many different arrangements there are (i) if no two people of the same sex are to stand next to each other, (ii) if the first and last people in the queue are both to be men.
(C)

9 [In this question, answers may be left in factorial form.] State the number of possible arrangements of the nine letters of the word *FACETIOUS*. Determine in how many of these arrangements: (i) the order in which the vowels occur is the same as in the original word; (ii) the vowels, in any order, are separated from each other by a consonant.
(C)

P30 Binomial Series
Power series, General binomial theorem, Applications, Approximations.

Power series

A **power series** is a series of the form:
$$a_0 + a_1 x + a_2 x^2 + a_3 x^3 + \ldots$$
where x is a variable and a_0, a_1, ... are constants. Its terms involve *regularly increasing powers* of a variable. These powers are positive integers.

The power series given by the general binomial theorem is called the **binomial series**.

ⓘ Examples of power series are:
$$1 + 2x + 3x^2 + 4x^3 + \ldots$$
$$1 - 3x^2 + 6x^4 - 10x^6 + \ldots$$
$$1 - \tfrac{1}{3}x^3 + \tfrac{1}{5}x^5 - \tfrac{1}{7}x^7 + \ldots$$
Exponential and logarithmic series are also power series (see P31).

General binomial theorem

The **general binomial theorem** gives the expansion of $(1+x)^n$ *for any rational value of n*, i.e.
$$(1+x)^n = 1 + nx + \frac{n(n-1)}{2!}x^2 + \frac{n(n-1)(n-2)}{3!}x^3 + \ldots$$

Note:
• The first term in the bionomial is 1.
• The general term is
$$\frac{n(n-1)(n-2)\ldots(n-r+1)}{r!}x^r.$$

• **If n is a positive integer**, the RHS is a **finite** binomial series (since $n(n-1)\ldots$ becomes zero when $r = n + 1$). Its last term is x^n. (See P19.) The expansion is valid for *all values of x*.

• **If n is not a positive integer**, the binomial series is **infinite** (since $n(n-1)\ldots$ will never become zero). The expansion is valid *only if* $-1 < x < 1$, i.e. $|x| < 1$. (It is not valid for $|x| \geq 1$.) The range of validity should always be stated.

ⓘ The expansion of $(1+x)^3$ is a finite series. It is valid for all values of x.
$$(1+x)^3 = 1 + 3x + \frac{3(2)}{2!}x^2 + \frac{3(2)(1)}{3!}x^3$$
$$= 1 + 3x + 3x^2 + x^3$$

ⓘ The expansions of $(1+x)^{-3}$ and $(1+x)^{\frac{1}{3}}$ are infinite series. Each is valid for $-1 < x < 1$.

$(1+x)^{-3}$
$$= 1 + (-3)x + \frac{(-3)(-4)}{2!}x^2 + \frac{(-3)(-4)(-5)}{3!}x^3 + \ldots$$
$$= 1 - 3x + 6x^2 - 10x^3 + \ldots$$

$(1+x)^{\frac{1}{3}}$
$$= 1 + (\tfrac{1}{3})x + \frac{(\tfrac{1}{3})(-\tfrac{2}{3})}{2!}x^2 + \frac{(\tfrac{1}{3})(-\tfrac{2}{3})(-\tfrac{5}{3})}{3!}x^3 + \ldots$$
$$= 1 + \tfrac{1}{3}x - \tfrac{1}{9}x^2 + \tfrac{5}{81}x^3 - \ldots$$

Applications

The binomial theorem is often used to give series for negative and fractional powers of expressions. Remember the other ways to write these powers:

reciprocal → *negative* power, e.g. $\dfrac{1}{a^n} = a^{-n}$

root → *fractional* power, e.g. $\sqrt[n]{a} = a^{\frac{1}{n}}$

The 'x' in the binomial theorem may be replaced by **another term or group of terms**. Write the given expression in the form $[1 + (x)]^n$ first. Then use the series for $(1+x)^n$ for the given value of n, replacing x by the chosen term or terms. *If n is not a positive integer*, find the range of values over which the expansion is valid, using:
$$-1 < (\text{replacement for } x) < 1$$

To expand $(a + x)^n$, if n is *not* a positive integer, it must be rewritten first:
$$(a+x)^n = a^n\left(1 + \frac{x}{a}\right)^n$$
The expansion is valid only for $-1 < \frac{x}{a} < 1$.

To **expand a compound function as a series**, it is usually easier to express it as the sum or product of *simpler* functions first. Partial fractions are often used to express rational functions as the sum of simpler functions (see P26 and P27). To find the range of validity for the combined expansion, work out the range of validity for each simpler expansion and find their 'overlap' (see worked example).

ⓘ Some useful expansions to know are:
$$(1+x)^{-1} = 1 - x + x^2 - x^3 + x^4 - \ldots$$
$$(1-x)^{-1} = 1 + x + x^2 + x^3 + x^4 + \ldots$$
$$(1+x)^{-2} = 1 - 2x + 3x^2 - 4x^3 + 5x^4 - \ldots$$
$$(1-x)^{-2} = 1 + 2x + 3x^2 + 4x^3 + 5x^4 + \ldots$$
These are valid for $-1 < x < 1$.

ⓘ *Find the first four terms of* $(1-2x)^{-\frac{3}{2}}$.
Treat $(1-2x)^{-\frac{3}{2}}$ as $[1 + (-2x)]^{-\frac{3}{2}}$.
Use the expansion of $(1+x)^{-\frac{3}{2}}$, replacing x by $(-2x)$.
$$(1-2x)^{-\frac{3}{2}} = 1 + (-\tfrac{3}{2})(-2x) + \frac{(-\tfrac{3}{2})(-\tfrac{5}{2})}{2!}(-2x)^2$$
$$+ \frac{(-\tfrac{3}{2})(-\tfrac{5}{2})(-\tfrac{7}{2})}{3!}(-2x)^3 + \ldots$$
$$= 1 + 3x + \tfrac{15}{2}x^2 + \tfrac{35}{2}x^3 + \ldots$$
This is valid for $-1 < -2x < 1$, i.e. $\tfrac{1}{2} > x > -\tfrac{1}{2}$.

ⓘ *Find the first three terms of* $(2 - x)^{-5}$
$$(2 - x)^{-5} = 2^{-5}(1 - \tfrac{1}{2}x)^{-5} = \tfrac{1}{32}[1 + (-\tfrac{1}{2}x)]^{-5}$$
$$= \tfrac{1}{32}\left[1 + (-5)(-\tfrac{1}{2}x) + \frac{(-5)(-6)}{2!}(-\tfrac{1}{2}x)^2 + \ldots\right]$$
$$= \tfrac{1}{32}[1 + \tfrac{5}{2}x + \tfrac{15}{4}x^2 + \ldots]$$
$$= \tfrac{1}{32} + \tfrac{5}{64}x + \tfrac{15}{128}x^2 + \ldots$$
This is valid for $-1 < -\tfrac{1}{2}x < 1$, i.e. $2 > x > -2$.

Approximations

The expansion of $(1+x)^n$ as a series may be used to find the **approximate values**, to any required degree of accuracy, of integral powers of numbers and roots of numbers. Always check that the series is valid for the numerical value used for the 'x term' in the expansion. Make sure that you take sufficient terms to give the accuracy required.

ⓘ *Evaluate $\sqrt{25.1}$ to four decimal places.*
$$\sqrt{25.1} = (25 + 0.1)^{\frac{1}{2}} = 5(1 + 0.004)^{\frac{1}{2}}$$
$$= 5\left[1 + (\tfrac{1}{2})(0.004) + \frac{(\tfrac{1}{2})(-\tfrac{1}{2})}{2!}(0.004)^2 + \ldots\right]$$
$$= 5(1 + 0.002 - 0.000002 + \ldots)$$
$$\approx 5(1.001998) = 5.00999$$
So $\sqrt{25.1} \approx 5.0100$ (to four decimal places)

Binomial Series
Worked examples and Exam questions.

 (a) *Find the first four terms in the expansion of* $\left(x^2 + \dfrac{1}{x^2}\right)^{-\frac{1}{2}}$ *in ascending powers of x.*

(b) *Find the value of* $\dfrac{1}{\sqrt{100.01}}$ *to 14 decimal places.*

(a) $\left(x^2 + \dfrac{1}{x^2}\right)^{-\frac{1}{2}} = \left(\dfrac{1}{x^2}(x^4 + 1)\right)^{-\frac{1}{2}}$

$= \left(\dfrac{1}{x^2}\right)^{-\frac{1}{2}}(1 + x^4)^{-\frac{1}{2}} = x(1 + x^4)^{-\frac{1}{2}}$

The first four terms of $x(1 + x^4)^{-\frac{1}{2}}$ are given by:

$x\left(1 + (-\tfrac{1}{2})(x^4) + \dfrac{(-\tfrac{1}{2})(-\tfrac{3}{2})(x^4)^2}{2 \times 1} + \dfrac{(-\tfrac{1}{2})(-\tfrac{3}{2})(-\tfrac{5}{2})(x^4)^3}{3 \times 2 \times 1}\right)$

$= x\left(1 - \tfrac{1}{2}x^4 + \tfrac{3}{8}x^8 - \tfrac{5}{16}x^{12}\right)$

$= x - \tfrac{1}{2}x^5 + \tfrac{3}{8}x^9 - \tfrac{5}{16}x^{13}$

(for $-1 < x^4 < 1 \Rightarrow 0 < x < 1$ since x^4 cannot be negative.

(b) $\dfrac{1}{\sqrt{100.01}} = (100.01)^{-\frac{1}{2}}$

To use the expansion in (a), the value of x must be in the range $0 < x < 1$.

$100.01 = 0.01 + 100 = 0.01 + \dfrac{1}{0.01} = 0.1^2 + \dfrac{1}{0.1^2}$

$\therefore (100.01)^{-\frac{1}{2}} = \left(0.1^2 + \dfrac{1}{0.1^2}\right)^{-\frac{1}{2}}$

Let $x = 0.1$ in the expansion in (a).

$(100.01)^{-\frac{1}{2}} \approx 0.1 - \dfrac{1}{2} \times 0.00001 + \dfrac{3}{8} \times 0.000\,000\,001$

$\qquad - \dfrac{5}{16} \times 0.000\,000\,000\,000\,1$

$\qquad = 0.099\,995\,000\,374\,968\,75$

$\qquad = 0.099\,995\,000\,374\,97$ (to 14 d.p.)

The next term in the expansion is too small to affect the result.

 (a) *Write down the expansion of* $(1 - x)^{-2}$ *and* $(1 + x)^{-2}$.

(b) *Use the above result to find the coefficient of* x^3 *in the expansion of* $(1 - x)^{-2}(1 + x)^{-2}$.

(c) *Use a shorter method to solve (b).*

(a) $(1 - x)^{-2} = 1 + 2x + 3x^2 + 4x^3 + \ldots$

$(1 + x)^{-2} = 1 - 2x + 3x^2 - 4x^3 + \ldots$

Both expansions are valid for $-1 < x < 1$.

(b) $(1 + 2x + 3x^2 + 4x^3 + \ldots)(1 - 2x + 3x^2 - 4x^3 + \ldots)$

Multiplying the terms given below gives the 'x^3 terms'.

'1st bracket'	$\times$	'2nd bracket'	$\rightarrow$	'result'
1	$\times$	$-4x^3$	$\rightarrow$	$-4x^3$
$+2x$	$\times$	$+3x^2$	$\rightarrow$	$+6x^3$
$+3x^2$	$\times$	$-2x$	$\rightarrow$	$-6x^3$
$+4x^3$	$\times$	1	$\rightarrow$	$+4x^3$

$\therefore$ the coefficient of x^3 is: $-4 + 6 - 6 + 4 = 0$.

(c) $(1 - x)^{-2}(1 + x)^{-2} = [(1 - x)(1 + x)]^{-2}$

$= (1 - x^2)^{-2}$

$= 1 + (-2)(-x^2) + (-2)(-3)(-x^2)^2 + \ldots$

$= 1 + 2x^2 + 3x^4 + \ldots$

There are no odd powers of x in this expression. So the coefficient of x^3 is 0.

 Expand $\dfrac{3x + 5}{(1 - x)(1 + 3x)}$ *as a series of ascending powers of x up to and including the term in* x^2.

Expressing the function in partial fractions gives:

$\dfrac{3x + 5}{(1 - x)(1 + 3x)} = \dfrac{2}{(1 - x)} + \dfrac{3}{(1 + 3x)}$

$\qquad = 2(1 - x)^{-1} + 3(1 + 3x)^{-1}$

$2(1 - x)^{-1} = 2(1 + x + x^2 + \ldots) = 2 + 2x + 2x^2 + \ldots$

$3(1 + 3x)^{-1} = 3(1 - 3x + 9x^2 + \ldots)$

$\qquad = 3 - 9x + 27x^2 + \ldots$

$2(1 - x)^{-1} + 3(1 + 3x)^{-1}$

$= (2 + 3) + (2x - 9x) + (2x^2 + 27x^2) + \ldots$

$= 5 - 7x + 29x^2 + \ldots$

$2(1 - x)^{-1}$ is valid for $-1 < -x < 1$, i.e. $1 > x > -1$.

$3(1 + 3x)^{-1}$ is valid for $-1 < 3x < 1$, i.e. $-\tfrac{1}{3} < x < \tfrac{1}{3}$.

$\therefore$ the combined expansion is valid for $-1 < 3x < 1$, i.e. $-\tfrac{1}{3} < x < \tfrac{1}{3}$

---

 1 (a) Find the first four terms in the expansion of $(1 - 4x)^{\frac{1}{2}}$ in ascending powers of x and state the range of validity of the expansion. Use the expansion to determine the value of $\sqrt{15.36}$, correct to 5 decimal places.

(b) The coefficient of x^2 in the expansion of $(1 + ax)^{\frac{1}{4}}$ is -6. Calculate the two possible values of a. *(S)*

2 Obtain the binomial expansion of $(1 + 2x)^{-3}$ in ascending powers of x as far as the term in x^3. *(L)*

3 Show that

$$\dfrac{1}{\left(1 - \dfrac{x}{3}\right)} + \dfrac{1}{\left(1 + \dfrac{x}{3}\right)} = \dfrac{18}{(9 - x^2)}.$$

Hence, or otherwise, express $\dfrac{18}{(9 - x^2)}$ as a series in ascending powers of x up to and including the term in x^4, assuming that the value of x is such as to make the expansions valid. *(A)*

4 Write down the first four terms of the binomial series expansion in ascending powers of x of the function $(1 - x)^{-\frac{1}{2}}$, and hence show that

$$\sqrt{10} = 3\left\{1 + \dfrac{1}{20} + \dfrac{1 \times 3}{20 \times 40} + \dfrac{1 \times 3 \times 5}{20 \times 40 \times 60} + \ldots\right\}.$$

(OLE)

5 Write down the expansion in ascending powers of x up to the term in x^2 of (i) $(1 + x)^{\frac{1}{2}}$, (ii) $(1 - x)^{-\frac{1}{2}}$, and simplify the coefficients. Hence, or otherwise, expand

$$\sqrt{\left(\dfrac{1 + x}{1 - x}\right)}$$

in ascending powers of x up to the term in x^2. By using $x = 1/10$ obtain an estimate, to three decimal places, for $\sqrt{11}$. *(J)*

6 (a) Expand $(1 - 2x)^{\frac{1}{2}}$ in ascending powers of x up to and including the term in x^4 and state the range for which this expansion is valid.

(b) Use this expansion to deduce the square root of 0.8 correct to *four* decimal places. *(N)*

P31 Exponential and Logarithmic Series

Exponential series, Logarithmic series.

Exponential series

e^x can be expressed as an **infinite series**.

$$e^x = 1 + \frac{x}{1!} + \frac{x^2}{2!} + \frac{x^3}{3!} + \ldots + \frac{x^n}{n!} + \ldots$$

The series is valid for all values of x.

The value of e can be calculated to a required degree of accuracy by substituting $x = 1$ in the series for e^x.

Other exponential functions such as e^{kx} and e^{x+k}, where k is a constant, can be expressed as infinite series.
To write e^{kx} as a series, replace x by kx in the expansion, so

$$e^{kx} = 1 + \frac{(kx)}{1!} + \frac{(kx)^2}{2!} + \frac{(kx)^3}{3!} + \ldots \frac{(kx)^n}{n!} + \ldots$$

To write e^{x+k} as a series, use $e^{x+k} = e^k . e^x$, so

$$e^{x+k} = e^k \left(1 + \frac{x}{1!} + \frac{x^2}{2!} + \frac{x^3}{3!} + \ldots + \frac{x^n}{n!} + \ldots \right)$$

These series are valid for all values of x too.

ℹ *Calculate e to six significant figures by using the series for e^x as far as the 10th term.*

$$e = e^1 = 1 + \frac{1}{1!} + \frac{1^2}{2!} + \frac{1^3}{3!} + \ldots + \frac{1^9}{9!}$$

Evaluating the terms using a calculator.
$e = 2.71828$ (to six significant figures)

ℹ *Expand e^{3x} and e^{x+2} as far as the terms in x^3.*

$$e^{3x} = 1 + \frac{(3x)}{1!} + \frac{(3x)^2}{2!} + \frac{(3x)^3}{3!} + \ldots$$

$$= 1 + 3x + \frac{9x^2}{2} + \frac{9x^3}{2} + \ldots$$

$$e^{x+2} = e^2 . e^x$$

$$= e^2 \left(1 + x + \frac{x^2}{2!} + \frac{x^3}{3!} + \ldots \right)$$

Logarithmic series

There is no simple series for **ln**x, but

$$\ln(1+x) = x - \frac{x^2}{2} + \frac{x^3}{3} - \frac{x^4}{4} + \ldots$$

This series converges provided $-1 < x \leqslant 1$.

To write $\ln(1+kx)$ as a series, replace x by kx in the expansion and find the new range of validity.

To express logarithms of products and quotients as series, rewrite them using the basic rules of logarithms first.

ℹ *Expand $\ln(1-x)$ as far as the third term and give the range over which it is valid.*

$$\ln(1-x) = \ln[1+(-x)] = (-x) - \frac{(-x)^2}{2} + \frac{(-x)^3}{3} - \ldots$$

$$= -x - \frac{x^2}{2} - \frac{x^3}{3} - \ldots$$

This series is valid for $-1 < (-x) \leqslant 1$
i.e. $-1 \leqslant x < 1$.

ℹ *Expand $\ln\{(1+x)/(1-x)\}$ as far as the third term and give the range over which it is stated.*

$\ln\{(1+x)/(1-x)\} = \ln(1+x) - \ln(1-x)$

$$= \left(x - \frac{x^2}{2} + \frac{x^3}{3} - \frac{x^4}{4} + \ldots \right) - \left(-x - \frac{x^2}{2} - \frac{x^3}{3} - \frac{x^4}{4} - \ldots \right)$$

$$= 2 \left(x + \frac{x^3}{3} + \frac{x^5}{5} + \ldots \right)$$

The two series are valid if $-1 < x \leqslant 1$ and $-1 \leqslant x < 1$. So for both to be valid $-1 < x < 1$.

Approximate values of logarithms can be calculated using logarithmic series.

The series for $\ln\left(\frac{1+x}{1-x}\right)$ is often used for these approximations because it converges rapidly.

ℹ *Find the value of $\ln 1.5$ to 4 decimal places.*

We use $\ln\left(\frac{1+x}{1-x}\right) = \ln 1.5$, i.e. $x = 0.2$.

So $\ln 1.5 = \ln\left(\frac{1+0.2}{1-0.2}\right)$

$$= 2\left[(0.2) + \frac{(0.2)^3}{3} + \frac{(0.2)^5}{5} + \ldots \right]$$

$$= 2(0.202\,731)$$

$$= 0.4055 \ (4 \text{ d.p.})$$

Exponential and Logarithmic Series
Worked examples, Guided example and Exam questions.

 (a) Expand e^{1-x^3} as a series of ascending powers of x as far as the term in x^9 and find the general term.

(b) Find the first four terms and the term in x^n in the expansion of $(1+x)e^x$.

(a) $e^{1-x^3} = e^1 \cdot e^{-x^3}$

$$= e\left[1 + (-x^3) + \frac{(-x^3)^2}{2!} + \frac{(-x^3)^3}{3!} + \ldots + \frac{(-x^3)^n}{n!} + \ldots\right]$$

$$= e\left[1 - x^3 + \frac{1}{2}x^6 - \frac{1}{6}x^9 + \ldots + \frac{(-1)^n}{n!}x^{3n} + \ldots\right]$$

Hence, $e^{1-x^3} = e(1 - x^3 + \frac{1}{2}x^6 - \frac{1}{6}x^9)$ as far as terms in x^9, and

the general term is $\dfrac{(-1)^n e}{n!}x^{3n}$.

(b) $(1+x)e^x = (1+x)\left(1 + \frac{x}{1!} + \frac{x^2}{2!} + \frac{x^3}{3!} + \ldots + \frac{x^n}{n!} + \ldots\right)$

$$= 1 + \frac{x}{1!} + \frac{x^2}{2!} + \frac{x^3}{3!} + \ldots + \frac{x^n}{n!} + \ldots$$
$$+ x + \frac{x^2}{1!} + \frac{x^3}{2!} + \frac{x^4}{3!} + \ldots + \frac{x^n}{(n-1)!} + \ldots$$

$$= 1 + \left(1 + \frac{1}{1!}\right)x + \left(\frac{1}{1!} + \frac{1}{2!}\right)x^2 + \left(\frac{1}{2!} + \frac{1}{3!}\right)x^3 +$$
$$\ldots + \left(\frac{1}{(n-1)!} + \frac{1}{n!}\right)x^n + \ldots$$

$$= 1 + \frac{2}{1!}x + \left(\frac{2}{2!} + \frac{1}{2!}\right)x^2 + \left(\frac{3}{3!} + \frac{1}{3!}\right)x^3 + \ldots$$
$$+ \left(\frac{n}{n!} + \frac{1}{n!}\right)x^n + \ldots$$

$$= 1 + \frac{2}{1!}x + \frac{3}{2!}x^2 + \frac{4}{3!}x^3 + \ldots + \frac{(n+1)}{n!}x^n + \ldots$$

 Express $\ln\sqrt{\dfrac{1+x}{1-x}}$ as a series of terms in ascending powers of x up to and including the term in x^5.

Use your series to obtain an approximate value for $\ln\left(\dfrac{\sqrt{11}}{3}\right)$ giving your answer correct to six decimal places.

$\ln\sqrt{\dfrac{1+x}{1-x}} = \ln(1+x)^{\frac{1}{2}} - \ln(1-x)^{\frac{1}{2}}$

$$= \frac{1}{2}[\ln(1+x) - \ln(1-x)]$$

$$= \frac{1}{2}\left[\left(x - \frac{x^2}{2} + \frac{x^3}{3} - \frac{x^4}{4} + \frac{x^5}{5}\right) - \right.$$
$$\left.\left(-x - \frac{x^2}{2} - \frac{x^3}{3} - \frac{x^4}{4} - \frac{x^5}{5}\right)\right]$$

$$= x + \frac{x^3}{3} + \frac{x^5}{5} + \ldots.$$

If $\sqrt{\dfrac{1+x}{1-x}} = \dfrac{\sqrt{11}}{3}$, then $x = \dfrac{1}{10}$.

Putting $x = \dfrac{1}{10}$ in the series obtained,

$\ln\left(\dfrac{\sqrt{11}}{3}\right) = \dfrac{1}{10} + \dfrac{\frac{1}{3}}{1000} + \dfrac{\frac{1}{5}}{100\,000}$

$$= 0.1 + 0.000\,333 + 0.000\,002$$

So $\ln\left(\dfrac{\sqrt{11}}{3}\right) = 0.100\,335$, correct to six decimal places.

GE *Expand $e^{-x}\ln(1+2x)$ in ascending powers of x as far as the term in x^4. Write down the range of values of x for which this series is valid.*

Expand e^{-x} as far as the term in x^3.

Expand $\ln(1+2x)$ as far as the term in x^4.

(Think why there is no need to expand e^{-x} as far as the term in x^4.)

Multiply the two series obtained together, discarding any terms which are of order x^5 or bigger.

Hence you have obtained the required series. Write down the ranges of validity for (i) e^{-x} and (ii) $\ln(1+2x)$.

Hence write down the range of values of x over which *both* series are valid.

EX 1 Expand $\dfrac{e^{2x}}{1+2x}$ as a series of ascending powers of x as far as the term in x^3 and give the set of values of x for which the expansion is valid.

(L)

2 Expand $\dfrac{e^x + e^{-x}}{2}$ as a series of ascending powers of x.

Deduce the general term in the expansion of $\dfrac{e^{\sqrt{x}} + e^{-\sqrt{x}}}{2}$.

(L)

3 (a) Write down the first 4 terms and the term in x^n in the expansion of e^x. Prove that the coefficient of x^n in the expansion of $(x^2 + x)e^x$ is

$$\frac{n}{(n-1)!} \text{ when } n \geq 2.$$

Deduce that $(x^2 + x)e^x - x$ is always positive when x is positive.

(b) Express $\dfrac{\sqrt{1-x}}{1+x}$ in ascending powers of x up to and

including the term in x^2. By substituting $x = \dfrac{1}{9}$, show that

$$\sqrt{2} \approx \frac{2755}{1944}.$$

(S)

4 Expand, in ascending powers of x as far as the term in x^3:
(a) $\log_e(1-2x)$; (b) $\log_e(1-3x)$.

Hence expand $\log_e\dfrac{(1-2x)^3}{(1-3x)^2}$ as far as the term in x^3 and find

the coefficient of x^n in this series. Write down the range of values of x for which this series is valid.

(A)

5 (a) Expand $e^{\frac{1}{2}x}\log_e(1+x)$ in ascending powers of x as far as the term in x^4 and hence show that, for certain values of x to be stated,

$$e^{\frac{1}{2}x}\log_e(1+x) + e^{-\frac{1}{2}x}\log_e(1-x) = ax^4 + \ldots$$

and give the value of a.

(b) Expand $(1+x)^{-\frac{1}{2}}$ in ascending powers of x, giving the first four terms and the general term. Hence, without using tables or calculator, obtain the value of $1/\sqrt{101}$, correct to 6 decimal places, showing all working.

(S)

6 Express $\log_e\left(\dfrac{1+2x}{1-2x}\right)$ as a series of terms in ascending

powers of x up to and including the term in x^5. Use your series to obtain an approximate value for $\log_e(5/3)$, giving your answer to 5 decimal places. (A)

Equations

The general equation of a **straight line** is

$$ax + by + c = 0$$

where a, b and c are constants.

The line with **gradient** m and **intercept** c on the y-axis has equation

$$y = mx + c.$$

Note: $y = mx$ passes through the origin $(0, 0)$.
  $y = c$ is parallel to the x-axis.
  $x = k$ (k is a constant) is parallel to the y-axis.

The line which cuts the x-axis at $(a, 0)$ and the y-axis at $(0, b)$ has equation

$$\frac{x}{a} + \frac{y}{b} = 1$$

The line of gradient m, through (x_1, y_1) has equation

$$y - y_1 = m(x - x_1)$$

The line through (x_1, y_1) and (x_2, y_2) has equation

$$\frac{y - y_1}{y_2 - y_1} = \frac{x - x_1}{x_2 - x_1}$$

If the perpendicular from the origin to the line is of length p and at an angle θ to the x-axis, then the equation of the line is

$$x\cos\theta + y\sin\theta = p$$

Note: $ax + by + c = 0$ and $x\cos\theta + y\sin\theta = p$ represent the same straight line if

$$\cos\theta = \pm\frac{a}{\sqrt{(a^2 + b^2)}}, \sin\theta = \pm\frac{b}{\sqrt{(a^2 + b^2)}},$$

$$p = \mp\frac{c}{\sqrt{(a^2 + b^2)}}$$

The signs are chosen so as to ensure p is positive.

Perpendicular distance

The **length of the perpendicular** from (x_1, y_1) to the straight line $ax + by + c = 0$ is

$$\pm\frac{ax_1 + by_1 + c}{\sqrt{(a^2 + b^2)}}$$

The perpendicular distance from the origin is taken as positive.

Points on the same side of a line give the same sign.
Points on opposite sides of a line give different signs.

$\boxed{i}$ *Show that $(-1, 2)$ and $(3, 4)$ are on opposite sides of the line $x + 2y = 6$.*

Perpendicular distance from $(-1, 2)$ to $x + 2y - 6 = 0$

$$= \frac{(-1) + 2(2) - 6}{\sqrt{(1^2 + 2^2)}} = \frac{-3}{\sqrt{5}}$$

Perpendicular distance from $(3, 4)$ to $x + 2y - 6 = 0$

$$= \frac{(3) + 2(4) - 6}{\sqrt{(1^2 + 2^2)}} = \frac{5}{\sqrt{5}}$$

Since these distances are oppositely signed they are on opposite sides of the line.

Pairs of lines

The **angle θ between two straight lines** with gradients m_1 and m_2 ($m_1 > m_2$) is given by

$$\tan\theta = \frac{m_1 - m_2}{1 + m_1 m_2}$$

The two lines are (a) parallel if $m_1 = m_2$,
          (b) perpendicular if $m_1 m_2 = -1$.

$\boxed{i}$ *Find the angle between the lines $y = \sqrt{3}x + 2$ and $\sqrt{3}y = x - 4$.*

$$y = \sqrt{3}x + 2 \Rightarrow m_1 = \sqrt{3}; \sqrt{3}y = x - 4 \Rightarrow m_2 = \frac{1}{\sqrt{3}}$$

$$\tan\theta = \frac{m_1 - m_2}{1 + m_1 m_2} = \frac{\sqrt{3} - \frac{1}{\sqrt{3}}}{1 + \sqrt{3} \times \frac{1}{\sqrt{3}}} = \frac{3 - 1}{\sqrt{3}(1 + 1)} = \frac{1}{\sqrt{3}}$$

$$\Rightarrow \theta = \tan^{-1}\frac{1}{\sqrt{3}} = 30°$$

The **equations of the bisectors** of the angles between the lines $a_1x + b_1y + c_1 = 0$ and $a_2x + b_2y + c_2 = 0$ are given by

$$\frac{a_1x + b_1y + c_1}{\sqrt{(a_1^2 + b_1^2)}} = \pm\frac{a_2x + b_2y + c_2}{\sqrt{(a_2^2 + b_2^2)}}$$

$\boxed{i}$ *Find the equations of the bisectors of the angles between $5x + 12y + 4 = 0$ and $3x - 4y + 1 = 0$.*

The equations are $\dfrac{5x + 12y + 4}{\sqrt{(5^2 + 12^2)}} = \pm\dfrac{3x - 4y + 1}{\sqrt{(3^2 + (-4)^2)}}$

$$\Rightarrow 5(5x + 12y + 4) = \pm 13(3x - 4y + 1)$$

giving $2x - 16y - 1 = 0$ and $64x + 8y + 33 = 0$.

The **equation of a line through the intersection of the lines** $a_1x + b_1y + c_1 = 0$ and $a_2x + b_2y + c_2 = 0$ is given by

$$(a_1x + b_1y + c_1) + \lambda(a_2x + b_2y + c_2) = 0$$

where λ is a constant.

λ is usually found from the given conditions.

$\boxed{i}$ *Find the equation of the line through the origin and concurrent with $2x - 5y - 3 = 0$ and $3x - 4y + 2 = 0$.*

Any line concurrent with the given lines has an equation of the form
$(2x - 5y - 3) + \lambda(3x - 4y + 2) = 0$

Since $(0, 0)$ lies on the required line

$$-3 + 2\lambda = 0 \Rightarrow \lambda = \frac{3}{2}$$

So the required line is $13x - 22y = 0$.

The Straight Line
Worked examples and Exam questions.

 A triangle has vertices at $A(-4, 10)$, $B(2, 2)$, $C(5, 8)$. Calculate the coordinates of D, the midpoint of AB. The line through D parallel to AC meets BC at E. Calculate the equation of the line DE and the coordinates of the point E.

D has coordinates $\left(\dfrac{-4+2}{2}, \dfrac{10+2}{2}\right) = (-1, 6)$

Gradient of $AC = \dfrac{10-8}{-4-5} = -\dfrac{2}{9}$

$\therefore$ equation of line through D parallel to AC is

$\dfrac{y-6}{x+1} = -\dfrac{2}{9}$

i.e. $9y - 54 = -2x - 2$
$2x + 9y = 52$ [1]

Equation of BC is

$\dfrac{y-2}{x-2} = \dfrac{8-2}{5-2} = 2$

i.e. $y - 2 = 2x - 4$
$2x - y = 2$ [2]

The coordinates of E are found by solving [1] and [2]
$[1]-[2]$ $10y = 50$ $y = 5$
$y = 5$ in [2], $x = 3.5$
$\therefore$ coordinates of E are $(3.5, 5)$.

 The points $A(-4, 6)$ and $C(-1, 1)$ are opposite vertices of a parallelogram $ABCD$. The sides BC, CD of the parallelogram lie along the lines

$$x + 3y - 2 = 0 \text{ and } x - y + 2 = 0$$

respectively. Calculate:

(i) the coordinates of D;
(ii) the tangent of the acute angle between the diagonals of the parallelogram;
(iii) the length of the perpendicular from A to the side CD;
(iv) the area of the parallelogram.

Gradient of BC and AD is $-\frac{1}{3}$.
Gradient of AB and CD is 1.
Equation of AD is

$\dfrac{y-6}{x+4} = -\dfrac{1}{3}$

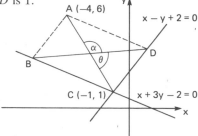

i.e. $3y - 18 = -x - 4$
$x + 3y = 14$ [1]
Similarly, equation of AB is $x - y = -10$ [2]
Given equation of BC is $x + 3y = 2$ [3]
and equation of CD is $x - y = -2$ [4]
(i) $[1]-[4]$ $4y = 16$, $y = 4$
$y = 4$ in [4] gives $x = 2$
$\therefore$ coordinates of D are $(2, 4)$.
(ii) $[3]-[2]$ $4y = 12$, $y = 3$
$y = 3$ in [2] gives $x = -7$
$\therefore$ coordinates of B are $(-7, 3)$.

$m_1 = $ gradient $AC = \dfrac{6-1}{-4+1} = \dfrac{5}{-3} = -\dfrac{5}{3}$

$m_2 = $ gradient $BD = \dfrac{4-3}{2+7} = \dfrac{1}{9}$

$\tan \alpha = \dfrac{m_1 - m_2}{1 + m_1 m_2} = \dfrac{-\dfrac{5}{3} - \dfrac{1}{9}}{1 + \left(-\dfrac{5}{3}\right)\left(\dfrac{1}{9}\right)} = -\dfrac{16}{9} \times \dfrac{27}{22} = -\dfrac{24}{11}$

Hence $\tan \theta = \dfrac{24}{11}$.

(iii) Let p be the length of the perpendicular from A to DC then

$p = \dfrac{(x_1 - y_1 + 2)}{\sqrt{1^2 + (-1)^2}}$ where $(x_1, y_1) = (-4, 6)$

$= \dfrac{(-4 - 6 + 2)}{\sqrt{2}} = 4\sqrt{2}$ units

(iv) Length of $CD = \sqrt{(2+1)^2 + (4-1)^2}$
$= \sqrt{9+9} = 3\sqrt{2}$ units
$\therefore$ Area of parallelogram $= p \times CD = 4\sqrt{2} \times 3\sqrt{2} = 24$ units^2

---

 1 Three points have coordinates $A(1, 7)$ $B(7, 5)$, and $C(0, -2)$. Find: (i) the equation of the perpendicular bisector of AB, (ii) the point of intersection of this perpendicular bisector and BC.

          (C)

2 The midpoint of the line joining the points $A(7,3)$ and $B(-1,-5)$ is C. Find both values of k if the straight line joining C to the point $P(k^2, k)$ is perpendicular to AB.

          (A)

3 The perpendicular bisector of the line joining the points $(1, 2)$ and $(5, 4)$ meets the y-axis at the point $(0, k)$. Calculate k.

          (S)

4 P and Q are the points of intersection of the line

$$\dfrac{x}{a} + \dfrac{y}{b} = 1, \ (a > 0, \ b > 0),$$

with the x and y axes respectively. The distance PQ is 10 and the gradient of PQ is -2. Find the value of a and b.

          (C)

5 Find the equation of the perpendicular bisector of the line joining the points $A(0, 8)$ and $B(4, 2)$.

          (S)

6 The triangle OAB has vertices $O(0, 0)$, $A(25, 0)$ and $B(18, 24)$. Prove that $AO = AB$ and find the equation of the internal bisector of the angle OAB. Given that the internal bisector of the angle AOB is $x - 2y = 0$, deduce the equation of the circle which touches the sides of the triangle OAB and has its centre inside this triangle. State the coordinates of the point of contact of the circle with the side OB.

          (O & C)

7 The equations of the sides of a triangle ABC are:
AB $x - 2y + 11 = 0$, BC $y = 7$, AC $2x - y + 7 = 0$. Without using tables or calculator, find: (i) the tangent of the angle BAC; (ii) the area of the triangle ABC.

          (A)

The Circle

Equations, tangents, Intersecting circles.

Equations

The **general equation of a circle** is of the form
$$x^2+y^2+2gx+2fy+c=0$$
It is a second degree equation in which
(a) the coefficients of x^2 and y^2 are unity,
(b) there is no xy term.
This circle has centre $(-g, -f)$
and radius $\sqrt{(g^2+f^2-c)}$.

The circle, centre (a, b), radius r, has equation
$$(x-a)^2+(y-b)^2=r^2,$$
If (a, b) is the origin, the circle equation is
$$x^2+y^2=r^2$$

The **equation of the circle on AB as diameter** where A is (x_1, y_1) and B is (x_2, y_2) is given by
$$(x-x_1)(x-x_2)+(y-y_1)(y-y_2)=0$$

To find the **equation of a circle through three points**
(a) Substitute the coordinates of each point in turn in the general equation of the circle.
(b) Solve the three simultaneous equations to find the values of g, f and c.
(c) Substitute g, f and c in the general equation.

ⓘ *Find the coordinates of the centre and the radius of the circle given by $3x^2+3y^2+6x+12y+9=0$.*

The circle equation can be rewritten as
$$x^2+y^2+2x+4y+3=0$$
Comparing this with the general equation of a circle
$$x^2+y^2+2gx+2fy+c=0$$
gives $g=1$, $f=2$, $c=3$.
So, the centre of the circle is $(-1, -2)$,
its radius is $\sqrt{(1^2+2^2-3)}=\sqrt{2}$.

ⓘ The equation of the circle with $(0, 0)$ and $(2, 2)$ as end points of a diameter is given by
$$(x-0)(x-2)+(y-0)(y-2)=0$$
i.e. $x^2+y^2-2x-2y=0$

ⓘ *Find the equation of the circle which circumscribes the triangle with vertices $(1, 0)$, $(2, 1)$ and $(0, 2)$.*

Let the equation be $x^2+y^2+2gx+2fy+c=0$.
Substituting the coordinates in turn gives
$$1+2g+c=0;$$
$$5+4g+2f+c=0;$$
$$4+4f+c=0$$
Solving these equations gives $g=-\frac{5}{6}$, $f=-\frac{7}{6}$, $c=\frac{2}{3}$.
Hence the equation of the circle is
$$3x^2+3y^2-5x-7y+2=0.$$

Tangents

The **equation of the tangent** at (x_1, y_1) to the circle
$$x^2+y^2+2gx+2fy+c=0$$
is $xx_1+yy_1+g(x+x_1)+f(y+y_1)+c=0$
Note the relation between these equations:
$x^2 \rightarrow xx_1$, $y^2 \rightarrow yy_1$, $2x \rightarrow (x+x_1)$, $2y \rightarrow (y+y_1)$.

To find the **condition that** $y=mx+c$ **be a tangent** to $x^2+y^2+2gx+2fy+c=0$, see **WE**

The **length of the tangent** from (x_1, y_1) to the circle $x^2+y^2+2gx+2fy+c=0$ is
$$\sqrt{(x_1^2+y_1^2+2gx_1+2fy_1+c)}.$$

ⓘ *Find the equation of the tangent at $(1, -2)$ to the circle $2x^2+2y^2-3x+4y+1=0$.*

Rewrite the circle equation as
$$x^2+y^2-\tfrac{3}{2}x+2y+\tfrac{1}{2}=0$$
So the tangent equation is
$$(1)x+(-2)y-\tfrac{3}{4}(x+1)+(y-2)+\tfrac{1}{2}=0$$
i.e. $x-4y-9=0$.

ⓘ *Find the length of the tangent from $(-5, 8)$ to the circle $x^2+y^2-4x-6y+3=0$.*

The length of the tangent is
$$\sqrt{[(-5)^2+8^2-4(-5)-6(8)+3]}=\sqrt{64}=8$$

Intersecting circles

The equation of any circle through the intersections of the circles
$$x^2+y^2+2g_1x+2f_1y+c_1=0$$
and $$x^2+y^2+2g_2x+2f_2y+c_2=0$$
is given by an equation of the form
$$(x^2+y^2+2g_1x+2f_1y+c_1)+$$
$$\lambda(x^2+y^2+2g_2x+2f_2y+c_2)=0$$
where λ is a constant.

λ is usually found from the given conditions.

If $\lambda=-1$, the equation reduces to a straight line. This is the **common chord** of the two circles and is known as the **radical axis** of the circles.

ⓘ *Find the equation of the circle which passes through the point $(-3, 1)$ and the points of intersection of $x^2+y^2-y-5=0$ and $x^2+y^2+2x+5y-1=0$.*

A circle through the intersection of the given circles has equation of the form
$$(x^2+y^2-y-5)+\lambda(x^2+y^2+2x+5y-1)=0.$$

Since $(-3, 1)$ must lie on this circle
$$[(-3)^2+1^2-1-5]+\lambda[(-3)^2+1^2+2(-3)+5(1)-1]=0$$
$$\Rightarrow \lambda=-\tfrac{1}{2}$$

So the required equation is
$$(x^2+y^2-y-5)-\tfrac{1}{2}(x^2+y^2+2x+5y-1)=0$$
i.e. $x^2+y^2-2x-7y-9=0$

The Circle

Worked example, Guided example and Exam questions.

WE *Find the values of c such that the line $x + y = c$ shall be a tangent to the circle $x^2 + y^2 - 4x + 2 = 0$. For each value of c find the co-ordinates of the point of contact. Draw a sketch of the circle and the two tangents.*

To find the points of intersection of $x + y = c$ and $x^2 + y^2 - 4x + 2 = 0$ put $y = c - x$ in the circle equation.
$$x^2 + (c - x)^2 - 4x + 2 = 0,$$
i.e. $2x^2 - x(2c + 4) + (2 + c^2) = 0$ [1]

If $x + y = c$ is a tangent to the circle then this quadratic will have equal roots,

i.e. $\triangle = b^2 - 4ac = 0$

i.e. $(2c + 4)^2 - 4 \times 2(2 + c^2) = 0$

$\quad 4c^2 + 16c + 16 - 16 - 8c^2 = 0$

$\quad\quad -4c^2 + 16c = 0, \quad \therefore c = 0$ or 4

The equations of the tangents are $x + y = 0$ and
$$x + y = 4$$

$c = 0$ in [1] gives $x = 1$, when $x + y = 0$ gives $y = -1$

$c = 4$ in [1] gives $x = 3$, when $x + y = 4$ gives $y = 1$

$\therefore$ the coordinates of the points of contact are $(1, -1)$ and $(3, 1)$.

The diagram below is a sketch of the circle and the two tangents.

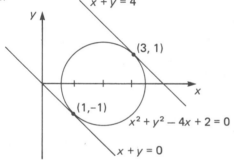

GE *Find the centre and radius of each of the circles C_1 and C_2 whose equations are $x^2 + y^2 - 16y + 32 = 0$, $x^2 + y^2 - 18x + 2y + 32 = 0$ respectively and show that the circles touch externally. Find the coordinates of their point of contact and show that the common tangent at that point passes through the origin. The other tangents from the origin, one to each circle, are drawn. Find, correct to the nearest degree, the angle between these tangents.*

Find the centre and radius of C_1.
Find the centre and radius of C_2.
Find the distance between the centres and show that it is equal to the sum of the radii, thus showing that the circles touch externally.
Eliminate x^2 and y^2 from the equations of C_1 and C_2 to obtain $x = y$ which is substituted into C_1 giving a quadratic in x (or y) which has equal roots, thus the coordinates of the point of contact can be found. A sketch at this stage is useful.

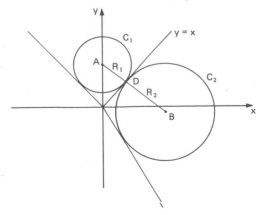

Note: The section formula could also be used to find the coordinates of D, the point of contact, which is the point dividing AB in the ratio $R_1 : R_2$.

Let $y = mx$ be the line through the origin tangential to C_1. Applying the tangency condition gives $m = \pm 1$.
So the required tangent is $y = -x$.
Similarly let $y = Mx$ be the required tangent to C_2.

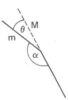

Apply the tangency condition to find the value of M. The angle between the tangents will be calculated as θ, hence the required angle α is easily found.

EX

1 Obtain the equation of the circle which passes through the origin and has its centre at the point $(3, -4)$. The line $y = x - 6$ meets this circle at the points P and Q. Find the coordinates of P and Q. Calculate the distance PQ.
     (A)

2 Find the distance between the centres of the circles $x^2 + y^2 + 6y + 8 = 0$ and $x^2 + y^2 - 12x - 10y - 60 = 0$ and prove that these circles touch one another. Obtain the equation of the smallest circle that passes through the centres of the given circles.
     (S)

3 Prove that the circles $x^2 + y^2 + 2x + 2y = 23$ and $x^2 + y^2 - 10x - 7y + 31 = 0$ touch each other externally, and calculate the coordinates of the point of contact. (A graphical solution will not be acceptable.)
     (O & C)

4 [In this question the use of tables, a calculator or accurate drawing is forbidden.]
The triangle ABC has vertices $A(0, 12)$, $B(-9, 0)$, $C(16, 0)$. Find the equations of the internal bisectors of the angles ABC and ACB. Hence, or otherwise, find the equation of the inscribed circle of the triangle ABC. Find also the equation of the circle passing through A, B and C.
     (C)

5 Find the equation of the circle which touches the line $y = x$ at the point $(4, 4)$ and whose centre lies on the line which passes through the point $(-1, -3)$ and the origin. Deduce the equation of the circle which touches the line $y = x$ at the point $(4, 4)$ and whose centre is on the line $3y = x$. Find the equations of the three tangents common to the two circles.
     (O & C)

6 The points A and B have coordinates $(8, 0)$ and $(0, 6)$ respectively and O is the origin. Find the equation of:
(i) the circumcircle; (ii) the inscribed circle of the triangle AOB.
     (A)

P34 Experimental Laws

Introduction, Linear relations, Non-linear relations.

Introduction   It is often necessary to find a relationship between two connected quantities. A table of experimental data, showing corresponding values of the two quantities, and a suggestion as to the form of the expected relationship are given. The data are usually displayed graphically and, if the expected relationship is confirmed, the graph is used to obtain the unknown constants in this relationship.

Linear relations

The simplest case is when the expected relation is a straight line of the form $y = mx + c$.

In this case simply plot y against x. If the points plotted lie approximately on a straight line then the given linear relation is approximately true.

The points rarely lie exactly on a straight line, so the line of 'best fit' is drawn 'by eye'. Consequently there is usually a small range of values in which acceptable answers will lie.

The values of m and c can be found from the graph by

either (a) finding the gradient (m) of the line and its intercept (c) on the y-axis,

or (b) substituting the coordinates of two points on the line in $y = mx + c$ and solving the resulting simultaneous equations.

Note: Do not use given values to find m and c since they may not give points on the line of 'best fit'.

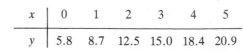 *The following data are believed to satisfy a law of the form $y = ax + b$. Find suitable values of a and b.*

x	0	1	2	3	4	5
y	5.8	8.7	12.5	15.0	18.4	20.9

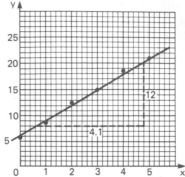

Figure 1

From the graph;

The gradient of the line gives

$$a = \frac{12}{4.1} = 2.9$$

'y-intercept' gives
$b = 6.2$

So,
$$y = 2.9x + 6.2$$

Non-linear relations

If the expected relation is not in the form $y = mx + c$, then it must be transformed to a linear form before proceeding as before. The transformations for some common relationships are given below.

Relationships of the form $y = ax^n + b$ (n known)
Compare $y = ax^n + b$
with $Y = mX + c$
Plot $Y = y$ against $X = x^n$ to give a straight line.
Gradient gives a, 'Y-intercept' gives b.

Relationships of the form $\dfrac{1}{y} + \dfrac{1}{x} = \dfrac{1}{a}$
Rewrite as $\dfrac{1}{y} = -\dfrac{1}{x} + \dfrac{1}{a}$.

Compare with $Y = mX + c$.

Plot $Y = \dfrac{1}{y}$ against $X = \dfrac{1}{x}$ to give a straight line.

Gradient is -1, 'Y-intercept' gives $\dfrac{1}{a}$.

Relationships of the form $y = ax^n$ (n unknown)

Rewrite $y = ax^n$
as $\log y = n \log x + \log a$.

Compare with $Y = mX + c$
Plot $Y = \log y$ against $X = \log x$ to give a straight line.
Gradient gives n, 'Y-intercept' gives $\log a$.

Relationships of the form $y = ab^x$
Rewrite $y = ab^x$
as $\log y = x \log b + \log a$
Compare with $Y = mX + c$
Plot $Y = \log y$ against $X = x$ to give a straight line.
Gradient gives $\log b$, 'Y-intercept' gives $\log a$.

The data of the following table are thought to obey a law of the form $y = ax^2 + b$. Find suitable values for a and b.

x	0	1	2	3
y	−5	3	24	67

Compare $y = ax^2 + b$
with $Y = mX + c$

Constructing a table for $X = x^2$ and $Y = y$ gives

$X(=x^2)$	0	1	4	9
$Y(=y)$	−5	3	24	67

The straight line represents $Y = aX + b$.
Gradient gives a, 'Y-intercept' gives b.

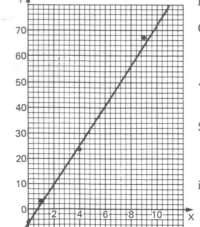

Figure 2

From the graph:

Gradient gives

$$a = \frac{70}{9}$$

'Y-intercept' gives
$b = -6$

So,
$$Y = \frac{70}{9}X - 6$$

i.e.
$$y = \frac{70}{9}x^2 - 6$$

Experimental Laws
Worked example and Exam questions.

The following corresponding values of x and y are believed to be related by the equation $y = x + ax^b$.

x	2	3	4	5	6	10
y	7.54	9.33	11.00	12.59	14.12	19.90

Draw a suitable graph to show that this may be so, and use your graph to find the probable values of a and b.

Write $y = x + ax^b$ as $y - x = ax^b$.

Taking logarithms gives $\log_{10}(y - x) = \log_{10} a + b \log_{10} x$

Let $\log_{10}(y - x) = Y$ and $\log_{10} x = X$

i.e. $Y = \log_{10} a + bX$

i.e. a straight line with slope b and y-intercept $\log_{10} a$

x	2	3	4	5	6	10
y	7.54	9.33	11.00	12.59	14.12	19.90
$y - x$	5.54	6.33	7.00	7.59	8.12	9.90
$Y = \log_{10}(y - x)$	0.74	0.80	0.85	0.88	0.91	1.00
$X = \log_{10} x$	0.30	0.48	0.60	0.70	0.78	1.00

The graph is drawn as shown.

From the graph $b = \dfrac{1.1 - 0.6}{1} = 0.50$

$\log_{10} a = 0.6$, $a = 3.98$

$\therefore y = x + 3.98x^{0.50}$

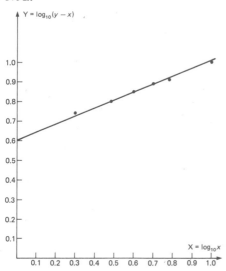

1 It is believed that two variables x and y are related by $y = ka^x$, where k and a are constants. For the following values, plot $\log_{10} y$ against x and hence estimate k and a.

x	0.5	1	2	4
y	0.28	0.45	1.13	7.03

(S)

2 The points (0.5, 0.265), (1.6, 1.352), (2.1, 1.978) and (3.4, 3.883) very nearly satisfy the relation $y = ax^n$, where a and n are constants. Draw a graph of $\log y$ against $\log x$, and use the points where the graph cuts the axes to determine the values of a and n. Use these values to calculate the value of y when $x = 1 \cdot 8$.

(OLE)

3 It is believed that two variables x and y are related by $y = ax^b$, where a and b are constants. For the following

values, plot $\log_{10} y$ against $\log_{10} x$ and hence estimate a and b.

x	0.6	1.2	1.8	2.4	3.0
y	0.35	1.04	1.95	3.06	4.33

(S)

4 The variables x and y satisfy an equation of the form $y = ax^k$, where a and k are constants. Express $\log_{10} y$ in terms of $\log_{10} x$.

In an experiment values of y corresponding to values of x are as given in the table below:

x	1.6	2.0	2.8	3.9	5.0
y	5.1	7.1	11.7	19.2	28.0

By drawing a straight-line graph estimate to one decimal place the values of a and k. Use your graph to estimate:
(a) the value of x when $y = 10$;
(b) the value of y when $x = \sqrt{10}$.   *(A)*

5 Measured values of x and y are given in the following table:

x	1	2	3	4	5	6	7
y	5.1	4.6	4.2	3.8	3.2	2.4	1.4

It is known that x and y are related by the equation $y^2 = a + bx$. Explain how a straight line graph may be drawn to represent the given equation and draw it for the values given. Use the graph to estimate the value of a and b. Estimate the greatest possible value of x.   *(C)*

6 Given that the values of x and y in the table below are experimental values of variables that satisfy $y = ax + b$, estimate graphically the constants a and b.

x	2	4	7	8	10
y	1.8	1.2	0.5	0.3	-0.2

(L)

7 Rewrite the following equations in suitable form to display a linear relationship in each case between two of the variables, x, $\ln x$, y and $\ln y$.

(a) $\dfrac{2}{x} + \dfrac{3}{y} = \dfrac{4}{xy}$,   (b) $5x = 6^y$.   *(L)*

8 A relation of the form $y = ae^x + b$ is known to exist between two variables x and y. By plotting y against e^x, use the following table of experimental values of x and y to estimate the constants a and b to 1 significant figure.

x	1	2	3	4
y	24	56.7	145.6	387.2

(L)

9

v	5	10	15	20	25
R	149	175	219	280	359

The table shows corresponding values of variables R and v obtained in an experiment. By drawing a suitable linear graph, show that these pairs of values may be regarded as approximations to values satisfying a relation of the form $R = a + bv^2$, where a and b are constants. Use your graph to estimate the values of a and b, giving your answers to 2 significant figures.   *(L)*

10 In each of the following cases, given experimental values of x and y, explain how straight line graphs may be drawn, using ordinary graph paper only:
(i) $y = ab^{x+1}$;
(ii) $px^2 + qy = x$, where a, b, p, q are constants.
In each case express the gradient of the line and its ordinate for $x = 0$ in terms of the constants.   *(A)*

Unknown curves

Sketching a graph of an **unknown curve** $y=f(x)$ is like building up an identikit picture. In general, the important features can be built up by answering the following questions (as appropriate) and systematically adding the findings to a pair of axes.

(a) What is the **domain** of the function?
If $f(x)$ is a polynomial, then the domain is the set of real numbers.
If $f(x)$ is a rational function, say $P(x)/Q(x)$, then the values of x for which $Q(x)=0$ will give discontinuities, i.e. the curve will have asymptotes at these values of x.

(b) Does the curve cut the **y-axis**?
If possible, let $x=0$ and find the corresponding value of y.

(c) Does the curve cut the **x-axis**?
Let $y=0$ and, if possible, find the corresponding value(s) of x.

(d) Does the curve have **symmetry**?
If $f(x)=f(-x)$, then $x=0$ is an axis of symmetry.
If $f(-x)=-f(x)$, then the part of the graph for which $x<0$ is a half-turn about the origin of the part of the graph for which $x>0$.

(e) How does the curve behave as $x\to\pm\infty$?
If $f(x)$ is a rational function, say $P(x)/Q(x)$, then divide $P(x)$ and $Q(x)$ by the highest power of x in $P(x)$ to find how $f(x)$ behaves as $x\to\pm\infty$.

(f) How does the curve behave near any **asymptotes**?
If x_1 is a discontinuity, then look at the curve as:
(i) $x\to x_1^-$, i.e. values of x just less than x_1,
(ii) $x\to x_1^+$, i.e. values of x just greater than x_1.

(g) Has the curve any **special points** (maximum, minimum or inflexion)? (See Special Points, p. 44.)

(h) Are there any **regions** of the xy-plane where the curve does not exist?
If $f(x)$ is a rational function, then rewrite $y=f(x)$ as a quadratic in x. For real x, the quadratic's discriminant $\geqslant 0$ (see Quadratics, p. 8). This gives the regions of the plane where the curve does exist.

$\boxed{\text{i}}$ *Sketch the graph of* $y=\dfrac{2x-1}{(x-2)^2}$.

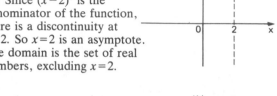

(a) Since $(x-2)^2$ is the denominator of the function, there is a discontinuity at $x=2$. So $x=2$ is an asymptote. The domain is the set of real numbers, excluding $x=2$.

(b) When $x=0$, $y=-\frac{1}{4}$. Plot $(0, -\frac{1}{4})$.

(c) When $y=0$, $x=\frac{1}{2}$. Plot $(\frac{1}{2}, 0)$

(d) No symmetry since
$$f(x)\neq f(-x)$$
and $f(-x)\neq -f(x)$.

(e) $y=\dfrac{2x-1}{(x-2)^2}=\dfrac{2x-1}{x^2-4x+4}$

Dividing numerator and denominator by x (the highest power of x in the numerator) gives

$$y=\frac{2-\frac{1}{x}}{x-4+\frac{4}{x}}$$

As $x\to\infty$, $y\to 0^+$.
As $x\to -\infty$, $y\to 0^-$.

(f) There is a discontinuity at $x=2$.
As $x\to 2^-$, $y\to +\infty$.
As $x\to 2^+$, $y\to +\infty$.

(g) $y'=\dfrac{-2(x+1)}{(x-2)^3}$

When $y'=0$, $x=-1$, i.e. $(-1, -\frac{1}{3})$ is a stationary point.

$$y''=\frac{2(2x+5)}{(x-2)^4}$$

When $x=-1$, $y''>0$, i.e. a local minimum.

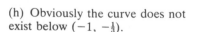

(h) Obviously the curve does not exist below $(-1, -\frac{1}{3})$.

Sketching Unknown Curves
Worked example, Guided example and Exam questions.

 Sketch the curve $y = \dfrac{3(x-2)}{x(x+6)}$.

(a) Since $x(x+6)$ is the denominator of the function, there are discontinuities at $x=0$ and $x=-6$.
So, $x=0$ and $x=-6$ are asymptotes.
The domain of the function is the set of real numbers excluding $x=0$ and $x=-6$.
(b) Since $x=0$ is a discontinuity, the curve does not cut the y-axis.
(c) When $y=0$, $x=2$. Plot $(2, 0)$.
(d) No symmetry.
(e) $y = \dfrac{3x-6}{x^2+6x} = \dfrac{3-\dfrac{6}{x}}{x+6}$

As $x \to +\infty$, $y \to 0^+$
As $x \to -\infty$, $y \to 0^-$.
(f) Discontinuity at $x=0$.
As $x \to 0^-$, $y \to +\infty$.
As $x \to 0^+$, $y \to +\infty$.
Discontinuity at $x=-6$.
As $x \to -6^-$, $y \to -\infty$.
As $x \to -6^+$, $y \to -\infty$.
(g) $y' = \dfrac{-3(x^2-4x-12)}{x^2(x+6)^2} = \dfrac{-3(x+2)(x-6)}{x^2(x+6)^2}$,

So, $y'=0$ when $x=-2$ or 6.
As we pass through $x=-2$, y' goes $-$ve, 0, $+$ve, so $x=-2$ is a point of local minimum.
As we pass through $x=6$, y' goes $+$ve, 0, $-$ve, so $x=6$ is a point of local maximum.

(h) Rewrite $y = \dfrac{3(x-2)}{x(x+6)}$ as $yx^2 + 3(2y-1)x + 6 = 0$.

For real x, $9(2y-1)^2 \geqslant 4.y.6$.
i.e. $12y^2 - 20y + 3 \geqslant 0$.
$\Rightarrow y \leqslant \dfrac{1}{6}$ or $y \geqslant \dfrac{3}{2}$.

So, for $\dfrac{1}{6} < y < \dfrac{3}{2}$, the curve does not exist.

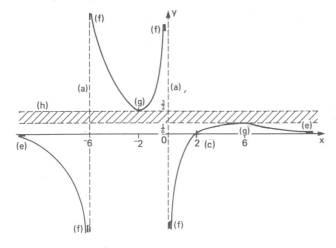

 Sketch the curve $y^2 = x(x-3)^2$.

First sketch the graph of $f(x) = x(x-3)^2$.
Since $y = \pm\sqrt{(f(x))} = \pm(x-3)\sqrt{x}$, notice,
(a) $y^2 = x(x-3)^2$ is symmetrical about the x-axis,
(b) for $x<0$, y is non-real, i.e. graph does not exist,
(c) $(0, 0)$ and $(3, 0)$ lie on the graph,
(d) for $0 < f(x) < 1$, $|y| > f(x)$, since $\sqrt{(|f(x)|)} > f(x)$,
(e) for $f(x) > 1$, $|y| < f(x)$.
Hence sketch the curve $y^2 = x(x-3)^2$.

[EX] 1 Sketch the curve $y = \dfrac{2}{x+1}$.
(S)

2 Given that $f(x) = x - 1 + \dfrac{1}{x+1}$, x real, $x \neq -1$, find the values of x for which $f'(x) = 0$. Sketch the graph of f, showing the co-ordinates of the turning points and indicating clearly the form of the graph when $|x|$ becomes large. *(J)*

3 Sketch, on separate diagrams, the graphs of:
(i) $y = x^3(1-x)$; (ii) $y = (x+1)/(x+2)^2$.
(O & C)

4. Given that $y = \dfrac{x^2+1}{x^2+x+1}$,
(i) state the limiting value of y: (a) as x tends to ∞; (b) as x tends to $-\infty$,
(ii) show that y is finite for all real values of x,
(iii) determine the set of values which y must take for real values of x,
(iv) determine the values of x for which y has a stationary value. Sketch the curve which represents the given equation. *(A)*

5 Sketch (on separate diagrams) the graphs of:
(a) $y = x^2 - x^3$; (b) $y = 1 - e^x$; (c) $y = 1/(1-e^x)$.
You are only asked for rough sketches; details of maxima and minima are not required but you should indicate the behaviour of the curves for numerically large and small values of x. *(O & C)*

6 Find the turning points on the curve $y = e^x \sin x$ for $0 \leqslant x \leqslant 2\pi$. Sketch the curve over this interval. *(A)*

7 The function f is defined by $f(x) = \dfrac{4x+5}{x^2-1}$. Show that $f(x)$ cannot take values between -4 and -1. Sketch the graph of the function showing clearly the behaviour of f as $x \to \pm 1$ and as $x \to \pm\infty$. *(W)*

8 If $y = 2x^4 - x^2 + 1$, find $\dfrac{dy}{dx}$ and deduce the three values of x for which $\dfrac{dy}{dx} = 0$. Find the corresponding values of y.
Distinguish between maximum and minimum values of y **either** by considering the signs of $\dfrac{dy}{dx}$ or by considering $\dfrac{d^2y}{dx^2}$. Hence sketch the curve for values of x from -1 to $+1$. *(O & C)*

9 (Throughout this question, $-\frac{1}{2}\pi \leqslant \sin^{-1} x \leqslant \frac{1}{2}\pi$.)
(i) Prove that, for $-1 < x < 1$, $\dfrac{d}{dx}(\sin^{-1} x) = (1-x^2)^{-\frac{1}{2}}$.
(ii) Given that $y = \dfrac{(1-x^2)^{\frac{1}{2}}}{x}$, $(-1 < x < 1, x \neq 0)$, prove that $\dfrac{dy}{dx}$ is always negative, and sketch the graph of y.
(iii) Given that $z = (1-x^2)^{\frac{1}{2}} \sin^{-1} x$, $(-1 < x < 1)$, find $\dfrac{dz}{dx}$.
Using your sketch in (ii), or otherwise, determine how many turning points there are on the graph of z.
(iv) Sketch the graph of z. (No co-ordinates of turning points are required.)
(C)

P36 More Trigonometry

General solutions of trig equations, Using more identities, Linear combinations of cos and sin.

General solutions of trig equations

The general solution of a trig equation describes all the angles that satisfy the equation. Since trig functions are periodic, there may be an infinite number of angles in a general solution. So general solutions are usually given as expressions in terms of n, where n is an integer.

General solutions for angles in radians

$\sin\theta = a \Rightarrow \theta = n\pi + (-1)^n\alpha$ where $\sin\alpha = a$

$\cos\theta = a \Rightarrow \theta = 2n\pi \pm \alpha$ where $\cos\alpha = a$

$\tan\theta = a \Rightarrow \theta = n\pi + \alpha$ where $\tan\alpha = a$

(To give these results in degrees, use $\pi = 180°$.)

To find α (one solution of the equation), use a calculator or known exact trig ratios.

When the equation is in terms of a multiple angle, such as $k\theta$, or a compound angle, such as $(\theta + \beta)$, find the general solution for $k\theta$ or $(\theta + \beta)$ first. Then work out the values of θ from this.

$\boxed{i}$ Some solutions to $\sin\theta = \alpha$ are marked on this diagram. To obtain them from the general solution, $\theta = n\pi \pm (-1)^n\alpha$, put $n = -1, 0, 1, 2, 3$.

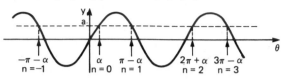

$\boxed{i}$ *Find the general solution of* (a) $\cos\theta = 0.8$ *in degrees* (b) $\tan(\theta + \pi) = 1$ *in radians.*

(a) One solution of $\cos\theta = 0.8$ is $36.9°$ (to 1 d.p.). General solution: $\theta = (360n \pm 36.9)°$ degrees (to 1 d.p.)

(b) One solution of $\tan(\theta + \pi) = 1$ is $45° = \frac{1}{4}\pi$.

General solution: $(\theta + \pi) = n\pi + \frac{1}{4}\pi$

$\Rightarrow \theta = n\pi - \frac{3}{4}\pi$

Using more identities

In Unit P16, trig identities are used to simplify expressions, solve equations, etc. At this stage, the identities given opposite on page 73 may also be used.

The **factor formulae** change sums or differences of two terms into products, i.e. they factorise these expressions. This is often useful when solving equations involving two or more terms. The pair of terms chosen to be factorised by the formula must give:

'an expression that will factorise' = 0.

The **half-angle formulae ('little-t' formulae)** give the trig ratios of one angle in terms of the tangent of half that angle. So different ratios in an expression can all be given in terms of one ratio. The t-notation is a useful shorthand. Choose t to match the angle in the trig ratios.

For $\sin A$, $\cos A$, $\tan A$, use $t = \tan\frac{1}{2}A$.

For $\sin 2A$, $\cos 2A$, $\tan 2A$, use $t = \tan\frac{1}{2}(2A) = \tan A$.

And so on (see Worked example).

$\boxed{i}$ *Find, in radians, the general solution of*
$\sin\theta - \sin 3\theta + \sin 5\theta = 0$.

$\sin\theta - \sin 3\theta + \sin 5\theta = 0$

$\Rightarrow (\sin\theta + \sin 5\theta) - \sin 3\theta = 0$ (rearranging terms)

$\Rightarrow 2\sin 3\theta\cos 2\theta - \sin 3\theta = 0$ (by factor formula)

$\Rightarrow \sin 3\theta(2\cos 2\theta - 1) = 0$

$\Rightarrow \sin 3\theta = 0$ or $(2\cos 2\theta - 1) = 0$

$\Rightarrow \sin 3\theta = 0$ or $\cos 2\theta = \frac{1}{2}$.

One solution of $\sin 3\theta = 0$ is 0.

$\therefore \sin 3\theta = 0 \Rightarrow 3\theta = n\pi + (-1)^n 0 \Rightarrow \theta = \frac{1}{3}n\pi$

One solution of $\cos 2\theta = \frac{1}{2}$ is $60° = \frac{1}{3}\pi$.

$\therefore \cos 2\theta = \frac{1}{2} \Rightarrow 2\theta = 2n\pi \pm \frac{1}{3}\pi \Rightarrow \theta = n\pi \pm \frac{1}{6}\pi$

Linear combinations of cos and sin

$a\cos\theta + b\sin\theta$, where a and b are constants, is called a **linear combination of cos and sin.** It can be **expressed as a single term** in the form:

$R\sin(\theta \pm \alpha)$ or $R\cos(\theta \pm \alpha)$

where $R > 0$ and α is an acute angle.

R and α depend on a and b. To find their values, use a compound angle formula to expand the chosen single term first. Then compare coefficients of $\cos\theta$ and $\sin\theta$ in the two equivalent expressions to obtain $a = \ldots$ and $b = \ldots$ Squaring these equations and adding gives R^2 and hence R. Dividing them gives $\tan\alpha$ and hence α.

The **graph and features of** $y = a\cos\theta + b\sin\theta$ can be found from $y = R\sin(\theta \pm \alpha)$ or $y = R\cos(\theta \pm \alpha)$.

These are known transformations of $y = \sin\theta$ and $y = \cos\theta$ respectively (see P12). Each is a stretch (by factor R, parallel to the y-axis) combined with a translation (distance α along the θ-axis, with $+\alpha$ to the left and $-\alpha$ to the right) (see Worked example).

Solving equations of the form $a\cos\theta + b\sin\theta = c$

Note: for real roots $c \le \sqrt{a^2 + b^2}$.
Method 1: express LHS as a single trig function first. Then solve the simple trig equation obtained.
Method 2: use $t = \tan\frac{1}{2}\theta$. Substitute 'little-$t$' formulae for $\cos\theta$ and $\sin\theta$. Solve the quadratic in t. Hence find θ. (See Guided example.)

$\boxed{i}$ (a) *Express* $12\cos\theta + 5\sin\theta$ *as* $R\cos(\theta - \alpha)$, *where* $R > 0$ *and* α *is an acute angle in degrees.*

(b) *Hence solve* $12\cos\theta + 5\sin\theta = 3$ *for* θ *in degrees.*

(a) Let $12\cos\theta + 5\sin\theta = R\cos(\theta - \alpha)$

$\Rightarrow 12\underline{\cos\theta} + 5\underline{\underline{\sin\theta}} = R\underline{\cos\theta}\cos\alpha + R\underline{\underline{\sin\theta}}\sin\alpha$

Comparing coefficients of $\underline{\cos\theta}$ and $\underline{\underline{\sin\theta}}$ gives:

$12 = R\cos\alpha$ [1] and $5 = R\sin\alpha$ [2]

Squaring [1] and [2] and adding gives:

$12^2 + 5^2 = R^2(\cos^2\alpha + \sin^2\alpha) \Rightarrow R^2 = 169 \Rightarrow R = 13$

Dividing [2] by [1] gives:

$\frac{5}{12} = \frac{R\sin\alpha}{R\cos\alpha} \Rightarrow \tan\alpha = \frac{5}{12} \Rightarrow \alpha = 22.6°$ (to 1 d.p.)

$\therefore 12\cos\theta + 5\sin\theta = 13\cos(\theta - 22.6)$.

(b) $12\cos\theta + 5\sin\theta = 3 \Rightarrow 13\cos(\theta - 22.6) = 3$

$\Rightarrow \cos(\theta - 22.6) = \frac{3}{13}$

One solution is $76.7°$ (to 1 d.p.).

General solution: $(\theta - 22.6) = 360n \pm 76.7$ degrees

$\theta - 22.6 = 360n + 76.7$

$\Rightarrow \theta = 360n + 99.3$ degrees

$\theta - 22.6 = 360n - 76.7$

$\Rightarrow \theta = 360n - 54.1$ degrees

More Trigonometry
More trig identities.
Worked examples, Guided example and Exam questions.

More trig identities

Other standard identities are given on page 33.

Triple angle formulae

$$\sin 3A = 3\sin A - 4\sin^3 A$$
$$\cos 3A = 4\cos^3 A - 3\cos A$$
$$\tan 3A = \frac{3\tan A - \tan^3 A}{1 - 3\tan^2 A}$$

Half-angle formulae
(also given as 'little-t' formulae,
$t = \tan\tfrac{1}{2}A$)

$$\sin A = \frac{2\tan\tfrac{1}{2}A}{1 + \tan^2\tfrac{1}{2}A} \quad \text{or} \quad \sin A = \frac{2t}{1 + t^2}$$
$$\cos A = \frac{1 - \tan^2\tfrac{1}{2}A}{1 + \tan^2\tfrac{1}{2}A} \quad \text{or} \quad \cos A = \frac{1 - t^2}{1 + t^2}$$
$$\tan A = \frac{2\tan\tfrac{1}{2}A}{1 - \tan^2\tfrac{1}{2}A} \quad \text{or} \quad \tan A = \frac{2t}{1 - t^2}$$

Factor formulae

$$\sin A + \sin B = 2\sin\tfrac{1}{2}(A + B)\cos\tfrac{1}{2}(A - B)$$
$$\sin A - \sin B = 2\cos\tfrac{1}{2}(A + B)\sin\tfrac{1}{2}(A - B)$$
$$\cos A + \cos B = 2\cos\tfrac{1}{2}(A + B)\cos\tfrac{1}{2}(A - B)$$
$$\cos A - \cos B = 2\sin\tfrac{1}{2}(A + B)\sin\tfrac{1}{2}(B - A)$$
$$\tan A + \tan B = \frac{\sin(A + B)}{\cos A \cos B}$$
$$\tan A - \tan B = \frac{\sin(A - B)}{\cos A \cos B}$$

 If $\tan A = \tfrac{5}{12}$, find, without a calculator, the possible values of
(a) $\tan\tfrac{1}{2}A$ (b) $\cos 2A$.

(a) Let $t = \tan\tfrac{1}{2}A$

$$\tan A = \frac{2t}{1 - t^2} \Rightarrow \frac{5}{12} = \frac{2t}{1 - t^2}$$
$$\Rightarrow 5(1 - t^2) = 12(2t)$$
$$\Rightarrow 0 = 5t^2 + 24t - 5$$
$$\Rightarrow 0 = (5t - 1)(t + 5)$$
$$\Rightarrow t = \tfrac{1}{5} \text{ or } t = -5$$

Therefore $\tan\tfrac{1}{2}A = \tfrac{1}{5}$ or $\tan\tfrac{1}{2}A = -5$.

(b) Let $t = \tan\tfrac{1}{2}(2A)$, i.e. $t = \tan A = \tfrac{5}{12}$.

$$\cos 2A = \frac{1 - t^2}{1 + t^2} = \frac{1 - (\tfrac{5}{12})^2}{1 + (\tfrac{5}{12})^2} = \frac{12^2 - 5^2}{12^2 + 5^2} = \frac{119}{169}$$

 Describe the main features of the graph of
$$f(\theta) = 12\cos\theta + 5\sin\theta$$

From $\boxed{\text{i}}$ opposite, $f(\theta) = 13\cos(\theta - 22.6)$. Its graph is a cosine wave, amplitude 13 and phase shift 22.6°.

$\cos\theta$ cuts the θ-axis where $\theta = (360n \pm 90)°$.

So $f(\theta)$ cuts the θ-axis where $(\theta - 22.6) = (360n \pm 90)°$
$$\Rightarrow \theta = (360n \pm 90)° + 22.6°$$

Max. and min. values of $f(\theta)$ are ± 13.

Max. values of $\cos\theta$ occur at $\theta = \pm 360n°$

So max. values of $f(\theta)$ occur at $(\theta - 22.6) = \pm 360n°$
$$\Rightarrow \theta = (22.6 \pm 360n)°.$$

Min. values of $\cos\theta$ occur at $\theta = (180 \pm 360n)°$.

So min. values of $f(\theta)$ occur at $(\theta - 22.6) = (180 \pm 360n)°$
$$\Rightarrow \theta = (202.6 \pm 360n)°$$

 (a) *Show that $\dfrac{1 - \sin\theta}{1 + \sin\theta} = \tan^2(\tfrac{1}{4}\pi - \tfrac{1}{2}\theta)$.*
Hence, or otherwise, show that $\tan 22\tfrac{1}{2}° = \sqrt{2} - 1$.

(b) *Solve $2\cos\theta - \sin\theta = 1$ for $-90° \le \theta \le 90°$.*

(a) LHS: deal with numerator and denominator separately at first. Use $t = \tan\tfrac{1}{2}\theta$. Substitute 'little-$t$' formulae for $\sin\theta$ and simplify each expression by using a common denominator $(1 + t^2)$. Simplify 'numerator $\div$ denominator' to $\dfrac{(1 - t)^2}{(1 + t)^2}$.

RHS: expand $\tan(\tfrac{1}{4}\pi - \tfrac{1}{2}\theta)$ using compound angle formulae.

Substitute $\tan\tfrac{1}{4}\pi = 1$. Simplify expression to $\dfrac{1 - t}{1 + t}$. Square this to obtain $\tan^2(\tfrac{1}{4}\pi - \tfrac{1}{2}\theta)$.

LHS = RHS, i.e. the required result.

Write $22\tfrac{1}{2}°$ in radians in the form $(\tfrac{1}{4}\pi - \tfrac{1}{2}\theta)$:
$$22\tfrac{1}{2}° = \tfrac{1}{8}\pi = \tfrac{1}{4}\pi - \tfrac{1}{8}\pi = \tfrac{1}{4}\pi - \tfrac{1}{2}(\tfrac{1}{4}\pi)$$
Put $\theta = \tfrac{1}{4}\pi$ in result (a) to obtain $\tan^2 22\tfrac{1}{2}°$. Substitute $\sin\tfrac{1}{4}\pi = \dfrac{1}{\sqrt{2}}$. Simplify in surd form. Take the square root and rearrange to give $\sqrt{2} - 1$.

(b) Use $t = \tan\tfrac{1}{2}\theta$. Substitute 'little-$t$' formulae for $\cos\theta$ and $\sin\theta$ in the equation. Simplify to $3t^2 + 2t - 1 = 0$. Factorise quadratic. Solve for t. Substitute each value of t in $\tan\tfrac{1}{2}\theta = t$. Find values of $\tfrac{1}{2}\theta$ such that $-45° \le \tfrac{1}{2}\theta \le 45°$. Hence find θ such that $-90° \le \tfrac{1}{2}\theta \le 90°$.

---

 1 (a) Prove the identity $\tan A + \cot A \equiv 2\operatorname{cosec} 2A$.
(b) It is given that $\tan B = \tfrac{4}{3}$ and that B is acute. Without using tables or a calculator, find the value of (i) $\cos 2B$,

(ii) $\tan\dfrac{B}{2}$.   *(C)*

2 By expressing $\sin\theta$ and $\cos\theta$ in terms of t, where $t = \tan(\theta/2)$, in the equation $5\sin\theta + 2\cos\theta = 5$, form a quadratic equation in t and solve this equation to find θ, correct to the nearest $0.1°$, in the range $40° < \theta < 50°$.

(*L*)

3 (a) (i) Show that $\tan 3\theta = \dfrac{3\tan\theta - \tan^3\theta}{1 - 3\tan^2\theta}$.

(ii) If $\theta = \tan^{-1}(\tfrac{1}{2})$ and $\alpha = \tan^{-1}(\tfrac{9}{13})$ show, without using a calculator, that $\tan(3\theta - \alpha) = 1$.
(b) (i) Express $4\sin\theta - 3\cos\theta$ in the form $R\sin(\theta - \alpha)$, where R is positive and a is an acute angle.
(ii) Hence, or otherwise, find the greatest and least values of the expression: $\dfrac{1}{10 - 3\cos\theta + 4\sin\theta}$.   (*N*)

4 Find the general solution, in radians, of the equation
$$3 - \cos 2x = 7\cos x.$$ (*O*)

5 Find the positive constant R and the acute angle A for which $\cos x + \sin x \equiv R\cos(x - A)$.
(a) Find the general solution, in radians, of the equation
$$\cos x + \sin x = 1.$$
(b) Deduce the greatest value of $\cos x + \sin x$.   (*L*)

6 (i) Find the value of the acute angle a for which
$$5\cos x - 3\sin x = \sqrt{34}\cos(x + \alpha)\text{ for all } x.$$

Giving your answers correct to one decimal place,
(ii) solve the equation
$$5\cos x - 3\sin x = 4 \text{ for } 0° \le x \le 360°$$
(iii) solve the equation
$$5\cos 2x - 3\sin 2x = 4 \text{ for } 0° \le x \le 360°.$$ (*O & C*)

P37 Vectors

Representation, Definitions, Addition and subtraction, Multiplication by a scalar, Position vectors, Ratio theorem.

Representation

A **vector** has **magnitude** and **direction**.
In print a vector is denoted by bold type e.g. **a,** or by two capital letters and an arrow, e.g. $\vec{AB}$.

In **2-dimensions**, the vector **a** can be represented by

$$\mathbf{a} = \begin{pmatrix} x \\ y \end{pmatrix} \text{ or } \mathbf{a} = (x\mathbf{i} + y\mathbf{j})$$

where $\mathbf{i} = \begin{pmatrix} 1 \\ 0 \end{pmatrix}$ and $\mathbf{j} = \begin{pmatrix} 0 \\ 1 \end{pmatrix}$ are called base vectors.

In **3-dimensions**, $\mathbf{a} = \begin{pmatrix} x \\ y \\ z \end{pmatrix}$ or $\mathbf{a} = (x\mathbf{i} + y\mathbf{j} + z\mathbf{k})$

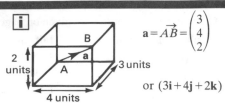

$$\mathbf{a} = \vec{AB} = \begin{pmatrix} 3 \\ 4 \\ 2 \end{pmatrix}$$

or $(3\mathbf{i} + 4\mathbf{j} + 2\mathbf{k})$

Base vectors in 3-dimensions:

$$\mathbf{i} = \begin{pmatrix} 1 \\ 0 \\ 0 \end{pmatrix}, \mathbf{j} = \begin{pmatrix} 0 \\ 1 \\ 0 \end{pmatrix}, \mathbf{k} = \begin{pmatrix} 0 \\ 0 \\ 1 \end{pmatrix}$$

Definitions

The **magnitude** of **a**, $|\mathbf{a}|$, is $\sqrt{(x^2 + y^2)}$ in 2-d and $\sqrt{(x^2 + y^2 + z^2)}$ in 3-d.
A **unit vector** has magnitude 1. $\hat{\mathbf{a}}$ is the unit vector in the direction of **a**.
The **zero vector, 0,** is any vector with zero magnitude.

The inverse of **a** is $-\mathbf{a}$

Two vectors $x\mathbf{i} + y\mathbf{j} + z\mathbf{k}$ and $a\mathbf{i} + b\mathbf{j} + c\mathbf{k}$ are **equal**, if and only if $x = a$, $y = b$ and $z = c$.

ⓘ *If* $\mathbf{a} = 5\mathbf{i} - s\mathbf{j} - 2\mathbf{k}$ *and* $\mathbf{b} = t\mathbf{i} + 2\mathbf{j} - u\mathbf{k}$ *are equal vectors, find (a)* s, t *and* u, (b) $|\mathbf{a}|$.

(a) Since $\mathbf{a} = \mathbf{b}$, then $5 = t$, $-s = 2$ and $-2 = -u$
$\Rightarrow t = 5$, $s = -2$ and $u = 2$

(b) $\mathbf{a} = 5\mathbf{i} + 2\mathbf{j} - 2\mathbf{k}$

$|\mathbf{a}| = \sqrt{[5^2 + 2^2 + (-2)^2]} = \sqrt{33}$

Addition and subtraction

The **triangle law** is used to add and subtract vectors.
Addition:
$\mathbf{a} + \mathbf{b} = \mathbf{c}$
Addition is commutative,
i.e. $\mathbf{a} + \mathbf{b} = \mathbf{b} + \mathbf{a}$
and associative,
i.e. $(\mathbf{a} + \mathbf{b}) + \mathbf{c} = \mathbf{a} + (\mathbf{b} + \mathbf{c})$

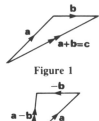

Figure 1

Subtraction:
$\mathbf{a} - \mathbf{b} = \mathbf{a} + (-\mathbf{b})$

Figure 2

ⓘ *Given* $\mathbf{a} = \begin{pmatrix} 2 \\ -1 \\ 3 \end{pmatrix}$ *and* $\mathbf{b} = \begin{pmatrix} -1 \\ 5 \\ -3 \end{pmatrix}$, *find*

(a) $\mathbf{a} + \mathbf{b}$ (b) $\mathbf{a} - \mathbf{b}$.

(a) $\mathbf{a} + \mathbf{b} = \begin{pmatrix} 2 \\ -1 \\ 3 \end{pmatrix} + \begin{pmatrix} -1 \\ 5 \\ -3 \end{pmatrix} = \begin{pmatrix} 1 \\ 4 \\ 0 \end{pmatrix}$

(b) $\mathbf{a} - \mathbf{b} = \begin{pmatrix} 2 \\ -1 \\ 3 \end{pmatrix} - \begin{pmatrix} -1 \\ 5 \\ -3 \end{pmatrix} = \begin{pmatrix} 3 \\ -6 \\ 6 \end{pmatrix}$

Multiplication by a scalar

A **scalar** is a real number, it has only magnitude.
If k is a scalar, then $k\mathbf{a}$ is a vector parallel to **a** but with k times the magnitude.
If $k > 0$, then $k\mathbf{a}$ is in the same direction as **a**.
If $k < 0$, then $k\mathbf{a}$ is in the opposite direction to **a**.

Multiplication by a scalar is distributive over vector addition, i.e. $k(\mathbf{a} + \mathbf{b}) = k\mathbf{a} + k\mathbf{b}$.

ⓘ *Solve the vector equation* $s\begin{pmatrix} -2 \\ 1 \end{pmatrix} + t\begin{pmatrix} 1 \\ 1 \end{pmatrix} = \begin{pmatrix} -5 \\ 1 \end{pmatrix}$.

$$s\begin{pmatrix} -2 \\ 1 \end{pmatrix} + t\begin{pmatrix} 1 \\ 1 \end{pmatrix} = \begin{pmatrix} -5 \\ 1 \end{pmatrix}$$

$\Rightarrow \left.\begin{array}{r} -2s + t = -5 \\ s + t = 1 \end{array}\right\} \Rightarrow s = 2, \ t = -1.$

Position vectors

The **position of a point** $P(x, y)$ in the plane can be given by the vector

$$\vec{OP} = \mathbf{r} = \begin{pmatrix} x \\ y \end{pmatrix} \text{ or } (x\mathbf{i} + y\mathbf{j}).$$

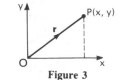

Figure 3

In 3-dimensions, $\mathbf{r} = \begin{pmatrix} x \\ y \\ z \end{pmatrix}$ or $(x\mathbf{i} + y\mathbf{j} + z\mathbf{k})$.

ⓘ The 3-dimensional position vector $\vec{OQ}$ can be written as

$$\vec{OQ} = \mathbf{q} = \begin{pmatrix} 2 \\ 5 \\ 3 \end{pmatrix}$$

or $(2\mathbf{i} + 5\mathbf{j} + 3\mathbf{k})$.

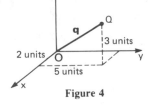

Figure 4

Ratio theorem

If C divides AB **internally** in the ratio $\lambda : \mu$, then

$$\mathbf{c} = \frac{\lambda\mathbf{b} + \mu\mathbf{a}}{\lambda + \mu}.$$

If the division is **external,**

then $\mathbf{c} = \frac{\lambda\mathbf{b} - \mu\mathbf{a}}{\lambda - \mu}$.

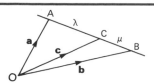

Figure 5

ⓘ *If* $\mathbf{a} = (2\mathbf{i} + 3\mathbf{j})$ *and* $\mathbf{b} = (8\mathbf{i} + 9\mathbf{j})$ *are the position vectors of A and B, find the position vector,* **c***, of C which divides AB internally in the ratio 1:2.*

$$\mathbf{c} = \frac{1(8\mathbf{i} + 9\mathbf{j}) + 2(2\mathbf{i} + 3\mathbf{j})}{1 + 2} = \frac{12\mathbf{i} + 15\mathbf{j}}{3} = 4\mathbf{i} + 5\mathbf{j}.$$

Vectors
Worked example, Guided example and Exam questions.

WE *In the diagram, $ST = 2TQ$, $\overrightarrow{PQ} = a$, $\overrightarrow{SR} = 2a$ and $\overrightarrow{SP} = b$.*
(a) Find in terms of a and b:

   (i) $\overrightarrow{SQ}$

   (ii) $\overrightarrow{TQ}$

   (iii) $\overrightarrow{RQ}$

   (iv) $\overrightarrow{PT}$

   (v) $\overrightarrow{TR}$

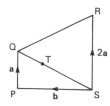

(b) What do your answers to (iv) and (v) tell you about the the points P, T, R?

(a) (i) $\overrightarrow{SQ} = \overrightarrow{SP} + \overrightarrow{PQ} = b + a$ (or $a + b$ by commutativity)

   (ii) $\overrightarrow{TQ} = \frac{1}{3}\overrightarrow{SQ} = \frac{1}{3}(a + b)$

   (iii) $\overrightarrow{RQ} = \overrightarrow{RS} + \overrightarrow{SQ} = -2a + (a + b)$
$$= b - a$$

   (iv) $\overrightarrow{PT} = \overrightarrow{PS} + \overrightarrow{ST}$

$$= -b + \frac{2}{3}\overrightarrow{SQ} \text{ (since } \overrightarrow{ST} = \frac{2}{3}\overrightarrow{SQ}, \text{ i.e. } \overrightarrow{ST} = 2\overrightarrow{TQ})$$

$$= -b + \frac{2}{3}(a + b) = \frac{2}{3}a - \frac{1}{3}b$$

$$= \frac{1}{3}(2a - b)$$

   (v) $\overrightarrow{TR} = \overrightarrow{TS} + \overrightarrow{SR}$

$$= -\frac{2}{3}(a + b) + 2a$$

$$= \frac{4}{3}a - \frac{2}{3}b = \frac{2}{3}(2a - b).$$

(b) Since $\overrightarrow{PT} = \frac{1}{3}(2a - b)$ and $\overrightarrow{TR} = \frac{2}{3}(2a - b)$, $\overrightarrow{PT}$ and $\overrightarrow{TR}$ are both multiples of the same vector $(2a - b)$. Hence PT and TR are parallel and T is common to both lines, so, P, T, R lie on the same line, i.e. they are collinear.

GE *(a) $\overrightarrow{OS}$ and $\overrightarrow{OT}$ represent the vectors $\lambda i + \mu j$ and $\mu i + \lambda j$ where λ and μ are scalars and i and j are unit vectors in two mutually perpendicular directions Ox and Oy. Show that $|\overrightarrow{OS}| = |\overrightarrow{OT}|$. Given that OS and OT are two adjacent sides of a rhombus $OSUT$, find the vectors represented by the diagonals OU and ST.*

(b) $\overrightarrow{PQ}$ and $\overrightarrow{PR}$ are represented by the sides PQ and PR of the triangle PQR, Show that
$$\overrightarrow{PQ} + \overrightarrow{PR} = 2\overrightarrow{PS}$$
where S is the midpoint of QR.
Hence, or otherwise, find the position of the point O within the triangle PQR such that
$$\overrightarrow{OP} + \overrightarrow{OQ} + \overrightarrow{OR} = 0$$

(a) Use the definition of the magnitude of a vector to show that $OS = OT$.

Sketch the rhombus $OSUT$. Use, $\overrightarrow{OU} = \overrightarrow{OS} + \overrightarrow{SU}$ and $\overrightarrow{ST} = \overrightarrow{SO} + \overrightarrow{OT}$ to find the required vectors.

(b) Use the ratio theorem to express $\overrightarrow{PS}$ in terms of $\overrightarrow{PQ}$ and $\overrightarrow{PR}$. Hence, required result.

Consider a point O on RT (where T is the midpoint of PQ). Write down $\overrightarrow{OP} + \overrightarrow{OQ}$ using the result just established. Hence show that
$$\overrightarrow{OP} + \overrightarrow{OQ} + \overrightarrow{OR} = 0,$$
where O is the point which divides RT in a certain ratio. State what this point O is called.

EX 1 The vector p has magnitude 7 units and bearing 052°, and the vector q has magnitude 12 units and bearing 163°. Draw a diagram (which need not be to scale) showing p, q and the resultant $p + q$. Calculate, correct to one decimal place, the magnitude of $p + q$.

                                               (L)

2 From an origin O the points A, B, C have position vectors a, b, $2b$ respectively. The points O, A, B are not collinear. The midpoint of AB is M, and the point of trisection of AC nearer to A is T. Draw a diagram to show O, A, B, C, M, T. Find, in terms a and b, the position vectors of M and T. Use your results to prove that O, M, T are collinear, and find the ratio in which M divides OT.

                                               (L)

3 Given that $OA = a$, $OB = b$, $OP = \frac{4}{5}OA$ and that Q is the midpoint of AB, express AB and PQ in terms of a and b. PQ is produced to meet OB produced at R, so that $QR = nPQ$ and $BR = kb$. Express QR: (i) in terms of n, a and b; (ii) in terms of k, a and b. Hence find the value of n and of k.

                                               (C)

4 The position vectors of three points A, B and C relative to an origin O are p, $3q - p$, and $9q - 5p$ respectively. Show that the points A, B and C lie on the same straight line, and state the ratio $AB : BC$. Given that $OBCD$ is a parallelogram and that E is the point such that $DB = \frac{1}{3}DE$, find the position vectors of D and E relative to O.

                                               (C)

5 The points A, B and C have position vectors a, b and c respectively referred to an origin O.
(a) Given that the point X lies on AB produced so that $AB : BX = 2 : 1$, find x, the position vector of X, in terms of a and b.
(b) If Y lies on BC, between B and C so that $BY : YC = 1 : 3$, find y, the position vector of Y, in terms of b and c.
(c) Given that Z is the mid-point of AC, show that X, Y and Z are collinear.
(d) Calculate $XY : YZ$.

                                               (L)

6 O, A and B are three non-collinear points; the position vectors of A and B with respect to O are a and b respectively. M is the mid-point of OB, T is the point of trisection of AB nearer B, $AMTX$ is a parallelogram and OX cuts AB at Y. Find, in terms of a and b, the position vectors of:
    (a) M;   (b) T;   (c) X;   (d) Y.
                                              (O & C)

7 The vertices A, B and C of a triangle have position vectors a, b and c respectively relative to an origin O. The point P is on BC such that $BP : PC = 3 : 1$; the point Q is on CA such that $CQ : QA = 2 : 3$; the point R is on BA produced such that $BR : AR = 2 : 1$. The position vectors of P, Q and R are p, q and r respectively. Show that q can be expressed in terms of p and r and hence or otherwise show that P, Q and R are collinear. State the ratio of the lengths of the line segments PQ and QR.

                                               (J)

8 The points P and Q have position vectors p and q respectively relative to an origin O, which does not lie on PQ. Three points R, S, T have respective position vectors $r = \frac{1}{4}p + \frac{3}{4}q$, $s = 2p - q$, $t = p + 3q$. Show in one diagram the positions of O, P, Q, R, S and T.

                                               (J)

P38 Vectors and Geometry

Equation of a straight line, Pairs of lines, Scalar (or dot) product, Applications of the scalar product, Equation of a plane.

Equation of a straight line

The equation of a straight line **parallel to vector b through a point** with position vector **a** is
$$\mathbf{r}=\mathbf{a}+t\mathbf{b}$$
where t is a real parameter.
r is the position vector of any point on the line.

The equation of a straight line **through two fixed points** with position vectors **a** and **b** is
$$\mathbf{r}=\mathbf{a}+t(\mathbf{b}-\mathbf{a})$$
where t is a real parameter.
Note: the equation is not unique.

ⓘ The equation of the straight line parallel to the vector $\mathbf{i}+2\mathbf{j}-5\mathbf{k}$ through the point with position vector $2\mathbf{i}-3\mathbf{j}+\mathbf{k}$ is
$$\mathbf{r}=(2\mathbf{i}-3\mathbf{j}+\mathbf{k})+t(\mathbf{i}+2\mathbf{j}-5\mathbf{k}).$$

ⓘ The equation of the straight line through two points with position vectors $2\mathbf{i}+\mathbf{j}-\mathbf{k}$ and $3\mathbf{i}-\mathbf{j}-3\mathbf{k}$ is
$$\mathbf{r}=(2\mathbf{i}+\mathbf{j}-\mathbf{k})+t[(3\mathbf{i}-\mathbf{j}-3\mathbf{k})-(2\mathbf{i}+\mathbf{j}-\mathbf{k})]$$
i.e. $\mathbf{r}=(2\mathbf{i}+\mathbf{j}-\mathbf{k})+t(\mathbf{i}-2\mathbf{j}-2\mathbf{k}).$

Pairs of lines

Two lines in space, $\mathbf{r}_1=\mathbf{a}_1+t\mathbf{b}_1$ and $\mathbf{r}_2=\mathbf{a}_2+s\mathbf{b}_2$, **intersect** if:
(a) $\mathbf{r}_1=\mathbf{r}_2$, i.e. $\mathbf{a}_1+t\mathbf{b}_1=\mathbf{a}_2+s\mathbf{b}_2$, and
(b) unique values for t and s can be found.

If unique values of t and s cannot be found, then the lines do not intersect and they are said to be **skew**.

ⓘ Find the point of intersection of
$\mathbf{r}_1=(2\mathbf{i}+3\mathbf{j})+t(-\mathbf{i}+2\mathbf{j})$ and $\mathbf{r}_2=(-\mathbf{i}+\mathbf{j})+s(3\mathbf{i}-2\mathbf{j})$.

The lines intersect where $\mathbf{r}_1=\mathbf{r}_2$,
i.e. $(2\mathbf{i}+3\mathbf{j})+t(-\mathbf{i}+2\mathbf{j})=(-\mathbf{i}+\mathbf{j})+s(3\mathbf{i}-2\mathbf{j})$
$\Rightarrow 2-t=-1+3s$, i.e. $t+3s=3$
and $3+2t=1-2s$, i.e. $t+s=-1$
giving $t=-3$ and $s=2$.
So, the lines meet at $(2\mathbf{i}+3\mathbf{j})-3(-\mathbf{i}+2\mathbf{j})=5\mathbf{i}-3\mathbf{j}$.
So, the point of intersection is $(5,-3)$.

Scalar (or dot) product

The **scalar (or dot) product** of vectors **a** and **b** is
$$\mathbf{a}.\mathbf{b}=|\mathbf{a}||\mathbf{b}|\cos\theta$$
where θ is the angle between **a** and **b**.

If **a** and **b** are **parallel**, i.e. $\theta=0$, $\mathbf{a}.\mathbf{b}=|\mathbf{a}||\mathbf{b}|$.
If **a** and **b** are **perpendicular**, i.e. $\theta=\dfrac{\pi}{2}$, $\mathbf{a}.\mathbf{b}=0$.

If $\mathbf{a}=x_1\mathbf{i}+y_1\mathbf{j}+z_1\mathbf{k}$ and $\mathbf{b}=x_2\mathbf{i}+y_2\mathbf{j}+z_2\mathbf{k}$
$\mathbf{a}.\mathbf{b}=(x_1\mathbf{i}+y_1\mathbf{j}+z_1\mathbf{k}).(x_2\mathbf{i}+y_2\mathbf{j}+z_2\mathbf{k})$
$\quad=x_1x_2+y_1y_2+z_1z_2$
since $\mathbf{i}.\mathbf{i}=\mathbf{j}.\mathbf{j}=\mathbf{k}.\mathbf{k}=1$
and $\mathbf{i}.\mathbf{j}=\mathbf{j}.\mathbf{k}=\mathbf{k}.\mathbf{i}=0.$

ⓘ Show that the vector $3\mathbf{i}+2\mathbf{j}-\mathbf{k}$ is at right angles to the straight line $\mathbf{r}=(\mathbf{i}+7\mathbf{j}+2\mathbf{k})+s(2\mathbf{i}-5\mathbf{j}-4\mathbf{k})$.

The direction of the straight line is parallel to the direction of the vector $(2\mathbf{i}-5\mathbf{j}-4\mathbf{k})$.
If the vector $3\mathbf{i}+2\mathbf{j}-\mathbf{k}$ is at right angles to the straight line, the scalar product of the vectors $2\mathbf{i}-5\mathbf{j}-4\mathbf{k}$ and $3\mathbf{i}+2\mathbf{j}-\mathbf{k}$ will be zero.

$(2\mathbf{i}-5\mathbf{j}-4\mathbf{k}).(3\mathbf{i}+2\mathbf{j}-\mathbf{k})=$
$\qquad\qquad (3)(2)+(-5)(2)+(-4)(-1)=0$
Hence, the given vector and the straight line are perpendicular.

Applications of the scalar product

The **angle θ between vectors a and b** is given by
$$\cos\theta=\frac{\mathbf{a}.\mathbf{b}}{|\mathbf{a}||\mathbf{b}|}$$

The **projection of a on b**, i.e. the resolved part of **a** in the direction of **b**, is
$$OP=|\mathbf{a}|\cos\theta$$
$$=\frac{\mathbf{a}.\mathbf{b}}{|\mathbf{b}|}$$

Figure 1

ⓘ Find, for the vectors $\mathbf{a}=\mathbf{i}+2\mathbf{j}$ and $\mathbf{b}=3\mathbf{i}+\mathbf{j}$,
(a) the acute angle θ between **a** and **b**,
(b) the resolved part of **a** in the direction of **b**.

(a) $\cos\theta=\dfrac{(\mathbf{i}+2\mathbf{j}).(3\mathbf{i}+\mathbf{j})}{\sqrt{(1^2+2^2)}.\sqrt{(3^2+1^2)}}=\dfrac{(1)(3)+(2)(1)}{\sqrt{5}.\sqrt{10}}=\dfrac{1}{\sqrt{2}}.$
So, $\theta=45°$.
(b) The resolved part of **a** in the direction of **b** is
$$\frac{\mathbf{a}.\mathbf{b}}{|\mathbf{b}|}=\frac{(1)(3)+(2)(1)}{\sqrt{(3^2+1^2)}}=\frac{5}{\sqrt{10}}=\frac{\sqrt{10}}{2}.$$

Equation of a plane

The equation of a plane **through a point** with position vector **a**, **perpendicular to a vector n**, is
$$(\mathbf{r}-\mathbf{a}).\mathbf{n}=0$$
i.e. $\mathbf{r}.\mathbf{n}=\mathbf{a}.\mathbf{n}$

The equation of a plane **through any three points** with position vectors **a**, **b** and **c** is
$$\mathbf{r}.(d\mathbf{i}+e\mathbf{j}+f\mathbf{k})=1$$
where d, e and f are found by
(a) substituting **a**, **b** and **c** in turn for **r**,
(b) solving the three simultaneous equations formed.

ⓘ Find the equation of the plane through the point with position vector $2\mathbf{i}-3\mathbf{j}+\mathbf{k}$ and perpendicular to the vector $\mathbf{i}-\mathbf{j}-2\mathbf{k}$.

If **r** is the position vector of any point lying in the plane, then the equation of the plane is
$\mathbf{r}.(\mathbf{i}-\mathbf{j}-2\mathbf{k})=(2\mathbf{i}-3\mathbf{j}+\mathbf{k}).(\mathbf{i}-\mathbf{j}-2\mathbf{k})$
$\qquad\qquad =(2.1)+(-3.-1)+(1.-2)$
$\qquad\qquad =2+3-2$
i.e. $\mathbf{r}.(\mathbf{i}-\mathbf{j}-2\mathbf{k})=3$

Vectors and Geometry
Worked example, Guided example and Exam questions.

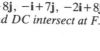

WE *Relative to an origin the points A, B, C, D and E shown in the diagram have position vectors* $\mathbf{i}+11\mathbf{j}$, $2\mathbf{i}+8\mathbf{j}$, $-\mathbf{i}+7\mathbf{j}$, $-2\mathbf{i}+8\mathbf{j}$ *and* $-4\mathbf{i}+6\mathbf{j}$ *respectively. The lines AB and DC intersect at F.*

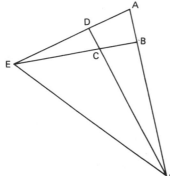

Calculate:
    (*i*) *the vector equations of the lines AB and DC.*
    (*ii*) *the position vector of the point F.*
Show that FD is perpendicular to EA and hence find
    (*iii*) *the position vector of the centre of the circle through E,*
    D and F.

(i) First find $\overrightarrow{AB}$ and $\overrightarrow{DC}$.

$\overrightarrow{AB} = (2\mathbf{i}+8\mathbf{j}) - (\mathbf{i}+11\mathbf{j}) = \mathbf{i}-3\mathbf{j}$,

$\overrightarrow{DC} = (-\mathbf{i}+7\mathbf{j}) - (-2\mathbf{i}+8\mathbf{j}) = \mathbf{i}-\mathbf{j}$
Equation of line AB is $\mathbf{r}=\mathbf{i}+11\mathbf{j}+s(\mathbf{i}-3\mathbf{j})$ and, equation of line DC is $\mathbf{r}=-2\mathbf{i}+8\mathbf{j}+t(\mathbf{i}-\mathbf{j})$.

(ii) F is the point of intersection of AB and DC.
AB and DC intersect where
$$\mathbf{i}+11\mathbf{j}+s(\mathbf{i}-3\mathbf{j}) = -2\mathbf{i}+8\mathbf{j}+t(\mathbf{i}-\mathbf{j})$$
i.e. $(3+s-t)\mathbf{i}+(3-3s+t)\mathbf{j}=0$
$\Rightarrow 3+s-t=0$, and $3-3s+t=0$,
giving $s=3$ and $t=6$.

    So, the lines intersect at the point F with position vector $\mathbf{r}=\mathbf{i}+11\mathbf{j}+3(\mathbf{i}-3\mathbf{j})$
    i.e. $\mathbf{r}=4\mathbf{i}+2\mathbf{j}$.

$\overrightarrow{FD} = (-2\mathbf{i}+8\mathbf{j}) - (4\mathbf{i}+2\mathbf{j}) = 6\mathbf{i}+6\mathbf{j}$

$\overrightarrow{EA} = (\mathbf{i}+11\mathbf{j}) - (-4\mathbf{i}+6\mathbf{j}) = 5\mathbf{i}+5\mathbf{j}$

$\overrightarrow{FD}.\overrightarrow{EA} = (-6\mathbf{i}+6\mathbf{j}).(5\mathbf{i}+5\mathbf{j}) = -30+30 = 0$

    Hence, FD and EA are perpendicular.

(iii) Since FD is perpendicular to ED, the circle passing through E, D and F must have the midpoint of EF as centre. (Angle in a semicircle is a right angle). Hence, position vector of the centre is
$$\frac{(-4\mathbf{i}+6\mathbf{j})+(4\mathbf{i}+2\mathbf{j})}{2} = 4\mathbf{j}.$$

 GE *Let* $\boldsymbol{a}=\mathbf{i}-2\mathbf{j}+\mathbf{k}$, $\boldsymbol{b}=2\mathbf{i}+\mathbf{j}-\mathbf{k}$. *Given that* $\boldsymbol{c}=\lambda\boldsymbol{a}+\mu\boldsymbol{b}$ *and that* $\boldsymbol{c}$ *is perpendicular to* $\boldsymbol{a}$, *find the ratio of* λ *to* μ.

Let A, B be the points with position vectors $\boldsymbol{a}$, $\boldsymbol{b}$ *respectively with respect to an origin O. Write down in terms of* $\boldsymbol{a}$ *and* $\boldsymbol{b}$, *a vector equation of the line l through A, in the plane of O, A and B, which is perpendicular to OA.*

Find the position vector of P, the point of intersection of l and OB.

Since **a** and **c** are perpendicular, calculate **a.c** $=0$.
Hence find ratio of λ to μ.
Since **c** is perpendicular to **a** and coplanar with **a** and **b** the equation of l can be written $\mathbf{r}=\mathbf{a}+k\mathbf{c}$.
Write $k\mathbf{c}$ as $t(\alpha\mathbf{i}+\beta\mathbf{j}+\gamma\mathbf{k})$ using $\mathbf{c}=\lambda\mathbf{a}+\mu\mathbf{b}$ and **a** and **b** as given and the ratio λ to μ as found. Hence, equation of l is found as $\mathbf{r}=\mathbf{a}+t(\alpha\mathbf{i}+\beta\mathbf{j}+\gamma\mathbf{k})$ with α,β and γ determined from your working. l meets OB where $\mathbf{r}=\mathbf{b}$.

EX 1 Given that $\mathbf{a}=\begin{pmatrix}4\\-3\end{pmatrix}$, $\mathbf{b}=\begin{pmatrix}2\\4\end{pmatrix}$ and $\mathbf{c}=\begin{pmatrix}22\\-11\end{pmatrix}$, find:

    (i) a unit vector perpendicular to $\mathbf{a}$;
    (ii) the value of the constants m and n for which $m\mathbf{a}+n\mathbf{b}=\mathbf{c}$.
Evaluate the scalar product of $\mathbf{a}$ and $\mathbf{b}$ and hence find the cosine of the angle between the direction of $\mathbf{a}$ and the direction of $\mathbf{b}$.   *(C)*

2 Find the position vector of the point of intersection of the two lines
$$\mathbf{r}=\begin{pmatrix}3\\4\end{pmatrix}+s\begin{pmatrix}1\\-2\end{pmatrix}$$
and
$$\mathbf{r}=\begin{pmatrix}1\\-1\end{pmatrix}+t\begin{pmatrix}2\\2\end{pmatrix}.$$

Show that this position vector is perpendicular to the first line, and find its projection on the second line. Write down in vector form the equations of the lines parallel to the given lines and passing through $(0, 0)$, and find the exact value of the cosine of the angle between these two lines.
    (O & C)

3 A, B and C are the points $(0,5,5)$, $(4,1,1)$ and $(2\frac{1}{2}, 2\frac{1}{2}, 2\frac{1}{2})$ respectively.
    (a) Prove that A, B and C are collinear and find the ratio in which C divides AB.
    (b) O is the origin. Prove that OC bisects angle AOB.
    (c) Given that $\mathbf{p}$, $\mathbf{q}$ and $\mathbf{r}$ are position vectors of P, Q and R relative to the origin O and that OQ bisects angle POR prove that
$$\frac{\mathbf{p}\cdot\mathbf{q}}{\mathbf{r}\cdot\mathbf{q}} = \frac{|\mathbf{p}|}{|\mathbf{r}|} \qquad (H)$$

4 Find the angle between the lines with vector equations $\mathbf{r}=\mathbf{a}+t\mathbf{c}$ and $\mathbf{r}=\mathbf{b}+s\mathbf{d}$, where
$$\mathbf{a}=\begin{pmatrix}1\\2\\-1\end{pmatrix} \quad \mathbf{b}=\begin{pmatrix}5\\5\\-4\end{pmatrix} \quad \mathbf{c}=\begin{pmatrix}0\\1\\-1\end{pmatrix} \quad \mathbf{d}=\begin{pmatrix}2\\1\\-1\end{pmatrix}.$$

Show that these lines intersect, and find the position vector of P, the point of intersection. Express in the vector form $\mathbf{r.n}=k$ the equation of the plane which passes through the point P, and which is perpendicular to the line joining the two points with position vectors $\mathbf{a}$ and $\mathbf{b}$.   *(OLE)*

5 The lines L_1 and L_2 are given by the equations
$$L_1:\mathbf{r}=\begin{pmatrix}1\\6\\3\end{pmatrix}+t\begin{pmatrix}2\\-1\\1\end{pmatrix}, \qquad L_2:\mathbf{r}=\begin{pmatrix}3\\3\\8\end{pmatrix}+s\begin{pmatrix}1\\0\\1\end{pmatrix}.$$

    (i) Calculate the angle between the directions of L_1, L_2;
    (ii) Show that the lines do not intersect;
    (iii) Verify that the vector $\mathbf{a}=\begin{pmatrix}1\\1\\-1\end{pmatrix}$ is perpendicular to each of the lines.
The point P on L_1 is given by $t=p$; the point Q on L_2 is given by $s=q$. Write down the column vector representing $\overrightarrow{PQ}$. Hence calculate p and q so that the vectors $\overrightarrow{PQ}$ and $\mathbf{a}$ are parallel.   *(J)*

6 The point A has position vector $\mathbf{i}+4\mathbf{j}-3\mathbf{k}$ referred to the origin O. The line L has vector equation $\mathbf{r}=t\mathbf{i}$. The plane Π contains the line L and the point A. Find:
    (a) a vector which is normal to the plane Π;
    (b) a vector equation for the plane Π;
    (c) the cosine of the acute angle between OA and the line L.   *(L)*

P39 Matrices

Definitions, Operations, Transformation of points, Transformation of lines.

Definitions

A **matrix** may be considered as a rectangular array of numbers. The entries in a matrix are called **elements**.
The **order** of a matrix is the number of rows × the number of columns.
A **row matrix** has only one row of elements. A **column matrix** has only one column of elements.
A **square matrix** has the same number of rows as columns, i.e. its order is of the form $(n \times n)$.
Matrices are **equal** if and only if they are of the same order and corresponding elements are equal.
A **zero** or **null matrix, 0,** is a matrix in which every element is zero.
The **identity** or **unit matrix, I,** is a square matrix in which each element in the leading diagonal is 1 and every other element is zero.

The **determinant** of a 2×2 matrix $A = \begin{pmatrix} a & b \\ c & d \end{pmatrix}$ is the number $\det A = \begin{vmatrix} a & b \\ c & d \end{vmatrix} = ad - bc$.

If $\det A = 0$, then A is called a **singular** matrix.
Every non-singular $n \times n$ matrix A has an **inverse** A^{-1} such that $AA^{-1} = A^{-1}A = I$.

If $A = \begin{pmatrix} a & b \\ c & d \end{pmatrix}$, then $A^{-1} = \dfrac{1}{\det A} \begin{pmatrix} d & -b \\ -c & a \end{pmatrix}$.

Operations

Matrices may be **added** (or **subtracted**) if and only if they are of the **same order**. Add (or subtract) corresponding elements.
Matrix addition is commutative and associative.

To **multiply** a matrix by a **scalar**, multiply each element of the matrix by the scalar.

Two matrices A and B may be **multiplied** together if and only if they are **compatible**, i.e. if the number of columns of A equals the number of rows of B. Each element of AB comes from a row in A and a column in B.
In general, matrix multiplication is not commutative. However, it is associative.

ℹ️ If $A = \begin{pmatrix} 2 & 3 & 5 \\ 4 & 7 & 1 \end{pmatrix}$ and $B = \begin{pmatrix} 0 & -1 & 3 \\ 8 & 2 & -5 \end{pmatrix}$, then

$$A + B = \begin{pmatrix} 2 & 2 & 8 \\ 12 & 9 & -4 \end{pmatrix} \text{ and } A - B = \begin{pmatrix} 2 & 4 & 2 \\ -4 & 5 & 6 \end{pmatrix}$$

ℹ️ $3 \begin{pmatrix} 5 & -3 & 6 \\ -1 & 0 & 7 \end{pmatrix} = \begin{pmatrix} 15 & -9 & 18 \\ -3 & 0 & 21 \end{pmatrix}$

ℹ️ $\begin{pmatrix} a & b & c \\ d & e & f \end{pmatrix} \begin{pmatrix} p & q \\ r & s \\ t & u \end{pmatrix} = \begin{pmatrix} ap+br+ct & aq+bs+cu \\ dp+er+ft & dq+es+fu \end{pmatrix}$

$(2 \times 3 \text{ matrix}) \times (3 \times 2 \text{ matrix}) \rightarrow (2 \times 2 \text{ matrix})$

Transformations of points

Transformations in the plane, other than translations, can be produced and described using 2×2 matrices.

Any point (x, y) can be mapped to (x_1, y_1) using a 2×2 matrix M, where $\begin{pmatrix} x_1 \\ y_1 \end{pmatrix} = M \begin{pmatrix} x \\ y \end{pmatrix}$.

To find the matrix describing a given transformation,
(a) find the image of $P(1, 0)$, say $P_1(a, b)$,
(b) find the image of $Q(0, 1)$, say $Q_1(c, d)$,
(c) the required matrix is $\begin{pmatrix} a & c \\ b & d \end{pmatrix}$.

If M is the matrix which represents a transformation in the plane and $\det M \neq 0$, then M^{-1} is the matrix which represents the **inverse transformation.**

If M and N are two matrices representing two transformations for which the origin is an invariant point, then NM is the matrix which represents the result M **followed by** N.

ℹ️ If $M = \begin{pmatrix} 0 & -1 \\ -1 & 0 \end{pmatrix}$, a reflection in $y = -x$, then

(2, 3) is mapped to $(-3, -2)$ by M, since

$$\begin{pmatrix} 0 & -1 \\ -1 & 0 \end{pmatrix} \begin{pmatrix} 2 \\ 3 \end{pmatrix} = \begin{pmatrix} -3 \\ -2 \end{pmatrix}$$

ℹ️ For rotation of $+90°$ about 0,
$P(1, 0) \rightarrow P_1(0, 1)$
$Q(0, 1) \rightarrow Q_1(-1, 0)$.

The matrix is $M = \begin{pmatrix} 0 & -1 \\ 1 & 0 \end{pmatrix}$.

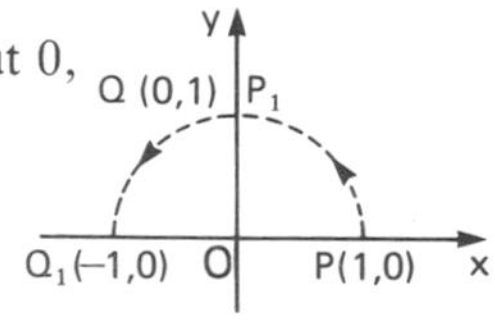

Figure 1

ℹ️ $M = \begin{pmatrix} 0 & -1 \\ 1 & 0 \end{pmatrix}$ and $M^{-1} = \begin{pmatrix} 0 & 1 \\ -1 & 0 \end{pmatrix}$.

M^{-1} is a rotation of $-90°$ about 0.

ℹ️ $NM = \begin{pmatrix} -1 & 0 \\ 0 & 1 \end{pmatrix} \begin{pmatrix} 0 & 1 \\ 1 & 0 \end{pmatrix} = \begin{pmatrix} 0 & -1 \\ 1 & 0 \end{pmatrix}$

M, a reflection in $y = x$, followed by N, a reflection in $x = 0$, is equivalent to a rotation of $+90°$ about 0.

Transformations of lines

The **linear transformation** T of the plane defined by

$$\begin{pmatrix} x \\ y \end{pmatrix} \rightarrow T \begin{pmatrix} x \\ y \end{pmatrix},$$

where $T = \begin{pmatrix} a & b \\ c & d \end{pmatrix}$ and $ad - bc \neq 0$,

maps any line in the plane to a line in the plane.

ℹ️ *Find the image of $y = 3x$ under the mapping* $\begin{pmatrix} 2 & 3 \\ 1 & 2 \end{pmatrix}$.

Let any point on $y = 3x$ be $(\lambda, 3\lambda)$, where λ is a parameter. The image of $(\lambda, 3\lambda)$ is given by

$$\begin{pmatrix} 2 & 3 \\ 1 & 2 \end{pmatrix} \begin{pmatrix} \lambda \\ 3\lambda \end{pmatrix} = \begin{pmatrix} 11\lambda \\ 7\lambda \end{pmatrix}$$

This is the position vector of any point on $11y = 7x$.
So $11y = 7x$ is the required image of $y = 3x$.

Matrices
Worked example, Guided example and Exam questions.

 (a) *A transformation T is equivalent to a shear parallel to the x-axis (the invariant line) which takes (1, 2) to (7, 2), followed by a reflection in the line $y = x$. Find the matrix which defines T.*
(b) *A linear transformation P of the plane maps the points (1, 3), (−2, −3) to the points (2, 4), (−3, −11), respectively. Find the matrix of this transformation.*

(a) The matrix $\begin{pmatrix} 1 & k \\ 0 & 1 \end{pmatrix}$ represents a shear parallel to the x-axis (the invariant line).
Since $(1, 2) \rightarrow (7, 2)$, we have
$$\begin{pmatrix} 1 & k \\ 0 & 1 \end{pmatrix}\begin{pmatrix} 1 \\ 2 \end{pmatrix} = \begin{pmatrix} 1+2k \\ 2 \end{pmatrix} = \begin{pmatrix} 7 \\ 2 \end{pmatrix} \Rightarrow k = 3.$$
So $S = \begin{pmatrix} 1 & 3 \\ 0 & 1 \end{pmatrix}$ defines the shear.

The matrix R which defines reflection in $y = x$ is $\begin{pmatrix} 0 & 1 \\ 1 & 0 \end{pmatrix}$.

Hence, the matrix which represents the shear followed by the reflection is $RS = \begin{pmatrix} 0 & 1 \\ 1 & 0 \end{pmatrix}\begin{pmatrix} 1 & 3 \\ 0 & 1 \end{pmatrix} = \begin{pmatrix} 0 & 1 \\ 1 & 3 \end{pmatrix}$.

(b) Let $\begin{pmatrix} a & b \\ c & d \end{pmatrix}$ be the matrix which defines P.

Now $\begin{pmatrix} a & b \\ c & d \end{pmatrix}\begin{pmatrix} 1 \\ 3 \end{pmatrix} = \begin{pmatrix} a+3b \\ c+3d \end{pmatrix} = \begin{pmatrix} 2 \\ 4 \end{pmatrix}$,

and $\begin{pmatrix} a & b \\ c & d \end{pmatrix}\begin{pmatrix} -2 \\ -3 \end{pmatrix} = \begin{pmatrix} -2a-3b \\ -2c-3d \end{pmatrix} = \begin{pmatrix} -3 \\ -11 \end{pmatrix}$.

So, $a + 3b = 2$,
and $2a + 3b = 3$,
$\Rightarrow a = 1$, $b = \frac{1}{3}$.
Also, $c + 3d = 4$,
and $2c + 3d = 11$,
$\Rightarrow c = 7$, $d = -1$.

Hence $\begin{pmatrix} 1 & \frac{1}{3} \\ 7 & -1 \end{pmatrix}$ is the matrix which defines P.

GE *Prove that the map T of the plane defined by*
$$\begin{pmatrix} x \\ y \end{pmatrix} \rightarrow \begin{pmatrix} a & b \\ c & d \end{pmatrix}\begin{pmatrix} x \\ y \end{pmatrix}, \text{ where } ad - bc \neq 0, \text{ maps any line in the}$$
plane to a line in the plane.
If the line $l(m_1)$ of slope m_1 through the origin is mapped onto the line $l(m_2)$ of slope m_2 through the origin, prove that
$$bm_1m_2 - dm_1 + am_2 - c = 0.$$
Given that there is a pair of distinct lines $l(m_1)$, $l(m_2)$ such that T maps $l(m_1)$ onto $l(m_2)$ and maps $l(m_2)$ onto $l(m_1)$ where
$$m_1 \neq m_2,$$
(a) prove that $a + d = 0$,
(b) prove that $T^2 = kI$, giving k in terms of a, b, c.

Let $\begin{pmatrix} \lambda \\ m\lambda + n \end{pmatrix}$ be the position vector of any point on $y = mx + n$.

Find $\begin{pmatrix} a & b \\ c & d \end{pmatrix}\begin{pmatrix} \lambda \\ m\lambda + n \end{pmatrix}$ and equate the result to $\begin{pmatrix} X \\ Y \end{pmatrix}$, say.

Write down two equations in λ and eliminate λ. Hence get $Y = f(X)$, the equation of a straight line.

Let $\begin{pmatrix} \lambda \\ m_1\lambda \end{pmatrix}$ be the position vector of any point on $l(m_1)$.

Find $\begin{pmatrix} a & b \\ c & d \end{pmatrix}\begin{pmatrix} \lambda \\ m_1\lambda \end{pmatrix} = \begin{pmatrix} \alpha \\ \beta \end{pmatrix}$, say.

Since (α, β) lies on $l(m_2)$, $\beta = m_2\alpha$. Use this to obtain the required equation.

Since T maps $l(m_2)$ onto $l(m_1)$, write down a corresponding equation to that obtained. Use the two equations to establish $a + d = 0$.
Evaluate T^2, remembering $a + d = 0$. Hence obtain the required result and give k in terms of a, b, c.

---

 1 (i) If $\mathbf{M} = \begin{pmatrix} 2 & -1 \\ 1 & 3 \end{pmatrix}$, find the values of $\mathbf{M}^2$, $\mathbf{M}^3$ and $\mathbf{M}^{-1}$.

Find x and y, given that $\mathbf{M}\begin{pmatrix} x \\ y \end{pmatrix} = \begin{pmatrix} 3 \\ 5 \end{pmatrix}$

(ii) A transformation T is equivalent to an enlargement with centre at the origin, scale factor 2, followed by a reflection in the line $x + y = 0$. What matrix defines T? If T maps a point P onto (6, 2), what are the coordinates of P?
(O & C)

2 A transformation M is represented by the matrix $\mathbf{M}$ where
$$\mathbf{M} = \begin{pmatrix} 4 & 1 \\ 2 & 3 \end{pmatrix}.$$

(i) Find the image of the point (−2, 5) under $\mathbf{M}$.
(ii) Find the inverse of $\mathbf{M}$.
(iii) Given that the point (11, 13) is the image of the point (a, b) under $\mathbf{M}$, find the value of a and of b.
(iv) Find, in terms of α, the image of the point (α, α) under $\mathbf{M}$.
(v) State the equation of the invariant line under $\mathbf{M}$.
(C)

3 If $\mathbf{A} = \begin{pmatrix} 2 & 1 & 1 \\ 1 & 0 & 1 \\ 0 & -1 & 0 \end{pmatrix}$ and $\mathbf{B} = \begin{pmatrix} 1 & -1 & 1 \\ 0 & 0 & -1 \\ -1 & 2 & -1 \end{pmatrix}$, find
(a) $\mathbf{AB}$;
(b) a matrix $\mathbf{X}$ such that $\mathbf{AX} + \mathbf{B} = \mathbf{A}$.
(O & C)

4 Let $\mathbf{A} = \begin{pmatrix} 1 & 1 \\ 0 & 1 \end{pmatrix}$.

(a) The plane is mapped onto itself by the map under which the point P of co-ordinates (x_1, y_1) is mapped to the point Q of co-ordinates (x_2, y_2), where $\begin{pmatrix} x_2 \\ y_2 \end{pmatrix} = \mathbf{A}\begin{pmatrix} x_1 \\ y_1 \end{pmatrix}$.

By considering $\mathbf{A}\begin{pmatrix} x \\ m_1x + c \end{pmatrix}$, prove that the line $y = m_1x + c$ is mapped onto a line of slope m_2, determining m_2 in terms of m_1. Hence or otherwise determine whether any line through the origin is mapped onto itself, and find any such line.
(b) Prove that there is no non-singular matrix $\mathbf{P}$ such that
$$\mathbf{P}^{-1}\mathbf{AP} = \begin{pmatrix} k_1 & 0 \\ 0 & k_2 \end{pmatrix} \text{ for real } k_1, k_2.$$
(O & C)

5 The transformation with matrix $\mathbf{T}$, where $\mathbf{T} = \begin{pmatrix} 2 & 1 \\ 2 & -2 \end{pmatrix}$, maps the point (x, y) into the point (x', y') so that
$$T\begin{pmatrix} x \\ y \end{pmatrix} = \begin{pmatrix} x' \\ y' \end{pmatrix}.$$

Find the equation of the image of the line $y = 3x$ under this transformation. Find also the equations of the lines through the origin which are turned through a right angle about the origin under this transformation.
(J)

P40 Complex Numbers

Definitions, Operations, Operations with the conjugate, Roots of equations.

Definitions

A **complex number**, z, is a number of the form
$$z = x + iy$$

where x and y are **real** numbers and $i = \sqrt{-1}$.
x is called the **real part** of z; y the **imaginary part**.

Since $i = \sqrt{-1}$
$$i^2 = -1,\ i^3 = -i,\ i^4 = 1,\ldots$$

The **modulus** of z is $|z| = \sqrt{x^2 + y^2}$.

The **argument of** z is $\arg(z) = \tan^{-1}\left(\dfrac{y}{x}\right)$

where $-\pi < \arg(z) \leqslant \pi$.
The **conjugate** of z, denoted by z^* or $\bar{z}$, is $x - iy$.

$z_1 = a + ib$ and $z_2 = c + id$ are **equal** if and only if $a = c$ and $b = d$, i.e. if the real parts are equal and the imaginary parts are equal.

$z = x + iy$ is **zero** if and only if $x = 0$ and $y = 0$.

[i] *For the complex number* $z = \dfrac{\sqrt{3}}{2} + \dfrac{1}{2}i$, *find*:

(a) $|z|$, (b) $\arg z$, (c) z^*.

(a) $|z| = \sqrt{\left(\dfrac{\sqrt{3}}{2}\right)^2 + \left(\dfrac{1}{2}\right)^2} = 1$

(b) $\arg z = \tan^{-1}\left(\dfrac{1/2}{\sqrt{3}/2}\right) = \tan^{-1}\left(\dfrac{1}{\sqrt{3}}\right) = \dfrac{\pi}{6}$

(c) $z^* = \dfrac{\sqrt{3}}{2} - \dfrac{1}{2}i$

[i] *Find the real values of x and y if*
$$(x - 1) + i(y - 2) = 0.$$

If $(x - 1) + i(y - 2) = 0$
then $(x - 1) = 0$ and $(y - 2) = 0$.
So $x = 1$ and $y = 2$.

Operations

Let $z_1 = a + ib$ and $z_2 = c + id$.

Addition: $z_1 + z_2 = (a + ib) + (c + id)$
$$= (a + c) + i(b + d)$$

Subtraction: $z_1 - z_2 = (a + ib) - (c + id)$
$$= (a - c) + i(b - d)$$

Multiplication: $z_1 z_2 = (a + ib)(c + id)$
$$= ac + i^2 bd + iad + ibc$$
$$= (ac - bd) + i(ad + bc)$$

Division: $z_1 \div z_2 = \dfrac{(a + ib)}{(c + id)} = \dfrac{(a + ib)(c - id)}{(c + id)(c - id)}$

$$= \left(\dfrac{ac + bd}{c^2 + d^2}\right) + i\left(\dfrac{bc - ad}{c^2 + d^2}\right)$$

[i] *If* $p = -2 + 3i$ *and* $q = 1 + 2i$, *express as complex numbers in the form* $x + iy$,

(a) $p + q$, (b) $p - q$, (c) pq, (d) $p \div q$.

(a) $p + q = (-2 + 3i) + (1 + 2i) = -1 + 5i$.
(b) $p - q = (-2 + 3i) - (1 + 2i) = -3 + i$.

(c) $pq = (-2 + 3i)(1 + 2i)$
$$= -2 + 6i^2 + 3i - 4i$$
$$= -2 - 6 - i = -8 - i.$$

(d) $p \div q = \dfrac{(-2 + 3i)}{(1 + 2i)} = \dfrac{(-2 + 3i)(1 - 2i)}{(1 + 2i)(1 - 2i)}$

$$= \left(\dfrac{-2 + 6}{1 + 4}\right) + i\left(\dfrac{3 - -4}{1 + 4}\right) = \dfrac{4}{5} + \dfrac{7}{5}i$$

Operations with the conjugate

Addition: $z + z^* = (x + iy) + (x - iy) = 2x$

Subtraction: $z - z^* = (x + iy) - (x - iy) = 2iy$

Multiplication: $zz^* = (x + iy)(x - iy) = x^2 + y^2$

Division: $\dfrac{z}{z^*} = \dfrac{(x + iy)}{(x - iy)} = \dfrac{(x + iy)(x + iy)}{(x - iy)(x + iy)}$

$$= \left(\dfrac{x^2 - y^2}{x^2 + y^2}\right) + i\left(\dfrac{2xy}{x^2 + y^2}\right)$$

[i] *If* $z = 3 + 4i$, *evaluate*:

(a) $z + z^*$ (b) $z - z^*$ (c) zz^* (d) $z \div z^*$.

(a) $z + z^* = (3 + 4i) + (3 - 4i) = 6$.

(b) $z - z^* = (3 + 4i) - (3 - 4i) = 8i$.
(c) $zz^* = (3 + 4i)(3 - 4i) = 9 + 16 = 25$.

(d) $z \div z^* = \dfrac{3 + 4i}{3 - 4i} = \dfrac{(3 + 4i)(3 + 4i)}{(3 - 4i)(3 + 4i)} = \left(\dfrac{-7}{25}\right) + \left(\dfrac{24}{25}\right)i$

Roots of equations

If the complex number $p + iq$ is a root of a polynomial equation with real coefficients then its conjugate, $p - iq$, is also a root.

[i] *If* $(2 + 3i)$ *is a root of a quadratic equation with real coefficients, find the equation.*

Since $(2 + 3i)$ is a root, $(2 - 3i)$ is the other root.
The required equation is
$$[x - (2 + 3i)][x - (2 - 3i)] = 0$$
i.e. $x^2 - [(2 + 3i) + (2 - 3i)]x + (2 + 3i)(2 - 3i) = 0$
i.e. $x^2 - 4x + 13 = 0$

Complex Numbers
Worked example, Guided example and Exam questions.

 (a) *Given that $z_1 = 2-3i$ and $z_2 = 3+4i$ find*
(i) *$z_1 z_2$,*

(ii) *$\dfrac{z_1}{z_2}$, in the form $p+iq$ where p and q are real.*

(b) *Given that $2+3i$ is a root of the equation*
$z^3 - 6z^2 + 21z - 26 = 0$, find the other two roots.

(a)
(i) $z_1 z_2 = (2-3i)(3+4i)$
$\quad = (6+12) + i(-9+8)$
$\quad = 18 - i$

(ii) $\dfrac{z_1}{z_2} = \dfrac{2-3i}{3+4i}$

$\quad = \dfrac{(2-3i)(3-4i)}{(3+4i)(3-4i)}$

$\quad = \dfrac{(6-12) + i(-9-8)}{9+16}$

$\quad = -\dfrac{6}{25} - \dfrac{17}{25}i$

(b) $z^3 - 6z^2 + 21z - 26 = 0$
We are given that $2+3i$ is a root of this equation. Since the coefficients of the equation are real, $2-3i$ is also a root. Hence $z-(2+3i)$ and $z-(2-3i)$ are factors of the equation. The product of these factors is
$[z-(2+3i)][z-(2-3i)]$
$\quad = z^2 - 4z + 13$
Dividing the LHS of the original equation by $z^2 - 4z + 13$ gives $z-2$.
Hence $z^3 - 6z^2 + 21z - 26 = 0$ can be written as
$(z-2)[z-(2+3i)][z-(2-3i)] = 0$,
giving the other two required roots as $z = 2$ and $z = 2-3i$.

 (i) *Express the square roots of $-2i$ in the form $\pm(a+ib)$ where a and b are real numbers.*
(ii) *Solve the equation*
$$z^2 - 3(1+i)z + 5i = 0$$
giving your answers in the form $a+ib$. Hence or otherwise solve the equation
$$z^2 - 3(1-i)z - 5i = 0$$
(i) Let $(a+ib)^2 = -2i$. Work out $(a+ib)^2$. Equate real and imaginary parts. Find a and b. Hence roots are $\pm(a+ib)$.
(ii) Let $z = a+ib$. Work out LHS. Equate real and imaginary parts. Find a and b. Hence roots are $a+ib$. Second equation is obtained from first by replacing i by $-i$. Hence the roots are $a-ib$.

---

 1 Express $(6+5i)(7+2i)$ in the form $a+ib$. Write down $(6-5i)(7-2i)$ in a similar form. Hence find the prime factors of $32^2 + 47^2$. *(J)*

2 Expand $z = (1+ic)^6$ in powers of c and find the five real finite values of c for which z is real. *(J)*

3 If $(1+i)z - iw + i = iz + (1-i)w - 3i = 6$, find the complex numbers z, w, expressing each in the form $a+bi$ where a, b are real. *(O & C)*

4 (a) Express $\dfrac{-1+i\sqrt{3}}{-1-i\sqrt{3}}$ in the form $a+ib$, where a and b are real numbers.
(b) Find the quadratic equation whose roots are $-3+4i$ and $-3-4i$, expressing your answer in the form $x^2 + px + q = 0$, where p and q are real numbers. *(C)*

5 Find the real values of a and b such that $(a+ib)^2 = i$. Hence, or otherwise, solve the equation $z^2 + 2zi + 1 - i = 0$, giving your solutions in the form $z = p+iq$. *(OLE)*

6 Let $z = x+iy$ be any non-zero complex number.
Express $\dfrac{1}{z}$ in the form $u+iv$.

Given that $z + \dfrac{1}{z} = k$ with k real, prove that either
$y = 0$ or $x^2 + y^2 = 1$. Show
(i) that if $y = 0$ then $|k| \geqslant 2$,
(ii) that if $x^2 + y^2 = 1$ then $|k| \leqslant 2$. *(J)*

7 (a) Given that $z = x+iy$, where x and y are real numbers, find z^2 in terms of x and y. Hence, or otherwise, find both square roots of i.
(b) One root of a quadratic equation with real coefficients is $(7-24i)/5$. State the other root of this equation, and find the equation in its simplest form. *(A)*

8 The roots of the quadratic equation $z^2 + pz + q = 0$ are $1+i$ and $4+3i$. Find the complex numbers p and q. It is given that $1+i$ is also a root of the equation $z^2 + (a+2i)z + 5 + ib = 0$, where a and b are real. Determine the values of a and b. *(J)*

9 Obtain a quadratic function: $f(z) = z^2 + az + b$, where a and b are real constants such that $f(-1-2i) = 0$. *(L)*

10 Show that $1+i$ is a root of the equation $x^4 + 3x^2 - 6x + 10 = 0$. Hence write down one quadratic factor of $x^4 + 3x^2 - 6x + 10$, and find all the roots of the equation. *(OLE)*

11 Given that $\alpha = 1+3i$ is a root of the equation $z^2 - (p+2i)z + q(1+i) = 0$, and that p and q are real, determine p, q and the other root of the equation. *(J)*

12 Given that $(x+iy)^2 = a+ib$, where x, y, a, b are real, prove that $4x^4 - 4ax^2 - b^2 = 0$. Hence, or otherwise, find the values of $(5+12i)^{1/2}$. What are the values of $(5-12i)^{1/2}$? Solve the equation $z^2 - (7+4i)z + (7+11i) = 0$. State the roots of $z^2 - (7-4i)z + (7-11i) = 0$. [Give all your answers in the form $u+iv$ where u, v are real.] *(O & C)*

13 In the quadratic equation $x^2 + (p+iq)x + 3i = 0$, p and q are real. Given that the sum of the squares of the roots is 8, find all possible pairs of values of p and q. *(J)*

14 Given that ω denotes either one of the non-real roots of the equation: $z^3 = 1$, show that: (i) $1 + \omega + \omega^2 = 0$; and (ii) the other non-real root is ω^2. Show that the non-real roots of the equation
$$\left(\dfrac{1-u}{u}\right)^3 = 1$$
can be expressed in the form $A\omega$ and $B\omega^2$, where A and B are real numbers, and find A and B. *(J)*

P41 Complex Numbers and Graphs

Argand diagram, Polar form, Multiplication and division in polar form,
Geometric representation of operations, Loci.

Argand diagram

Any complex number $z = x + iy$ may be represented on an **Argand diagram** by

either (a) the point $P(x, y)$,

or   (b) the position vector $\overrightarrow{OP}$.

The **modulus** of z, $|z|$, is the length of OP.
The **argument** of z, $\arg z$, is the angle θ between OP and the positive real axis, where $-\pi < \theta \leqslant \pi$.

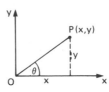

imaginary axis

Figure 1   **real** axis

$$|z| = \sqrt{(x^2 + y^2)}$$

$$\arg z = \theta = \tan^{-1}\left(\frac{y}{x}\right)$$

Polar form (also called modulus-argument form)

The **polar form** of a complex number is
$z = r(\cos\theta + i\sin\theta)$,
where $r = OP$ and $\theta = x\hat{O}P$.

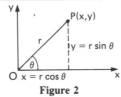

Figure 2

$|z| = r$, where $r \geqslant 0$.
$\arg z = \theta$, where $-\pi < \theta \leqslant \pi$.

$z^* = r(\cos\theta - i\sin\theta)$
$ = r(\cos(-\theta) + i\sin(-\theta))$

$|z^*| = r$ and $\arg z^* = -\theta$.

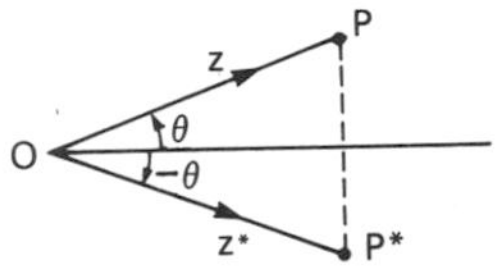

Figure 3

ℹ️ *Express the complex number $\sqrt{3} - i$ in polar form and illustrate it on an Argand diagram.*

Let $\sqrt{3} - i = r(\cos\theta + i\sin\theta)$.

$r = |z|$
$ = \sqrt{((\sqrt{3})^2 + (-1)^2)} = 2$
$\theta = \arg z$
$ = \tan^{-1}\left(\frac{-1}{\sqrt{3}}\right) = -\frac{\pi}{6}$

So, in polar form $\sqrt{3} - i$ is
$2(\cos(-\pi/6) + i\sin(-\pi/6))$

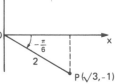

Figure 4

Multiplication and division in polar form

Let $z_1 = r_1(\cos\theta + i\sin\theta)$ and $z_2 = r_2(\cos\phi + i\sin\phi)$.

multiplication: $z_1 z_2 = r_1 r_2[\cos(\theta + \phi) + i\sin(\theta + \phi)]$

$|z_1 z_2| = |z_1||z_2|$ and $\arg(z_1 z_2) = \arg z_1 + \arg z_2$

division: $\dfrac{z_1}{z_2} = \dfrac{r_1}{r_2}[\cos(\theta - \phi) + i\sin(\theta - \phi)]$

$\left|\dfrac{z_1}{z_2}\right| = \dfrac{|z_1|}{|z_2|}$ and $\arg\left(\dfrac{z_1}{z_2}\right) = \arg z_1 - \arg z_2$

ℹ️ *If $z_1 = 4(\cos\pi/3 + i\sin\pi/3)$ and $z_2 = 2(\cos\pi/6 + i\sin\pi/6)$, evaluate:*
(a) $z_1 z_2$ and (b) $z_1 \div z_2$.

(a) $z_1 z_2 = 4(\cos\pi/3 + i\sin\pi/3) \times 2(\cos\pi/6 + i\sin\pi/6)$
$ = 8[\cos(\pi/3 + \pi/6) + i\sin(\pi/3 + \pi/6)]$
$ = 8(\cos\pi/2 + i\sin\pi/2)$

(b) $z_1 \div z_2 = \dfrac{4(\cos\pi/3 + i\sin\pi/3)}{2(\cos\pi/6 + i\sin\pi/6)}$
$ = 2[\cos(\pi/3 - \pi/6) + i\sin(\pi/3 - \pi/6)]$
$ = 2(\cos\pi/6 + i\sin\pi/6)$

Geometric representation of operations

addition $z_1 + z_2$

Figure 5

subtraction $z_1 - z_2$

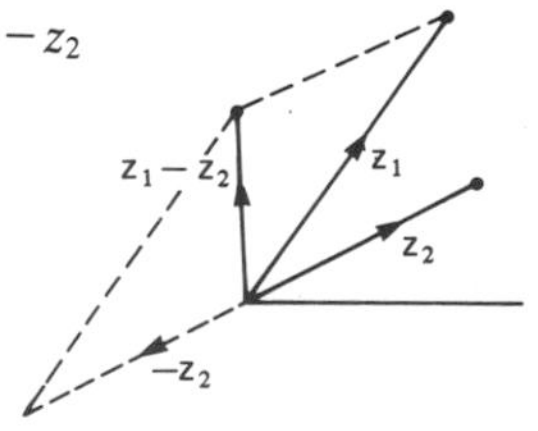

Figure 6

multiplication $z_1 z_2$

Figure 7

division $z_1 \div z_2$

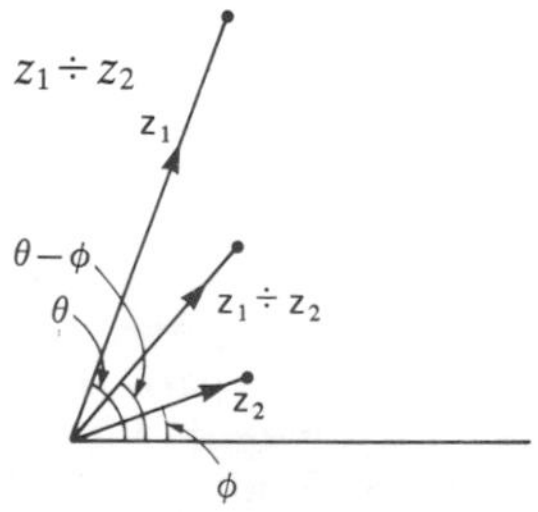

Figure 8

Loci

If z is a **variable complex number**, represented by the position vector $\overrightarrow{OZ}$, then the **locus** of Z under certain conditions can be sketched. Four common loci are illustrated below.

The locus of Z when
$|z| = a$
is a circle, centre O radius a.

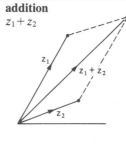

Figure 9

The locus of Z when
$\arg z = \alpha$, $(-\pi < \alpha \leqslant \pi)$
is a half line from 0, at an angle α with the real axis.

Figure 11

The locus of Z when
$|z - p| = a$,
where p is a fixed complex number, is a circle, centre P, radius a.

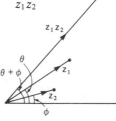

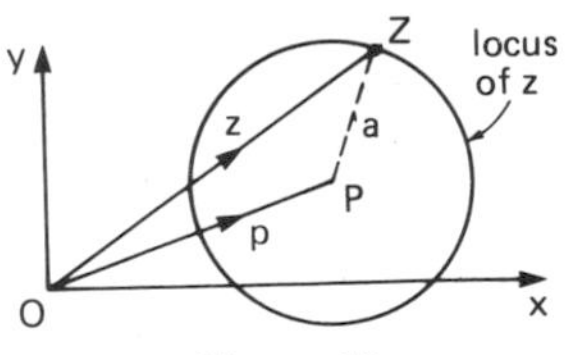

Figure 10

The locus of Z when
$\arg(z - p) = \arg q$,
where p and q are fixed complex numbers, is a half line from P, parallel to OQ.

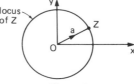

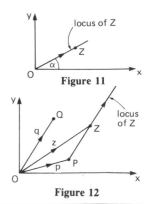

Figure 12

Complex Numbers and Graphs
Worked example, Guided example and Exam questions.

WE (a) *Indicate on an Argand diagram the region in which z lies if* $|z-2+3i| \leq 2$.

(b) *If the real part of* $\dfrac{z+1}{z-1}$ *is zero, show that the locus of the point representing z in the Argand plane is a circle and write down its centre and radius.*

(a) $|z-2+3i| \leq 2$ can be rewritten as $|z-(2-3i)| \leq 2$. This says that the distance between the fixed point $2-3i$ and the variable point z in the Argand plane must always be less than or equal to 2. i.e. the region in which z lies is the circular disc, centre $2-3i$ and radius 2, shown in the Argand diagram.

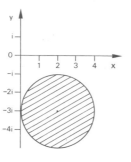

(b) Let $z = x + iy$,

then $\dfrac{z+1}{z-1} = \dfrac{x+iy+1}{x+iy-1}$

$= \dfrac{[(x+1)+iy][(x-1)-iy]}{[(x-1)+iy][(x-1)-iy]}$

$= \dfrac{(x^2-1+y^2)+i(-2y)}{(x-1)^2+y^2}$

If the real part of $\dfrac{z+1}{z-1} = 0$,

then $x^2 - 1 + y^2 = 0$
$\Rightarrow \quad x^2 + y^2 = 1$.
Hence the locus of z is a circle, centre $(0,0)$, radius 1.

GE *Express the complex numbers* $z = \sqrt{2} + i\sqrt{2}$ *and*

$w = -3 + i3\sqrt{3}$ *in modulus-argument form and hence write down the modulus and argument of each of the following:*

(i) $\dfrac{1}{z}$ (ii) zw (iii) $\dfrac{z}{w}$

Show in an Argand diagram the points representing the complex

numbers $\dfrac{1}{z}, zw, \dfrac{z}{w}$.

Let $z = r(\cos\theta + i\sin\theta) = \sqrt{2} + i\sqrt{2}$, and find r and θ.
Hence z can be written in modulus-argument form.
Do the same for $w = -3 + i3\sqrt{3}$.

(i) $\dfrac{1}{z} = \dfrac{1}{r}(\cos\theta - i\sin\theta)$

(ii) To find zw, multiply the moduli and add the arguments.

(iii) To find $\dfrac{z}{w}$, divide the moduli and subtract the arguments.

Having written down (i), (ii) and (iii), the points representing these complex numbers can easily be shown in an Argand diagram.

EX **1** (a) The complex number $z_1 = 2i$. Find the values of a and b such that: $(a+ib)^2 = z_1$.
If these two resulting complex numbers are z_2 and z_3, express z_1, z_2 and z_3 in modulus-argument form and display all three on the same Argand diagram.
(b) The complex number $z_4 = \sqrt{3} + i$. Find $(z_4)^2$. Express z_4 and $(z_4)^2$ in modulus-argument form and display them on the same Argand diagram. Deduce a further complex number z_5 such that: $(z_5)^2 = (z_4)^2$.   *(S)*

2 Express $\dfrac{1}{1+i\sqrt{3}}$ in the form $r(\cos\theta + i\sin\theta)$ where $r > 0$ and $-\pi < \theta \leq \pi$.   *(J)*

3 Given that $z = \sqrt{3} + i$, find the modulus and argument of (a) z^2, (b) $\dfrac{1}{z}$.
Show in an Argand diagram the points representing the complex numbers z, z^2 and $\dfrac{1}{z}$.   *(L)*

4 You are given that $z = \cos\theta + i\sin\theta$ ($0 < \theta < \frac{1}{2}\pi$). Draw an Argand diagram to illustrate the relative positions of the points representing z, $z+1$, $z-1$. Hence, or otherwise,
(a) determine the modulus and argument of each of these three complex numbers;
(b) prove that the real part of $\dfrac{z-1}{z+1}$ is zero.   *(O & C)*

5 Shade in an Argand diagram the region of the z-plane in which one or the other, but not both, of the following inequalities is satisfied: (i) $|z| \leq 1$, (ii) $|z-1-i| \leq 2$. Your diagram should show clearly which parts of the boundary are included.   *(J)*

6 (a) The points P and Q in an Argand diagram represent the complex numbers $7-i$ and $12+4i$ respectively, and O is the origin. Prove that the triangle OPQ is isosceles, and calculate to the nearest degree the size of angle OPQ.
(b) Identify the locus of the point representing the complex number z in each of the following cases:
(i) $|z-(1+i)| = 1$; (ii) $|z-1| = |z+i|$; (iii) $\arg(z-1) = \frac{1}{2}\pi$.   *(C)*

7 Sketch on the same Argand diagram the loci of z and w, where $|z| = |z-4i|$ and $|w+2| = 1$. State (i) the minimum value of $|z-w|$; (ii) the cartesian form of z for which $\arg z = \dfrac{\pi}{4}$.   *(A)*

8 If $z = 5+5i$ and $w = 7+i$, find (a) $z-w$, (b) $1/(z+w)$, expressing each in the form $x+iy$, where x and y are real. Verify that the real part of $(z-w)/(z+w)$ is zero. If, in the Argand diagram, P represents the position of $z-w$ and Q the position of $z+w$, what does the result imply about $P\hat{O}Q$?   *(O & C)*

9 In an Argand diagram, the point P represents the complex number z, where $z = x+iy$. Given that $z+2 = \lambda i(z+8)$, where λ is a real parameter, find the Cartesian equation of the locus of P as λ varies.
If also $z = \mu(4+3i)$, where μ is real, prove that there is only one possible position for P.   *(J)*

10 Find the modulus and argument of the complex number $\dfrac{1-3i}{1+3i}$. Show that, as the real number t varies, the point representing $\dfrac{1-it}{1+it}$ in the Argand diagram moves round a circle, and write down the radius and centre of the circle.   *(OLE)*

11 Indicate on an Argand diagram the region in which z lies, given that both $|z-(3+i)| \leq 3$ and $\dfrac{\pi}{4} \leq \arg[z-(1+i)] \leq \dfrac{\pi}{2}$ are satisfied.   *(J)*

P42 Methods of Differentiation
Implicit differentiation, Parametric differentiation, Logarithmic differentiation.

Implicit differentiation

An **implicit function** in two variables, x and y say, is one in which neither variable can be easily expressed in terms of the other.

To differentiate such an implicit function
(a) Differentiate it term by term to give an equation

in $\dfrac{dy}{dx}$, x and y.

(b) Make $\dfrac{dy}{dx}$ the subject of the equation.

To obtain the second derivative
(a) Differentiate the '$\dfrac{dy}{dx}$ equation' to obtain an

equation for $\dfrac{d^2y}{dx^2}$.

(b) Substitute for $\dfrac{dy}{dx}$ if necessary.

Repeat the procedure for higher derivatives.

|i| *Find $\dfrac{dy}{dx}$ when $x^3+y^3=3xy$*

$x^3+y^3=3xy$ is an implicit function.

Differentiating term by term gives

$$3x^2+3y^2.\frac{dy}{dx}=3y+3x.\underbrace{\frac{dy}{dx}}_{\text{product rule}}$$

$$(y^2-x)\frac{dy}{dx}=(y-x^2)$$

$$\frac{dy}{dx}=\frac{(y-x^2)}{(y^2-x)}$$

Parametric differentiation

If x and y are each expressed in terms of a third variable, t say, called the **parameter**, then $x=f(t)$ and $y=g(t)$ give the **parametric form** of the equation relating x and y.

To differentiate such a parametric form of an equation
(a) Find $\dfrac{dx}{dt}$ and $\dfrac{dy}{dt}$ separately. Do not attempt

to eliminate the parameter.

(b) Use $\dfrac{dy}{dx}=\dfrac{dy}{dt}.\dfrac{dt}{dx}$.

To obtain the second derivative
(a) Find $\dfrac{d}{dt}\left(\dfrac{dy}{dx}\right)$.

(b) Use $\dfrac{d^2y}{dx^2}=\dfrac{d}{dx}\left(\dfrac{dy}{dx}\right)=\dfrac{d}{dt}\left(\dfrac{dy}{dx}\right).\dfrac{dt}{dx}$.

|i| *The parametric equation of an ellipse is $x=a\cos\theta$, $y=b\sin\theta$, where a and b are constants. Find $\dfrac{dy}{dx}$ as a function of θ.*

$$x=a\cos\theta \qquad\qquad y=b\sin\theta$$
$$\frac{dx}{d\theta}=-a\sin\theta \qquad\qquad \frac{dy}{d\theta}=b\cos\theta$$

Using $\dfrac{dy}{dx}=\dfrac{dy}{d\theta}.\dfrac{d\theta}{dx}=b\cos\theta.\dfrac{1}{-a\sin\theta}=-\dfrac{b}{a}\cot\theta$

|i| *The coordinates of a point on a curve are given parametrically by $x=t+\dfrac{1}{t}$ and $y=t-\dfrac{1}{t}$. Find $\dfrac{dy}{dx}$ and $\dfrac{d^2y}{dx^2}$ in terms of t.*

$$x=t+\frac{1}{t}=t+t^{-1} \qquad\qquad y=t-\frac{1}{t}=t-t^{-1}$$
$$\frac{dx}{dt}=1-t^{-2} \qquad\qquad \frac{dy}{dt}=1+t^{-2}$$

Using $\dfrac{dy}{dx}=\dfrac{dy}{dt}.\dfrac{dt}{dx}=(1+t^{-2})\dfrac{1}{1-t^{-2}}=\dfrac{t^2+1}{t^2-1}$.

$$\frac{d}{dt}\left(\frac{dy}{dx}\right)=\frac{d}{dt}\left(\frac{t^2+1}{t^2-1}\right)$$
$$=\frac{(t^2-1)2t-(t^2+1)2t}{(t^2-1)^2}=\frac{-4t}{(t^2-1)^2}$$

$$\frac{d^2y}{dx^2}=\frac{d}{dt}\left(\frac{dy}{dx}\right).\frac{dt}{dx}=\frac{-4t}{(t^2-1)^2}.\frac{t^2}{(t^2-1)}=\frac{-4t^3}{(t^2-1)^3}.$$

Logarithmic differentiation

To differentiate a function of the form $y=[f(x)]^{g(x)}$
(a) Take logarithms of the given function.
(b) Differentiate the new function as usual.

This method is useful when differentiating complicated products and quotients.

|i| *Differentiate x^{2x} with respect to x.*

Let $y=x^{2x}$

so $\ln y=2x\ln x$

$$\frac{1}{y}\frac{dy}{dx}=2\ln x+2x.\frac{1}{x}$$

$$\frac{dy}{dx}=2y(\ln x+1)$$

$$=2x^{2x}(\ln x+1)$$

(a) *Given that $x^2 - 3xy + 2y^2 - 2x = 4$, find the value of $\dfrac{dy}{dx}$ at the point·$(1, -1)$.*

(b) *If $x = \dfrac{2t}{t+2}$ and $y = \dfrac{3t}{t+3}$, find the value of $\dfrac{dy}{dx}$ at the point $\left(\dfrac{2}{3}, \dfrac{3}{4}\right)$.*

(a) $x^2 - 3xy + 2y^2 - 2x = 4$ is an implicit function.
Differentiating with respect to x gives

$$2x - 3 \cdot \underbrace{\left(y + x\frac{dy}{dx}\right)}_{\substack{\text{product rule} \\ \text{and chain rule}}} + \underbrace{4y\frac{dy}{dx}}_{\text{chain rule}} - 2 = 0.$$

Factorise to find $\dfrac{dy}{dx}$ explicitly,

i.e. $(4y - 3x)\dfrac{dy}{dx} = 2 - 2x + 3y$

$\Rightarrow \qquad \dfrac{dy}{dx} = \dfrac{2 - 2x + 3y}{4y - 3x}.$

At the point $(1, -1)$,

$$\frac{dy}{dx} = \frac{2 - 2 \times 1 + 3\,(-1)}{4\,(-1) - 3}$$

$$= \frac{3}{7}.$$

(b) x and y are expressed in parametric form.

$x = \dfrac{2t}{t+2}$,

so, $\dfrac{dx}{dt} = \dfrac{(t+2).2 - 2t.1}{(t+2)^2} = \dfrac{4}{(t+2)^2}$ (using quotient rule).

$y = \dfrac{3t}{t+3}$,

so, $\dfrac{dy}{dt} = \dfrac{(t+3).3 - 3t.1}{(t+3)^2} = \dfrac{9}{(t+3)^2}$ (using quotient rule).

Using $\dfrac{dy}{dx} = \dfrac{dy}{dt} \times \dfrac{dt}{dx}$, we have,

$$\frac{dy}{dx} = \frac{9}{(t+3)^2} \times \frac{(t+2)^2}{4}.$$

At the point $\left(\dfrac{2}{3}, \dfrac{3}{4}\right)$, $t = 1$,

so, $\dfrac{dy}{dx} = \dfrac{9}{(1+3)^2} \times \dfrac{(1+2)^2}{4}$

$$= \frac{81}{64}.$$

 A function y of x is given by the equation

$$y = \frac{(1 - x^2)e^{-x}}{1 + x^2} \quad (|x| < 1)$$

Find $\dfrac{dy}{dx}$ when $x = 0$.

$y = \dfrac{(1 - x^2)e^{-x}}{1 + x^2} \quad (|x| < 1)$

So, $\ln y = \ln\left[\dfrac{(1 - x^2)e^{-x}}{1 + x^2}\right]$

$= \ln(1 - x^2) + \ln e^{-x} - \ln(1 + x^2)$

$= \ln(1 - x^2) - x - \ln(1 + x^2).$

Differentiating with respect to x gives:

$$\frac{1}{y}\frac{dy}{dx} = \frac{-2x}{1 - x^2} - 1 - \frac{2x}{1 + x^2}$$

$\Rightarrow \qquad \dfrac{dy}{dx} = \left(\dfrac{(1 - x^2)e^{-x}}{1 + x^2}\right)\left(\dfrac{-2x}{1 - x^2} - 1 - \dfrac{2x}{1 + x^2}\right)$

When $x = 0$, $\dfrac{dy}{dx} = (1)(-1) = -1$.

 1 Find expressions for $\dfrac{dy}{dx}$ for the following curves.
Give your answers in terms of x and y.
(a) $x^2 - y^2 = 10$ (b) $x^3 - 2y^2 + 7 = 0$
(c) $x^4 - y^4 = 2xy$ (d) $x^2 + 6xy + y^2 = 5$.

2 The parametric equations of a curve are
$x = 3t^2 - 1, \quad y = t(t^2 - 3)$.
(a) Find $\dfrac{dy}{dx}$, leaving your answer in terms of t.
(b) Calculate the two values of t for which $\dfrac{dy}{dx} = 0$ and find the cartesian coordinates of the points on the curve where $\dfrac{dy}{dx} = 0$.

3 Given that $x = \dfrac{2t}{t-2}$ and $y = \dfrac{3t}{t-3}$, find $\dfrac{dy}{dx}$ in terms of the parameter, t.
Find the values of t for which
(a) $\dfrac{dy}{dx}$ is not defined   (b) $\dfrac{dy}{dx} = 0$ (c) $\dfrac{dy}{dx} = 1$.

4 Use logarithmic differentiation to find $\dfrac{dy}{dx}$ when
(a) $y = \sqrt{\dfrac{x - 1}{x + 1}}$ (b) $y = x^{\sin x}$ (c) $y = x^{e^x}$
(d) $y = \sqrt{\dfrac{(2x - 1)(2x - 2)}{2x - 3}}$.

5 A function y of x is defined parametrically by
$x = t - \sin t, \; y = 1 - \cos t$.
(i) Find $\dfrac{dy}{dx}$.   (ii) Show that $y^2\dfrac{d^2 y}{dx^2} + 1 = 0$.
                                                 (N)

For questions 6 to 8, see also Unit P43.

6 A curve is defined parametrically by the equations
$x = t^3 - 6t + 4, \; y = t - 3 + \dfrac{2}{t}$. Find
(i) the equations of the normals to the curve at the points where the curve mets the x-axis .
(ii) the coordinates of their point of intersection.
                                                 (C)

7 Show that the normal to the curve $y = \tan x$ at the point P whose coordinates are $\left(\dfrac{\pi}{4}, 1\right)$ meets the x-axis at the point A $\left(\dfrac{\pi + 8}{4}, 0\right)$.   (L)

8 (i) Derive an expression for the gradient, at any point (x, y), on the curve whose equation is given by
$ye^x + \log_e(x + 1) - y^2 + 2 = 0$.
(ii) Find the equation of the normal to this curve at the point $(0, 2)$.   (N)

Applications of Differentiation
Gradient, tangent and normal, Velocity and acceleration, Small changes.

Gradient, tangent and normal

The gradient of a curve at any point P is defined to be equal to the gradient of the tangent at P.

Gradient of curve = gradient of tangent = $\dfrac{dy}{dx}$.

To find the gradient of curve $y = f(x)$ at $P(x_1, y_1)$, find $\dfrac{dy}{dx}$ and calculate its value when $x = x_1$, $y = y_1$.

The normal to a curve at a point is perpendicular to the tangent at that point.
If tangent and normal at $P(x_1, y_1)$ have gradients m_1 and m_2, then $m_1 m_2 = -1$
$\Rightarrow\ m_2 = \dfrac{-1}{m_1}$.

Equation of tangent at $P(x_1, y_1)$: $y - y_1 = m_1(x - x_1)$
Equation of normal at $P(x_1, y_1)$: $y - y_1 = m_2(x - x_1)$
or $y - y_1 = \dfrac{-1}{m_1}(x - x_1)$

The same method is also used when the equation of the curve is given as an implicit function of x or in parametric form (see Worked example).

---

i *Find the gradient and equations of the tangent and normal to* $y = 5x^3 - 7x^2 + 3x - 3$ *at the point* $(1, -2)$.

$$y = 5x^3 - 7x^2 + 3x - 3 \ \Rightarrow\ \frac{dy}{dx} = 15x^2 - 14x + 3.$$

At $(1, -2)$, $x = 1$ and $\dfrac{dy}{dx} = 15(1)^2 - 14(1) + 3 = 4$.

$\therefore$ the gradient of the curve at $(1, -2)$ is 4.

Gradient of tangent at $(1, -2)$ is 4.

The equation of the tangent at $(1, -2)$ is:
$$y - (-2) = 4(x - 1)$$
$$\Leftrightarrow\ y = 4x - 6$$

If m is the gradient of the normal at $(1, -2)$, then
$$4 \times m = -1\ \Rightarrow\ m = -\tfrac{1}{4}.$$

The equation of the normal at $(1, -2)$ is:
$$y - (-2) = -\tfrac{1}{4}(x - 1)$$
$$\Leftrightarrow\ 4y + x + 7 = 0$$

Velocity and acceleration

A particle is moving in a straight line so that its displacement s from a fixed point on the line after time t is given by $s = f(t)$.

Velocity v is the **rate of change of displacement** s with respect to time t, i.e. $v = \dfrac{ds}{dt}$.

If $v = 0$, the particle is **at rest**.
If $v < 0$, the particle is moving in the **opposite direction** to that in which s is measured.

Acceleration a is the **rate of change of velocity** v with respect to time t, i.e $a = \dfrac{dv}{dt}$.

But $v = \dfrac{ds}{dt}$, so $a = \dfrac{dv}{dt} = \dfrac{d}{dt}\left(\dfrac{ds}{dt}\right) = \dfrac{d^2 s}{dt^2}$.

Also $a = \dfrac{dv}{dt} = \dfrac{dv}{ds} \cdot \dfrac{ds}{dt}$ and $\dfrac{ds}{dt} = v$,

so $a = \dfrac{dv}{ds} \cdot v$ or $v \cdot \dfrac{dv}{ds}$.

So acceleration a is given by $\dfrac{dv}{dt}$ or $\dfrac{d^2 s}{dt^2}$ or $v \cdot \dfrac{dv}{ds}$.

If $a = 0$, the velocity of the particle is **constant**.
If $a > 0$, the particle is **accelerating**.
If $a < 0$, the particle is being **retarded**.

---

i *A particle moves in a straight line so that its distance from a fixed point 0 after t seconds is s metres where* $s = \tfrac{1}{3}t^3 - \tfrac{3}{2}t^2 + 2t$. *Show that the particle is at rest at two different times and find these times. Find the acceleration of the particle at these times and interpret the results.*

$$s = \tfrac{1}{3}t^3 - \tfrac{3}{2}t^2 + 2t$$

So velocity $v = \dfrac{ds}{dt} = t^2 - 3t + 2$.

The particle is at rest when $v = 0$,
i.e. when $t^2 - 3t + 2 = 0$
or $(t - 1)(t - 2) = 0 \ \Rightarrow\ t = 1$ or $t = 2$.

So the particle is at rest at two different times: after 1 second and after 2 seconds.

Acceleration $a = \dfrac{dv}{dt} = \dfrac{d^2 s}{dt^2} = 2t - 3$.

When $t = 1$, $a = 2(1) - 3 = -1$,
i.e. acceleration is -1 m s^{-2}.

So after 1 second, the particle is being retarded (slowing down).

When $t = 2$, $a = 2(2) - 3 = 1$,
i.e. acceleration is 1 m s^{-2}. So after 2 seconds, the particle is being accelerated (speeding up).

Small changes

If $y = f(x)$, then by definition: $\displaystyle\lim_{\delta x \to 0}\left(\dfrac{\delta y}{\delta x}\right) = \dfrac{dy}{dx}$. So when δx is small, we can say $\dfrac{\delta y}{\delta x} \approx \dfrac{dy}{dx} \Rightarrow \delta y \approx \dfrac{dy}{dx} \cdot \delta x$.

This approximation can be used to estimate the small change δy in y due to a small change δx in x (see **i**). It can also be used to estimate percentage changes.

If x is changed by $P\%$, then $\delta x = \dfrac{P}{100} \times x$.

This expression of δx is used to estimate δy. Then the approximate percentage change in y is given by:
$$\dfrac{\delta y}{y} \times 100\%.$$

(See Guided example.)

---

i *The radius r of a circle is* 5 cm. *Find the increase in the area A of the circle when the radius expands by* 0.01 cm.

Let the small increase in A be δA and the small increase in r be δr.

For a circle, radius r: $A = \pi r^2$ and $\dfrac{dA}{dr} = 2\pi r$.

Since $\delta A \approx \dfrac{dA}{dr} \cdot \delta r$, we have $\delta A \approx 2\pi r \cdot \delta r$.

When $r = 5$ cm and $\delta r = 0.01$ cm,

$\delta A \approx 2\pi(5)(0.01)$ cm$^2 \approx 0.314$ cm^2.

So the area increases by approximately 0.314 cm^2.

Applications of Differentiation
Worked examples, Guided example and Exam questions.

 A rectangular hyperbola has parametric equations
$x = at$, $y = \dfrac{a}{t}$, *where t is a parameter* $(t \in \mathbb{R}, \; t \neq 0)$, *a is a*
positive constant.
(a) Find and simplify the equation of the tangent at the point
with parameter t.
(b) The normal at A (parameter t = 3) meets the curve again
at B. Find the value of t at B.

(a) $\quad x = at \qquad$ and $\quad y = \dfrac{a}{t}$ i.e. $y = at^{-1}$

$\Rightarrow \dfrac{dx}{dt} = a \qquad\qquad \Rightarrow \dfrac{dy}{dt} = -at^{-2} = \dfrac{-a}{t^2}.$

Gradient of tangent: $\dfrac{dy}{dx} = \dfrac{dy}{dt} \cdot \dfrac{dt}{dx} = -\dfrac{a}{t^2} \times \dfrac{1}{a} = -\dfrac{1}{t^2}.$

Equation of tangent: $\quad y - \dfrac{a}{t} = -\dfrac{1}{t^2}(x - at)$

$\Rightarrow t^2 y + x - 2at = 0.$

(b) At A, $t = 3 \Rightarrow x = 3a$, $y = \frac{1}{3}a$.
Gradient of tangent $= -\frac{1}{9} \Rightarrow$ Gradient of normal $= 9$.
Equation of normal: $y - \frac{1}{3}a = 9(x - 3a)$
$\Rightarrow 3y = 27x - 80a.$

This line meets the curve where $3\left(\dfrac{a}{t}\right) = 27(at) - 80a$

$\Rightarrow 0 = a(27t^2 - 80t - 3) \Rightarrow 0 = a(t - 3)(27t + 1)$
$\Rightarrow t = 3$ or $t = -\frac{1}{27}$ since $a \neq 0$.
$\therefore$ at A, $t = 3$. At B, $t = -\frac{1}{27}$.

 A curve has the equation $x^3 + x^2 y + y^3 = 3$. *Show that, at the*
point $(2, -1)$, *the slope of the curve is* $-\frac{8}{7}$ *and the equation*
of the normal is $8y = 7x - 22$.

Differentiating the implicit function $x^3 + x^2 y + y^3 = 3$ gives:

$3x^2 + 2xy + x^2 \dfrac{dy}{dx} + 3y^2 \dfrac{dy}{dx} = 0 \Rightarrow \dfrac{dy}{dx} = \dfrac{-3x^2 - 2xy}{x^2 + 3y^2}.$

At the point $(2, -1)$, $x = 2$, $y = -1$ and the slope is:

$\dfrac{dy}{dx} = \dfrac{-3(2)^2 - 2(2)(-1)}{(2)^2 + 3(-1)^2} = \dfrac{-12 + 4}{4 + 3} = -\dfrac{8}{7}.$

Gradient of normal is $\frac{7}{8}$ since $-\frac{8}{7} \times \frac{7}{8} = -1$.

Equation of normal is $y - (-1) = \frac{7}{8}(x - 2)$
$\Rightarrow 8y + 8 = 7x - 14$
$\Rightarrow 8y = 7x - 22.$

A particle P moves in a straight line such that its distance
s metres from a fixed point O at time t seconds, where $t \geq 0$, *is*
given by $s = 9t^2 - 2t^3$. *What is the velocity and acceleration*
of P when t = 3? Find also the distance of P from O when t = 4
and show that it is then moving towards O.

distance (s) $\qquad$ velocity (v) $\qquad$ acceleration (a)

$s = 9t^2 - 2t^3 \Rightarrow v = \dfrac{ds}{dt} = 18t - 6t^2 \Rightarrow a = \dfrac{d^2 s}{dt^2} = 18 - 12t$

When $t = 3$, $v = 18t - 6t^2 = 18(3) - 6(3)^2 = 0$, and
$a = 18 - 12t = 18 - 12(3) = -18.$

$\therefore$ the velocity of P is 0 m s^{-1} (i.e. P is stationary) and
the acceleration of P is -18 m s^{-2} (i.e. a retardation).

When $t = 4$, $s = 9t^2 - 2t^3 = 9(4)^2 - 2(4)^3 = 16$, and
$v = 18t - 6t^2 = 18(4) - 6(4)^2 = -24.$

$\therefore$ P is 16 m from O, moving with a velocity of -24 m s^{-1}.
The negative sign shows that P is moving towards O.

 The period T of a simple pendulum is calculated using the
formula $T = 2\pi \sqrt{\dfrac{l}{g}}$ *where l is the length of the pendulum*
and g is a constant. Find the percentage change in the period
if the pendulum is lengthened by 2%.

Use $\delta T \approx \dfrac{dT}{dl} \cdot \delta l$ to estimate the δT caused by δl.

When finding $\dfrac{dT}{dl}$, write $\sqrt{l}$ as $l^{\frac{1}{2}}$ in the formula for T.

Write δl (the increase of 2%) as a fraction of l.

To give δT as a percentage of T, use $\dfrac{\delta T}{T} \times 100\%.$

---

1 A ball is thrown vertically upwards. The height, h metres,
of the ball above the ground at time t seconds, can be
modelled using the formula $h = 2 + 10t - 5t^2$.
Find the velocity of the ball when $t = 1.5$ seconds.
$\hfill (OLE)$

2 A particle moves along a line so that its distance x metre
from O after t second is given by $x = t^3 - 9t^2 + 24t$.
  (i) Find the velocity v in terms of t, and the values of t
  for which the particle is at rest.
  (ii) Calculate the distance between the two points where
  the particle is instantaneously at rest.
  (iii) Calculate the acceleration of the particle at the times
  when it is instantaneously at rest.
  (iv) Find the distance of the particle from O when its
  acceleration is zero. $\hfill (O \& C)$

3 A speaker uses an amplifier to carry her words to
members of the audience x metre away. The power output,
P watt, is given by the formula $P = 0.0004 x^2$.
  (i) To increase the distance by a small amount δx metre,
  the output must be increased by δP watt. Find an
  approximate expression for δP in terms of x and δx.
  (ii) Show that $\dfrac{\delta P}{P} \approx 2 \dfrac{\delta x}{x}$.
  (iii) If the power output of the amplifier is increased by
  2%, by what percentage approximately is the
  distance her voice will carry increased? $\hfill (O \& C)$

4 Find the gradient of the curve $y + y^3 = x - x^2$ at the point
$(2, -1)$. $\hfill (C)$

5 A curve has the equation $y = x \sin 2x$. Find the gradient of
the curve at $x = \pi / 3$. $\hfill (J)$

6 The point on the graph of $y = \ln x$ for which $x = e$ is
denoted by A.
  (i) State the y-coordinate of A in its simplest form.
  (ii) Find the gradient of the graph at A.
  (iii) Find the equation of the tangent to the graph at A, in
  as simple a form as possible.
  (iv) Show that the tangent at A passes through the origin.
$\hfill (O \& C)$

7 A curve is defined by the parametric equations
$x = \theta - \sin \theta$, $y = 1 - \cos \theta$, $0 < \theta < 2\pi$.
Show that $\dfrac{dy}{dx} = \cot \dfrac{\theta}{2}$, and find the equation of the
tangent and of the normal to the curve at the point
where $\theta = \dfrac{\pi}{2}$. $\hfill (J)$

P44 Methods of Integration II
Trig functions, Trig substitution, Fractions.

Trig functions

1. Simple trig functions

Use standard results (given on p. 47 and p. 89).

2. Product of the form $f'(x)g[f(x)]$

Use the algebraic substitution $u = f(x)$ (see P24, p. 48) if one factor of the product is the derivative of the function in the other factor.

3. Even powers of sin x or cos x only

Rewrite using a double angle formula (see p. 33).

4. Odd powers of sin x or cos x

Rewrite the odd power in one of these forms:
odd power of $\sin x$ = (even power of $\sin x$) $\times \sin x$
odd power of $\cos x$ = (even power of $\cos x$) $\times \cos x$

Then use $\sin^2 x + \cos^2 x = 1$ to rewrite the even power.

This gives (even power of $\sin x$) in terms of $\cos x$, or (even power of $\cos x$) in terms of $\sin x$.

5. Powers of tan x

Rewrite using $\tan^2 x = \sec^2 x - 1$.

6. Products of the form sin mx cos nx

Use a factor formula (see p. 73) to rewrite the product as a sum or difference.

$\boxed{i}$ $\int \cos 2x = \frac{1}{2}\sin 2x + c$

$\boxed{i}$ For $I = \int \sin^2 x \cos x\, dx$, use $u = \sin x$;
$$\frac{du}{dx} = \cos x.$$
$$I = \int u^2 . \frac{du}{dx} . dx = \int u^2 du = \frac{1}{3}u^3 + c = \frac{1}{3}\sin^3 x + c$$

$\boxed{i}$ $\int \cos^2 x\, dx = \int \frac{1}{2}(1 + \cos 2x)dx = \frac{1}{2}x + \frac{1}{4}\sin 2x + c$

$\boxed{i}$ $\int \cos^3 x\, dx = \int \cos^2 x \cos x\, dx$
$$= \int (1 - \sin^2 x)\cos x\, dx$$
$$= \int \cos x\, dx - \int \sin^2 x \cos x\, dx$$
$$= \sin x - \frac{1}{3}\sin^3 x + c$$

$\boxed{i}$ $\int \tan^2 x\, dx = \int (\sec^2 x - 1)dx = \tan x - x + c$

$\boxed{i}$ $\int \sin 3x \cos x\, dx = \int \frac{1}{2}(\sin 4x + \sin 2x)dx$
$$= -\frac{1}{8}\cos 4x - \frac{1}{4}\cos 2x + c$$

Trig substitution

To integrate some functions we use an algebraic substitution (see P24, p. 48). In some cases substituting a trig function instead of an algebraic one gives a simpler integral.

To integrate $f(x)$ in this way, follow these steps:

(a) Let $x = g(\theta)$. Find $\frac{dx}{d\theta}$.

(b) Replace x in $f(x)$ by $g(\theta)$ to give $f(g(\theta))$. Simplify. Use trig identities if necessary.

(c) Use $\int f(x)dx = \int f(g(\theta))\frac{dx}{d\theta}.d\theta$.

Indefinite integral: give the result in terms of x.
Definite integral: change the limits from x values to θ values and use these to find the answer (see Worked example).

$\boxed{i}$ Find $\int \frac{x}{\sqrt{1 - x^2}}dx$.

Let $x = \sin\theta$. So $\frac{dx}{d\theta} = \cos\theta$.

$\sqrt{1 - x^2} = \sqrt{1 - \sin^2\theta} = \sqrt{\cos^2\theta} = \cos\theta$

$\therefore \int \frac{x}{\sqrt{1 - x^2}}dx = \int \frac{\sin\theta}{\cos\theta}.\cos\theta\, d\theta$
$$= \int \sin\theta\, d\theta$$
$$= -\cos\theta + c = -\sqrt{1 - x^2} + c$$

Fractions

1. Using standard forms

Standard results are given on p. 47 and p. 89.

2. Using recognition

If the numerator is the derivative of all of the denominator, use $\int \frac{f'(x)}{f(x)}dx = \ln|f(x)| + c$.

3. Using substitution

If the numerator is the derivative of a function within the denominator, i.e. $\frac{f'(x)}{g[f(x)]}$, use a suitable substitution, such as $u = f(x)$.

4. Separating the numerator

If the numerator is a simple polynomial, each term in it may give a separate fraction that is easy to integrate.

5. Using partial fractions

If the function is a proper fraction, express it in terms of partial fractions (see p. 52 and p. 54) if this makes it easier to integrate.

6. Using long division

If the function is an improper fraction, divide out to obtain terms that are not fractions together with a proper fraction (see 2nd Worked example). Integrate each term.

$\boxed{i}$ $\int \frac{1}{ax + b}dx = \frac{1}{a}\ln|ax + b| + c$

$\boxed{i}$ $\int \frac{e^x}{e^x + 5}dx = \ln|e^x + 5| + c$ since $\frac{d}{dx}(e^x + 5) = e^x$.

$\boxed{i}$ For $I = \int \frac{\sin x}{\cos^3 x}dx$, use $u = \cos x$; $\frac{du}{dx} = -\sin x$.
$$I = \int \frac{-1}{u^3}du = \int -u^{-3}du = \frac{1}{2}u^{-2} + c = \frac{1}{2\cos^2 x} + c$$

$\boxed{i}$ $\int \frac{x + 1}{1 + x^2}dx = \int \frac{x}{1 + x^2}dx + \int \frac{1}{1 + x^2}dx$
$$= \frac{1}{2}\ln|1 + x^2| + \tan^{-1}x + c$$

$\boxed{i}$ $\int \frac{3x^2 + 2x + 4}{(2x + 1)(1 + x^2)}dx = \int \left[\frac{3}{(2x + 1)} + \frac{1}{(1 + x^2)}\right]dx$
$$= \frac{3}{2}\ln|2x + 1| + \tan^{-1}x + c$$

Methods of Integration II
More standard integrals, Worked examples, Guided example, Exam questions

More standard integrals

At this stage you should know the following standard integrals. In each case, c is the constant of integration.

	function	integral
trigonometrical (x in radians)	$\tan x$	$\ln|\sec x| + c$
	$\operatorname{cosec} x$	$\ln|\tan\tfrac{1}{2}x| + c$
	$\sec x$	$\ln|\sec x + \tan x| + c$
	$\cot x$	$\ln|\sin x| + c$

	function	integral
inverse trigonometrical	$\dfrac{1}{a^2 + x^2}$	$\dfrac{1}{a}\tan^{-1}\left(\dfrac{x}{a}\right) + c$
	$\dfrac{1}{\sqrt{a^2 - x^2}}$	$\sin^{-1}\left(\dfrac{x}{a}\right) + c$

 Using the substitution $x = \tan\theta$, find $\displaystyle\int_0^1 \frac{dx}{(1+x^2)^2}$.

Let $x = \tan\theta$.

Then $\dfrac{dx}{d\theta} = \sec^2\theta$.

Limits:

x	θ
1	$\pi/4$
0	0

Using the substitution gives

$$\int_0^1 \frac{dx}{(1+x^2)^2} = \int_0^{\frac{\pi}{4}} \frac{1}{(1+\tan^2\theta)^2}\sec^2\theta\, d\theta$$

$$= \int_0^{\frac{\pi}{4}} \frac{\sec^2\theta}{\sec^4\theta}\, d\theta = \int_0^{\frac{\pi}{4}} \frac{1}{\sec^2\theta}\, d\theta$$

$$= \int_0^{\frac{\pi}{4}} \cos^2\theta\, d\theta = \frac{1}{2}\int_0^{\frac{\pi}{4}}(1+\cos 2\theta)\, d\theta$$

$$= \left[\frac{\theta}{2} + \frac{1}{4}\sin 2\theta\right]_0^{\frac{\pi}{4}} = \left[\frac{\pi}{8} + \frac{1}{4}\right] - [0+0] = \frac{\pi}{8} + \frac{1}{4}$$

 Evaluate: $\displaystyle\int \frac{x^3 + 2x^2 - 10x - 9}{x^2 - 9}\, dx$.

The function to be integrated is a rational function which is an improper fraction. So divide first.

$$\frac{x^3 + 2x^2 - 10x - 9}{x^2 - 9} = x + 2 + \frac{9 - x}{x^2 - 9}$$

$$= x + 2 + \frac{1}{x - 3} - \frac{2}{x + 3}$$

Hence

$$\int \frac{x^3 + 2x^2 - 10x - 9}{(x-3)(x+3)}\, dx = \int \left[x + 2 + \frac{1}{x-3} - \frac{2}{x+3}\right] dx$$

$$= \tfrac{1}{2}x^2 + 2x + \ln|x-3| - 2\ln|x+3| + c$$

GE *Find the following integrals:*

(a) $\displaystyle\int \frac{2x^2 + 2x + 3}{(x+2)(x^2+3)}\, dx$ (b) $\displaystyle\int \frac{x^2 - 2}{x^2 - 1}\, dx$ (c) $\displaystyle\int \frac{1}{\sqrt{1+x^2}}\, dx$.

(a) Notice that the integrand can be written in partial fractions.

(b) Notice the integrand is a rational function with numerator and denominator of equal degree. This cannot be expressed in partial fractions immediately. Divide out the integrand first, and express in partial fractions. Now integrate.

(c) Use the substitution $x = \tan u$ (since $1 + \tan^2 u = \sec^2 u$). Now integrate the function and substitute for $u = \tan^{-1} x$ at the end.

EX 1 Evaluate (a) $\displaystyle\int_1^4 \left(\sqrt{x} + \frac{1}{\sqrt{x}}\right)^3 dx$ (b) $\displaystyle\int_0^{\frac{\pi}{2}} \cos 2x \sin 4x\, dx$

(c) $\displaystyle\int_0^{\frac{3}{4}} \frac{1 - x}{(x+1)(x^2+1)}\, dx$. *(L)*

2 Given that $y = \dfrac{2x - 1}{(x-2)(5-x)}$

(i) express y in partial fractions (ii) evaluate $\displaystyle\int_3^4 y\, dx$. *(A)*

3 Evaluate the indefinite integrals:

(i) $\displaystyle\int \frac{1}{\sqrt{2x+1}}\, dx$ (ii) $\displaystyle\int \frac{x}{2x+1}\, dx$ (iii) $\displaystyle\int \frac{e^x}{4 - e^{2x}}\, dx$.

(You may find the substitution $e^x = t$ helpful in (iii).) *(O & C)*

4 (a) Using the substitution $y = x + 1$, or otherwise, evaluate: $\displaystyle\int_{-1}^2 \frac{3}{x^2 + 2x + 10}\, dx$.

(b) Find $\displaystyle\int 2x e^{2x}\, dx$.

(c) Find $\displaystyle\int \frac{x - 4}{(x-1)^2(2x+1)}\, dx$. *(W)*

5 Express $f(x) = \dfrac{2x + 1}{x^2(x+1)}$ in partial fractions.

Hence find $\displaystyle\int f(x)\, dx$ for $x > 0$. *(A)*

6 Use partial fractions to find the exact value of $\displaystyle\int_0^{\frac{1}{2}} \frac{1}{1 - x^2}\, dx$, giving your answer in a simplified form involving a single logarithm. *(C)*

7 Using the substitution $2x = \sin\theta$, or otherwise, find the exact value of $\displaystyle\int_0^{\frac{1}{4}} \frac{1}{\sqrt{1 - 4x^2}}\, dx$. *(J)*

8 $f(x) \equiv \dfrac{x^2 + 6x + 7}{(x+2)(x+3)}$, $x \in \mathbf{R}$.

Given that $f(x) \equiv A + \dfrac{B}{x+2} + \dfrac{C}{x+3}$

(a) find the values of the constants A, B and C

(b) show that $\displaystyle\int_0^2 f(x)\, dx = 2 + \ln\left[\frac{25}{18}\right]$. *(L)*

9 Use the substitution $x = 2\cos\theta$, or otherwise, to evaluate $\displaystyle\int_1^{\sqrt{2}} \frac{1}{x^2\sqrt{4 - x^2}}\, dx$, giving your answer in surd form. *(O)*

89

Areas

Before calculating areas, sketch the curve.

1. Area between a curve and the y-axis
The area bounded by
the curve $x = g(y)$,
the y-axis and the
lines $y = c$, $y = d$
is given by

$$\int_c^d x \, dy.$$

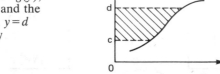

2. Area between two curves
To find the area between two curves, calculate

(a) the x-coordinates of the points of intersection of the curves to give the limits of integration,
(b) the area under each curve separately,
(c) the difference between the areas.

(See Worked example.)

i   *Find the area bounded by the curve $y = x^2 + 2$ ($x \geq 0$), the y-axis and the lines $y = 3$ and $y = 5$.*

Since $x \geq 0$, the required
area, A, is shown shaded
in this sketch.

$$y = x^2 + 2$$
$$\Rightarrow \ x = \sqrt{y - 2} = (y - 2)^{\frac{1}{2}}$$

$$\text{Area } A = \int_3^5 (y - 2)^{\frac{1}{2}} \, dy$$

$$= \left[\frac{2}{3}(y - 2)^{\frac{3}{2}} \right]_3^5$$

$$= \frac{2}{3}\left[(5 - 2)^{\frac{3}{2}} \right] - \frac{2}{3}\left[(3 - 2)^{\frac{3}{2}} \right]$$

$$= \frac{2}{3} \times 3^{\frac{3}{2}} - \frac{2}{3} \times 1^{\frac{3}{2}}$$

$$= \frac{2}{3} \times 3 \times \sqrt{3} - \frac{2}{3}$$

$$= 2\sqrt{3} - \frac{2}{3}$$

$$= \frac{6\sqrt{3} - 2}{3} \quad \text{square units.}$$

Volumes of revolution

Before calculating volumes, sketch the curve.

1. Rotation about the x-axis
The area bounded by
the curve $y = f(x)$,
the x-axis and the
lines $x = a$, $x = b$ is
rotated once about
the x-axis.

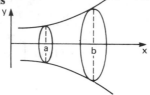

The volume of the solid formed is given by $\int_a^b \pi y^2 \, dx$.

2. Rotation about the y-axis
The area bounded by
the curve $x = g(y)$,
the y-axis and the
lines $y = c$, $y = d$ is
rotated once about
the y-axis.

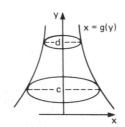

The volume of the solid formed is given by $\int_c^d \pi x^2 \, dy$.
(See Guided example.)

---

i   *Find the volume of the solid formed when the area between the x-axis, the lines $x = 2$ and $x = 4$ and the curve $y = x^2$ is rotated once about the x-axis. Leave your answer as a multiple of π.*

Volume of revolution

$$= \int_2^4 \pi y^2 \, dx$$

$$= \int_2^4 \pi (x^2)^2 \, dx$$

$$= \int_2^4 \pi x^4 \, dx$$

$$= \left[\frac{\pi x^5}{5} \right]_2^4 = \frac{\pi}{5}(4^5 - 2^5)$$

$$= \frac{\pi}{5}(1024 - 32)$$

$$= \frac{992}{5} \pi \text{ cubic units}$$

Mean value

The **mean value** of $y = f(x)$ over a closed interval $a \leq x \leq b$ is defined to be

$$\frac{1}{b - a} \int_a^b y \, dx.$$

---

i   *Find the mean value of $y = \sin x$ over the interval 0 to π.*

$$\text{Mean value} = \frac{1}{\pi - 0} \int_0^\pi \sin x \, dx$$

$$= \frac{1}{\pi}[-\cos x]_0^\pi$$

$$= \frac{1}{\pi}\{[-(-1)] - [-(1)]\}$$

$$= \frac{2}{\pi}$$

Applications of Integration
Worked examples, Guided example and Exam questions.

WE

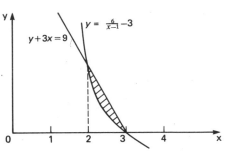

Calculate the shaded area shown between the curve $y = \dfrac{6}{x-1} - 3$

and the straight line $y + 3x = 9$.

The curve $y = \dfrac{6}{x-1} - 3$ and the line $y + 3x = 9$ intersect at $x = 2$

and $x = 3$.

We first calculate Area₁ between $y + 3x = 9$, $x = 2$, $x = 3$ and the x-axis.

Since the shape formed is a trapezium,

$$\text{Area}_1 = \frac{1}{2}[(9 - 3 \times 2) + 0]. \, 1 = \frac{3}{2} \text{ square units.}$$

Area₂ between the curve, $x = 2$, $x = 3$ and the x-axis is

$$\text{Area}_2 = \int_2^3 \left(\frac{6}{x-1} - 3 \right) dx$$

$$= \left[6 \ln |x-1| - 3x \right]_2^3$$

$$= (6 \ln 2 - 9) - (6 \ln 1 - 6)$$

$$= (6 \ln 2 - 3) \text{ square units.}$$

Required area $= \text{Area}_1 - \text{Area}_2$

$$= \frac{3}{2} - (6 \ln 2 - 3)$$

$$= \frac{3}{2} (3 - 4 \ln 2) \text{ square units.}$$

WE *Sketch, on the same axes, those parts of the curve* $y = 16 - x^2$ *and the line* $y = 6x$ *which lie in the same quadrant. Shade the area which satisfies* $y \le 16 - x^2$, $y \ge 6x$ *and* $x \ge 0$. *Find the volume generated when this area is rotated completely about the x-axis, leaving your answer as a multiple of* π.

The required volume is obtained by rotating the area below the curve and between the lines $x = 0$ and $x = 2$ and the x-axis around the x-axis and then subtracting the volume obtained by rotating the triangle with base 2 and height 12 around the x-axis.

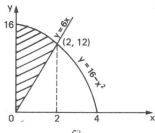

So, volume required $= \displaystyle\int_0^2 \pi(16 - x^2)^2 \, dx - \int_0^2 \pi(6x)^2 \, dx$

$$= \pi \int_0^2 (256 - 32x^2 + x^4 - 36x^2) \, dx$$

$$= \pi \int_0^2 (256 - 68x^2 + x^4) \, dx$$

$$= \pi \left[256x - \frac{68}{3}x^3 + \frac{x^5}{5} \right]_0^2$$

$$= \pi [(512 - 68.\tfrac{8}{3} + \tfrac{32}{5}) - (0)]$$

$$= 337\tfrac{1}{15} \pi \text{ cubic units.}$$

GE *A bowl is formed by rotating about the y-axis the area contained between that part of the curve* $2y = x^2$ *from* $x = 0$ *to* $x = 4$, *the line* $x = 4$ *and the x-axis. Calculate (a) the maximum volume of water the bowl could hold (b) the volume of material forming the bowl.*

First sketch the required area.
To find the volume of water the bowl could hold evaluate the

integral $\displaystyle\int_0^8 \pi \, x^2 \, dy$.

To find the volume of material forming the bowl, calculate the volume of a circular cylinder of radius 4 and height 8 units. Subtract the first volume from this to give the required volume of material.

EX

1. A function $f(x)$ is defined by the formula $f(x) = 2x^4 + 2x^3$, $x \in R$, where R is the set of real numbers.
   (a) Find the stationary points of $f(x)$ and determine their nature, justifying your answers.
   (b) Find where the graph of $f(x)$ meets the x and y axes and make a rough sketch of the graph.
   (c) Calculate the finite area bounded by the x-axis and the graph of $f(x)$. *(H)*

2. Sketch the curve: $y = 1 - \dfrac{4}{x^2}$. The region R is bounded by

   the curve $y = 1 - \dfrac{4}{x^2}$, the x-axis and the lines $x = \frac{1}{2}$ and

   $x = 1$. Find the volume generated when R is rotated completely about the x-axis, leaving your answer as a multiple of π. *(S)*

3. Sketch the graphs of $y^2 = 16x$ and $y = x - 5$. Find
   (i) the co-ordinates of their points of intersection;
   (ii) the area of the finite region enclosed between the graphs. *(A)*

4. Draw a rough sketch of the circle $x^2 + y^2 = 100$, and the curve $9y = 2x^2$; find the co-ordinates of the points A and B where they meet. Calculate the area bounded by the minor arc AB of the circle and the other curve, and the volume obtained by rotating this area about the axis Oy. *(OLE)*

5. The region R in the first quadrant is bounded by the y-axis, the x-axis, the line $x = 3$ and the curve $y^2 = 4 - x$.
   (i) Draw a sketch showing the region R and calculate its area.
   (ii) Calculate the volume formed when R is rotated about the y-axis through one revolution. *(C)*

6. (a) The diagram shows part of the curve $y = \dfrac{12}{x + 2}$. Find

   (i) the area of the shaded region
   (ii) the volume obtained, in terms of π, when the shaded region is rotated through 360° about the x-axis.

   (b) A particle moves in a straight line so that, at time t seconds after leaving a fixed point O, its velocity, v m s⁻¹, is given by $v = 15 \sin \frac{1}{2} t$. Find:
   (i) the time at which the particle first has a speed of 10 m s⁻¹
   (ii) the acceleration of the particle when $t = 0$
   (iii) an expression for the displacement of the particle from O in terms of t. *(C)*

Definitions

A **differential equation** is an equation which contains at least one differential coefficient.
Only **first order** differential equations will be considered here.

The **solution** of a differential equation is an equation relating the variables involved but containing no differential coefficients.
The **general solution** contains an arbitrary constant.
A **particular solution** may be obtained if an 'x value' and a corresponding 'y value' are given. These values are called **boundary conditions** or **initial conditions** and enable the constant to be calculated.

Graphically a differential equation describes a property of a **family of curves**. Its general solution is the equation of any member of that family. Its particular solution is the equation of one particular member of that family.

$\boxed{\text{i}}$ $\dfrac{dy}{dx} = 3x$ is a first order differential equation

because the only differential coefficient is $\dfrac{dy}{dx}$.

Its general solution is $y = \tfrac{3}{2}x^2 + c$.

If $x = 0$ when $y = 1$, then $c = 1$.
So a particular solution is $y = \tfrac{3}{2}x^2 + 1$.

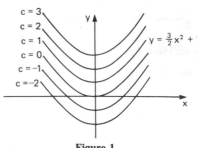

$c = 3$
$c = 2$
$c = 1$
$c = 0$
$c = -1$
$c = -2$
$y = \frac{3}{2}x^2 + 1$

Figure 1

Solution

1. Equations of the form $\dfrac{dy}{dx} = f(x)$

Integrate directly so that $y = \displaystyle\int f(x)\, dx$.

$\boxed{\text{i}}$ *Solve* $\dfrac{dy}{dx} = \dfrac{1}{x}$

$y = \displaystyle\int \dfrac{1}{x}\, dx$

$y = \ln|x| + c$

2. Equations of the form $\dfrac{dy}{dx} = f(y)$

(a) Rewrite the equation in the form $\dfrac{1}{f(y)} \cdot \dfrac{dy}{dx} = 1$.

(b) Integrate directly $\displaystyle\int \dfrac{1}{f(y)} \cdot dy = \int dx$.

$\boxed{\text{i}}$ *Solve* $\dfrac{dy}{dx} = \operatorname{cosec} y$

$\dfrac{1}{\operatorname{cosec} y} \cdot \dfrac{dy}{dx} = 1$

$\displaystyle\int \sin y \cdot dy = \int dx$

$-\cos y = x + c$

3. Equations in which the variables are separable

i.e. of the form $\dfrac{dy}{dx} = \dfrac{f(x)}{g(y)}$ or $f(x) \cdot g(y)$

(a) Separate the variables and rewrite in the form

$$g(y) \cdot \dfrac{dy}{dx} = f(x).$$

(b) Integrate each side separately

$$\int g(y)\, dy = \int f(x)\, dx.$$

$\boxed{\text{i}}$ *Solve* $y(1+x^2)\dfrac{dy}{dx} - 2(1+y^2) = 0$.

Separate the variables $\dfrac{y}{(1+y^2)} \cdot \dfrac{dy}{dx} = \dfrac{2}{(1+x^2)}$

Integrate $\displaystyle\int \dfrac{y}{(1+y^2)} dy = \int \dfrac{2}{(1+x^2)}\, dx$

$\tfrac{1}{2}\ln|(1+y^2)| = 2\tan^{-1}(x) + c$

Formation

Many situations in science and nature are concerned with the rate at which a quantity changes. These can be expressed mathematically as differential equations which can then be solved.
Remember that

'rate of decrease' = −'rate of increase'

$\boxed{\text{i}}$ 1. The rate of decay of the nuclei of radioactive substances is proportional to the number x of nuclei remaining.
Rate of decay of x is $\dfrac{dx}{dt} \propto -x$

So $\dfrac{dx}{dt} = -kx$ (where k is a constant)

2. Suppose that the velocity v of a particle is proportional to the square of its displacement s.
This gives $v \propto s^2$
     i.e. $v = ks^2$ (where k is a constant).

But $v = \dfrac{ds}{dt}$, so $\dfrac{ds}{dt} = ks^2$.

Differential Equations
Worked example, Guided example and Exam questions.

 Solve the differential equation $\dfrac{dy}{dx} = \dfrac{\sin^2 x}{y^2}$ *given that* $y = 1$ *when* $x = 0$.

$\dfrac{dy}{dx} = \dfrac{\sin^2 x}{y^2}$ is a variables separable differential equation.

It can be rewritten as

$$y^2 \frac{dy}{dx} = \sin^2 x.$$

Integrating, $\displaystyle\int y^2 \, dy = \int \sin^2 x \, dx$

giving, $\dfrac{y^3}{3} = \dfrac{1}{2} \displaystyle\int (1 - \cos 2x) \, dx$

i.e. $\dfrac{y^3}{3} = \dfrac{1}{2}\left(x - \dfrac{\sin 2x}{2} \right) + c.$

$$\left[\text{Since } \sin^2 x = \frac{1}{2}(1 - \cos 2x) \right]$$

Since $y = 1$ when $x = 0$,

$\dfrac{1^3}{3} = \dfrac{1}{2}\left(0 - \dfrac{\sin 0}{2} \right) + c$

$\Rightarrow \quad c = \dfrac{1}{3}.$

So the solution is

$\dfrac{y^3}{3} = \dfrac{1}{4}(2x - \sin 2x) + \dfrac{1}{3},$

or $4y^3 = 3(2x - \sin 2x) + 4.$

 Newton's law of cooling states that the rate at which a body, at T°C above the temperature of its surroundings, cools is proportional to T.
A body at 68°C is placed in a room at 16°C and after 5 minutes it has cooled to 55°C. What will be its temperature after a further 5 minutes?

Newton's law gives $\dfrac{dT}{dt} = -kT$, where k is a constant to be determined.

Integrating, $\displaystyle\int \frac{dT}{T} = -k \int 1 \, dt,$

i.e. $\ln T = c - kt$, c is the constant of integration.

So, $T = e^c \cdot e^{-kt}.$

When $t = 0$, $T = 68 - 16 = 52 \Rightarrow e^c = 52$

$\therefore \quad T = 52e^{-kt}$

When $t = 5$, $T = 55 - 16 = 39$

$\therefore \quad 39 = 52e^{-5k} \Rightarrow e^{-5k} = \dfrac{39}{52} = \dfrac{3}{4}$

After a further 5 minutes, i.e. $t = 10$,

$T = 52e^{-10k}$

$= 52(e^{-5k})^2$

$= 52(\tfrac{3}{4})^2$

$= 29\tfrac{1}{4}$

The temperature of the body is therefore $16 + 29\tfrac{1}{4} = 45\tfrac{1}{4}$°C.

 Find the solution of the differential equation $(x+1)\dfrac{dy}{dx} = y$, *given that* $y = 4$ *when* $x = 1$.

Rewrite the differential equation in the form of $\dfrac{dy}{dx} = \dfrac{f(x)}{g(y)}$.

Separate the variables and integrate both sides. Include an arbitrary constant of integration. Use the conditions $y = 4$ when $x = 1$ to find the constant of integration.

 1 Find y in terms of x given that $x\dfrac{dy}{dx} = y(y+1)$ and $y = 4$ when $x = 2$.

(L)

2 Find the solution of the differential equation $\dfrac{dy}{dx} = xy \ln x$ which satisfies the initial conditions $x = 1$, $y = 1$, giving $\ln y$ in terms of x.

(O & C)

3 Find the solution of the differential equation

$2\dfrac{dy}{dx} = 2xe^{-2y} + e^{-2y}$ for which $y = 0$ when $x = 0$.

(S)

4 Solve the differential equation $(1 + e^y)\dfrac{dy}{dx} = e^{2y}\cos^2 x$, given that $y = 0$ when $x = 0$.

(A)

5 Solve the differential equation

$(1 + x)\dfrac{dy}{dx} = 1 - \sin^2 y$ for which $y = \dfrac{\pi}{4}$ when $x = 0$.

6 Find y in terms of x given that $\dfrac{dy}{dx} = y(1 - y)$ and that $y = \tfrac{1}{2}$ when $x = 0$.

(C)

7 During a chemical reaction two substances A and B decompose. The number of grams, x, of substance A present at time t is given by $x = \dfrac{10}{(1+t)^3}$.

There are y grams of B present at time t and $\dfrac{dy}{dt}$ is directly proportional to the product of x and y. Given that $y = 20$ and $\dfrac{dy}{dt} = -40$ when $t = 0$, show that $\dfrac{dy}{dt} = \dfrac{-2y}{(1+t)^3}$.

Hence determine y as a function of t. Determine the amount of substance B remaining when the reaction is essentially complete.

(A)

8 A plant grows in a pot which contains a volume V of soil. At time t the mass of the plant is m and the volume of soil utilised by the roots is αm, where α is a constant. The rate of increase of the mass of the plant is proportional to the mass of the plant times the volume of soil not yet utilised by the roots. Obtain a differential equation for m, and verify that it can be written in the form

$$V\beta \frac{dt}{dm} = \frac{1}{m} + \frac{\alpha}{V - \alpha m}, \text{ where } \beta \text{ is a constant.}$$

The mass of the plant is initially $\dfrac{V}{4\alpha}$. Find, in terms of V and β, the time taken for the plant to double its mass. Find also the mass of the plant at time t.

(J)

P47 Numerical Integration
Introduction, Trapezium rule, Simpson's rule.

Introduction

Sometimes it is impossible to evaluate the integral $\int_a^b f(x)\,dx$ exactly. Since this integral gives the area bounded by the curve $y=f(x)$, the x-axis and the lines $x=a$ and $x=b$, an approximate value for the integral can be found by estimating this area by another method.

Two common methods are the **trapezium rule** and **Simpson's rule.**

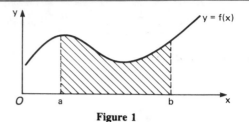

Figure 1

Trapezium rule

This method divides the area into n trapezia, each of width h.

Area under curve ≈ sum of areas of trapezia.

This gives

$$\int_a^b f(x)\,dx \approx \frac{h}{2}\{(y_0+y_n)+2(y_1+y_2+\dots+y_{n-1})\}$$

where $h=\dfrac{b-a}{n}$.

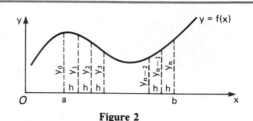

Figure 2

Simpson's rule

This method divides the area into an even number of parallel strips n, of width h, and approximates the area of pairs of strips using parabolas.

This gives

$$\int_a^b f(x)\,dx \approx \frac{h}{3}\{(y_0+y_n)+4(y_1+y_3+\dots y_{n-1})+2(y_2+y_4+\dots+y_{n-2})\}$$

Note: the number of strips must be even.

ⓘ *Evaluate $\int_1^9 \log_e x\,dx$ using 8 strips (a) by the trapezium rule (b) by Simpson's rule.*

The integration interval $(b-a)=9-1=8$ units

So $h=\dfrac{b-a}{n}=\dfrac{8}{8}=1$.

The values of x at which y is calculated are: 1, 2, 3, 4, 5, 6, 7, 8, 9.

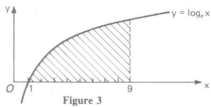

Figure 3

(a) Trapezium rule

Tabulating the results as follows helps the final calculation:

x	y	First and last ordinates	Remaining ordinates
1	y_0	0	
2	y_1		0.693
3	y_2		1.099
4	y_3		1.386
5	y_4		1.609
6	y_5		1.792
7	y_6		1.946
8	y_7		2.079
9	y_8	2.197	
Totals		2.197	10.604

$\int_1^9 \log_e x\,dx \approx \frac{1}{2}\{(y_0+y_8)+2(y_1+\dots+y_7)\}$

$=\frac{1}{2}\{2.197+2(10.604)\}$

$=11.703$

(b) By Simpson's rule

The working can be arranged as follows to aid calculation:

x	y	First and last ordinates	'Odd' ordinates	Remaining ordinates
1	y_0	0		
2	y_1		0.693	
3	y_2			1.099
4	y_3		1.386	
5	y_4			1.609
6	y_5		1.792	
7	y_6			1.946
8	y_7		2.079	
9	y_8	2.197		
Totals		2.197	5.950	4.654

$\int_1^9 \log_e x\,dx$

$\approx \frac{1}{3}\{(y_0+y_8)+4(y_1+\dots+y_7)+2(y_2+\dots+y_6)\}$

$=\frac{1}{3}\{2.197+4(5.950)+2(4.654)\}$

$=11.768$

It can be shown by exact methods that the integral is 11.775 021 …

Numerical Integration
Worked examples and Exam questions.

WE *Tabulate, to two decimal places, the values of the expression $\sqrt{1+x^2}$ at unit intervals from $x=2$ to $x=7$ inclusive. Use these values to find an estimate by the trapezoidal rule of the mean value of the expression for $2 \leq x \leq 7$.*

x	2	3	4	5	6	7
$f(x)$	$\sqrt{5}$	$\sqrt{10}$	$\sqrt{17}$	$\sqrt{26}$	$\sqrt{37}$	$\sqrt{50}$
	2.24	3.16	4.12	5.10	6.08	7.07
	y_0	y_1	y_2	y_3	y_4	y_5

Using the trapezium rule with six ordinates and $h=1$ gives

$$\int_2^7 \sqrt{1+x^2}\, dx \approx \tfrac{1}{2}[(y_0+y_5)+2(y_1+y_2+y_3+y_4)]$$

$$\therefore \int_2^7 \sqrt{1+x^2}\, dx \approx \tfrac{1}{2}[(2.24+7.07)$$
$$+2(3.16+4.12+5.10+6.08)]$$
$$=\tfrac{1}{2}(9.31+2\times18.46)$$
$$=23.115$$

$$\therefore \text{ mean value} = \frac{1}{7-2}\int_2^7 \sqrt{1+x^2}\, dx$$

$$\approx \frac{1}{5}\times 23.115 = 4.62 \text{ (2 d.p.)}$$

WE *Use Simpson's rule with 7 ordinates (6 strips) to find an approximate value of*
$$\int_0^6 xe^{-x}\, dx$$

Give the answer correct to two decimal places.

x	0	1	2	3	4	5	6
$f(x)$	0	e^{-1}	$2e^{-2}$	$3e^{-3}$	$4e^{-4}$	$5e^{-5}$	$6e^{-6}$
	0	0.368	0.271	0.149	0.073	0.034	0.015
	y_0	y_1	y_2	y_3	y_4	y_5	y_6

Simpson's rule with seven ordinates and $h=1$ gives

$$\int_0^6 xe^{-x}\, dx \approx \tfrac{1}{3}[(y_0+y_6)+4(y_1+y_3+y_5)+2(y_2+y_4)]$$

$$\therefore \int_0^6 xe^{-x}\, dx \approx \tfrac{1}{3}[(0+0.015)+4(0.368+0.149+0.034)$$
$$+2(0.271+0.073)]$$
$$=\tfrac{1}{3}(0.015+4\times0.551+2\times0.344)$$
$$=\tfrac{1}{3}(0.015+2.204+0.688)$$
$$=0.969=0.97 \text{ (2 d.p.)}$$

EX 1 Use Simpson's rule with three ordinates to find an approximate value of
$$\int_{\frac{1}{2}}^{\frac{3}{2}} \frac{1}{x}\, dx. \tag{L}$$

2 The integral $\int_0^{\frac{1}{2}} \sqrt{(1-x^2)}\, dx$ is denoted by I. The value of I is to be estimated by using the trapezoidal rule, and T_1, T_2 denote the estimates obtained when one and two strips respectively are used. Calculate T_1 and T_2, giving your answers correct to three decimal places. Assuming that the error when the trapezoidal rule is used is approximately proportional to h^3, where h denotes the width of a strip,

show that an improved estimate of I is given by $(8T_2-T_1)/7$ and evaluate this expression correct to three decimal places. Given that $y^2=1-x^2$ is the equation of the circle whose centre is the origin and whose radius is 1 unit, show that $I=\tfrac{1}{12}\pi+\tfrac{1}{8}\sqrt{3}$. Hence calculate an estimate for the value of π. (C)

3 Use Simpson's rule with five ordinates to estimate
$$\int_0^{\frac{2\pi}{9}} \log_{10}(\cos x)\, dx$$
giving your answer to 3 decimal places. (A)

4 Use Simpson's Rule with five ordinates (i.e. 4 strips of equal width), working to four significant figures, to obtain an approximate value for
$$\int_0^{90} \sin\frac{\pi x}{180}\, dx.$$
Evaluate the integral directly. (J)

5 By considering suitable areas, or otherwise, show that, for any $n>0$,
$$\tfrac{1}{2} \leq \int_0^1 (1+x^n)^{-1}\, dx \leq 1.$$
When $n=4$, find a value (to three significant figures) for the integral, using Simpson's rule with five ordinates. (O & C)

6 Values of a continuous function f were found experimentally as given below.

t	0	0.3	0.6	0.9	1.2	1.5	1.8
$f(t)$	2.72	3.00	3.32		4.06	4.48	4.95

Use linear interpolation to estimate $f(0.9)$. Then use Simpson's rule with seven ordinates to estimate $\int_0^{1.8} f(t)\, dt$, tabulating your working and giving your answer to two places of decimals. (J)

7 Tabulate, to three places of decimals, the values of $(1+x^4)^{\frac{1}{4}}$ for $x=0, 0.2, 0.4, 0.6, 0.8$. Using Simpson's rule with five ordinates, estimate, to 3 significant figures, the value of
$$\int_0^{0.8} (1+x^4)^{\frac{1}{4}}\, dx.$$
By expanding $(1+x^4)^{\frac{1}{4}}$ in powers of x as far as and including the term in x^8, obtain, to 3 significant figures, a second estimate for the value of this integral. (L)

8 The region defined by the inequalities $0 \leq x \leq \pi$, $0 \leq y \leq \log_{10}(1+\sin x)$ is rotated completely about the x-axis. Using any appropriate rule for approximate integration with five ordinates, find the volume of the solid of revolution formed, giving your answer to 3 significant figures. (A)

9 Given that $x \geq 4$, show that $e^{-\frac{1}{4}x^2} \leq e^{-2x}$ and hence show that
$$\int_4^8 e^{-\frac{1}{4}x^2}\, dx < 0.0002.$$
[Take e^{-8} to be 0.0003.]
Use Simpson's rule with 5 ordinates to estimate the value of $\int_0^4 e^{-\frac{1}{4}x^2}\, dx$ and hence obtain an estimate of $\int_{-8}^8 e^{-\frac{1}{4}x^2}\, dx$. (J)

PURE MATHEMATICS QUESTION BANK

Answers are given on pages 105–121. **A**, **AS** and **SH** denote A-level, AS-level and Scottish Higher questions, respectively.

1 A   9 mins
$$f(x) \equiv 2x^3 + px^2 + qx + 6,$$
where p and q are constants.
When $f(x)$ is divided by $(x + 1)$, the remainder is 12. When $f(x)$ is divided by $(x - 1)$, the remainder is –6.
(a) Find the value of p and the value of q.
(b) Show that $f\left(\frac{1}{2}\right) = 0$ and hence write $f(x)$ as the product of three linear factors.

(L)

2 AS   5 mins
Prove that $x - 2$ is a factor of
$2x^3 - 9x^2 + 7x + 6$.
Hence, or otherwise, solve the equation
$2x^3 - 9x^2 + 7x + 6 = 0$.

(J)

3 SH   5 mins
The set of factors of
$2x^3 + 3x^2 - 5x - 6$ contains which of the following?
(1) $(x + 1)$
(2) $(x + 2)$
(3) $(2x - 3)$
A (1) only
B (2) only
C (3) only
D (1), (2) and (3)
E Some other combination of (1), (2) and (3)

(H)

4 A

Express $f(x) = \dfrac{x^2 + x + 1}{(2x + 1)(x + 1)^2}$ in the form

$$\frac{A}{(2x + 1)} + \frac{B}{(x + 1)} + \frac{C}{(x + 1)^2}.$$

(OLE)

5 AS   5 mins

Show that $\left(\dfrac{1 + x^2}{1 - x^2}\right)^2 - \left(\dfrac{2x}{1 - x^2}\right)^2$

has the same numerical value for all $x(\neq \pm 1)$ and determine this value.

(J)

6 SH   5 mins
For all x, except $x = 1$,
$\dfrac{x^2 + 1}{x - 1}$ equals

A $x - 1$

B $x + 1$

C $x + 1 + \dfrac{1}{x - 1}$

D $x + 1 + \dfrac{2}{x - 1}$

E $x - 1 + \dfrac{2}{x - 1}$

(H)

7 A   13 mins
The roots of the equation
$$2x^2 + 6x + 3 = 0$$
are α and β.

(a) Show that $\alpha^2 + \beta^2 = 6$.
(b) The roots of the equation
$2x^2 + px + q = 0$
are $2\alpha + \beta$ and $\alpha + 2\beta$.
Calculate the value of p and the value of q.

(A)

8 AS   9 mins
The two roots of the quadratic equation
$$x^2 + 2x + 3 = 0$$
are denoted by α, β. Without solving the equation, find the quadratic equation whose roots are $\alpha + \dfrac{1}{\beta}, \beta + \dfrac{1}{\alpha}$.

(W)

9 SH   12 mins
(a) For what range of real values of k does the equation
$kx^2 + kx - 2 = 0$ have real roots?
(b) If the roots are denoted by α and β, determine the value of k for which $\alpha = -\dfrac{5}{\beta}$.

(H)

10 A   7 mins
For the geometric series
$$a + ar + ar^2 + \dots$$
the sum of the first two terms is 24 and the sum to infinity is 27.
(i) Show that $r = \pm \dfrac{1}{3}$.
(ii) Find the two possible values of a.

(W)

11 AS   12 mins
The first three terms of a geometric series are
$3(q + 5)$, $3(q + 3)$ and $(q + 7)$ respectively.
(a) Calculate the possible values of q.
(b) For each possible value of q find the common ratio, r, of the geometric series.
(c) For the value of r such that $-1 < r < 1$, find the sum to infinity of the geometric series.

(L)

12 SH   5 mins
$k - 6$, k and $k + 18$ are successive terms of a geometric series. Which of the following is/are true about k?
(1) k is even   (2) k is odd
(3) k is prime
A (1) only
B (1) and (3) only
C (2) only
D (2) and (3) only
E None of (1), (2) or (3)

(H)

13 A   7 mins
The sum of the first ten terms of an arithmetic series is 60; the sum of the first twenty-two terms is 220. Find the common difference and the first term of the series.

(J)

14 AS   10 mins
(i) Find $\displaystyle\sum_{r=1}^{100} \frac{2r}{3}$.

(ii) Find the sum to infinity of
$$\frac{7}{10} + \frac{7}{100} + \frac{7}{1000} + \frac{7}{10\,000} + \dots,$$

giving your answer in the form $\frac{p}{q}$, where p and q are positive integers.

Hence, or otherwise, find the value of
$\sum_{r=1}^{\infty} \frac{k}{10^r}$ in terms of k.

(L)

15 SH   10 mins

Show that the series $\frac{1}{x} + \frac{1}{x^2} + \frac{1}{x^3} + \dots,\ \ x \neq 0,$ is geometric.

State the range of values of x for which a sum to infinity exists and express this sum to infinity in a simplified form.

Find the sum to infinity of the series
$$\frac{1}{3} + \frac{1}{9} + \frac{1}{27} + \dots$$

and hence the sum to infinity of
$$\left(\frac{1}{3} - \frac{1}{4}\right) + \left(\frac{1}{9} - \frac{1}{16}\right) + \left(\frac{1}{27} - \frac{1}{64}\right) + \dots$$

(H)

16 A   6 mins

Find the number of ways a committee of 4 people can be chosen from a group of 5 men and 7 women when it contains

(a) only people of the same sex,

(b) people of both sexes and there are at least as many women as men.

(L)

17 AS   9 mins

A company which has 10 directors has to send 3 of them to a conference.

(a) In how many different ways can the 3 directors who attend be chosen?

It is now decided that at least one of those attending should be able to speak French. Four out of the 10 directors speak French.

(b) In how many different ways can the 3 directors now be chosen?

(C)

18 A   14 mins

Write down the expansion of $(1+x)^{-\frac{1}{2}}$ in ascending powers of x up to and including the term in x^3.

Obtain the expansion of $\dfrac{(1-x)^2}{(1+x)^{\frac{1}{2}}}$ in ascending powers of x up to and including the term in x^3.

(O & C)

19 AS   9 mins

Write down and simplify the binomial expansion of $(1+2x)^{-\frac{1}{2}}$ up to and including the term in x^3. By putting $x = \frac{1}{8}$, use your expansion to obtain an approximation to $\sqrt{5}$, giving your answer as a ratio of two integers.

(W)

20 A   6 mins

Given that $|x| \neq 1$, find the complete set of values of x for which $\dfrac{x}{x-1} > \dfrac{1}{x+1}$.

(L)

21 AS   5 mins

Find the set of values of x such that
$$3x - 2 > x^2 + 2x - 14.$$

(J)

22 A   11 mins

(a) Express as a single logarithm in its simplest form
$$\log 2 + 2 \log 18 - \tfrac{3}{2} \log 36.$$

(b) Solve the equation
$$3^x = 4^{x-2}$$
giving your answer to three significant figures.

(OLE)

23 AS   5 mins

Given that
$$\ln x + 3 \ln y - \ln 2 = \ln x^4 - \ln 54,$$
find the value of $\frac{x}{y}$.

(J)

24 SH   5 mins

Given that $\log_2 2x + \log_2 8x = 6$, then x equals

A   1.5

B   2

C   3.6

D   6.4

E   none of these.

(H)

25 A   11 mins

Determine the expansions, in ascending powers of x, up to and including the term in x^3 of

(a) $\ln(1 + 2x)$;

(b) $\ln(1 - 3x)$.

Hence obtain the expansion, in ascending powers of x, up to and including the term in x^3 of
$$f(x) = \ln\left[\frac{(1+2x)^{\frac{1}{2}}}{(1-3x)^2}\right].$$

State the range of values of x for which the expansion of $f(x)$ is valid.

(OLE)

26 AS   8 mins

Use appropriate series to show that $y = e^{2x} - \sqrt{(1+4x)}$ is approximately proportional to x^2 for small values of x. Hence sketch the graph of y near the origin.

(A)

27 A   9 mins

The line $3x + 4y = 15$ intersects the curve $2xy = 9$ at A and B. Find

(i) the coordinates of A and of B,

(ii) the distance AB.

(C)

28 AS   9 mins

Sketch, on the same axes, the graphs of

        (i) $y = 2e^x$

and   (ii) $y = 4 - x^2$

stating the coordinates of the points where the graphs cross the coordinate axes. State the number of real roots of the equation
$$2e^x + x^2 = 4.$$

Show that one of the roots lies between 0.55 and 0.65.

(W)

29 SH   5 mins

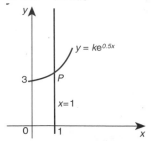

The figure shows part of the graph of $y = ke^{0.5x}$.
(a) Find the value of k.
(b) The line with equation $x = 1$ intersects the graph at P.
Find the coordinates of the point P.

(H)

30 A   10 mins
The vertices of $\triangle ABC$ are the points $A(-1, 5)$, $B(-5, 2)$ and $C(8, -7)$.
(a) Find in the form $px + qy + r = 0$, where p, q and r are integers, an equation of the line passing through B and C.
(b) Show, by calculation, that AB and AC are perpendicular.
The point D lies on the line BA produced and is such that $3BA = BD$.
(c) Determine the coordinates of D.

(L)

31 AS   18 mins
Solutions to this question by accurate drawing will not be accepted.
The diagram shows a trapezium $ABCD$ in which AB is parallel to DC. The point A lies on the y-axis. Points B and D are $(6, 13)$ and $(1, -2)$ respectively.

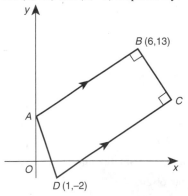

Angles ABC and BCD are $90°$.
Given that the equation of DC is $3y = 4x - 10$, find
(i) the equation of AB,
(ii) the equation of BC,
(iii) the coordinates of A and of C,
(iv) the area of the trapezium.

(C)

32 SH   6 mins
(a) Find the equation of the line through the point $(3, -5)$ which is parallel to the line with equation $3x + 2y - 5 = 0$.
(b) The points A and B have coordinates (a, a^2) and $(2b, 4b^2)$ respectively.
Determine the gradient of AB in its simplest form.

(H)

33 A   18 mins
The points P, Q and R have coordinates $(2, 4)$, $(8, -2)$ and $(6, 2)$ respectively.
(a) Find the equation of the straight line l which is perpendicular to the line PQ and which passes through the midpoint of PR.
(b) The line l cuts PQ at S. Find the ratio $PS : SQ$.
(c) The circle passing through P, Q and R has centre C. Find the coordinates of C and the radius of the circle.

(A)

34 AS   15 mins
Find the equation of the circle C which passes through the points $O(0, 0)$, $A(3, 3)$ and $B(3, 1)$. Show that the radius of C is $\sqrt{5}$ and find the coordinates of the centre.
Verify that the point $P(2, 4)$ lies on C.
Show that the gradient of the tangent at P to C is $-\frac{1}{2}$ and hence find the equation of this tangent.

(W)

35 SH   15 mins
The equation of a circle is
$$x^2 + y^2 + 14x - 20y + 129 = 0.$$
(a) State the centre and radius of the circle.
(b) Verify that the point $P(-3, 12)$ lies on the circumference of the circle and show that the equation of the tangent to the circle at P is $y = 6 - 2x$.
(c) Show that the line $y = 6 - 2x$ is also a tangent to the circle with equation
$$x^2 + y^2 - 28x + 4y + 120 = 0$$
and find the coordinates of the point of contact.

(H)

36 A   14 mins

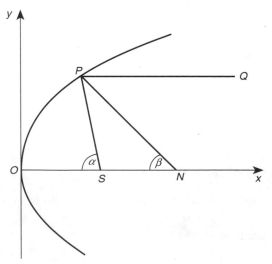

The point $P(p^2, 2p)$ is on the parabola $y^2 = 4x$ and S is the point $(1, 0)$. The normal to the parabola at P intersects the x-axis at N and PQ is parallel to the x-axis. Given that the angle $PSO = \alpha$ and that the angle $PNO = \beta$, where O is the origin,
(i) find $\tan \alpha$ in terms of p,
(ii) show that $\tan \beta = p$.
Deduce that $\alpha = 2\beta$, and hence prove that PN bisects the angle SPQ.

(J)

37 AS 9 mins

Show that the equation of the normal to the parabola $y^2 = 4ax$ at the point $P(at^2, 2at)$ is $y + tx = at(2 + t^2)$.

This normal meets the x-axis at Q; the perpendicular from P to the x-axis meets the x-axis at R. Show that the length of QR is independent of t.

(W)

38 SH 16 mins

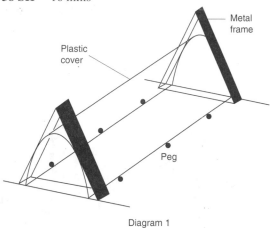

Diagram 1

Diagram 2

Diagram 1 shows a rectangular sheet of transparent plastic moulded into a parabolic shape and pegged to the ground to form a cover for growing plants. Triangular metal frames are placed over the cover to support it and prevent it blowing away in the wind.

Diagram 2 shows an end view of the cover and the triangular frame related to the origin O and axes Ox and Oy. (All dimensions are given in centimetres.)

(a) Show that the equation of the parabolic end is

$$y = 40 - \frac{x^2}{10}, \; -20 \le x \le 20.$$

(b) Show that the triangular frame touches the cover without disturbing the parabolic shape.

(H)

39 A 9 mins

A curve is defined by the parametric equations

$$x = t^2, \quad y = \frac{2}{t} \quad (t \neq 0).$$

Show that the equation of the tangent to the curve at the point $P\left(p^2, \dfrac{2}{p}\right)$ is $x + p^3 y = 3p^2$.

Given that this tangent passes through the point $(1, 2)$, determine the possible values of p.

(J)

40 AS 9 mins

(i) Find the range of values of x for which $x(8 - x) \le 15$.

(ii) Find the value of m for which the straight line $y = mx + 12$ is a tangent to the curve $x^2 + xy + 9 = 0$.

(C)

41 A 11 mins

The variables x and y are known to satisfy an equation of the form

$$\frac{1}{x} + \frac{1}{y} = \frac{1}{c},$$

where c is a constant. For five chosen values of x, corresponding approximate values of y were obtained experimentally. The results, rounded to one place of decimals, are given in the following table, although one of the results has been recorded incorrectly.

x	1.5	2.5	3.5	4.5	5.5
y	6.2	3.2	1.8	1.6	1.5

By drawing a suitable linear graph, identify the value of y which has been recorded incorrectly and write down what you think it should have been. Use your graph to estimate the value of c to one place of decimals.

(J)

42 AS 17 mins

The population P thousands, to one decimal place, of a new town T years after 1975 is summarised in the table.

T	1	2	3	4	5
P	15.4	24.6	47.2	88.3	144.4

It is believed that the above data are connected by a relationship of the form

$$P = kc^T$$

where k and c are constants.

By plotting $\ln P$ against T, obtain estimates for the values of k and c, giving your answers to 2 decimal places.

(L)

43 SH 9 mins

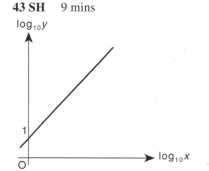

As shown in the diagram, a set of experimental results gives a straight line graph when $\log_{10} y$ is plotted against $\log_{10} x$. The straight line passes through $(0, 1)$ and has a gradient of 2. Express y in terms of x.

(H)

44 A   8 mins

(a) The angle in a sector of a given circle is 20° and the area of the sector is 2m². Calculate the arc-length of the sector.

(b) Given that θ is so small that powers of θ above the second may be neglected, find an approximate value for the acute angle θ (measured in radians) which satisfies the equation

$$\cos 3\theta - \cos 5\theta = \frac{2}{625}.$$

(N)

45 AS   8 mins

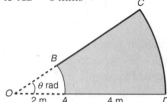

AB and DC are arcs of concentric circles, centre O, where OA = 2 m and AD = 4 m. Given that angle $AOB = \theta$ radians and that the perimeter of the figure $ABCD$, shown in the diagram, is 12 m, calculate

(i) θ

(ii) the shaded area $ABCD$.

(C)

46 SH   3 mins

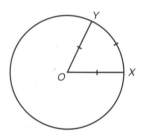

Arc XY is equal in length to the radius of the circle. Given that r is the radius of the circle, then the area of the sector OXY is

A r

B $\frac{1}{3}\pi r$

C $\frac{1}{2}r^2$

D $\frac{1}{6}\pi r^2$

E $\frac{\sqrt{3}}{4}r^2$

(H)

47 A   6 mins

Sketch the graph of $y = \sec\left(x - \frac{\pi}{4}\right)$ for $0 \le x \le \frac{\pi}{2}$,

stating the y-coordinate corresponding to $x = 0$, $x = \frac{\pi}{4}, x = \frac{\pi}{2}$.

(J)

48 AS   6 mins

Sketch the graph of

$$y = \cos x, 0 \le x \le 2\pi.$$

Hence, or otherwise, determine the ranges of values of x in the interval $0 \le x \le 2\pi$ for which

$$|\cos x| \le \frac{1}{2}.$$

(J)

49 SH   3 mins

The maximum value of $1 - \cos\left(x - \frac{\pi}{6}\right), 0 \le x < 2\pi$, occurs when x is

A   0

B $\frac{\pi}{6}$

C $\frac{2\pi}{3}$

D $\frac{7\pi}{6}$

E $\frac{4\pi}{3}$

(H)

50 A   11 mins

Prove the identity

$$\tan \theta + \cot \theta \equiv 2 \operatorname{cosec} 2\theta$$

Find, in radians, all the solutions of the equation

$$\tan x + \cot x = 8 \cos 2x$$

in the interval $0 < x < \pi$.

(A)

51 AS   8 mins

Solve, for $0 \le x \le \pi$. the equation

$$\sin 2x = \cos x$$

giving your answers in terms of π.

(L)

52 SH   5 mins

Given that $\sin A = \frac{3}{4}$, where $0 < A < \frac{\pi}{2}$, find the **exact** value of $\sin 2A$.

(H)

53 A   11 mins

The figure shows a triangle ABC with the usual notation.

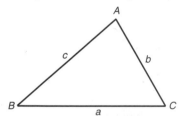

(a) Show that its area is $\frac{1}{2}ac \sin B$.

(b) In a case when $AB = 8$ cm and $BC = 6$ cm, the area of the triangle ABC is 12 cm². Find the two possible values of
(i) angle B,
(ii) the length of AC.

(OLE)

54 AS   4 mins

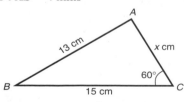

The figure shows $\triangle ABC$ in which $AB = 13$ cm, $BC = 15$ cm and $\angle ACB = 60°$. Given that AC = x cm, calculate the possible values of x.

(L)

55 A   22 mins

[In this question you may give lengths to three significant figures and angles to the nearest 0.1°.]

The pyramid *VABCD* has vertex *V* and a square base *ABCD*. Each side of the base has length 12 cm and the lengths of *VA*, *VB*, *VC*, and *VD* are each 11 cm. The centre of the base is *O* and the midpoints of the sides *AB* and *CD* are *P* and *Q* respectively.
Calculate
(a) the height *VO*,
(b) the size of the angle between the edges *VA* and *VC*,
(c) the length of the perpendicular from *B* to *VA*,
(d) the size of the angle between the planes *VAB* and *VAD*.
A sphere is placed inside the pyramid so that it touches the base and the four sloping faces. Calculate the size of angle *VPQ* and hence, or otherwise, find the radius of the sphere.

(OLE)

56 AS   12 mins

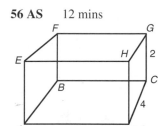

For a tank of these dimensions, calculate the length of *DF*.
Find
(i) the angle between *DF* and the base *ABCD*,
(ii) the angle between *DF* and *DA*.
Deduce the angle between *DF* and *AB*.

(W)

57 A   27 mins
(a) The points *A*, *B* have position vectors **a**,**b** respectively with respect to an origin *O*. The point *C* lies on *AB* and *AC/AB* = λ.
Show that the position vector of *C* is given by
c = (1 − λ)**a** + λ**b**.
(b) *ABCD* is a quadrilateral and *X*,*Y* denote respectively the midpoints of the diagonals *AC* and *BD*. Prove that
4**YX** = **BA** + **BC** + **DA** + **DC**.
(c) (i) *OABCDE* is a regular hexagon and **a**,**b** denote respectively the position vectors of *A*, *B* with respect to *O*. Using the fact that **OC** = 2**AB**, obtain an expression for **OC** in terms of **a**,**b** and obtain similar expressions for **OD** and **OE**.
(ii) The lines *OB* and *AC* meet in *F*. Find an expression for **OF** in terms of **b**.

(W)

58 AS   9 mins
ORST is a parallelogram. *U* is the midpoint of *RS* and *V* is the midpoint of *ST*. Relative to the origin *O*, **r**, **s**, **t**, **u** and **v** are the position vectors of *R*, *S*, *T*, *U* and *V* respectively.
(a) Express **s** in terms of **r** and **t**.
(b) Express **v** in terms of **s** and **t**.
(c) Hence, or otherwise, show that
4(**u** + **v**) $\doteq$ 3(**r** + **s** + **t**).

(L)

59 SH   3 mins
A cuboidal crystal is placed relative to the coordinate axes as shown.

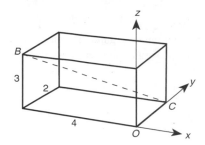

(a) Write down $\vec{BC}$ in component form.
(b) Calculate $|\vec{BC}|$.

(H)

60 A   22 mins
The unit vectors **i**, **j**, **k** are parallel to the *x*-, *y*-, and *z*-axes, respectively, of a Cartesian frame of reference *Oxyz*, where *O* denotes the origin. *A* and *B* are two points with position vectors

$$\vec{OA} = \mathbf{i} + \mathbf{j} + \mathbf{k}, \qquad \vec{OB} = 13\mathbf{i} + 10\mathbf{j} + 9\mathbf{k}.$$

(i) In terms of **i**, **j** and **k**, express the unit vector parallel to $\vec{AB}$.
(ii) Write down a vector equation of the straight line *AB*.
(iii) Find the point *P* on $\vec{AB}$ such that *AP* : *PB* = 1 : 7.
(iv) Verify that the angle *OPB* is 175.5° approximately.

(N)

61 AS   12 mins
(a) The vector equations of two lines are
r = 2**i** + **j** + λ(**i** + **j** + 2**k**)
and   r = 2**i** + 2**j** +*t***k** + μ(**i** + 2**j** + **k**)
where **i**, **j**, **k** are perpendicular unit vectors and *t* is a constant.
(i) Given that the two lines intersect, calculate *t* and find the position vector of the point of intersection.
(ii) Find the angle between the lines, giving your answer correct to the nearest degree.

(W)

62 A   15 mins
(i) If $j^2 = -1$, show that the product
$$\left(\cos\frac{\pi}{8} + j\sin\frac{\pi}{8}\right)\left(\cos\frac{3\pi}{8} + j\sin\frac{3\pi}{8}\right)\left(\cos\frac{\pi}{2} + j\sin\frac{\pi}{2}\right)$$
is a real number and evaluate it.
(ii) Find positive real surds *x* and *y* such that
$(x + jy)^2 = 1 + j$.

(N)

63 AS   7 mins
Given that
$(x + iy)^2 = 2i$,
where *x* and *y* are real, show that one solution of the equation is *x* = 1, *y* = 1 and find the other solution.
Let z_1 and z_2 denote the two possible values of *x* + i*y*.
Represent z_1 and z_2 in an Argand diagram. Write down the values of the conjugate complex numbers z_1^* and z_2^* and verify that

$$\arg z_2^* - \arg z_1 = \arg z_1^* - \arg z_2.$$

(J)

Pure Mathematics Question Bank

64 A   15 mins

The complex number $u = -10 + 9i$.

(a) Show the complex number u on an Argand diagram.

(b) Giving your answer to the nearest degree, calculate the argument of u.

(c) Find the complex number v which satisfies the equation $uv = -11 + 28i$.

(d) Verify that $|u + v| = 8\sqrt{2}$.

(A)

65 AS   10 mins

The complex number ω has modulus 3 and argument $\dfrac{\pi}{4}$.

Find the modulus and argument of

(i) ω^2 (ii) $i\omega$.

Mark in an Argand diagram the points P, Q and R representing the complex numbers ω, ω^2 and $i\omega$, respectively. Find the area of quadrilateral $OPQR$, where O is the origin.

(J)

66 A   4 mins

Differentiate with respect to x

(i) $e^{2x} \sec 3x$,

(ii) $(1 + x^3) / (1 + x)$.

(O & C)

67 A   11 mins

(i) Given that $y = \cos^2 x$, find $\dfrac{dy}{dx}$.

(ii) Given that $x = \dfrac{1}{1 + t^2}$ and $y = \dfrac{t}{1 + t^2}$,

where t is a parameter, find $\dfrac{dy}{dx}$ in terms of t.

(C)

68 A   25 mins

(a) Differentiate, with respect to x,

(i) $x \sin x$, (ii) e^{2-x}, (iii) $\tan^2 x$.

(b) Find the coordinates of the stationary points

on the curve $y = \dfrac{x^2}{3x - 1}$.

(c) Find the equation of the tangent to the curve $y^2 - 8x - 2y + 13 = 0$ at (2, 3).

(C)

69 A   10 mins

Given that $y = x^3 - 4x^2 + 5x - 2$, find $\dfrac{dy}{dx}$.

P is the point on the curve where $x = 3$.

(i)   Calculate the y-coordinate of P.

(ii) Calculate the gradient at P.

(iii) Find the equation of the tangent at P.

(iv) Find the equation of the normal at P.

Find the values of x for which the curve has a gradient of 5.

(O & C)

70 AS   12 mins

(a) Verify that the point P with coordinates (1, 3) lies on the curve with equation
$$y = x^3 - x + 3.$$

(b) Find an equation of the tangent to the curve at P.

(c) Find an equation of the normal to the curve at P.
The tangent to the curve at P meets the x-axis at A and the normal to the curve at P meets the y-axis at B.

(d) Calculate the area of the triangle AOB, where O is the origin.

(L)

71 A   13 mins

The volume of liquid V cm^3 in a container when the depth is x cm is given by

$$V = \frac{x^{\frac{1}{4}}}{(x + 2)^{\frac{1}{2}}}, \quad x > 0.$$

(a) Find $\dfrac{dV}{dx}$ and determine the value of x for which $\dfrac{dV}{dx} = 0$.

(b) Calculate the rate of change of volume when the depth is 1 cm and increasing at a rate of 0.01 cm s^{-1}, giving your answer in cm^3 s^{-1} to three significant figures.

(A)

72 AS   10 mins

A particle P moves along a straight line. At time t seconds after the motion begins, the displacement of P from a fixed point O on the line is x metres, where $x = 3\sin t - 2\cos t - 1$.

Find

(i)   the velocity and the acceleration of P when $t = 0$,

(ii) the time at which P first passes through O,

(iii) the greatest distance of P from O during the motion.

(J)

73 A   10 mins

Consider the function $y = e^{-x} \sin x$, where $-\pi \le x \le \pi$.

(i)   Find $\dfrac{dy}{dx}$.

(ii) Show that, at stationary points, $\tan x = 1$.

(iii) Determine the coordinates of the stationary points, correct to two significant figures.

(iv) Explain how you could determine whether your stationary points are maxima or minima. You are not required to do any calculations.

(O & C)

74 AS   15 mins

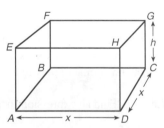

The above figure shows a water tank in the shape of a cuboid with a square base $ABCD$ and open top $EFGH$. Given that $AD = x$ and $CG = h$, write down expressions for the volume V of the tank and its total internal surface area S. Show that

$$S = x^2 + \frac{4V}{x}.$$

Given that $V = 32$,

(i) find the value of x which minimises S.

(ii) find the minimum value of S, and show that the corresponding value of h is 2.

For a tank of these dimensions, calculate the length of DF.

(W)

75 SH   10 mins

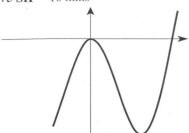

The diagram shows a part of the curve with equation
$$y = 2x^2(x - 3).$$
Find the coordinates of the stationary points on the graph and determine their nature.
(b) State the range of values of k for which $y = k$ intersects the graph in three distinct points.

(H)

76 A   26 mins

The curve with equation $y = \dfrac{ax + b}{x(x + 2)}$, where a and b are constants, has zero gradient at the point $(1, -2)$.
(a) Show that $a = -8$ and find the value of b.
(b) Show that the gradient is also zero at the point $(-\frac{1}{2}, -8)$.
(c) Find equations for the three asymptotes of this curve.
Sketch the curve, stating the coordinates of the point at which the curve meets the x-axis.
Using your sketch, or otherwise, find the set of values of y for which no part of the curve exists.

(A)

77 AS   25 mins

By writing $(x + h)$ in the form $x\left(1 + \dfrac{h}{x}\right)$,
show that for h sufficiently small,
$$(x + h)^n - x^n = nx^{n-1}h + \frac{n(n - 1)}{2}x^{n-2}h^2 + \dots$$

Deduce the derivative of x^n.
(b) The function $f(x)$ is defined on the domain $[0, 1]$ by
$$f(x) = \frac{2x^2}{1 + x^2}.$$

Obtain an expression for $f'(x)$ in its simplest form and show that
$$f''(x) = \frac{4(1 - 3x^2)}{(1 + x^2)^3}.$$

Hence find
(i) the coordinates of the point at which $f''(x) = 0$ and show that this point is a point of inflexion,
(ii) the largest and smallest values of $f'(x)$ stating the values of x for which these occur.
State the range of f and sketch its graph.

(W)

78 SH   9 mins

Integrate, with respect to x, the function
$$g(x) = \frac{4x^{\frac{1}{2}} - 5x^{-2}}{2x}, \quad x \neq 0.$$

(H)

79 A   15 mins

(a) Evaluate:
(i) $\displaystyle\int_0^1 xe^{2x}\, dx$

(ii) $\displaystyle\int_0^1 \frac{x - 1}{x + 1}\, dx$

(b) Use the substitution $x = 2\cos\theta$, or otherwise, to evaluate
$$\int_1^{\sqrt 2} \frac{1}{x^2\sqrt{(4 - x^2)}}\, dx.$$

(OLE)

80 AS   9 mins

Using the substitution $y = 2 - x$, show that
$$\int_0^1 \left(\frac{x}{2 - x}\right)^2 dx = 3 - 4\ln 2.$$

(W)

81 A   10 mins

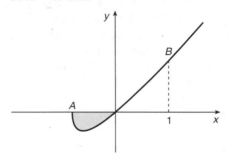

The sketch shows part of the graph of $y = x\sqrt{1 + x}$. (NB Not to scale.)
(i) Find the coordinates of point A and the range of values of x for which the function is defined.
(ii) Find the volume of the solid formed by rotating the curve from A to B through one complete turn about the x-axis. Leave π as a factor in your answer.
(iii) Show that the shaded area is 4/15. You may find the substitution $u = 1 + x$ useful.

(O & C)

82 AS   11 mins

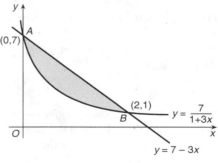

The diagram shows part of the curve $y = \dfrac{7}{1 + 3x}$ and part of the straight line $y = 7 - 3x$. The graphs intersect at the point A $(0, 7)$ and the point B $(2, 1)$. Calculate the area of the shaded region, giving your answer correct to three significant figures.

(C)

Pure Mathematics Question Bank

83 SH   18 mins

A function $f(x)$ is defined by the formula

$$f(x) = \frac{1}{3}x^3 - 2x^2 + 3x, \quad x \in R,$$

where R is the set of real numbers.

(a) Find the stationary points of $f(x)$ and determine their nature, justifying your answers.

(b) Find where the graph of $f(x)$ meets the x- and y-axes and make a rough sketch of the graph.

(c) Calculate the finite area bounded by the x-axis and the graph of $f(x)$.

(H)

84 A   7 mins

Solve the differential equation

$$\left(1 + x^2\right)\frac{dy}{dx} = x\left(4 + y^2\right)$$

given that $y = 0$ when $x = 0$, expressing y in terms of x.

(OLE)

85 AS   20 mins

Newton's law of cooling states that the rate at which a body cools is directly proportional to the excess temperature of the body over the temperature of its immediate surroundings. Given that at time t minutes a body has a temperature $T\,^\circ\text{C}$ and its surroundings a constant temperature $\theta\,^\circ\text{C}$, form a differential equation in terms of T, θ, t and the constant of proportionality k, $k > 0$.

Integrate this equation to show that

$$\ln(T - \theta) = -kt + c$$

where c is a constant.

Hence show that

$$T = \theta + Ae^{-kt}$$

where $\ln A = c$.

At 2.23 p.m., the water in a kettle boils at 100 °C in a room of constant temperature 21°C. After 10 minutes, the temperature of the water in the kettle is 84 °C. Use this information to find the values of k and A, giving your answers to two significant figures. Hence find the time, to the nearest minute, when the temperature of the water in the kettle will be 70 °C.

(L)

86 A   16 mins

Sketch the graph of the curve with equation $y = \ln(8 - x)$.

By drawing a suitable straight line show that the equation $x = \ln(8 - x)$ has just one real root α. Prove that α lies between 1 and 2.

Use an iterative method to calculate the value of α, giving your answer to two decimal places.

(OLE)

87 AS   11 mins

Given that the equation $x^3 + x - 12 = 0$ has a positive root α, find the two consecutive integers between which this root lies. Starting with the smaller of these two integers, use the

iteration $x_{n+1} = \frac{1}{4}\left(3x_n - \frac{1}{x_n} + \frac{12}{x_n^2}\right)$ to find the value of x correct

to three decimal places.

(C)

88 A   6 mins

Use the trapezium rule with 6 ordinates to estimate

$$\int_0^1 e^{x^2}\,dx$$

correct to two places of decimals.

(N)

89 AS   9 mins

Use Simpson's rule with 5 ordinates and an interval of 0.25 to find an approximate value of the integral

$$\int_0^1 \sqrt{x^3 + 1}\,dx.$$

Give your answer correct to two decimal places.

(W)

90 AS   15 mins

The flow of water over a weir was monitored over a 15-day period. The flow was measured on Sunday (day 0) and subsequently at noon on every third day. The results were as follows.

Day	0	3	6	9	12	15
Rate of flow (m³/day)	48 000	53 000	54 000	52 000	46 000	38 000

Plot these points on graph paper and draw a smooth curve through them. You may now assume that this smooth curve is a good representation of the actual rate of flow.

By applying the trapezium rule, estimate the total volume of water flowing over the weir in this 15-day period.

State, giving your reason, whether your result is likely to be an overestimate or an underestimate of the true value.

Why is Simpson's rule, though generally more accurate, inapplicable in this case?

(A)

91 A   22 mins

Functions f and g are defined as follows:

$$f{:}x \;\to\; \frac{1}{x}, x \in \mathbb{R}, \; x \neq 0.$$

$$g{:}x \;\to\; 1 - x, \; x \in \mathbb{R}.$$

Write down expressions for $fg(x)$ and $gf(x)$, where $x \neq 0$, $x \neq 1$, and hence show that $gfg(x) = fgf(x)$ for all such x.

The function h is defined by

$$h{:}x \;\to\; e^x, x \in \mathbb{R}.$$

On a single, clearly labelled diagram, sketch the graphs of fh and hg, and describe a single transformation which maps the graph of fh onto the graph of hg.

Show that $h^{-1}f(x) = (fh)^{-1}(x)$ for all $x > 0$.

(C)

92 A   18 mins

A function f is defined by $f{:}x \;\to\; \dfrac{2x}{x-4}$, for $x \neq 4$.

Find an expression for f^2 and for f^{-1}.

Hence find the non-zero value of x for which $f^2 = f^{-1}$.

A function g is defined by $g{:}x \;\to\; ax^2 + bx$. Given that $g(3) = 9$ and that $gf(2) = 14$, find the value of a and of b.

(C)

93 SH   15 mins
The function f is defined by $f(x) = x^3 - 2x^2 - 5x + 6$.
The function g is defined by $g(x) = x - 1$.
(a) Show that $f(g(x)) = x^3 - 5x^2 + 2x + 8$.

(b) Factorise fully $f(g(x))$.

(c) The function k is such that $k(x) = \dfrac{1}{f(g(x))}$.

For what values of x is the function k not defined?
(H)

94 A   20 mins
You are given the matrix $\mathbf{A} = \begin{pmatrix} -1 & -4 \\ 1 & 3 \end{pmatrix}$

(i)   Calculate $\mathbf{A}^2$ and $\mathbf{A}^3$.
(ii) Show that the formula $\mathbf{A}^n = \begin{pmatrix} 1 - 2n & -4n \\ n & 1 + 2n \end{pmatrix}$

is consistent with the given value of $\mathbf{A}$ and your calculations for $n = 2$ and $n = 3$.
(iii) Prove by induction that the formula for $\mathbf{A}^n$ is correct when n is a positive integer.
(iv) Find the values of p and q for which
$\mathbf{A}^2 = p\mathbf{A} + q\mathbf{I}$.
(v)   Deduce that
$\mathbf{A}^3 = p\mathbf{A}^2 + q\mathbf{A}$.
Using the result of part (iv) write this in the form
$\mathbf{A}^3 = r\mathbf{A} + s\mathbf{I}$ and find r and s.
(vi) Continue with this method to express $\mathbf{A}^4$ in terms of $\mathbf{A}$ and $\mathbf{I}$.
(vii) Propose a formula for $\mathbf{A}^n$ in terms of $\mathbf{A}$ and $\mathbf{I}$ and show that it gives the same matrix $\mathbf{A}^n$ as you found in part (ii).

95 AS   15 mins
Find the values of k for which the matrix

$$\mathbf{M} = \begin{pmatrix} k+1 & 6 \\ 1 & k \end{pmatrix}$$

does not have an inverse.
If k is **not** equal to either of these special values, write down $\mathbf{M}^{-1}$ in terms of k.
Consider the straight lines with equations
$$(k+1)x + 6y = 12$$
$$x + ky = 4.$$

Using $\mathbf{M}^{-1}$ find the coordinates of the point of intersection of these lines in the case when $k = 3$.
For each of the special values of k which you find above, state the geometrical reason why it is not possible to find an intersection point by this method.
(A)

Question Bank Answers

1 A
(a) $f(-1) = 2(-1)^3 + p(-1)^2 + q(-1) + 6 = 4 + p - q = 12$

$\Rightarrow p - q = 8$

$f(1) = 2(1)^3 + p(1)^2 + q(1) + 6 = 8 + p + q = -6$

$\Rightarrow p + q = -14$

$\left.\begin{matrix} p + q = -14 \\ p - q = 8 \end{matrix}\right\} \Rightarrow 2p = -6 \Rightarrow p = -3 \Rightarrow q = -11$

(b) $f\left(\tfrac{1}{2}\right) = 2\left(\tfrac{1}{2}\right)^3 - 3\left(\tfrac{1}{2}\right)^2 - 11\left(\tfrac{1}{2}\right) + 6 = \tfrac{1}{4} - \tfrac{3}{4} - 5\tfrac{1}{2} + 6 = 0$

$\therefore x - \tfrac{1}{2}$ is a factor of $f(x)$.

By long division, $f(x) = \left(x - \tfrac{1}{2}\right)\left(2x^2 - 2x - 12\right)$
$= 2\left(x - \tfrac{1}{2}\right)\left(x^2 - x - 6\right)$
$= 2\left(x - \tfrac{1}{2}\right)(x + 2)(x - 3)$
$= (2x - 1)(x + 2)(x - 3)$

2 AS
Let $f(x) = 2x^3 - 9x^2 + 7x + 6$
$f(2) = 2(2)^3 - 9(2)^2 + 7(2) + 6 = 16 - 36 + 14 + 6 = 0$
$\therefore x - 2$ is a factor of $f(x)$
By long division, $f(x) = (x - 2)\left(2x^2 - 5x - 3\right)$
$= (x - 2)(2x + 1)(x - 3)$

$f(x) = 0 \Rightarrow (x - 2)(2x + 1)(x - 3) = 0$
$\Rightarrow x - 2 = 0$ or $2x + 1 = 0$ or $x - 3 = 0$
Hence, $x = 2, -\tfrac{1}{2}$ or 3

3 SH
Let $f(x) = 2x^3 + 3x^2 - 5x - 6$

$f(-1) = 2(-1)^3 + 3(-1)^2 - 5(-1) - 6 = -2 + 3 + 5 - 6 = 0$

$\Rightarrow x + 1$ is a factor of $f(x)$

$f(-2) = 2(-2)^3 + 3(-2)^2 - 5(-2) - 6 = -16 + 12 + 10 - 6 = 0$

$\Rightarrow x + 2$ is a factor of $f(x)$

$f\left(\tfrac{3}{2}\right) = 2\left(\tfrac{3}{2}\right)^3 + 3\left(\tfrac{3}{2}\right)^2 - 5\left(\tfrac{3}{2}\right) - 6 = \tfrac{54}{8} + \tfrac{27}{4} - \tfrac{15}{2} - 6 = 0$

$\Rightarrow 2x - 3$ is a factor of $f(x)$

$\therefore$ The correct answer is D.

4 A
Let $f(x) = \dfrac{x^2 + x + 1}{(2x+1)(x+1)^2} = \dfrac{A}{2x+1} + \dfrac{B}{x+1} + \dfrac{C}{(x+1)^2}$

$= \dfrac{A(x+1)^2 + B(2x+1)(x+1) + C(2x+1)}{(2x+1)(x+1)^2}$

So $x^2 + x + 1 = A(x+1)^2 + B(2x+1)(x+1) + C(2x+1)$
$x = -1 \Rightarrow 1 = -C \Rightarrow C = -1$
$x = -\tfrac{1}{2} \Rightarrow \tfrac{3}{4} = \tfrac{1}{4}A \Rightarrow A = 3$
Comparing coefficients of $x^2 \Rightarrow 1 = A + 2B \Rightarrow B = -1$
Hence $f(x) = \dfrac{3}{2x+1} - \dfrac{1}{x+1} - \dfrac{1}{(x+1)^2}$

5 AS
$\left(\dfrac{1+x^2}{1-x^2}\right)^2 - \left(\dfrac{2x}{1-x^2}\right)^2 = \dfrac{\left(1+x^2\right)^2}{\left(1-x^2\right)^2} - \dfrac{(2x)^2}{\left(1-x^2\right)^2}$

$= \dfrac{1 + 2x^2 + x^4 - 4x^2}{\left(1-x^2\right)^2} = \dfrac{1 - 2x^2 + x^4}{\left(1-x^2\right)^2}$

$= \dfrac{\left(1-x^2\right)^2}{\left(1-x^2\right)^2} = 1$

Hence, for all $x \neq \pm 1$, $\left(\dfrac{1+x^2}{1-x^2}\right)^2 - \left(\dfrac{2x}{1-x^2}\right)^2 = 1$

6 SH

$$x-1\overline{\smash{\big)}\,x^2+1}\quad\genfrac{}{}{0pt}{}{x+1\ \ \text{R.2}}{}$$

$$\underline{x^2-x}$$
$$x+1$$
$$\underline{x-1}$$
$$2$$

gives $x+1+\dfrac{2}{x-1}$ $(x\neq 1)$

∴ The correct answer is D.

7 A

$\alpha+\beta=\dfrac{-6}{2}=-3$ $\alpha\beta=\dfrac{3}{2}$

(a) $\alpha^2+\beta^2=(\alpha+\beta)^2-2\alpha\beta=(-3)^2-2\left(\dfrac{3}{2}\right)=6$

(b) $(2\alpha+\beta)+(\alpha+2\beta)=\dfrac{-p}{2}\Rightarrow 3\alpha+3\beta=3(\alpha+\beta)=\dfrac{-p}{2}$

$\Rightarrow 3(-3)=\dfrac{-p}{2}\Rightarrow p=18$

$(2\alpha+\beta)(\alpha+2\beta)=\dfrac{q}{2}\Rightarrow 2\alpha^2+2\beta^2+5\alpha\beta$

$=2\left(\alpha^2+\beta^2\right)+5\alpha\beta=\dfrac{q}{2}$

$\Rightarrow 2(6)+5\left(\dfrac{3}{2}\right)=\dfrac{q}{2}$

$\Rightarrow q=39$

8 AS

$\alpha+\beta=\dfrac{-2}{1}=-2$ $\qquad\alpha\beta=\dfrac{3}{1}=3$

$\left(\alpha+\dfrac{1}{\beta}\right)+\left(\beta+\dfrac{1}{\alpha}\right)=\alpha+\beta+\dfrac{1}{\beta}+\dfrac{1}{\alpha}=\alpha+\beta+\dfrac{\alpha+\beta}{\alpha\beta}$

$\phantom{\left(\alpha+\dfrac{1}{\beta}\right)+\left(\beta+\dfrac{1}{\alpha}\right)}=-2+\dfrac{-2}{3}$

$\phantom{\left(\alpha+\dfrac{1}{\beta}\right)+\left(\beta+\dfrac{1}{\alpha}\right)}=-2\tfrac{2}{3}$

$\left(\alpha+\dfrac{1}{\beta}\right)\left(\beta+\dfrac{1}{\alpha}\right)=\alpha\beta+\dfrac{1}{\alpha\beta}+2=3+\dfrac{1}{3}+2=5\tfrac{1}{3}$

∴ The required quadratic equation is $x^2-\left(-2\tfrac{2}{3}\right)x+5\tfrac{1}{3}=0$

i.e. $x^2+2\tfrac{2}{3}x+5\tfrac{1}{3}=0$ or $3x^2+8x+16=0$

9 SH

(a) Real roots $\Rightarrow b^2-4ac\geq 0\Rightarrow k^2-4(k)(-2)\geq 0$

$\phantom{\text{(a) Real roots }}\Rightarrow k^2+8k\geq 0\Rightarrow k(k+8)\geq 0$

$\phantom{\text{(a) Real roots }}\Rightarrow k\leq -8\quad\text{or}\quad k\geq 0$

(b) $\alpha=\dfrac{-5}{\beta}\Rightarrow\alpha\beta=-5$

$\alpha\beta=\dfrac{-2}{k}=-5\Rightarrow k=\dfrac{2}{5}$

10 A

(i) $S_2=a+ar=a(1+r)=24\Rightarrow a=\dfrac{24}{1+r}$

$S_\infty=\dfrac{a}{1-r}=27\Rightarrow a=27(1-r)$

$a=\dfrac{24}{1+r}=27(1-r)\Rightarrow 24=27(1-r)(1+r)=27\left(1-r^2\right)$

so $\dfrac{24}{27}=1-r^2\Rightarrow r^2=1-\dfrac{24}{27}=\dfrac{3}{27}=\dfrac{1}{9}\Rightarrow r=\pm\dfrac{1}{3}$

(ii) $r=\dfrac{1}{3}\Rightarrow a=\dfrac{24}{1+\frac{1}{3}}=18$

$r=-\dfrac{1}{3}\Rightarrow a=\dfrac{24}{1-\frac{1}{3}}=36$

∴ The two possible values of a are 18 and 36.

11 AS

(a) $\dfrac{3(q+3)}{3(q+5)}=\dfrac{q+7}{3(q+3)}\Rightarrow\dfrac{q+3}{q+5}=\dfrac{q+7}{3(q+3)}$

$\Rightarrow 3(q+3)^2=(q+5)(q+7)$

$\Rightarrow 3q^2+18q+27=q^2+12q+35$

$\Rightarrow 2q^2+6q-8=0$

$\Rightarrow q=1\text{ or}-4$

(b) $r=\dfrac{q+7}{3(q+3)}\qquad q=1\Rightarrow r=\dfrac{8}{12}=\dfrac{2}{3}$

$\phantom{(b) r=\dfrac{q+7}{3(q+3)}\qquad}q=-4\Rightarrow r=\dfrac{3}{-3}=-1$

(c) $r=\dfrac{2}{3}\Rightarrow q=1$

∴ $a=3(1+5)=18$ and $S_\infty=\dfrac{18}{1-\frac{2}{3}}=54$

12 SH

$\dfrac{k}{k-6}=\dfrac{k+18}{k}\Rightarrow k^2=(k-6)(k+18)=k^2+12k-108$

$\Rightarrow 12k=108\Rightarrow k=9$

∴ Only (2) is true and the correct answer is C.

13 A

$S_{10}=\dfrac{10}{2}[2a+9d]=60\Rightarrow 2a+9d=12$

$S_{22}=\dfrac{22}{2}[2a+21d]=220\Rightarrow 2a+21d=20$

$2a+21d=20$

$\underline{2a+9d=12}$

$12d=8\Rightarrow d=\tfrac{8}{12}=\tfrac{2}{3}$

$2a=12-9d\Rightarrow a=\dfrac{1}{2}(12-9d)=\dfrac{1}{2}\left(12-9\left(\tfrac{2}{3}\right)\right)=3$

∴ The common difference is $\tfrac{2}{3}$ and the first term is 3.

14 AS

(i) $\displaystyle\sum_{r=1}^{100}\dfrac{2r}{3}=\dfrac{2}{3}\sum_{r=1}^{100}r=\dfrac{2}{3}\left[\tfrac{1}{2}(100)(101)\right]=3366\tfrac{2}{3}$

(ii) $\dfrac{7}{10}+\dfrac{7}{100}+\dfrac{7}{1000}+\ldots$ is a geometric series

with $a=\dfrac{7}{10}$, $r=\dfrac{1}{10}$.

So $S_\infty=\dfrac{\frac{7}{10}}{1-\frac{1}{10}}=\dfrac{\frac{7}{10}}{\frac{9}{10}}=\dfrac{7}{9}$

$\displaystyle\sum_{r=1}^{\infty}\dfrac{k}{10^r}=\dfrac{k}{10}+\dfrac{k}{100}+\dfrac{k}{1000}+\ldots$ is a geometric series in the

same pattern as $\dfrac{7}{10}+\dfrac{7}{100}+\dfrac{7}{1000}+\ldots$ with 7 replaced by k.

Hence $\displaystyle\sum_{r=1}^{\infty}\dfrac{k}{10^r}=\dfrac{k}{9}$

15 SH

The nth and $(n+1)$th terms in the series are $\dfrac{1}{x^n}$ and $\dfrac{1}{x^{n+1}}$

The common ratio, r, is $\dfrac{\frac{1}{x^{n+1}}}{\frac{1}{x^n}} = \dfrac{x^n}{x^{n+1}} = \dfrac{1}{x}$

Therefore, each term is $\dfrac{1}{x}$ $(x \neq 0)$ times the previous term so the series is geometric.

A sum to infinity, S_∞, exists when $\left|\dfrac{1}{x}\right| < 1$, i.e. when $|x| > 1$

$$S_\infty = \dfrac{\frac{1}{x}}{1 - \frac{1}{x}} = \dfrac{\frac{1}{x}}{\frac{x-1}{x}} = \dfrac{1}{x-1}$$

$\dfrac{1}{3} + \dfrac{1}{9} + \dfrac{1}{27} + \dots$ is a geometric series with

$a = \dfrac{1}{3}, r = \dfrac{1}{3} \therefore S_\infty = \dfrac{\frac{1}{3}}{1 - \frac{1}{3}} = \dfrac{1}{2}$

$\dfrac{1}{4} + \dfrac{1}{16} + \dfrac{1}{64} + \dots$ is a geometric series with

$a = \dfrac{1}{4}, r = \dfrac{1}{4} \therefore S_\infty = \dfrac{\frac{1}{4}}{1 - \frac{1}{4}} = \dfrac{1}{3}$

Hence $\left(\dfrac{1}{3} - \dfrac{1}{4}\right) + \left(\dfrac{1}{9} - \dfrac{1}{16}\right) + \left(\dfrac{1}{27} - \dfrac{1}{64}\right) + \dots$

$= \left(\dfrac{1}{3} + \dfrac{1}{9} + \dfrac{1}{27} + \dots\right) - \left(\dfrac{1}{4} + \dfrac{1}{16} + \dfrac{1}{64} + \dots\right)$

$= \dfrac{1}{2} - \dfrac{1}{3} = \dfrac{1}{6}$

16 A

(a) An all male committee can be chosen in

$^5C_4 = \dfrac{5!}{1!4!} = 5$ ways.

An all female committee can be chosen in

$^7C_4 = \dfrac{7!}{3!4!} = \dfrac{7 \times 6 \times 5}{1 \times 2 \times 3} = 35$ ways.

$\therefore$ There are $5 + 35 = 40$ ways of chosing a committee where all the members are of the same sex.

(b) The committee could consist of 2 Men 2 Women or 1M3W. (4W is not allowed because people of both sexes must be included.)

The number of ways to have 2M2W is

$^5C_2 \times {}^7C_2 = \dfrac{5!}{2!3!} \times \dfrac{7!}{2!5!} = 10 \times 21 = 210.$

The number of ways to have 1M3W is

$^5C_1 \times {}^7C_3 = \dfrac{5!}{1!4!} \times \dfrac{7!}{3!4!} = 5 \times 35 = 175.$

$\therefore$ The total number of ways is $210 + 175 = 385.$

17 AS

(a) The three directors may be chosen in $^{10}C_3$ ways i.e.

$^{10}C_3 = \dfrac{10!}{3!7!} = \dfrac{10 \times 9 \times 8}{1 \times 2 \times 3} = 120$ ways.

(b) 1 French speaker and 2 non-French speakers may be chosen in $^4C_1 \times {}^6C_2 = \dfrac{4!}{1!3!} \times \dfrac{6!}{2!4!} = 4 \times 15 = 60$ ways.

2 French speakers and 1 non-French speaker may be chosen in $^4C_2 \times {}^6C_1 = \dfrac{4!}{2!2!} \times \dfrac{6!}{1!5!} = 6 \times 6 = 36$ ways.

3 French speakers maybe chosen in

$^4C_3 = \dfrac{4!}{1!3!} = 4$ ways.

$\therefore$ Three directors may be chosen so that at least one of them speaks French in $60 + 36 + 4 = 100$ ways.

18 A

$(1+x)^{-\frac{1}{2}} = 1 + \left(-\frac{1}{2}\right)x + \dfrac{\left(-\frac{1}{2}\right)\left(-\frac{3}{2}\right)}{2!}x^2 + \dfrac{\left(-\frac{1}{2}\right)\left(-\frac{3}{2}\right)\left(-\frac{5}{2}\right)}{3!}x^3 + \dots$

$= 1 - \frac{1}{2}x + \frac{3}{8}x^2 - \frac{5}{16}x^3 + \dots$

$\dfrac{(1-x)^2}{(1+x)^{\frac{1}{2}}} = (1-x)^2(1+x)^{-\frac{1}{2}}$

$= \left(1 - 2x + x^2\right)(1+x)^{-\frac{1}{2}}$

$= \left(1 - 2x + x^2\right)\left(1 - \frac{1}{2}x + \frac{3}{8}x^2 - \frac{5}{16}x^3 + \dots\right)$

$= 1 - \frac{1}{2}x + \frac{3}{8}x^2 - \frac{5}{16}x^3 - 2x + x^2 - \frac{3}{4}x^3 + x^2 - \frac{1}{2}x^3 + \dots$

$= 1 - \frac{5}{2}x + \frac{19}{8}x^2 - \frac{25}{16}x^3 + \dots$

19 AS

$(1+2x)^{-\frac{1}{2}} = 1 + \left(-\frac{1}{2}\right)(2x) + \dfrac{\left(-\frac{1}{2}\right)\left(-\frac{3}{2}\right)}{2!}(2x)^2$

$+ \dfrac{\left(-\frac{1}{2}\right)\left(-\frac{3}{2}\right)\left(-\frac{5}{2}\right)}{3!}(2x)^3 + \dots$

$= 1 + \left(-\frac{1}{2}\right)(2x) + \left(\frac{3}{8}\right)(2x)^2 + \left(-\frac{5}{16}\right)(2x)^3 + \dots$

$= 1 - x + \frac{3}{2}x^2 - \frac{5}{2}x^3 + \dots$

Sub in $x = \frac{1}{8}$ to give:

$\left[1 + 2\left(\frac{1}{8}\right)\right]^{-\frac{1}{2}} = 1 - \left(\frac{1}{8}\right) + \frac{3}{2}\left(\frac{1}{8}\right)^2 - \frac{5}{2}\left(\frac{1}{8}\right)^3 + \dots$

$\left(\frac{10}{8}\right)^{-\frac{1}{2}} = 1 - \left(\frac{1}{8}\right) + \frac{3}{2}\left(\frac{1}{8}\right)^2 - \frac{5}{2}\left(\frac{1}{8}\right)^3 + \dots$

$\left(\frac{5}{4}\right)^{-\frac{1}{2}} = 1 - \frac{1}{8} + \frac{3}{128} - \frac{5}{1024} + \dots$

$\left(\frac{5}{4}\right)^{-\frac{1}{2}} \approx \dfrac{915}{1024}$

Invert $\dfrac{\sqrt{5}}{2} \approx \dfrac{1024}{915}$

Hence $\sqrt{5} \approx \dfrac{2048}{915}$

20 A

$\dfrac{x}{x-1} > \dfrac{1}{x+1} \Rightarrow \dfrac{x}{x-1} - \dfrac{1}{x+1} > 0$

$\Rightarrow \dfrac{x(x+1) - (x-1)}{(x-1)(x+1)} > 0$

$\Rightarrow \dfrac{x^2 + 1}{(x-1)(x+1)} > 0$

Note zero values in each bracket, i.e. $x = 1, x = -1$

	$x < -1$	$-1 < x < +1$	$x > +1$
$x^2 + 1$	+	+	+
$x - 1$	−	−	+
$x + 1$	−	+	+
Product	+	−	+

$\therefore$ The complete set of values for which $\dfrac{x}{x-1} > \dfrac{1}{x+1}$ is

$\{x : x < -1 \text{ or } x > 1\}$

Pure Mathematics Question Bank: Answers

21 AS

$3x - 2 > x^2 + 2x - 14 \Rightarrow x^2 - x - 12 < 0$

$\Rightarrow (x+3)(x-4) < 0$

By sketching the graph of $y = (x+3)(x-8)$

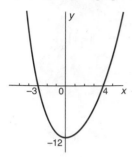

it can be seen that $y = (x+3)(x-4) < 0$ when x lies between -3 and 4

$\therefore$ The set of values for which $3x - 2 > x^2 + 2x - 14$ is $\{x : -3 < x < 4\}$

22 A

(a) $\log 2 + 2\log 18 - \frac{3}{2}\log 36 = \log 2 + \log 18^2 - \log 36^{\frac{3}{2}}$

$= \log \dfrac{(2)\left(18^2\right)}{36^{\frac{3}{2}}}$

$= \log 3$

(b) Taking logs of both sides gives

$\log 3^x = \log 4^{x-2} \Rightarrow x\log 3 = (x-2)\log 4$

$\Rightarrow x\log 3 = x\log 4 - 2\log 4$

$\Rightarrow x\log 3 - x\log 4 = -2\log 4$

$\Rightarrow x(\log 3 - \log 4) = -2\log 4$

$\Rightarrow x = \dfrac{-2\log 4}{\log 3 - \log 4} = 9.64 \ (3 \text{ s.f.})$

23 AS

$\ln x + 3\ln y - \ln 2 = \ln x^4 - \ln 54 \Rightarrow \ln x + \ln y^3 - \ln 2 = \ln\left(\dfrac{x^4}{54}\right)$

$\Rightarrow \ln\left(\dfrac{xy^3}{2}\right) = \ln\left(\dfrac{x^4}{54}\right)$

$\Rightarrow \dfrac{xy^3}{2} = \dfrac{x^4}{54}$

$\Rightarrow \dfrac{54}{2} = \dfrac{x^4}{xy^3}$

$\Rightarrow 27 = \dfrac{x^3}{y^3} = \left(\dfrac{x}{y}\right)^3$

$\Rightarrow 3 = \dfrac{x}{y}$

24 SH

$\log_2 2x + \log_2 8x = 6 \Rightarrow \log_2\left[(2x)(8x)\right] = 6$

$\Rightarrow \log_2\left[16x^2\right] = 6$

$\Rightarrow 2^6 = 16x^2$

$\Rightarrow x^2 = 4$

$\Rightarrow x = 2 \qquad [x > 0 \text{ for } \log x]$

$\therefore$ The correct answer is B.

25 A

(a) $\ln(1+2x) = (2x) - \dfrac{(2x)^2}{2} + \dfrac{(2x)^3}{3} - \ldots$

$= 2x - 2x^2 + \frac{8}{3}x^3 - \ldots$

(b) $\ln(1-3x) = (-3x) - \dfrac{(-3x)^2}{2} + \dfrac{(-3x)^3}{3} - \ldots$

$= -3x - \frac{9}{2}x^2 - 9x^3 - \ldots$

$f(x) = \ln\left[\dfrac{(1+2x)^{\frac{1}{2}}}{(1-3x)^2}\right] = \ln(1+2x)^{\frac{1}{2}} - \ln(1-3x)^2$

$= \tfrac{1}{2}\ln(1+2x) - 2\ln(1-3x)$

$= \tfrac{1}{2}\left[2x - 2x^2 + \tfrac{8}{3}x^3 - \ldots\right] - 2\left[-3x - \tfrac{9}{2}x^2 - 9x^3 - \ldots\right]$

$= 7x + 8x^2 + \tfrac{58}{3}x^3 + \ldots$

The expansion of $\ln(1+2x)$ converges when $-1 < 2x \le 1$

i.e. when $-\frac{1}{2} < x \le \frac{1}{2}$

The expansion of $\ln(1-3x)$ converges when $-1 < -3x \le 1$

i.e. when $-\frac{1}{3} \le x < \frac{1}{3}$

$\therefore$ The expansion of $f(x)$ is valid when $-\frac{1}{3} \le x < \frac{1}{3}$

26 AS

$e^{2x} = 1 + \dfrac{2x}{1!} + \dfrac{(2x)^2}{2!} + \dfrac{(2x)^3}{3!} + \ldots$

$= 1 + 2x + 2x^2 + \tfrac{4}{3}x^3 + \ldots$

$\sqrt{1+4x} = (1+4x)^{\frac{1}{2}} = 1 + \left(\tfrac{1}{2}\right)(4x) + \dfrac{\left(\tfrac{1}{2}\right)\left(-\tfrac{1}{2}\right)}{2!}(4x)^2$

$+ \dfrac{\left(\tfrac{1}{2}\right)\left(-\tfrac{1}{2}\right)\left(-\tfrac{3}{2}\right)}{3!}(4x)^3 + \ldots$

$= 1 + 2x - 2x^2 + 4x^3 - \ldots$

$\therefore y = e^{2x} - \sqrt{(1+4x)}$

$= (1 + 2x + 2x^2 + \tfrac{4}{3}x^3 + \ldots) - (1 + 2x - 2x^2 + 4x^3 - \ldots)$

$= 4x^2 - \tfrac{8}{3}x^3 \ldots$

For small values of x, $-\frac{8}{3}x^3$ may be neglected so y is approximately $4x^2$ $\therefore$ y is approximately proportional to x^2.

Near the origin when x is small, the graph of y is

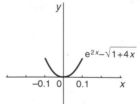

27 A

(i) The curves intersect when $2xy = 9 \Rightarrow y = \dfrac{9}{2x}$

$3x + 4\left(\dfrac{9}{2x}\right) = 15 \Rightarrow 3x + \dfrac{18}{x} = 15 \Rightarrow 3x^2 + 18 = 15x$

$\Rightarrow 3x^2 - 15x + 18 = 0 \Rightarrow x = 2 \text{ or } 3$

$x = 2 \Rightarrow y = \frac{9}{4}$ and $x = 3 \Rightarrow y = \frac{3}{2}$

$\therefore$ A has coordinates $\left(2, \frac{9}{4}\right)$ and B has coordinates $\left(3, \frac{3}{2}\right)$

(ii) The distance from A to B is

$$\sqrt{(3-2)^2 + \left(\frac{3}{2} - \frac{9}{4}\right)^2} = \sqrt{1 + \frac{9}{16}} = \frac{5}{4}$$

28 AS

(i) $y = 2e^x$ crosses the y-axis at $(0, 2)$ and does not touch or cross the x-axis.

(ii) $y = 4 - x^2$ crosses the y-axis at $(0, 4)$ and crosses the x-axis at $(-2, 0)$ and $(2, 0)$.

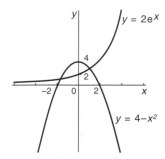

When the curves intersect, $2e^x = 4 - x^2$ or $2e^x + x^2 = 4$

This equation has two roots as the curves intersect twice.

When $x = 0.55$, $2e^{0.55} + (0.55)^2 < 4$

When $x = 0.65$, $2e^{0.65} + (0.65)^2 > 4$

Hence, one of the roots lies between 0.55 and 0.65.

29 SH

(a) $y = ke^{0.5x}$ cuts the y-axis at $(0, 3)$ so $3 = ke^{0.5(0)} \Rightarrow k = 3$

(b) At $x = 1$, $y = 3e^{0.5(1)} = 4.95$ (3 s.f.)

$\therefore$ The coordinates of P are $(1, 4.95)$.

30 A

(a)

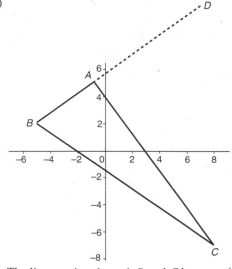

The line passing through B and C has equation

$$\frac{y-2}{-7-2} = \frac{x-(-5)}{8-(-5)} \Rightarrow \frac{y-2}{-9} = \frac{x+5}{13}$$

$$\Rightarrow 13(y-2) = -9(x+5) \Rightarrow 9x + 13y + 19 = 0$$

(b) Gradient of AB is $\dfrac{5-2}{-1-(-5)} = \dfrac{3}{4}$

Gradient of $AC = \dfrac{5-(-7)}{-1-8} = -\dfrac{4}{3}$

Gradient of $AB \times$ gradient of $AC = \dfrac{3}{4} \times -\dfrac{4}{3} = -1 \Rightarrow AB \perp AC$

(c)

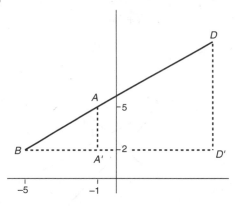

By similar triangles, $3BA = BD \Rightarrow 3BA' = BD'$

and $3AA' = DD'$

$BA' = 4 \Rightarrow BD' = 3BA' = 3(4) = 12$

$AA' = 3 \Rightarrow DD' = 3AA' = 3(3) = 9$

$\therefore$ The coordinates of D are $(7, 11)$.

31 AS

(i) Equation of DC is $y = \dfrac{4}{3}x - \dfrac{10}{3} \Rightarrow$ gradient of DC is $\dfrac{4}{3}$

$AB \parallel DC \Rightarrow$ gradient of AB is $\dfrac{4}{3}$

so equation is $y - 13 = \dfrac{4}{3}(x - 6)$

Hence the equation of AB is $4x - 3y + 15 = 0$

(ii) $BC \perp DC \Rightarrow$ gradient of BC $= \dfrac{-1}{\text{gradient of } DC} = -\dfrac{3}{4}$

Equation of BC is $y - 13 = -\dfrac{3}{4}(x - 6)$

or $3x + 4y - 70 = 0$

(iii) A lies on AB with x coordinate 0

so $4(0) - 3y + 15 = 0 \Rightarrow y = 5$

Hence the coordinates of A are $(0, 5)$.

BC and DC intersect at C.

BC has equation $3x + 4y - 70 = 0$ or $y = \dfrac{1}{4}(70 - 3x)$

DC has equation $3y = 4x - 10$ or $y = \dfrac{1}{3}(4x - 10)$

So at C, $\dfrac{1}{4}(70 - 3x) = \dfrac{1}{3}(4x - 10)$

$\Rightarrow 210 - 9x = 16x - 40 \Rightarrow x = 10$

$\Rightarrow y = 10$

$\therefore$ Coordinates of C are $(10, 10)$.

(iv) Length of $AB = \sqrt{(6-0)^2 + (13-5)^2} = 10$

Length of $BC = \sqrt{(6-10)^2 + (13-10)^2} = 5$

Length of $DC = \sqrt{(10-1)^2 + (10-(-2))^2} = 15$

$\therefore$ Area of trapezium

$= \frac{1}{2}(AB + DC) \times BC = \frac{1}{2}(10 + 15) \times 5 = 62\frac{1}{2}$

32 SH

(a) $3x + 2y - 5 = 0 \Rightarrow y = -\dfrac{3}{2}x + \dfrac{5}{2} \Rightarrow$ gradient is $-\dfrac{3}{2}$

Line through $(3, -5)$ parallel to $3x + 2y - 5 = 0$ also has gradient $-\frac{3}{2}$ so its equation is

$y - (-5) = -\frac{3}{2}(x - 3)$ i.e. $3x + 2y + 1 = 0$

(b) Gradient of AB is $\dfrac{4b^2 - a^2}{2b - a} = \dfrac{(2b - a)(2b + a)}{2b - a} = 2b + a$

33 A
(a)

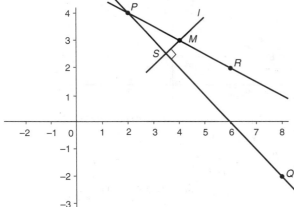

Let M be the midpoint of PR. Coordinates of M are $(4, 3)$.

Gradient of PQ is $\dfrac{4 - (-2)}{2 - 8} = -1$ so the gradient of l is

$\dfrac{-1}{-1} = 1$. Since l passes through M, it has equation

$y - 3 = 1(x - 4)$ i.e. $y = x - 1$

(b) PQ has equation $y - 4 = -1(x - 2)$ i.e. $y = 6 - x$

l and PQ intersect when $y = 6 - x = x - 1$

i.e. when $x = 3\frac{1}{2}$ and $y = 2\frac{1}{2}$

$\therefore$ Coordinates of S are $\left(3\frac{1}{2}, 2\frac{1}{2}\right)$.

The length of PS is $\sqrt{\left(2 - 3\frac{1}{2}\right)^2 + \left(4 - 2\frac{1}{2}\right)^2} = \dfrac{3}{\sqrt{2}}$

The length of SQ is $\sqrt{\left(3\frac{1}{2} - 8\right)^2 + \left(2\frac{1}{2} - (-2)\right)^2} = \dfrac{9}{\sqrt{2}}$

$\therefore$ ratio $PS : SQ$ is $\dfrac{3}{\sqrt{2}} : \dfrac{9}{\sqrt{2}}$ or $1 : 3$

(c) From the general equation of the circle passing through P, Q and R:

$(2)^2 + (4)^2 + 2g(2) + 2f(4) + c = 0 \Rightarrow 4g + 8f + c = -20$
$(8)^2 + (-2)^2 + 2g(8) + 2f(-2) + c = 0 \Rightarrow 16g - 4f + c = -68$
$(6)^2 + (2)^2 + 2g(6) + 2f(2) + c = 0 \Rightarrow 12g + 4f + c = -40$

Solving these simultaneous equations gives
$f = 3, g = -1, c = -40$
$\therefore$ The coordinates of C are $(1, -3)$ and the radius is
$\sqrt{(-1)^2 + (3)^2 + 40} = 5\sqrt{2}$

34 AS
From the general equation of a circle,
$x^2 + y^2 + 2gx + 2fy + c = 0,$

$(0)^2 + (0)^2 + 2g(0) + 2f(0) + c = 0 \Rightarrow c = 0$
$(3)^2 + (3)^2 + 2g(3) + 2f(3) + 0 = 0 \Rightarrow g + f = -3$
$(3)^2 + (1)^2 + 2g(3) + 2f(1) + 0 = 0 \Rightarrow 3g + f = -5$

Solving these simultaneous equations gives
$g = -1, f = -2, c = 0$

Hence, the equation of circle C is $x^2 + y^2 - 2x - 4y = 0$

The radius of C is $\sqrt{(-1)^2 + (-2)^2 - 0} = \sqrt{5}$

The coordinates of the centre of C are $(-g, -f)$ i.e. $(1, 2)$.

$(2)^2 + (4)^2 + 2(-1)(2) + 2(-2)(4) = 0$ so $P(2, 4)$ satisfies the general equation for C. Hence $P(2, 4)$ lies on C.

Let M be the centre of C so M is $(1, 2)$. The gradient of PM is $\dfrac{4 - 2}{2 - 1} = 2$ and as the tangent at P is perpendicular to the radius PM, its gradient is $-\frac{1}{2}$.

The tangent at P has equation $y - 4 = -\frac{1}{2}(x - 2)$

i.e. $x + 2y - 10 = 0$

35 SH
(a) Using the general equation of a circle,
$x^2 + y^2 + 2gx + 2fy + c = 0,$
$x^2 + y^2 + 14x - 20y + 129 = 0 \Rightarrow g = 7, f = -10, c = 129$
$\therefore$ The centre is $(-7, 10)$ and the radius is
$\sqrt{(7)^2 + (-10)^2 - 129} = 2\sqrt{5}$

(b) $(-3)^2 + (12)^2 + 14(-3) - 20(12) + 129 = 0$
$\Rightarrow P(-3, 12)$ lies on the circle.
The general equation of the tangent is
$xx_1 + yy_1 + g(x + x_1) + f(y + y_1) + c = 0$
so the equation of the tangent at $P(-3, 12)$ is
$-3x + 12y + 7(x - 3) - 10(y + 12) + 129 = 0$
i.e. $y = 6 - 2x$

(c) The points of contact are found by solving
$y = 6 - 2x$ and $x^2 + y^2 - 28x + 4y + 120 = 0$
$x^2 + (6 - 2x)^2 - 28x + 4(6 - 2x) + 120 = 0$
$\Rightarrow x^2 - 12x + 36 = 0 \Rightarrow x = 6, y = -6$

Only one solution means that $y = 6 - 2x$ is a tangent to the circle and touches it at $(6, -6)$.

36 A

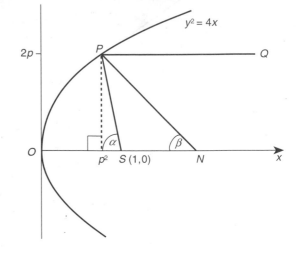

(i) $\tan \alpha = \dfrac{2p-0}{1-p^2} = \dfrac{2p}{1-p^2}$

(ii) Gradient of tangent at P is $\dfrac{dy}{dx} = \dfrac{2}{y} = \dfrac{1}{p}$

∴ Gradient of normal at P (PN) is $-p$.
Equation of PN is $y - 2p = -p\left(x - p^2\right)$

i.e. $y = p^3 + 2p - px$

At N, $y = 0$ so $x = p^2 + 2$

∴ $\tan \beta = \dfrac{2p-0}{\left(p^2+2\right)-p^2} = \dfrac{2p}{2} = p$

$PS = \sqrt{\left(2p\right)^2 + \left(1-p^2\right)^2} = \sqrt{1 + 2p^2 + p^4} = \sqrt{\left(1+p^2\right)^2} = 1 + p^2$

$SN = \left(p^2 + 2\right) - 1 = 1 + p^2$

∴ $PS = SN \Rightarrow \triangle PSN$ is isosceles $\Rightarrow S\hat{P}N = \beta \Rightarrow \alpha = 2\beta$

$N\hat{P}Q = \beta$ since $PQ \,||\, SN$

Hence PN bisects $S\hat{P}Q$.

37 AS

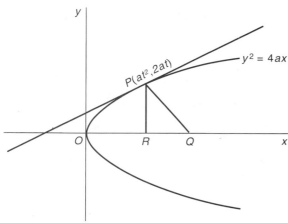

The gradient of the tangent is found by differentiating
$y^2 = 4ax$

$2y\dfrac{dy}{dx} = 4a \Rightarrow \dfrac{dy}{dx} = \dfrac{2a}{y}$

Gradient of tangent at P is $\dfrac{2a}{2at} = \dfrac{1}{t}$ so the gradient of the

normal at P is $-t$.

∴ The equation of the normal at P is $y - 2at = -t\left(x - at^2\right)$

i.e. $y + tx = at\left(2 + t^2\right)$

At Q, $y = 0$ so $0 + tx = at\left(2 + t^2\right) \Rightarrow x = a\left(2 + t^2\right)$

$QR = a\left(2 + t^2\right) - at^2 = 2a$ which is independent of t.

38 SH

(a) The general equation of a vertical parabola is
$y - y_1 = a(x - x_1)^2$. This parabola passes through $(0, 40)$
so $y - 40 = a(x - 0)^2 \Rightarrow y = ax^2 + 40$
The parabola also passes through $(20, 0)$ and $(-20, 0)$ so
$0 = a(20)^2 + 40$ and $0 = a(-20)^2 + 40 \Rightarrow a = -\dfrac{1}{10}$

∴ The equation of the parabola is $y = 40 - \dfrac{x^2}{10}$

Since $y \geq 0$, $-20 \leq x \leq 20$

(b)

Gradient of $AB = -\dfrac{50}{25} = -2$ and the equation of AB is

$y = -2x + 50$

Substituting this into $y = 40 - \dfrac{x^2}{10}$ gives

$-2x + 50 = 40 - \dfrac{x^2}{10} \Rightarrow x^2 - 20x + 100 = 0 \Rightarrow (x - 10)^2 = 0$

so $x = 10$ is the only solution
∴ AB is a tangent to the parabola and just touches it.
By symmetry, AC is also a tangent to the parabola. Hence
the triangular frame touches the cover without disturbing
the parabolic shape.

39 A
The gradient of the tangent
$\dfrac{dy}{dx} = \dfrac{dy}{dt} \bigg/ \dfrac{dx}{dt} = \dfrac{-2t^{-2}}{2t} = -\dfrac{1}{t^3}$

At $P\left(p^2, \dfrac{2}{p}\right)$, $\dfrac{dy}{dx} = -\dfrac{1}{p^3}$

∴ The equation of the tangent at P is $y - \dfrac{2}{p} = -\dfrac{1}{p^3}\left(x - p^2\right)$

so $p^3 y - 2p^2 = -x + p^2$ i.e. $x + p^3 y = 3p^2$
Tangent passes through $(1, 2) \Rightarrow 1 + 2p^3 = 3p^2$
$\Rightarrow 2p^3 - 3p^2 + 1 = 0$
By inspection, $p = 1$ is one solution so, by long division,
$2p^3 - 3p^2 + 1 = 0$
$\Rightarrow (p - 1)(2p^2 - p - 1) = 0$
$\Rightarrow (p - 1)(p - 1)(2p + 1) = 0$

∴ $p = 1$ or $-\dfrac{1}{2}$

40 AS
(i) $x(8 - x) \leq 15 \Rightarrow 8x - x^2 - 15 \leq 0 \Rightarrow x^2 - 8x + 15 \geq 0$
$\Rightarrow (x - 5)(x - 3) \geq 0 \Rightarrow x \leq 3$ or $x \geq 5$

(ii) When $y = mx + 12$ is a tangent to $x^2 + xy + 9 = 0$,
the equation $x^2 + x(mx + 12) + 9 = 0$ has only one solution.
$x^2 + mx^2 + 12x + 9 = 0 \Rightarrow (1 + m)x^2 + 12x + 9 = 0$
and for one solution '$b^2 - 4ac = 0$'
$\Rightarrow (12)^2 - 4(1 + m)(9) = 0 \Rightarrow m = 3$

41 A

Putting $X = \frac{1}{x}$, $Y = \frac{1}{y}$, and $K = \frac{1}{c}$, the equation has a linear

form $X + Y = K$ or $Y = K - X$.

Tabulating the values of X and Y to 3 d.p. gives:

X	0.667	0.400	0.286	0.222	0.182
Y	0.161	0.313	0.556	0.625	0.667

The graph of Y against X is:

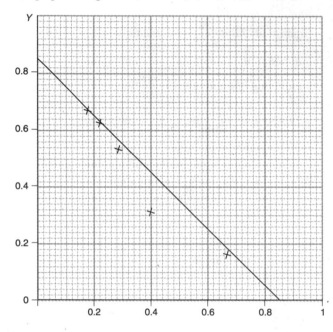

From the graph it can be seen that the incorrect value is
$Y = 0.313$ i.e. $y = 3.2$
The line gives a value of $Y = 0.45$ i.e. $y = 2.2$
From the y-intercept, $K = \frac{1}{c} \approx 0.85 \Rightarrow c = 1.2$ (1 d.p.)

42 AS

$P = kc^T \Rightarrow \ln P = \ln k + T \ln c$

T	1	2	3	4	5
P	15.4	24.6	47.2	88.3	144.4
$\ln P$	2.73	3.20	3.85	4.48	4.97

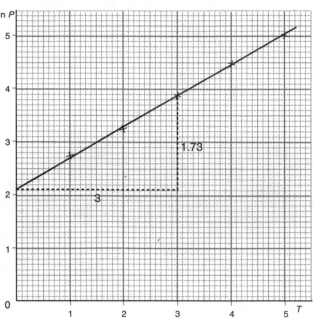

From the y-intercept of the graph, $\ln k = 2.12$
$\Rightarrow k = 8.33$ (2 d.p.)

The gradient $= \frac{1.73}{3} = 0.577 = \ln c \Rightarrow c = 1.78$ (2 d.p.)

43 SH

The equation of the straight line is $Y = 2X + 1$
where $Y = \log_{10} y$ and $X = \log_{10} x$.

So, since $\log_{10} 10 = 1, \log_{10} y = 2 \log_{10} x + \log_{10} 10 = \log_{10} 10x^2$

$\therefore y = 10x^2$

44 A

(a)

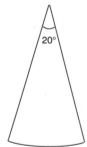

$180° \equiv \pi$ radians $\Rightarrow 20° \equiv \frac{\pi}{9}$ radians

Sector area $= \frac{1}{2} r^2 \theta = \frac{1}{2} r^2 \left(\frac{\pi}{9}\right) = 2 \Rightarrow r = \frac{6}{\sqrt{\pi}}$

Arc length $= r\theta = \left(\frac{6}{\sqrt{\pi}}\right)\left(\frac{\pi}{9}\right) = \frac{2}{3}\sqrt{\pi}$ (1.18 to 2 d.p.)

(b) Neglecting θ^2 and higher powers of θ gives

$\cos 3\theta \approx 1 - \frac{1}{2}(3\theta)^2 = 1 = \frac{9}{2}\theta^2$

$\cos 5\theta \approx 1 - \frac{1}{2}(5\theta)^2 = 1 - \frac{25}{2}\theta^2$

$\therefore \cos 3\theta - \cos 5\theta = \dfrac{2}{625} \Rightarrow \left(1 - \dfrac{9}{2}\theta^2\right) - \left(1 - \dfrac{25}{2}\theta^2\right) \approx \dfrac{2}{625}$

$\Rightarrow 8\theta^2 \approx \dfrac{2}{625} \Rightarrow \theta^2 \approx 0.0004 \Rightarrow \theta \approx \pm 0.02$

$\therefore$ 0.02 is an approximate value for θ.

45 AS

(i) Arc length $= r\theta \Rightarrow$ arc $AB = 2\theta$ and arc $CD = 6\theta$

Perimeter of $ABCD = 4 + 2\theta + 4 + 6\theta = 12 \Rightarrow \theta = \frac{1}{2}$

(ii) Sector area $= \dfrac{1}{2}r^2\theta \Rightarrow$ sector area $OCD = \dfrac{1}{2}(6)^2\left(\dfrac{1}{2}\right) = 9$

and sector area $OAB = \dfrac{1}{2}(2)^2\left(\dfrac{1}{2}\right) = 1$

$\therefore$ Shaded area $ABCD = 9 - 1 = 8$ m^2

46 SH

By definition, arc $XY =$ radius $\Rightarrow$ angle $XOY = 1$ radian

$\theta = 1 \Rightarrow$ area $OXY = \dfrac{1}{2}r^2(1) = \dfrac{1}{2}r^2$

$\therefore$ Correct answer is C.

47 A

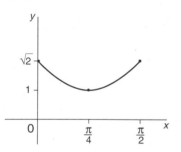

$x = 0 \Rightarrow y = \sec\left(-\dfrac{\pi}{4}\right) = \dfrac{1}{\cos\left(-\dfrac{\pi}{4}\right)} = \sqrt{2}$

$x = \dfrac{\pi}{4} \Rightarrow y = \sec(0) = \dfrac{1}{\cos 0} = 1$

$x = \dfrac{\pi}{2} \Rightarrow y = \sec\left(\dfrac{\pi}{4}\right) = \dfrac{1}{\cos\left(\dfrac{\pi}{4}\right)} = \sqrt{2}$

48 AS

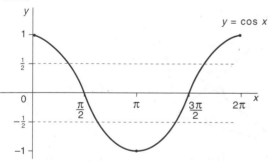

$|\cos x| \le \dfrac{1}{2} \Rightarrow -\dfrac{1}{2} \le \cos x \le \dfrac{1}{2}$

From the graph, since $\cos x = \dfrac{1}{2} \Rightarrow x = \dfrac{\pi}{3}$ or $\dfrac{5\pi}{3}$

and $\cos x = -\dfrac{1}{2} \Rightarrow x = \dfrac{2\pi}{3}$ or $\dfrac{4\pi}{3}$, it can be seen that

$|\cos x| \le \dfrac{1}{2}$ when $\dfrac{\pi}{3} \le x \le \dfrac{2\pi}{3}$ or $\dfrac{4\pi}{3} \le x \le \dfrac{5\pi}{3}$

49 SH

The maximum value of $1 - \cos\left(x - \dfrac{\pi}{6}\right)$ occurs when

$\cos\left(x - \dfrac{\pi}{6}\right)$ is minimum i.e. $\cos\left(x - \dfrac{\pi}{6}\right) = -1$.

This occurs when $x - \dfrac{\pi}{6} = \pi$ since $\cos \pi = -1$.

Hence $x = \pi + \dfrac{\pi}{6} = \dfrac{7\pi}{6}$ gives the minimum value of

$\cos\left(x - \dfrac{\pi}{6}\right)$ and the maximum value of $1 - \cos\left(x - \dfrac{\pi}{6}\right)$

in the range $0 \le x < 2\pi$.

$\therefore$ The correct answer is D.

50 A

$\tan\theta + \cot\theta = \dfrac{\sin\theta}{\cos\theta} + \dfrac{\cos\theta}{\sin\theta} = \dfrac{\sin^2\theta + \cos^2\theta}{\sin\theta\cos\theta}$

$= \dfrac{1}{\sin\theta\cos\theta} = \dfrac{2}{2\sin\theta\cos\theta} = \dfrac{2}{\sin 2\theta}$

$= 2\,\text{cosec}\,2\theta$

$\therefore \tan x + \cot x = 8\cos 2x \Rightarrow 2\,\text{cosec}\,2x = 8\cos 2x$

$\Rightarrow \text{cosec}\,2x = 4\cos 2x \Rightarrow \dfrac{1}{\sin 2x} = 4\cos 2x$

$\Rightarrow 1 = 4\sin 2x\cos 2x = 2\sin 4x \Rightarrow \sin 4x = \dfrac{1}{2}$

$\Rightarrow 4x = \dfrac{\pi}{6} + 2n\pi$ or $\dfrac{5\pi}{6} + 2n\pi \Rightarrow x = \dfrac{\pi}{24} + \dfrac{n\pi}{2}$ or $\dfrac{5\pi}{24} + \dfrac{n\pi}{2}$

For $0 < x < \pi$, $x = \dfrac{\pi}{24}, \dfrac{13\pi}{24}, \dfrac{5\pi}{24}, \dfrac{17\pi}{24}$

51 AS

$\sin 2x = \cos x \Rightarrow \sin 2x - \cos x = 0 \Rightarrow 2\sin x\cos x - \cos x = 0$

$\Rightarrow \cos x(2\sin x - 1) = 0$

$\cos x = 0 \Rightarrow x = \dfrac{\pi}{2}$ or $\dfrac{3\pi}{2}$

$2\sin x - 1 = 0 \Rightarrow \sin x = \dfrac{1}{2} \Rightarrow x = \dfrac{\pi}{6}$ or $\dfrac{5\pi}{6}$

$\therefore$ For $0 \le x \le 2\pi$, $x = \dfrac{\pi}{6}, \dfrac{\pi}{2}, \dfrac{3\pi}{2}, \dfrac{5\pi}{6}$

52 SH

$\sin 2A = 2\sin A\cos A$

$\sin A = \dfrac{3}{4} \Rightarrow \cos A = \sqrt{1 - \sin^2 A} = \sqrt{1 - \left(\dfrac{3}{4}\right)^2} = +\dfrac{\sqrt{7}}{4}$ (positive as A is in first quadrant)

$\therefore$ The exact value of $\sin 2A = 2\left(\dfrac{3}{4}\right)\left(\dfrac{\sqrt{7}}{4}\right) = \dfrac{3\sqrt{7}}{8}$

53 A

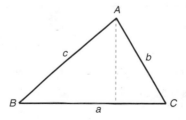

(a) Perpendicular height $= c\sin B$

Area $= \frac{1}{2}$ base $\times$ height $\Rightarrow$ Area $= \frac{1}{2}ac\sin B$

(b) (i) $B = \sin^{-1}\left(\dfrac{2\times 12}{8\times 6}\right) = \sin^{-1}0.5 \Rightarrow B = 30°$ or $B = 150°$

(ii) Using cosine rule with $B = 30°$

$AC^2 = 8^2 + 6^2 - 2.8.6.\cos 30° \Rightarrow AC = 4.11$ cm (3 s.f.)

Using cosine rule with $B = 150°$

$AC^2 = 8^2 + 6^2 - 2.8.6.\cos 150° \Rightarrow AC = 13.5$ cm (3 s.f.)

54 AS

Using the cosine rule

$13^2 = 15^2 + x^2 - 2.15.x.\cos 60° \Rightarrow x^2 - 15x + 56 = 0$

$\Rightarrow (x-8)(x-7) = 0 \Rightarrow x = 8$ cm or $x = 7$ cm

55 A

(a)

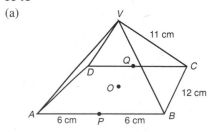

$OA = \dfrac{1}{2}\sqrt{12^2 + 12^2} = 6\sqrt{2}$ (Pythagoras)

$VO = \sqrt{11^2 - \left(6\sqrt{2}\right)^2} = 7$ cm

(b) $\cos O\hat{V}A = \dfrac{7}{11} \Rightarrow O\hat{V}A = 50.5°$ (3 s.f.)

$\Rightarrow$ angle between VA and VC is $50.5° \times 2 = 101°$

(c)

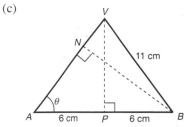

$BN = 12\sin\theta = 12 \times \dfrac{\sqrt{11^2 - 6^2}}{11} = 10.1$ cm (3 s.f.)

(d)

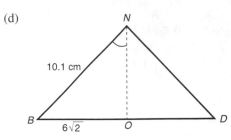

Required angle is $B\hat{N}D$

$\sin B\hat{N}O = \dfrac{6\sqrt{2}}{10.1} \Rightarrow B\hat{N}O = 57.2$ (3 s.f.)

$\Rightarrow$ angle between planes is $57.2 \times 2 = 114.4°$

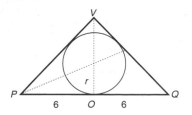

$\tan V\hat{P}Q = \dfrac{OV}{OP} = \dfrac{7}{6} \Rightarrow V\hat{P}Q = 49.4°$

Bisector of $V\hat{P}Q$ meets bisector of $P\hat{V}Q$ at centre of circle.

Thus, $\tan\frac{1}{2}V\hat{P}Q = \dfrac{r}{6} \Rightarrow r = 6\tan\frac{1}{2}V\hat{P}Q \Rightarrow r = 2.76$ cm

56 AS

(i) $BD = \sqrt{4^2 + 4^2} = \sqrt{32}$ (Pythagoras)

$DF = \sqrt{2^2 + \left(\sqrt{32}\right)^2} = 6$

$\tan\theta = \dfrac{2}{\sqrt{32}} \Rightarrow \theta = 19.5°$

(ii)

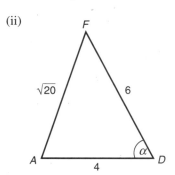

$AF = \sqrt{4^2 + 2^2} = \sqrt{20}$

Thus $\triangle AFD$ is right-angled at A, since it obeys Pythagoras' Theorem.

$\therefore \cos\alpha = \dfrac{4}{6} \Rightarrow \alpha = 48.2°$. By symmetry, the angle between DF and AB is also $48.2°$.

57 A

(a) $\dfrac{AC}{AB} = \lambda \Rightarrow \mathbf{AC} = \lambda\mathbf{AB} \Rightarrow \mathbf{c} - \mathbf{a} = \lambda(\mathbf{b} - \mathbf{a})$

$\Rightarrow \mathbf{c} = (1 - \lambda)\mathbf{a} + \lambda\mathbf{b}$

(b)

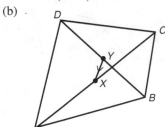

$\mathbf{YX} = \frac{1}{2}\mathbf{BD} + \mathbf{DA} + \frac{1}{2}\mathbf{AC} = \frac{1}{2}\mathbf{DA} + \frac{1}{2}\mathbf{BC}$ (1)

and $\mathbf{YX} = \frac{1}{2}\mathbf{DB} + \mathbf{BA} + \frac{1}{2}\mathbf{AC} = \frac{1}{2}\mathbf{DC} + \frac{1}{2}\mathbf{BA}$ (2)

Adding (1) and (2) gives

$2\mathbf{YX} = \frac{1}{2}\mathbf{DA} + \frac{1}{2}\mathbf{BC} + \frac{1}{2}\mathbf{DC} + \frac{1}{2}\mathbf{BA}$

$\Rightarrow 4\mathbf{YX} = \mathbf{BA} + \mathbf{BC} + \mathbf{DA} + \mathbf{DC}$

(c)(i)

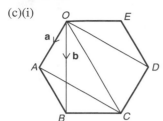

$AB = b - a$ and $OC = 2AB$

∴ $OC = 2(b - a)$

$OD = OC + CD = 2b - 3a$

$OE = OD + DE = b - 2a$

(ii) Let $OF = \lambda OB$. Using the ratio theorem and the fact that $OABC$ is an isosceles trapezium

$OF = \lambda a + (1 - \lambda)OC = \lambda a + 2(1 - \lambda)(b - a)$

$= 3\lambda a - 2a - 2\lambda b + 2b$

but $OF = \lambda b$ ∴ $\lambda b = 3\lambda a - 2\lambda b + 2b - 2a$

$\Rightarrow 3\lambda(b - a) = 2(b - a)$

$\Rightarrow \lambda = \dfrac{2}{3}$ ∴ $OF = \dfrac{2}{3} b$

58 AS

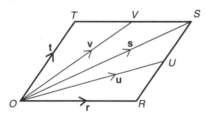

(a) $RS = OT \Rightarrow s = r + t$

(b) $v = t + \frac{1}{2} r = \frac{1}{2}(r + 2t) = \frac{1}{2}(s + t)$

(c) $u = r + \frac{1}{2} t = \frac{1}{2}(s + r)$

so $4(u + v) = 4s + 2t + 2r$

but $s = r + t$ ∴ $4(u + v) = 3s + 3t + 3r = 3(r + s + t)$

59 SH

$\overrightarrow{BC} = 4\mathbf{x} + 2\mathbf{y} - 3\mathbf{z}$

$|\overrightarrow{BC}| = \sqrt{4^2 + 2^2 + (-3)^2} = 5.39$ (3 s.f.)

60 A

(i) $\overrightarrow{AB} = \overrightarrow{OB} - \overrightarrow{OA} = 12\mathbf{i} + 9\mathbf{j} + 8\mathbf{k}$

Unit vector parallel to $\overrightarrow{AB}$

is $\dfrac{\overrightarrow{AB}}{|\overrightarrow{AB}|} = \dfrac{12\mathbf{i} + 9\mathbf{j} + 8\mathbf{k}}{\sqrt{12^2 + 9^2 + 8^2}} = \dfrac{1}{17}(12\mathbf{i} + 9\mathbf{j} + 8\mathbf{k})$

(ii) Vector equation of a line $\mathbf{r} = \mathbf{a} + t\mathbf{b}$

∴ $\mathbf{r} = (\mathbf{i} + \mathbf{j} + \mathbf{k}) + t(12\mathbf{i} + 9\mathbf{j} + 8\mathbf{k})$

(iii) $AP : PB = 1 : 7$ so by the ratio theorem

$\overrightarrow{OP} = \dfrac{1(13\mathbf{i} + 10\mathbf{j} + 9\mathbf{k}) + 7(\mathbf{i} + \mathbf{j} + \mathbf{k})}{1 + 7} = \dfrac{5}{2}\mathbf{i} + \dfrac{17}{8}\mathbf{j} + 2\mathbf{k}$

(iv) Using scalar product to find θ acute,

with $\overrightarrow{PB} = \dfrac{21}{2}\mathbf{i} + \dfrac{63}{8}\mathbf{j} + 7\mathbf{k}$

$\cos\theta = \dfrac{\overrightarrow{OP} \cdot \overrightarrow{PB}}{|\overrightarrow{OP}||\overrightarrow{PB}|} = \dfrac{\left(\frac{5}{2} \times \frac{21}{2}\right) + \left(\frac{17}{8} \times \frac{63}{8}\right) + (2 \times 7)}{3.8426 \times 14.875} = 0.997$

so acute $\theta = 4.5°$ and required angle is $180° - 4.5° = 175.5°$

61 AS

(i) Find position vector of point of intersection by equating components.

$(2 + \lambda)\mathbf{i} = (2 + \mu)\mathbf{i} \Rightarrow \lambda = \mu$

$(1 + \lambda)\mathbf{j} = (2 + 2\mu)\mathbf{j} \Rightarrow 1 + \lambda = 2 + 2\mu$

$\Rightarrow \lambda = -1$ and $\mu = -1$

$2\lambda\mathbf{k} = (t + \mu)\mathbf{k} \Rightarrow t = -1$

Substituting gives $r_1 = \mathbf{i} - 2\mathbf{k}$ and $r_2 = \mathbf{i} - 2\mathbf{k}$

so point of intersection is $(1, 0, -2)$

(ii) Consider the direction of the lines only.

Let $\mathbf{a} = -(\mathbf{i} + \mathbf{j} + 2\mathbf{k})$ and $\mathbf{b} = (\mathbf{i} + 2\mathbf{j} + \mathbf{k})$

$\Rightarrow |\mathbf{a}| = \sqrt{6}$ and $|\mathbf{b}| = \sqrt{6}$

$\cos\theta = \dfrac{\mathbf{a} \cdot \mathbf{b}}{|\mathbf{a}||\mathbf{b}|} = \dfrac{5}{\sqrt{6}\sqrt{6}} \Rightarrow \theta = 34°$ (to nearest degree)

62 A

(i) $\left(\cos\dfrac{\pi}{8} + j\sin\dfrac{\pi}{8}\right)\left(\cos\dfrac{3\pi}{8} + j\sin\dfrac{3\pi}{8}\right) = \cos\dfrac{\pi}{2} + j\sin\dfrac{\pi}{2}$

[See polar form multiplication, Unit P26]

∴ Original product is $\left(\cos\dfrac{\pi}{2} + j\sin\dfrac{\pi}{2}\right)^2 = -\sin^2\dfrac{\pi}{2} = -1$

(ii) $(x + jy)^2 = (x^2 - y^2) + 2jxy = 1 + j$

Equating real and imaginary parts gives $2xy = 1 \Rightarrow y = \dfrac{1}{2x}$

and $x^2 - y^2 = 1 \Rightarrow$ (substituting for y)

$4x^4 - 4x^2 - 1 = 0$

Solving by formula and taking positive roots gives

$x = \left(\dfrac{1 + \sqrt{2}}{2}\right)^{\frac{1}{2}}$

$y = \dfrac{1}{\left(2\left(1 + \sqrt{2}\right)\right)^{\frac{1}{2}}} = \left(\dfrac{\sqrt{2} - 1}{2}\right)^{\frac{1}{2}}$

63 AS

$(x + iy)^2 = (x^2 - y^2) + 2ixy = 2i$

Equating real and imaginary parts gives $(x^2 - y^2) = 0$ and $2xy = 2$

Solving the simultaneous equations $x = \pm1$ and $y = \pm1$ so the solutions are $x = 1$ and $y = 1$ or $x = -1$ and $y = -1$

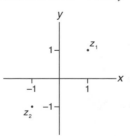

Let $z_1 = 1 + i$ then $z_1^* = 1 - i$ and arg $z_1 = 45°$, arg $z_1^* = 315°$

$z_2 = -1 - i$ then $z_2^* = -1 + i$ and arg $z_2 = 225°$, arg $z_2^* = 135°$

arg $z_2^* - $ arg $z_1 = 135° - 45° = 90°$

arg $z_1^* - $ arg $z_2 = 315° - 225° = 90°$

Thus arg $z_2^* - $ arg $z_1 = $ arg $z_1^* - $ arg z_2

64 A

(a) $u = -10 + 9i$

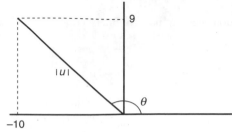

(b) $\arg u = \tan^{-1}\left(-\frac{9}{10}\right) = 138°$ (to nearest degree)

(c) Let $v = a + ib$ then $(-10 + 9i)(a + ib) = -11 + 28i$
$\Rightarrow (-10a - 9b) + (9a - 10b)i = -11 + 28i$
Equating real and imaginary parts and solving the
simultaneous equations gives $a = 2$ and $b = -1$ $\therefore$ $v = 2 - i$

(d) $|u + v| = |-8 + 8i| = \sqrt{-8^2 + 8^2} = 8\sqrt{2}$

65 AS

$|\omega| = 3$, $\arg \omega = \dfrac{\pi}{4} \Rightarrow \omega = 3\left(\cos\dfrac{\pi}{4} + i\sin\dfrac{\pi}{4}\right) \Rightarrow \omega = 3\left(\dfrac{1}{\sqrt{2}} + i\dfrac{1}{\sqrt{2}}\right)$

(i) $\omega^2 = 9\left(\dfrac{1}{\sqrt{2}} + i\dfrac{1}{\sqrt{2}}\right)^2 = 9i \Rightarrow |\omega^2| = 9$ and $\arg \omega^2 = \dfrac{\pi}{2}$

[or use polar form multiplication for $\omega \times \omega$]

(ii) $i\omega = 3\left(-\dfrac{1}{\sqrt{2}} + i\dfrac{1}{\sqrt{2}}\right) \Rightarrow |i\omega| = 3$ and $\arg i\omega = \dfrac{3\pi}{4}$

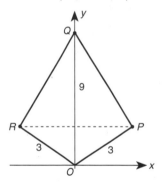

Area of $OPQR = \frac{1}{2} OQ \times PR$

Now $PR = 2 \times 3\cos\dfrac{\pi}{4} = \dfrac{6}{\sqrt{2}} = 3\sqrt{2}$

Area $= \frac{1}{2} \times 9 \times 3\sqrt{2} = \dfrac{27\sqrt{2}}{2}$

66 A

(i) Let $y = e^{2x}\sec 3x$

Product with $u = e^{2x}$ so $\dfrac{du}{dx} = 2e^{2x}$

$v = \sec 3x$ so $\dfrac{dv}{dx} = 3\sec 3x \tan 3x$

$\dfrac{dy}{dx} = 2e^{2x}\sec 3x + 3e^{2x}\sec 3x \tan 3x$

$= e^{2x}\sec 3x(2 + 3\tan 3x)$

(ii) Let $y = \dfrac{1+x^3}{1+x}$

Quotient with $u = 1 + x^3$ so $\dfrac{du}{dx} = 3x^2$

$v = 1 + x$ so $\dfrac{dv}{dx} = 1$

$\dfrac{dy}{dx} = \dfrac{3x^2(1+x) - (1+x^3)}{(1+x)^2} = \dfrac{2x^3 + 3x^2 - 1}{(1+x)^2}$

$= \dfrac{(1+x)^2(2x-1)}{(1+x)^2} = 2x - 1$

67 A

(i) $y = \cos^2 x$

Let $u = \cos x$ so $\dfrac{du}{dx} = -\sin x$

and $y = u^2$ so $\dfrac{dy}{du} = 2u$

$\dfrac{dy}{dx} = \dfrac{dy}{du} \cdot \dfrac{du}{dx} = -2u\sin x = -2\cos x\sin x = -\sin 2x$

(chain rule)

(ii) $\dfrac{dx}{dt} = \dfrac{-2t}{(1+t^2)^2}$ and $\dfrac{dy}{dt} = \dfrac{1-t^2}{(1+t^2)^2}$ (quotient formula)

$\dfrac{dy}{dx} = \dfrac{dy}{dt} \cdot \dfrac{dt}{dx} = \dfrac{1-t^2}{(1+t^2)^2} \cdot \dfrac{(1+t^2)^2}{-2t} = \dfrac{t^2-1}{2t}$

68 A

(a) (i) Let $y = x\sin x$

Product with $u = x$ so $\dfrac{du}{dx} = 1$

$v = \sin x$ so $\dfrac{dv}{dx} = \cos x$

$\dfrac{dy}{dx} = x\cos x + \sin x$

(ii) $y = e^{2-x}$

Let $u = 2 - x$ so $\dfrac{du}{dx} = -1$

and $y = e^u$ so $\dfrac{dy}{du} = e^u$

$\dfrac{dy}{dx} = -1 \times e^u = -e^u = -e^{2-x}$ (chain rule)

(iii) $y = \tan^2 x$

Let $u = \tan x$ so $\dfrac{du}{dx} = \sec^2 x$

and $y = u^2$ so $\dfrac{dy}{du} = 2u$

$\dfrac{dy}{dx} = 2u \times \sec^2 x = 2\tan x\sec^2 x$ (chain rule)

(b) $\dfrac{dy}{dx} = \dfrac{2x(3x-1) - 3x^2}{(3x-1)^2} = \dfrac{3x^2 - 2x}{(3x-1)^2}$ (quotient formula)

For stationary points $\dfrac{dy}{dx} = 0$

$\Rightarrow 3x^2 - 2x = 0 \Rightarrow x = 0$ or $x = \frac{2}{3}$

So coordinates of stationary points are $(0, 0)$ and $\left(\frac{2}{3}, \frac{4}{9}\right)$

(c) Differentiating with respect to x gives $2y\dfrac{dy}{dx} - 8 - 2\dfrac{dy}{dx} = 0$

$\Rightarrow (2y - 2)\dfrac{dy}{dx} = 8 \Rightarrow \dfrac{dy}{dx} = \dfrac{8}{(2y-2)}$

At $(2, 3)$ $\dfrac{dy}{dx} = 2$ so equation of tangent is

$y - 3 = 2(x - 2) \Rightarrow y = 2x - 1$

69 A

$\dfrac{dy}{dx} = 3x^2 - 8x + 5$

(i) At P, $x = 3$, $y = 3^3 - 4.3^2 + 5.3 - 2 = 4$

(ii) $\dfrac{dy}{dx} = 27 - 24 + 5 = 8$

(iii) Equation of tangent $y - 4 = 8(x - 3) \Rightarrow y = 8x - 20$

(iv) Gradient of normal is $-\dfrac{1}{8}$

Equation of normal $y - 4 = -\dfrac{1}{8}(x - 3) \Rightarrow 8y + x = 35$

$\dfrac{dy}{dx} = 5 \Rightarrow 3x^2 - 8x + 5 = 5 \Rightarrow 3x^2 - 8x = 0$

$\Rightarrow x = 0$ or $x = \dfrac{8}{3}$

70 AS

(a) $P(1, 3)$ When $x = 1$ $y = 1 - 1 + 3 = 3$ $\therefore$ P lies on the curve.

(b) $\dfrac{dy}{dx} = 3x^2 - 1$ At $x = 1$, $\dfrac{dy}{dx} = 2$

Equation of tangent is $(y - 3) = 2(x - 1) \Rightarrow y = 2x + 1$

(c) Gradient of normal $= -\dfrac{1}{2}$

$\therefore$ equation of normal is $(y - 3) = -\dfrac{1}{2}(x - 1) \Rightarrow 2y + x = 7$

(d) $A = (-\dfrac{1}{2}, 0)$ $B = (0, \dfrac{7}{2})$

Area $= \dfrac{1}{2} \times \dfrac{1}{2} \times \dfrac{7}{2} = \dfrac{7}{8}$

71 A

(a) Differentiate using the quotient formula

$\dfrac{dV}{dx} = \dfrac{\frac{1}{4}x^{-\frac{3}{4}}(x+2)^{\frac{1}{2}} - \frac{1}{2}x^{\frac{1}{4}}(x+2)^{-\frac{1}{2}}}{(x+2)} = \dfrac{(x+2) - 2x}{4x^{\frac{3}{4}}(x+2)^{\frac{3}{2}}}$

$= \dfrac{2 - x}{4x^{\frac{3}{4}}(x+2)^{\frac{3}{2}}}$

If $\dfrac{dV}{dx} = 0$ then $2 - x = 0 \Rightarrow x = 2$

(b) $\dfrac{dx}{dt} = 0.01\,\text{cm s}^{-1}$ and $\dfrac{dV}{dt} = \dfrac{dV}{dx} \cdot \dfrac{dx}{dt}$ (chain rule)

so $\dfrac{dv}{dt} = \dfrac{0.01(2 - x)}{4x^{\frac{3}{4}}(x+2)^{\frac{3}{2}}}$

When $x = 1$ cm, $\dfrac{dv}{dt} = 0.000481\ \text{cm}^3\text{s}^{-1}$ (3 s.f.)

72 AS

(i) $v = \dfrac{dx}{dt} = 3\cos t + 2\sin t$ When $t = 0$, $v = 3$ m s^{-1}

$a = \dfrac{dv}{dt} = -3\sin t + 2\cos t$ When $t = 0$, $a = 2$ m s^{-2}

(ii) $x = 0 \Rightarrow 3\sin t - 2\cos t - 1 = 0 \Rightarrow 3\sin t - 2\cos t = 1$

Comparing with the form $R\sin(\theta - \alpha)$ gives

$R = \sqrt{3^2 + 2^2} = \sqrt{13}$ and $\alpha = \tan^{-1}\frac{2}{3}$, $\alpha = 33.7°$

Thus $\sqrt{13}\sin(t - 33.7°) = 1 \Rightarrow t = 49.8$ s

(iii) Greatest distance at $v = 0 \Rightarrow 3\cos t + 2\sin t = 0$

$\tan t = -\dfrac{3}{2} \Rightarrow t = 123.7$s and $x = 2.6$ m

73 A

$y = e^{-x}\sin x$

(i) $\dfrac{dy}{dx} = -e^{-x}\sin x + e^{-x}\cos x = e^{-x}(\cos x - \sin x)$ (product rule)

(ii) For stationary points, $\dfrac{dy}{dx} = 0 \Rightarrow e^{-x} = 0$ no solution

or $\cos x - \sin x = 0 \Rightarrow \tan x = 1 \Rightarrow x = \dfrac{-\pi}{4}$ and $x = \dfrac{\pi}{4}$

(iii) This gives stationary points at $(-2.4, -7.5)$ and $(0.79, 0.32)$

(iv) To determine whether the points are maxima or minima, find $\dfrac{d^2y}{dx^2}$ and substitute the values of x at the stationary points. If the result is positive we have a minimum; if it is negative we have a maximum. If $\dfrac{d^2y}{dx^2}$ is zero it will be necessary to consider values just to the left and right of x.

74 AS

$V = x^2h \Rightarrow xh = \dfrac{V}{x}$

$S = x^2 + 4xh = x^2 + \dfrac{4V}{x}$

For $V = 32$, $S = x^2 + \dfrac{128}{x}$

(i) For minimum value $\dfrac{dS}{dx} = 2x - \dfrac{128}{x^2} = 0 \Rightarrow x = 4$

(ii) Minimum $S = 4^2 + \dfrac{128}{4} = 48$

and corresponding $h = \dfrac{32}{16} = 2$

$DF = \sqrt{BF^2 + BD^2} = \sqrt{2^2 + (\sqrt{32})^2} = 6$

75 SH

(a) $y = 2x^3 - 6x^2 \Rightarrow \dfrac{dy}{dx} = 6x^2 - 12x$

$\dfrac{dy}{dx} = 0$ for stationary points

Thus $x = 0$, $x = 2$ and stationary points are $(0, 0)$ and $(2, -8)$. From graph: $(0, 0)$ is a maximum and $(2, -8)$ is a minimum.

(b) For three distinct points of intersection $-8 < k < 0$.

76 A

(a) At $(1, -2)$, equation $\Rightarrow a + b = -6$ and

$\dfrac{dy}{dx} = \dfrac{ax(x+2) - (ax+b)(2x+2)}{x^2(x+2)^2} = 0 \Rightarrow -a - 4b = 0$

These give $a = -8$, $b = 2$

(b) $\dfrac{dy}{dx} = \dfrac{8x^2 - 4x - 4}{x^2(x+2)^2} = 0 \Rightarrow (8x + 4)(x - 1) = 0$

$\Rightarrow x = -\dfrac{1}{2}$ or $1 \Rightarrow$ points $\left(-\dfrac{1}{2}, -8\right)$, $(1, -2)$

(c) $y = \dfrac{2-8x}{x(x+2)} \Rightarrow$ asymptotes at $x = 0$ and $x = -2$

Also at $y = 0$ since $y \to 0$ as $x \to \pm\infty$.

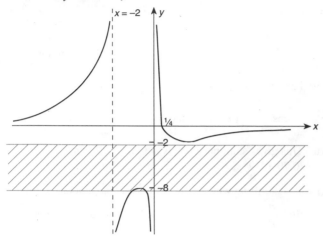

Curve meets x-axis at $\left(\dfrac{1}{4}, 0\right)$

For $-8 < y < -2$ no part of curve exists.
[Or, without using your sketch:
Make $y = \dfrac{2-8x}{x(x+2)}$ into a quadratic in x and solve for real values]

77 AS

(a) $(x+h)^n - x^n = x^n\left(1 + \dfrac{h}{x}\right)^n - x^n$

$= x^n\left(1 + \dfrac{nh}{x} + \dfrac{n(n-1)}{2!}\dfrac{h^2}{x^2} + \ldots\right) - x^n$

$= nx^{n-1}h + \dfrac{n(n-1)}{2!}x^{n-2}h^2 + \cdots$

$\therefore \lim_{h \to 0} \dfrac{(x+h)^n - x^n}{h} = nx^{n-1}$

(b) $f'(x) = \dfrac{4x(1+x^2) - 2x(2x^2)}{(1+x^2)^2} = \dfrac{4x}{(1+x^2)^2}$

(by quotient formula)

$f''(x) = \dfrac{4(1+x^2)^2 - 4x.4x(1+x^2)}{(1+x^2)^4} = \dfrac{4(1-3x^2)}{(1+x^2)^3}$

(quotient formula)

(i) $f''(x) = 0 \Rightarrow 1 - 3x^2 = 0 \Rightarrow x = \dfrac{1}{\sqrt{3}}$ and $y = \dfrac{1}{2}$ (on domain $[0, 1]$)

By considering $f'(x)$ to left and right

	$x < \dfrac{1}{\sqrt{3}}$	$\dfrac{1}{\sqrt{3}} < x$
$f'(x)$	+ ve	+ ve

Thus $\left(\dfrac{1}{\sqrt{3}}, \dfrac{1}{2}\right)$ is a point of inflexion

(ii) $f'(x)$ has minimum value 0 at $x = 0$

$f'(x)$ has maximum value $\dfrac{3\sqrt{3}}{4}$ at $x = \dfrac{1}{\sqrt{3}}$

Range of f is $[0, 1]$.

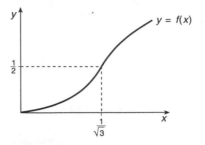

78 SH

$g(x) = \dfrac{4x^{\frac{1}{2}} - 5x^{-2}}{2x} = 2x^{-\frac{1}{2}} - \dfrac{5}{2}x^{-3}$

$\int g(x)\,dx = 4x^{\frac{1}{2}} + \dfrac{5}{4}x^{-2} + c$ where c is constant of integration

79 A

(a) (i) $\displaystyle\int_0^1 xe^{2x}\,dx$ requires integration by parts

Let $u = x$ then $\dfrac{du}{dx} = 1$, $\dfrac{dv}{dx} = e^{2x}$ then $v = \frac{1}{2}e^{2x}$

so $\displaystyle\int_0^1 xe^{2x}\,dx = \left[\frac{1}{2}xe^{2x}\right]_0^1 - \int_0^1 \frac{1}{2}e^{2x}\,dx$

$= \left[\frac{1}{2}xe^{2x}\right]_0^1 - \left[\frac{1}{4}e^{2x}\right]_0^1 = \frac{1}{2}e^2 - \left(\frac{1}{4}e^2 - \frac{1}{4}\right) = \frac{1}{4}\left(e^2 + 1\right)$

(ii) $\displaystyle\int_0^1 \dfrac{x-1}{x+1}\,dx = \int_0^1 1 - \dfrac{2}{x+1}\,dx = \left[x - 2\ln|x+1|\right]_0^1$

$= 1 - 2\ln 2$

(b) $x = 2\cos\theta \Rightarrow dx = -2\sin\theta\,d\theta$ and new limits are

$\theta = \dfrac{\pi}{3}, \theta = \dfrac{\pi}{4}$

so $\displaystyle\int_{\frac{\pi}{3}}^{\frac{\pi}{4}} \dfrac{-2\sin\theta}{4\cos^2\theta.2\sin\theta}\,d\theta = \int_{\frac{\pi}{3}}^{\frac{\pi}{4}} \dfrac{-1}{4\cos^2\theta}\,d\theta$

$= \left[-\dfrac{1}{4}\tan\theta\right]_{\frac{\pi}{3}}^{\frac{\pi}{4}} = \dfrac{1}{4}\left(\sqrt{3} - 1\right)$

80 AS

Let $y = 2 - x$, then $x = 2 - y$ and $dx = -dy$
New limits are $y = 2$ and $y = 1$

Hence $\displaystyle\int_0^1 \left(\dfrac{x}{2-x}\right)^2 dx = \int_2^1 -\left(\dfrac{2-y}{y}\right)^2 dy = \int_2^1 \left(\dfrac{2}{y} - 1\right)^2 dy$

$= -\displaystyle\int_2^1 \dfrac{4}{y^2} - \dfrac{4}{y} + 1\,dy$

$= -\left[-\dfrac{4}{y} - 4\ln y + y\right]_2^1 = 3 - 4\ln 2$

81 A

(i) $y = x\sqrt{1+x}$

At point A, $y = 0 \Rightarrow x\sqrt{1+x} = 0 \Rightarrow x = 0$ or $x = -1$
$\therefore$ point A has coordinates $(-1, 0)$

Function is defined for $1 + x \geq 0 \Rightarrow x \geq -1$

(ii) Vol of solid $= \pi \int_{-1}^{1} x^2(1+x)dx = \pi\left[\frac{1}{3}x^3 + \frac{1}{4}x^4\right]_{-1}^{1} = \frac{2}{3}\pi$

(iii) Area $= \int_{-1}^{0} x\sqrt{1+x}\,dx$

Use substitution $u = 1 + x$
then $dx = du$ and new limits are $u = 0$ and $u = 1$

So required area $= \int_{0}^{1} u^{\frac{1}{2}}(u-1)du = \left[\frac{2}{5}u^{\frac{5}{2}} - \frac{2}{3}u^{\frac{3}{2}}\right]_{0}^{1} = \frac{4}{15}$

82 AS
Find required area by subtracting area under curve from area under line.

Area $= \int_{0}^{2} 7 - 3x\,dx - \int_{0}^{2}\frac{7}{1+3x}dx = \left[7x - \frac{3}{2}x^2 - \frac{7}{3}\ln|1+3x|\right]_{0}^{2}$

$= \left(14 - 6 - \frac{7}{3}\ln 7\right) - 0 = 3.46 \quad (3 \text{ s.f.})$

83 SH
(a) $f'(x) = x^2 - 4x + 3 = 0$ for stationary points

$\Rightarrow$ stationary points are $x = 3$, $y = 0$ and $x = 1$, $y = \frac{4}{3}$

$f''(x) = 2x - 4$

When $x = 3$, $f''(x)$ is positive $\therefore$ minimum

When $x = 1$, $f''(x)$ is negative $\therefore$ maximum

(b) $f(0) = 0$, so curve meets y-axis at $(0, 0)$

$\frac{1}{3}x^3 - 2x^2 + 3x = 0 \Rightarrow x = 0$ and $x = 3$

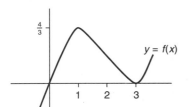

(c) Area $= \int_{0}^{3} \frac{1}{3}x^3 - 2x^2 + 3x\,dx = \left[\frac{1}{12}x^4 - \frac{2}{3}x^3 + \frac{3}{2}x^2\right]_{0}^{3}$

$= 2.25$

84 A

$(1+x^2)\frac{dy}{dx} = x(4+y^2) \Rightarrow \int\frac{1}{(4+y^2)}dy = \int\frac{x}{(1+x^2)}dx$

Integrating gives $\frac{1}{2}\tan^{-1}\left(\frac{1}{2}y\right) = \frac{1}{2}\ln(1+x^2) + C$

$y = 0$ and $x = 0 \Rightarrow 0 = \frac{1}{2}\ln 1 + C \Rightarrow C = 0$

$\therefore y = 2\tan\left(\ln(1+x^2)\right)$

85 AS

$\frac{dT}{dt} \propto (T - \theta) \Rightarrow \frac{dT}{dt} = -k(T-\theta) \Rightarrow \int\frac{1}{(T-\theta)}dT = -k\int dt$

Thus $\ln(T-\theta) = -kt + c \Rightarrow T - \theta = e^c e^{-kt}$

Let $A = e^c \Rightarrow \ln A = c$ then $T = \theta + Ae^{-kt}$
At $t = 0$ s, $T = 100$ °C and at $t = 600$ s, $T = 84$ °C. $\theta = 21$ °C

Thus $100 = 21 + A \Rightarrow A = 79$
and $84 = 21 + 79e^{-600k} \Rightarrow k = 0.00038$
Thus $T = \theta + 79e^{-0.00038t}$
When $T = 70$ °C $\quad 70 = 21 + 79e^{-0.00038t} \Rightarrow 0.00038t = \ln\left(\frac{79}{49}\right)$

$\Rightarrow t = 1256.9$ s, so kettle will be at 70 °C after 21 minutes (to nearest minute)
[Working in minutes gives $k = 0.0226$ (3s.f.) and same value for time.]

86 A
$x = 0 \Rightarrow y = \ln 8$
$y = 0 \Rightarrow x = 7$

function is not defined for $x = 8$

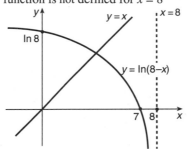

$y = x$ cuts $y = \ln(8-x)$ once, thus $x = \ln(8-x)$ has one root
$f(x) = x - \ln(8-x)$
$f(1) \approx -0.946$, $f(2) \approx 0.208$

$f(x)$ is continuous over $[1, 2]$, so change of sign $\Rightarrow$ root lies between 1 and 2
Using Newton–Raphson method $\quad f'(x) = 1 + \frac{1}{8-x}$

$x_0 = 2 f(x_0) = 0.2082$, $\quad f'(x_0) = 1.1667$

$x_1 = 2 - \frac{0.2082}{1.1667} = 1.8215$

and $\quad x_2 = 1.8215 - \frac{0.0004}{1.1619} = 1.8212$

so $\alpha = 1.82$ (2d.p.)

87 AS
Let $f(x) = x^3 + x - 12$, then $f(2) = 8 + 2 - 12 = -2 < 0$
and $f(3) = 27 + 3 - 12 = 18 > 0 \therefore \alpha$ lies between 2 and 3

Let $x_0 = 2$, $x_1 = \frac{1}{4}\left((3 \times 2) - \frac{1}{2} + \frac{12}{4}\right) = 2.125$,

$x_2 = 2.140$, $x_3 = 2.143$, $x_4 = 2.144$, $x_5 = 2.144$.

The solution is $x = 2.144$ (3 d.p.)

88 A

$\int_{0}^{1} e^{x^2}dx$ using trapezium rule with $h = 0.2$

x	0	0.2	0.4	0.6	0.8	1.0
$f(x)$	1	1.041	1.174	1.433	1.896	2.718
	y_0	y_1	y_2	y_3	y_4	y_5

$\int_{0}^{1} e^{x^2}dx \approx \frac{0.2}{2}\{(1 + 2.718) + 2(1.041 + 1.174 + 1.433 + 1.896)\}$
$= 1.48$ (2 d.p.)

Pure Mathematics Question Bank: Answers

89 AS

x	0	0.25	0.5	0.75	1
$f(x)$	1	1.008	1.061	1.192	1.414
	y_0	y_1	y_2	y_3	y_4

Simpson's rule with five ordinates and $h = 0.25$

$$\int_0^1 \sqrt{x^3 + 1}\, dx \approx \frac{0.25}{3}\left[(1 + 1.414) + 4(1.008 + 1.192) + 2(1.061)\right]$$

$$= 1.11 \text{ (2 d.p.)}$$

90 AS

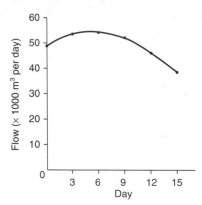

Using trapezium rule with six ordinates and $h = 3$

x	0	3	6	9	12	15
$f(x)$	48 000	53 000	54 000	52 000	46 000	38 000
	y_0	y_1	y_2	y_3	y_4	y_5

Total volume $\approx \dfrac{3}{2}\{(48000 + 38000)$

$$+ 2(53000 + 54000 + 52000 + 46000)\}$$

$$= 744\,000\,\text{m}^3$$

This is likely to be an underestimate, since curve is convex. Simpson's rule cannot be used since there is an odd number of strips.

91 A

$$fg(x) = \frac{1}{1-x} \qquad gf(x) = \left(1 - \frac{1}{x}\right)$$

$$gfg(x) = \left(1 - \frac{1}{1-x}\right) = \frac{x}{x-1}$$

$$fgf(x) = \left(\frac{1}{1 - \frac{1}{x}}\right) = \frac{x}{x-1}$$

$$\therefore fgf(x) = gfg(x)$$

$$fh(x) = \frac{1}{e^x}, \quad hg(x) = e^{1-x}$$

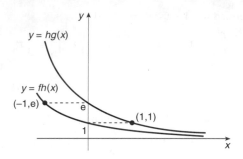

fh is mapped onto hg by a translation of one unit in the positive x direction.

$$h^{-1}(x) = \ln x \Rightarrow h^{-1}f(x) = \ln\left(\frac{1}{x}\right) \text{ and } (fh)^{-1} = \ln\left(\frac{1}{x}\right)$$

Thus $h^{-1}f(x) = (fh)^{-1}(x)$ for all $x > 0$

92 A

$$f^2 : x \rightarrow \frac{4x^2}{(x-4)^2}$$

Let $y = \dfrac{2x}{x-4} \Rightarrow y(x-4) = 2x \Rightarrow x(y-2) = 4y \Rightarrow x = \dfrac{4y}{y-2}$

thus $f^{-1} : x \rightarrow \dfrac{4x}{x-2}$

For $f^2 = f^{-1}$, $\dfrac{4x^2}{(x-4)^2} = \dfrac{4x}{x-2} \Rightarrow x^2 - 2x = (x-4)^2$

$$\Rightarrow x = \frac{8}{3}$$

$g(3) = 9a + 3b = 9$ and

$$gf(x) = a\left(\frac{4x^2}{(x-4)^2}\right) + b\left(\frac{2x}{x-4}\right)$$

$$\Rightarrow gf(2) = 4a - 2b = 14$$

Solving simultaneously gives $a = 2$ and $b = -3$

93 SH

(a) $f(g(x)) = (x-1)^3 - 2(x-1)^2 - 5(x-1) + 6$

$$= x^3 - 5x^2 + 2x + 8$$

(b) $f(g(-1)) = 0 \therefore (x+1)$ is a factor

$$
\begin{array}{r}
x^2 - 6x + 8 \\
x+1 \overline{\smash{)}\ x^3 - 5x^2 + 2x + 8} \\
\underline{x^3 + x^2} \\
-6x^2 + 2x \\
\underline{-6x^2 - 6x} \\
8x + 8
\end{array}
$$

$$\therefore f(g(x)) = (x+1)(x-2)(x-4)$$

(c) $k(x) = \dfrac{1}{(x+1)(x-2)(x-4)}$

k is not defined when denominator is zero
i.e. $x = 4$, $x = 2$ and $x = -1$

94 A

(i) $\mathbf{A}^2 = \begin{pmatrix} -1 & -4 \\ 1 & 3 \end{pmatrix}\begin{pmatrix} -1 & -4 \\ 1 & 3 \end{pmatrix} = \begin{pmatrix} -3 & -8 \\ 2 & 5 \end{pmatrix}$

$\mathbf{A}^3 = \begin{pmatrix} -1 & -4 \\ 1 & 3 \end{pmatrix}\begin{pmatrix} -3 & -8 \\ 2 & 5 \end{pmatrix} = \begin{pmatrix} -5 & -12 \\ 3 & 7 \end{pmatrix}$

(ii) With $n = 2$, $\mathbf{A}^2 = \begin{pmatrix} -3 & -8 \\ 2 & 5 \end{pmatrix}$

With $n = 3$, $\mathbf{A}^3 = \begin{pmatrix} -5 & -12 \\ 3 & 7 \end{pmatrix}$

(iii) Put $n = 1$

$A^1 = \begin{pmatrix} 1-(2\times 1) & -4\times 1 \\ 1 & 1+(2\times 1) \end{pmatrix}$

$= \begin{pmatrix} -1 & -4 \\ 1 & 3 \end{pmatrix}$

So formula holds for $n = 1$
Assume formula is true for $n = k$

Then $\mathbf{A}^{k+1} = \mathbf{A}\mathbf{A}^k = \begin{pmatrix} -1 & -4 \\ 1 & 3 \end{pmatrix}\begin{pmatrix} 1-2k & -4k \\ k & 1+2k \end{pmatrix}$

$= \begin{pmatrix} 1-2(k+1) & -4(k+1) \\ k+1 & 1+2(k+1) \end{pmatrix}$

Since this is the result for $\mathbf{A}^k$ with k replaced by $k + 1$, and since the formula has been shown to be true for $n = 1$, it is therefore true for all positive n, by mathematical induction.

(iv) $\begin{pmatrix} -3 & -8 \\ 2 & 5 \end{pmatrix} = \begin{pmatrix} -p & -4p \\ p & 3p \end{pmatrix} + \begin{pmatrix} q & 0 \\ 0 & q \end{pmatrix}$ which gives $p = 2$ and $q = -1$

$\therefore \mathbf{A}^2 = 2\mathbf{A} - \mathbf{I}$

(v) $\mathbf{A}^3 = \mathbf{A}\mathbf{A}^2 = \mathbf{A}(p\mathbf{A} + q\mathbf{I}) = p\mathbf{A}^2 + q\mathbf{A} = 2\mathbf{A}^2 - \mathbf{A}$
$= 3\mathbf{A} - 2\mathbf{I}$

(vi) $\mathbf{A}^4 = \mathbf{A}\mathbf{A}^3 = 3\mathbf{A}^2 - 2\mathbf{A} = 4\mathbf{A} - 3\mathbf{I}$

(vii) $\mathbf{A}^n = n\mathbf{A} - (n-1)\mathbf{I} = \begin{pmatrix} -n & -4n \\ n & 3n \end{pmatrix} - \begin{pmatrix} n-1 & 0 \\ 0 & n-1 \end{pmatrix}$

$= \begin{pmatrix} 1-2n & -4n \\ n & 1+2n \end{pmatrix}$

which is the formula given for $\mathbf{A}^n$ in part (ii) of the question.

95 AS

(a) det $\mathbf{M} = k(k+1) - 6 = 0$ for $\mathbf{M}$ to have no inverse
$\Rightarrow k^2 + k - 6 = 0 \Rightarrow k = 2$ and $k = -3$

$\mathbf{M}^{-1} = \frac{1}{k(k+1)-6}\begin{pmatrix} k & -6 \\ -1 & k+1 \end{pmatrix}$

If $k = 3$, $\mathbf{M}^{-1} = \frac{1}{6}\begin{pmatrix} 3 & -6 \\ -1 & 4 \end{pmatrix}$

Simultaneous equations can be written

$\mathbf{M}\begin{pmatrix} x \\ y \end{pmatrix} = \begin{pmatrix} 12 \\ 4 \end{pmatrix}$

$\Rightarrow \mathbf{M}^{-1}\mathbf{M}\begin{pmatrix} x \\ y \end{pmatrix} = \mathbf{M}^{-1}\begin{pmatrix} 12 \\ 4 \end{pmatrix} \Rightarrow \begin{pmatrix} x \\ y \end{pmatrix} = \frac{1}{6}\begin{pmatrix} 3 & -6 \\ -1 & 4 \end{pmatrix}\begin{pmatrix} 12 \\ 4 \end{pmatrix} = \begin{pmatrix} 2 \\ \frac{2}{3} \end{pmatrix}$

thus $x = 2$ and $y = \frac{2}{3}$
For $k = -3$ the equations become $-2x + 6y = 12$
and $x - 3y = 4$
For $k = 2$ the equations become $3x + 6y = 12$
and $x + 2y = 4$
In both cases the pairs of lines are parallel
and will not intersect.

M1 Force Diagrams

Definitions, Types of forces, Drawing force diagrams.

Definitions

Mechanics is concerned with the action of forces on bodies.

In mechanics a **body** is any object to which a force can be applied.

A **rigid body** is a body whose shape is unaltered by any force applied to it.

A **particle** is a body whose dimensions, except mass, are negligible.

A **lamina** is a flat body having area but negligible thickness.

A **hollow body** is a three-dimensional shell having negligible thickness.

Types of forces

Forces occur in mechanics in various ways. Some of the most common are described below.

Weight W

The weight of a body is the force with which the earth attracts the body. It acts at the body's centre of gravity and is always vertically downwards.

Figure 1

A light body is considered to be weightless.

Push and pull P

Pushes and pulls are forces which act on a body at the point(s) where they are applied.

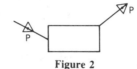

Figure 2

Normal reaction R

A normal reaction is a force which acts on a body in contact with a surface. It acts in a direction at right angles to the surfaces in contact.

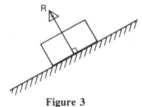

Figure 3

Friction F

Friction is a force which acts on a body in contact with a rough surface. It acts tangentially between the two surfaces and in a direction to resist the motion of the body.

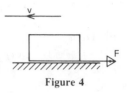

Figure 4

Smooth surfaces are considered to be frictionless. Air resistance is ignored unless stated otherwise.

Tension T

The tension in a string is a force which acts on a body to which the string is attached. Tensions can also come from springs, rods, etc.

Figure 5

Thrust S

The thrust from a spring or rod is similar to a tension but acts in the opposite direction.

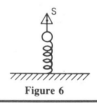

Figure 6

Drawing force diagrams

Drawing a clear **force diagram** is an essential first step in the solution of any problem in mechanics which is concerned with the action of forces on a body.

The following are important points to remember when drawing such a force diagram.

1. Make the diagram large enough to show clearly all the forces acting on the body and to enable any necessary geometry and trigonometry to be done.

2. Show only forces which are acting on the body being considered. A common fault is including forces which the body is applying to its surroundings (including other bodies).

3. Weight always acts on a body unless the body is described as light.

4. Contact with another object or surface gives rise to a normal reaction and sometimes friction.

5. Attachment to another object (by a string, spring, hinge, etc.) gives rise to a force on the body at the point of attachment.

6. Forces acting on a particle act at the same point. Forces acting on other bodies may act at different points.

7. Check that no forces have been omitted or included more than once.

ℹ️ Some simple force diagrams illustrate these points.

(a) Forces acting on a block on a smooth horizontal plane:

W – weight (vertically down)

R – normal reaction (at right angles to the surfaces in contact)

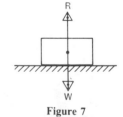

Figure 7

(b) Forces acting on a block at rest on a rough inclined plane:

W – weight

R – normal reaction

F – friction (acting to resist motion)

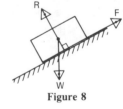

Figure 8

(c) Forces acting on a block being pulled (by a string) along a rough horizontal plane:

W – weight

R – normal reaction

F – friction

T – tension in string (acting away from body)

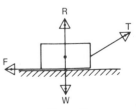

Figure 9

Force Diagrams
Exercises

The drawing of force diagrams is a skill it is essential to acquire during the study of mechanics. Although it does not appear by itself as an examination question it is often the first step in the solution of problems in this subject.
The following questions provide practice in this important skill.

EX In this exercise, identify clearly each type of force marked on your force diagrams.

1 Draw a diagram to show the force acting on a uniform ladder resting on horizontal rough ground and leaning against a smooth vertical wall.

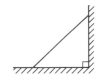

2 The sketch shows a uniform ladder resting on rough horizontal ground and leaning against a rough vertical wall with a man standing one quarter the way up the ladder. Draw diagrams to show the forces,
(a) on the ladder,
(b) on the man.

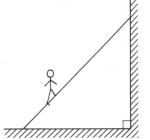

3 This diagram shows a bead resting on a rough inclined plane being acted on by the force *P* which is about to move it up the plane. Sketch the diagram and show all the forces acting on the bead.

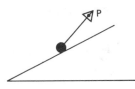

4 This diagram shows a bead resting on a rough inclined plane and just being prevented from moving down the plane by the force *Q*. Sketch the diagram and show all the forces acting on the bead.

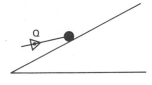

5 This sketch shows a large smooth sphere of weight *W* resting inside a smooth cylinder and being held in place by a small smooth sphere of weight *w*. Draw diagrams to show the forces acting on,
(a) the large sphere,
(b) the small sphere.

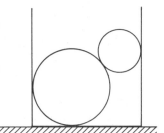

6 Draw two diagrams showing the forces acting on a block of wood which is
(a) sliding down a rough inclined plane at steady speed,
(b) accelerating down a rough inclined plane.

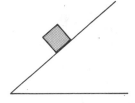

7 Draw a sketch showing the forces acting on a car which is being driven up an incline at steady speed.

8 This diagram shows a car travelling at steady speed on a level road and pulling a caravan.

Draw diagrams to show the forces acting on,
(a) the car,
(b) the caravan.

9 A particle is suspended from a fixed point by a light inextensible string. Draw a force diagram showing the forces acting on the particle when it is moving with steady speed in a horizontal circle below the fixed point.

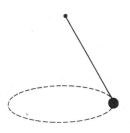

10 This sketch shows a rough rod resting against a rough cylinder with its lower end on rough ground. Draw diagrams showing the forces acting on:
(a) the rod;
(b) the cylinder.

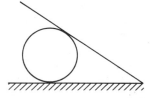

11 A stone is thrown through the air. Draw a force diagram,
(a) if air resistance is ignored,
(b) if air resistance is present.

12 Two housebricks, one resting exactly on top of the other, stand on horizontal ground. Draw sketches to show the forces acting on,
(a) the top brick, (b) the bottom brick.

13 A man is standing alone in a moving lift. Draw diagrams to show the forces acting on,
(a) the man, (b) the lift, when the lift is:
 (i) accelerating upwards,
 (ii) travelling at steady speed,
 (iii) accelerating downwards.

14 A railway engine is pulling a train up an incline against frictional resistances. If the combined engine and train is experiencing a retardation, draw diagrams showing the forces acting on,
(a) the engine, (b) the train.

M2 1-D Kinematics
Definitions, Motion in one dimension, Equations for uniform acceleration, Vertical motion under gravity.

Definitions

Kinematics is the study of displacement, velocity and acceleration.

Displacement is the position of a point relative to an origin O. It is a **vector**.
SI unit is the **metre** (m). Other metric units are centimetre (cm), kilometre (km).
Distance is the magnitude of the displacement. It is a **scalar**.

Velocity is the rate of change of displacement with respect to time. It is a **vector**.
SI unit: **metre per second** (m s^{-1} or m/s). Other metric units: cm s^{-1} or cm/s, km h^{-1} or km/h.
Speed is the magnitude of the velocity. It is a **scalar**.
Uniform velocity is constant speed in a fixed direction.

Average velocity is $\dfrac{\text{change in displacement}}{\text{time taken}}$.   **Average speed** is $\dfrac{\text{total distance travelled}}{\text{time taken}}$.

Acceleration is the rate of change of velocity with respect to time. It is a **vector**.
SI unit: **metre per second squared** (m s^{-2} or m/s^2). Other metric units: cm s^{-2} or cm/s^2, km h^{-2} or km/h^2.
Negative acceleration is sometimes called **retardation**.
Uniform acceleration is constant acceleration in a fixed direction.

Motion in one dimension

When a particle moves in **one dimension**, i.e. along a straight line, it has only two possible directions in which to move. Positive and negative signs are used to identify the two directions.

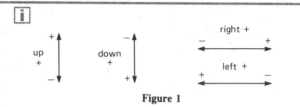

Figure 1

Equations for uniform acceleration

The **equations for uniform acceleration** in a straight line are:

$$v = u + at$$
$$s = \tfrac{1}{2}(u + v)t$$
$$v^2 = u^2 + 2as$$
$$s = ut + \tfrac{1}{2}at^2$$

The notation used is:
s – displacement; t – time; u – initial velocity;
v – velocity at time t; a – acceleration.
Units must be consistent, e.g. if s is in metres and t in seconds, then u and v must be in m s^{-1} and a in m s^{-2}.

To solve problems using these equations of motion:
(a) Choose the positive direction.
(b) List the five quantities (s, t, u, v, a), fill in known values and mark which are to be found.
(c) Use the appropriate equation(s) to find the required unknown(s). If any three of the quantities are known, then the other two can always be found.

Note: These equations do not apply to acceleration which is not uniform.
Problems about non-uniform acceleration must be solved by graphical methods or by calculus.

A particle moves in a straight line with constant acceleration. Its initial velocity is $6\,m\,s^{-1}$ and its velocity after 8 s is $10\,m\,s^{-1}$. Find the acceleration and the displacement of the particle after 16 s.

Assume the motion is horizontal.
Choose the direction of motion as positive.

1st stage
$s = ?$ m, $t = 8$ s, $u = 6$ m s^{-1}, $v = 10$ m s^{-1}, $a = ?$ m s^{-2}

Use $v = u + at$
$$10 = 6 + a(8)$$
$$a = 0.5 \text{ m s}^{-2}$$
So the uniform acceleration is 0.5 m s^{-2}.

2nd stage
$s = ?$ m, $t = 16$ s, $u = 6$ m s^{-1}, $v = ?$ m s^{-1}, $a = 0.5$ m s^{-2}.

Use $s = ut + \tfrac{1}{2}at^2$
$$= (6)(16) + \tfrac{1}{2}(0.5)(16)^2$$
$$= 160 \text{ m}$$
So the displacement after 16 s is 160 m.

Vertical motion under gravity

The motion of a body thrown **vertically upward** or falling **freely downward** (ignoring air resistance) is a special case of uniform acceleration in a straight line.

This uniform acceleration is due to **gravity** and acts vertically downwards towards the centre of the earth. It is denoted by g and common approximate values are **10 m s^{-2}** and **9.8 m s^{-2}**.

A body is thrown vertically upward.

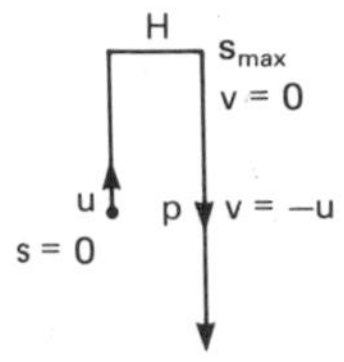

Taking up as positive,
$a = -g$.
At highest point H
s is maximum, $v = 0$.
At point of projection P
$s = 0$, $v = \pm u$.

Figure 2

1-D Kinematics
Worked example, Guided example and Exam questions

WE *A stone is projected vertically upwards from the top of a cliff 20 m high. After a time of 3 s it passes the edge of the cliff on its way down. Calculate*

(a) *the speed of projection,*
(b) *the speed when it hits the ground,*
(c) *the times when it is 10 m above the top of the cliff,*
(d) *the time when it is 5 m above the ground.*

Take up as positive.
(a) $s = 0$, $t = 3$ s, $u = ?$, $v = ?$, $a = -10$ m s^{-2}
Use $s = ut + \frac{1}{2}at^2$
so, $0 = u.3 + \frac{1}{2}(-10) \, 3^2$
$\Rightarrow u = 15$ m s^{-1}.
(b) $s = -20$ m, $t = ?$, $u = 15$ m s^{-1}, $v = ?$, $a = -10$ m s^{-2}
Use $v^2 = u^2 + 2as$
so, $v^2 = 15^2 + 2\,(-10)(-20)$
$\quad = 625$
$\Rightarrow v = -25$ m s^{-1} — particle is moving downwards with speed 25 m s^{-1}.
(c) $s = 10$ m, $t = ?$, $u = 15$ m s^{-1}, $v = ?$, $a = -10$ m s^{-2}
Use $s = ut + \frac{1}{2}at^2$
so, $10 = 15t + \frac{1}{2}(-10)t^2$
i.e. $t^2 - 3t + 2 = 0$
$\Rightarrow t = 1$ s or $t = 2$ s — the two times when it is 10 m above the top of the cliff.
(d) $s = -15$ m, $t = ?$, $u = 15$ m s^{-1}, $v = ?$, $a = -10$ m s^{-2}
Use $\quad s = ut + \frac{1}{2}at^2$
so, $-15 = 15t + \frac{1}{2}(-10)t^2$
i.e. $t^2 - 3t - 3 = 0$
i.e. $t = \dfrac{3 \pm \sqrt{[9 - 4.1.(-3)]}}{2} = \dfrac{3 \pm \sqrt{21}}{2}$
$\Rightarrow t \approx 3.7$ s (discounting the negative root).

GE *A stone is thrown vertically upwards with a speed of* 20 m s^{-1}. *A second stone is thrown vertically upwards from the same point and with the same initial speed* 20 m s^{-1} *but* 2 s *later than the first one. Show that the two stones collide at a distance of* 15 m *above the point of projection.*

Take up as positive. Let $s = h$ m be the displacement of each stone when they collide.
For first stone, $s = h$ m, $t = T$ s (say), $u = 20$ m s^{-1}, $v = ?$, $a = -10$ m s^{-2}.
For second stone, $s = h$ m, $t = (T-2)$ s, $u = 20$ m s^{-1}, $v = ?$, $a = -10$ m s^{-2}.
Use $s = ut + \frac{1}{2}at^2$ for each stone. Equate the two expressions for h and so find T. Use formula again with value for T found to calculate h.

EX **1** A train is uniformly retarded from 35 m/s to 21 m/s over a distance of 350 m. Calculate:
(a) the retardation;
(b) the total time taken under this retardation to come to rest from a speed of 35 m/s.
(L)

2 Two particles, X and Y, are moving in the same direction on parallel horizontal tracks. At a certain point O, the particle X, travelling with a speed of 16 m/s and retarding uniformly at 6 m/s^2, overtakes Y, which is travelling at 8 m/s and accelerating uniformly at 2 m/s^2. Calculate:
(i) the distance of Y from O when the velocities of X and Y are equal;
(ii) the velocity of X when Y overtakes X.
(C)

3 A car is moving along a straight horizontal road at constant speed 18 m/s. At the instant when the car passes a lay-by, a motor-cyclist leaves the lay-by, starting from rest, and moves with constant acceleration 2·5 m/s^2 in pursuit of the car. Given that the motor-cyclist overtakes the car T seconds after leaving the lay-by, calculate:
(a) the value of T;
(b) the speed of the motor-cyclist at the instant of passing the car.
(L)

4 Two points A and B lie on a horizontal plane. A particle is projected vertically upwards from A with an initial speed of 20 m/s. One second later another particle is projected vertically upwards from B with an initial speed of 17·5 m/s. Calculate, at the instant at which the two particles are at the same vertical height above the plane:
(a) the time which has elapsed since the first particle was projected from A;
(b) the speeds of the two particles.
(A)

5 A balloon is ascending at a constant speed of 3 m/s. The crew release some gas and as a result the balloon experiences a constant downward acceleration of 0·25 m/s^2. How much farther will the balloon ascend, and how long will it be before the balloon returns to its original height? If this height is 80 m above the ground and the balloon continues to descend with the same acceleration, how much longer will it be before the balloon strikes the ground and what will be its velocity at impact?
(C)

6 A particle moves in a straight line with uniform acceleration α. Its initial velocity was u. Prove that the distance x travelled in time t is given by $x = ut + \frac{1}{2}\alpha t^2$. A motor-car is timed between three successive points X, Y and Z, where $XY = YZ = 2$ km. It takes 100 seconds to travel from X to Y and 150 seconds to travel from Y to Z. Given that the retardation of the car is uniform from the point X onwards, calculate the value of this retardation. Find also how far the car travels beyond Z before it stops.
(W)

7 A particle X is projected vertically upwards from the ground with a velocity of 80 m/s. Calculate the maximum height reached by X. A particle Y is held at a height of 300 m above the ground. At the moment when X has dropped 80 m from its maximum height, Y is projected downwards with a velocity of v m/s. The particles reach the ground at the same time. Calculate the value of v.
(C)

8 (a) A particle moves in a straight line with uniform acceleration α. Given that its initial velocity was u and its velocity after it had travelled for time t was v, derive an expression for v in terms of u, α and t.
(b) The driver of an express travelling at uniform speed u suddenly sees ahead of him, on the same track, a train at rest. He immediately applies the brakes, thus giving his train a retardation of f_1. At the same instant the stationary train starts to move away from the express with an acceleration of f_2.
Given that the two trains were originally x apart, find
(i) the distance the two trains are apart after time t (measured from the instant the driver of the express applied his brakes),
(ii) the speeds of the two trains after time t,
(iii) the value of x in terms of u, f_1 and f_2 if a collision is *just averted*.
Given that $u = 60$ m s^{-1}, $f_1 = 6$ m s^{-2} and $f_2 = 8$ m s^{-2}, find the value of x in metres. Calculate the speeds of the two trains at the moment of 'near-collision'.
(W)

In these questions assume $g = 10$ m s^{-2} unless an alternative value is stated.

M3 Graphs in Kinematics

Displacement-time graph, Velocity-time graph, Acceleration-time graph.

Displacement -time graph

A **displacement-time** graph (or *s-t* **graph**) for a body moving in a straight line shows its displacement *s* from a fixed point on the line plotted against time *t*. The **velocity** *v* of the body at time *t* is given by the **gradient** of the *s-t* graph at *t*, since $v = \dfrac{ds}{dt}$.

The *s-t* graph for a body moving with **constant velocity** is a **straight line**. The velocity *v* of the body is given by the gradient of the line.

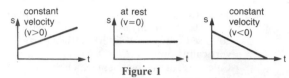

Figure 1

The *s-t* graph for a body moving with **variable velocity** is a **curve**.

The velocity at any time may be estimated from the gradient of the tangent to the curve at that time. The average velocity between two times may be estimated from the gradient of the chord joining them.

ⓘ The *s-t* graph below shows the displacement *s* of a car from its starting point at given instants *t*.

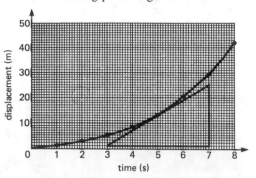

Figure 2

To estimate the velocity of the car after 5 s, draw the tangent to the graph at *t* = 5 s.

$$\therefore \text{ velocity after 5 s} \approx \frac{25-1}{7-3} = \frac{24}{4} = 6 \text{ m s}^{-1}$$

Velocity-time graph

A **velocity-time graph** (or *v-t* **graph**) for a body moving in a straight line shows its velocity *v* plotted against time *t*.

The **acceleration** *a* of the body at time *t* is given by the **gradient** of the *v-t* graph at *t*, since $a = \dfrac{dv}{dt}$.

The **displacement** *s* in a time interval is given by the **area** under the *v-t* graph for that time interval, since $s = \int v\, dt$.

The *v-t* graph for a body moving with **uniform acceleration** is a **straight line**. The acceleration *a* of the body is given by the gradient of the line.

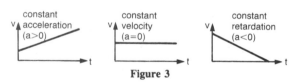

Figure 3

The total displacement *s* of a body can be found from a *v-t* graph of the above type by calculating the area of the trapezium.

The *v-t* graph for a body moving with **variable acceleration** is a **curve**.

The acceleration *a* of the body at any time may be estimated from the gradient of the tangent to the curve at that time.

The displacement *s* of the body in a given time interval may be estimated by finding the area under the *v-t* graph in that interval by a numerical method (see Numerical Integration p. 76).

The velocity-time graph for a moving vehicle is shown below.

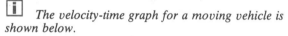
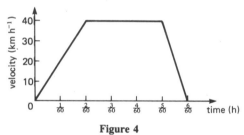

Figure 4

Use the graph to calculate:
(a) the acceleration during the first two minutes,
(b) the retardation during the last minute,
(c) the total displacement of the vehicle.

(a) The acceleration during the first two minutes
= change in velocity ÷ time taken
$$= 40 \div \frac{2}{60} = 1200 \text{ km h}^{-2}$$

(b) The retardation during the last minute
= change in velocity ÷ time taken
$$= 40 \div \frac{1}{60} = 2400 \text{ km h}^{-2}$$

(c) The total displacement of the vehicle is given by the area under the graph. This area is a trapezium.

Total displacement $= \dfrac{1}{2}\left(\dfrac{3}{60} + \dfrac{6}{60}\right) \cdot 40 = 3$ km.

Acceleration- time graph

An **acceleration-time graph** for a body moving in a straight line shows its acceleration *a* plotted against time *t*.

The final **velocity** *v* of the body after a time interval is given by the **area** under the acceleration-time graph for that time interval, since $v = \int a\, dt$

Use the trapezium rule, with intervals of 1 s, to verify from this graph that the velocity after 4 s is 8.1 m s⁻¹ approximately.

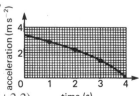

Figure 5

Velocity $= \frac{1}{2}\{(3.4+2.8) + (2.8+2.2)$
$+ (2.2+1.4) + (1.4+0)\}$
$= \frac{1}{2} \times 16.2 = 8.1 \text{ m s}^{-1}$

Graphs in Kinematics
Worked example, Guided example and Exam questions

 Two points P and Q are x metres apart in the same straight line. A particle starts from rest at P and moves directly towards Q with an acceleration a m s^{-2} until it acquires a speed of V m s^{-1}. It maintains this speed for a time T seconds and is then brought to rest at Q under a retardation a m s^{-2}. Prove that

$$T = \frac{x}{V} - \frac{V}{a}.$$

Let t_1 and t_2 be the times for which the particle is accelerating and being retarded respectively.

Sketch the velocity–time graph.

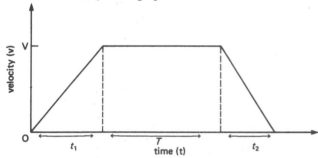

Using the definitions of acceleration and retardation,

$$a = \frac{V}{t_1} \Rightarrow t_1 = \frac{V}{a} \qquad [1]$$

and $\qquad a = \frac{V}{t_2} \Rightarrow t_2 = \frac{V}{a} \qquad [2]$

We know that the total distance travelled between P and Q is x m and this is represented by the area under the graph.

So $x = \frac{1}{2}Vt_1 + VT + \frac{1}{2}Vt_2$

Using the values of t_1 and t_2 from [1] and [2] we have,

$$x = \frac{V^2}{2a} + VT + \frac{V^2}{2a}$$

i.e. $x = \frac{V^2}{a} + VT$

$$TV = x - \frac{V^2}{a}$$

$$T = \frac{x}{V} - \frac{V}{a}$$

 Two cars, C and D, travel equal distances of 9 km in the same time of 18 minutes, finishing at rest. Car C starts from rest, accelerates uniformly to a speed of 45 km/h, travels steadily at this speed and is then brought to rest with uniform retardation. Car D moves at a constant speed for the first 3.6 km and is then brought to rest with uniform retardation. Sketch speed–time graphs for the motion of each car and hence, or otherwise, calculate

(a) *the distance, in km C travels at steady speed,*
(b) *the initial speed in km/h of D,*
(c) *the retardation of D, stating the units.*

Sketch the two graphs. (Remember to change km/h to m/s, km to m, minutes to seconds, etc,)

(a) Let T (say) be the time for which C travels at constant speed. Work out the area under the graph (a trapezium) put it equal to 9 km ($=9 \times 10^3$ m) the distance gone. Hence T.

(b) Let V m/s (say) be the initial speed of D and T_1 seconds be the time for which D travels at V m/s. Then $VT_1 = 3 \cdot 6 \times 10^3$ — the distance travelled at V m/s. Work out the total area under the graph (a trapezium) and get a second equation connecting V and T_1. Solve the two equations for V.

(c) Now find T_1 from (b).
Retardation is $V \div (18 \times 60 - T_1)$ m/s^2.

 1 A train travels between two stations, 3.9 km apart, in 6 minutes, starting and finishing at rest. During the first $\frac{3}{4}$ minute the acceleration is uniform, for the next $3\frac{3}{4}$ minutes the speed is constant and for the remainder of the journey the train is retarded uniformly. Sketch a speed–time graph of the journey and hence, or otherwise, calculate:
  (i) the maximum speed, in km/h, attained by the train;
  (ii) the acceleration of the train during the first $\frac{3}{4}$ minute, stating the units. *(A)*

2 A motorist starting a car from rest accelerates uniformly to a speed of v m/s in 9 seconds. He maintains this speed for another 50 seconds and then applies the brakes and decelerates uniformly to rest. His deceleration is numerically equal to three times his previous acceleration.
  (i) Sketch a velocity–time graph.
  (ii) Calculate the time during which deceleration takes place.
  (iii) Given that the total distance moved is 840 m calculate the value of v.
  (iv) Calculate the initial acceleration. *(C)*

3
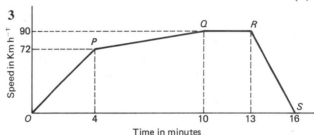

The figure, not drawn to scale, shows the speed/time diagram for a train journey taking 16 minutes. The train reaches a speed of 72 km h^{-1} after 4 minutes and 90 km h^{-1} after a further 6 minutes. The train maintains a steady speed for the next 3 minutes and then decelerates to rest in the last 3 minutes. Calculate:
  (i) the accelerations in m s^{-2} during those parts of the journey corresponding to OP and PQ;
  (ii) the total length of the journey;
  (iii) the average speed for the whole journey in km h^{-1}.

(O & C)

4 Trials are being undertaken on a horizontal road to test the performance of an electrically powered car. The car has a top speed V. In a test run the car moves from rest with uniform acceleration a and is brought to rest with uniform retardation r.
  (i) If the car is to achieve top speed during a test run, by using a velocity–time sketch, or otherwise, show that the length of the test run must be at least

$$\frac{V^2(a+r)}{2ar}.$$

  (ii) Find the least time taken for a test run of length

(a) $\dfrac{2V^2(a+r)}{9ar}$, (b) $\dfrac{2V^2(a+r)}{3ar}$.

  (iii) Find, in terms of V, the average speed of the car for the test run described in (ii) (b). *(A)*

5 Starting from rest at the point A, a particle moves, in a straight line, with constant acceleration until it reaches the point B. The particle then moves with constant retardation until it comes to rest at C, where $AB = 3BC$. The time taken to travel from A to B is T and the speed at B is V. Find, in terms of V and T;
  (i) the time taken for the whole journey from A to C;
  (ii) the distance AC. *(C)*

M4 Relative Motion
Velocity triangle, Relative velocity, Problem solving.

Velocity triangle

When an aircraft flies through the air, its motion over the ground is affected by the way the air is moving.

To describe the motion of an aircraft we need:

ground-speed (GS) – speed of aircraft over ground,
track (T) – direction in which aircraft moves,
airspeed (AS) – speed of aircraft through air,
course (C) – direction in which aircraft points,
wind-speed (WS) – speed of wind,
wind direction (WD) – direction in which wind blows.

These give three vectors connected by the law of **vector addition:**

$(GS, T) = (AS, C) + (WS, WD)$
This gives the **velocity triangle.**

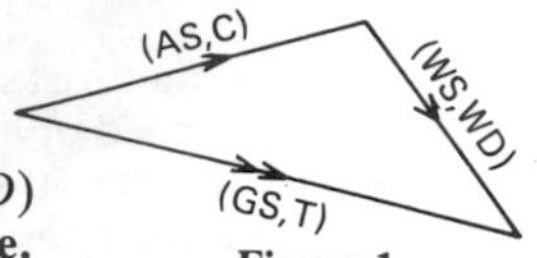

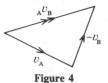

Figure 1

Similarly, when a body travels through water, its motion is affected by the way the water is moving. Instead of wind speed and direction, there is the speed and direction of the flow of water. The speed of the body in still water replaces the airspeed.

📖 *A river, 0.4 km wide, flows from E to W at a steady speed of 1 km h⁻¹. A swimmer, whose speed in still water is 2 km h⁻¹, starts from the S bank and heads N across the river. Find his speed over the river bed and how far downstream he is when he reaches the N bank.*

For swimmer: speed in still water 2 km h⁻¹, course N.
For river: speed 1 km h⁻¹, direction E.

We need to find GS and T
for the swimmer.
$\tan \alpha = \frac{1}{2}$
$\Rightarrow \alpha \approx 26.6°$.

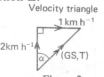

Figure 2

Speed over river bed $= \sqrt{2^2 + 1^2} = \sqrt{5} = 2.24$ km h⁻¹.

Displacement diagram

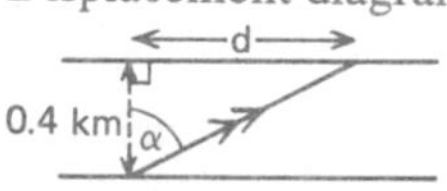

Distance, d, downstream
$= 0.4 \tan \alpha$
$= 0.2$ km

Figure 3

Relative velocity

When we say that A is moving with constant velocity v_A we mean that A is moving with constant velocity v_A relative to a fixed observer on earth.

If A and B are moving with constant velocities v_A and v_B respectively, then, to an observer on B, A will have a velocity $_Av_B$, where:

$_Av_B = v_A - v_B$.

Figure 4

$_Av_B$ is often called the **velocity of A relative to B.**

A and B may be two bodies, e.g. ships, aircraft, cars, cyclists, etc. or one of them could be one of the elements, e.g. rain, wind, etc.

Note: On the diagrams the magnitudes of the vectors are given. The arrows show the directions of the vectors.

📖 *To a motor-cyclist travelling due N at 50 km h⁻¹ the wind appears to come from NW at 60 km h⁻¹. What is the true velocity of the wind?*

Imagine yourself to be the motor-cyclist.
In the velocity triangle:
$_Wv_C = v_W - v_C$
The magnitudes of $_Wv_C$ and v_C are
$_Wv_C = 60$ km h⁻¹
$v_C = 50$ km h⁻¹

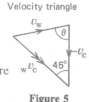

Figure 5

By the cosine rule, $v_W^2 = 60^2 + 50^2 - 2.60.50 \cos 45°$
$\Rightarrow v_W \approx 43.1$ km h⁻¹

By the sine rule, $\dfrac{\sin \theta}{60} = \dfrac{\sin 45°}{43.1} \Rightarrow \theta \approx 79.9°$

∴ true wind velocity is 43.1 km h⁻¹ from S $79.9°$ W.

Problem solving

Two bodies A and B, moving with constant velocities v_A and v_B respectively, will reach either a position of **interception** or of **closest approach.**

When solving such relative motion problems:
1. Draw an initial sketch using the given information.
2. Imagine yourself to be on one of the bodies, B say.
In an interception problem, B should be the body being intercepted.
3. State the relative velocity rule, i.e. $_Av_B = v_A - v_B$.
4. Draw the correct velocity triangle for $_Av_B$.
5. To find the magnitude and direction of $_Av_B$, use the trigonometry of the velocity triangle.

If it is an 'interception' problem:
the time, t, at which interception occurs is given by

$$t = \frac{\text{initial distance apart}}{_Av_B}.$$

If it is a 'closest approach' problem:
(a) draw a displacement diagram showing the initial positions A_0 and B_0 of A and B respectively and $_Av_B$.

Figure 6

(b) find d, the shortest distance between A and B during motion, by trigonometry or scale drawing.

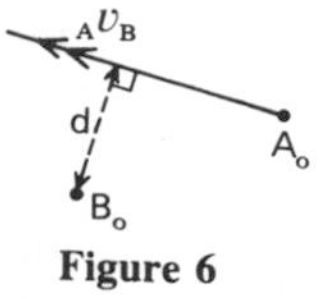

📖 *A dinghy in distress is 6 km S 50° W of a lifeboat and drifting S 20° E at 5 km h⁻¹. In what direction should the lifeboat travel to reach the dinghy as quickly as possible if the maximum speed of the lifeboat is 35 km h⁻¹?*

Initial sketch

Imagine yourself on the dinghy D. The lifeboat will appear to travel directly towards you, i.e. $_Lv_D$ will be in a direction S 50° W.

Figure 7

Velocity triangle

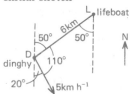

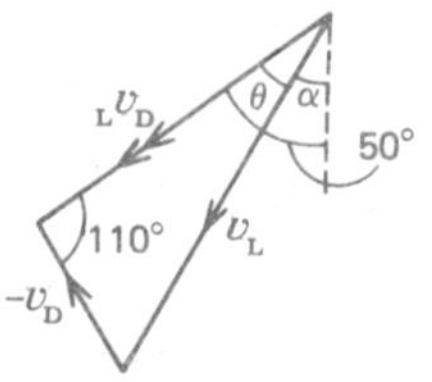

Figure 8

In the velocity triangle:
$_Lv_D = v_L - v_D$
The magnitudes of v_L and v_D are:
$v_L = 35$ km h⁻¹
$v_D = 5$ km h⁻¹.

By the sine rule:
$$\frac{\sin \theta}{5} = \frac{\sin 110°}{35}$$
$\Rightarrow \theta \approx 7.7°$
So $\alpha \approx 50° - 7.7° = 42.3°$.
∴ the lifeboat must travel S 42.3° W.

Two straight roads, one running North-South and the other running East-West, intersect at a crossroads O. Two men A and B are cycling at steady speeds towards O. At a certain instant, A is 20 m from O and travelling due North at 3 m s^{-1} and B is 20 m from O and cycling due West at 4 m s^{-1}. Calculate the shortest distance apart of the two cyclists and the time which elapses before this is attained.

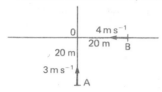

Initial sketch (situation seen by fixed observer)

We view the situation from A, i.e. we need $_B v_A$.

In this velocity triangle the magniture of $_B v_A$ is:

Velocity triangle

$_B v_A = 5$ m s^{-1} (from 3:4:5 $\triangle$)

The direction of $_B v_A$ is given by θ where:

$$\tan \theta = \frac{4}{3},$$

$$\text{so } \sin \theta = \frac{4}{5},$$

$$\text{and } \cos \theta = \frac{3}{5}.$$

Displacement diagram (as seen from A)

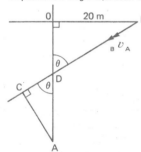

A sees B travelling along the direction BC.
The cyclists are closest together when A sees B to be at a position C, where AC is perpendicular to BC.
The shortest distance apart is, therefore, AC.

Using this displacement diagram,
in $\triangle OBD$, $OD = 20 \cot \theta = 15$ m.
Since $OA = 20$ m and $OD = 15$ m, $AD = 5$ m.
In $\triangle ACD$, $AC = AD \sin \theta = 4$ m.
Hence the shortest distance between the cyclists is 4 m.

To find the time taken to reach the 'closest position' we first calculate the distance BC.
$BC = BD + DC$
$\quad = 20 \operatorname{cosec} \theta + 5 \cos \theta$
$\quad = 25 + 3 = 28$ m.
A sees B travelling along BC at $_B v_A = 5$ m s^{-1}.
So the time taken to travel the 28 m is $28 \div 5 = 5\frac{3}{5}$ s.
Hence, the cyclists are at the 'closest position' after $5\frac{3}{5}$ s.

 At 12 noon a battleship, whose maximum speed is 30 knots, sights a submarine which is moving due North at 10 knots. When first sighted, the submarine is 15 nautical miles North-East of the battleship. Calculate,
(a) the direction in which the battleship must be steered in order to intercept the submarine as quickly as possible,
(b) the time at which they meet,
(c) their distance apart at 1215 hours.

Make an initial sketch. The problem is best solved by viewing the interception from the submarine. The battleship appears to come directly towards you with a velocity $_B v_S = v_B - v_S$. You know the direction of $_B v_S$ is 045°. You know also the speed and direction of v_S and the speed v_B.
(a) Draw the velocity triangle.
(b) Use the sine rule to calculate the direction in which the battleship must be steered.
(c) Calculate $_B v_S$. The battleship covers the 15 nm distance to intercept the submarine at a speed of $_B v_S$. Hence find the time taken to meet.
(d) At 1215 hours, the battleship has travelled for 15 minutes at a speed of $_B v_S$. Find the distance covered in this time and subtract it from the initial separation of 15 nm. This gives their distance apart at 1215 hours.

1 To a cyclist riding due North at 3 m s^{-1} the wind appears to be blowing from the East. If the cyclist doubles his speed, but does not change his direction, the wind appears to be blowing from N60°E. Find, by drawing or calculation, the true wind speed and direction. The cyclist now turns around and cycles due South at 3 m s^{-1}. Calculate the apparent wind direction. *(S)*

2 A ship A, steaming in a direction 030° with a steady speed of 12 knots, sights a ship B. The relative velocity of B to A is 10 knots in a direction 270°. Find the magnitude and direction of the velocity of B. A changes direction but the magnitude of its velocity does not change so that the relative velocity of A to B is in the direction due North. Find the new direction of A. *(O & C)*

3

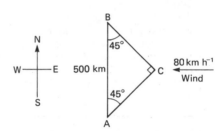

Three cities A, B and C are at the vertices of an isosceles triangle. B is 500 km due north of A, and C is due south-east from B and due north-east from A. A steady wind blows from East to West at a speed of 80 km h^{-1} (see diagram). An aircraft, whose speed in still air is 200 km h^{-1}, flies direct from A to B then from B to C and then from C to A. Using a graphical method, or otherwise, find the time taken for each part of the journey, giving each answer in hours, to one place of decimals. *(C)*

4 A ship P is travelling due East at 30 kilometres per hour and a ship Q is travelling due South at 40 kilometres per hour. Both ships keep constant speed and course. At noon they are each 10 km from the point of intersection, O, of their courses, and moving towards O.
Find the co-ordinates, with respect to axes Ox eastwards and Oy northwards, of P and Q at time t hours past noon, and find the distance PQ at this time. Find the time at which P and Q are closest to one another. Find the magnitude and direction of the velocity of Q relative to P, indicating the direction on a diagram. Show that, at the position of closest approach, the bearing of Q from P is $\theta°$ South of East, where $\tan \theta° = \frac{3}{4}$.

(J)

M5 1-D Particle Dynamics

Force, Mass and weight, Newton's laws of motion, Problem solving.

Force	A **force** is necessary to cause a body to **accelerate**. More than one force may act on a body. If the forces on a body are in **equilibrium**, i.e. balance out, then the body may be at rest or moving in a straight line at constant speed. If there is a resultant force on the body, then the body will accelerate. Force is a **vector**, i.e. it has magnitude and direction. SI unit of force is the **newton** (N). 1 newton is the force needed to give a body of mass 1 kg an acceleration of $1 \, \text{m s}^{-2}$.

Mass and weight	**Mass** and **weight** are different. The **mass** of a body is a measure of the matter contained in the body. A massive body will need a large force to change its motion. The mass of a body may be considered to be constant, whatever the position of the body, provided that none of the body is destroyed or changed. Mass is a **scalar**, i.e. it has magnitude only. SI unit of mass is the **kilogram** (kg). The **weight** of a body is the force with which the earth attracts it. It is dependent upon the body's distance from the earth, so a body 'weighs' less at the top of Everest than it does at sea level. Weight is a **vector**, since it is a force. SI unit of weight is the **newton** (N). The weight W, in newtons, and mass m, in kilograms, of a body are connected by the relation $W = mg$, where g is the acceleration due to gravity, in m s^{-2}. Common approximate values for g are $10 \, \text{m s}^{-2}$ and $9.8 \, \text{m s}^{-2}$.

Newton's laws of motion	**Newton's three laws of motion** are the fundamental basis of the study of mechanics at this level. Although there is no direct proof of these laws, predictions made using them agree very closely with observations.

statement	consequence(s)
1st law Every body will remain at rest or continue to move in a straight line at constant speed unless an external force acts on it.	(a) If a body has an acceleration, then there must be a force acting on it. (b) If a body has no acceleration, then the forces acting on it must be in equilibrium.

2nd law
The rate of change of momentum of a moving body is proportional to the external force acting on it and takes place in the direction of that force.
So when an external force acts on a body of constant mass, the force produces an acceleration which is directly proportional to the force.
	(a) The basic equation of motion for constant mass is:
	    Force = mass × acceleration
	    (in N) (in kg) (in m s^{-2})
	(b) The force and acceleration of the body are both in the same direction.
	(c) A constant force on a constant mass gives a constant acceleration.

3rd law If a body A exerts a force on a body B, then B exerts an equal and opposite force on A.	These forces between bodies are often called reactions. In a rigid body the internal forces occur as equal and opposite pairs and the net effect is zero. So only external forces need to be considered.

Problem solving	The following are important points to remember when solving problems using Newton's laws of motion. 1. Draw a clear force diagram (see Force Diagrams p. 108). 2. If there is no acceleration, i.e. the body is either at rest or moving with uniform velocity, then the forces balance in each direction. 3. If there is an acceleration: (a) mark it on the diagram using $\longrightarrow^{a}$ (b) write down, if possible, an expression for the resultant force, (c) use Newton's 2nd law, i.e. write the equation of motion: force = mass × acceleration

i Body at rest on a rough inclined plane.

Figure 1

No acceleration so forces balance:
∥ to plane $\Rightarrow F = mg \sin \alpha$
⊥ to plane $\Rightarrow R = mg \cos \alpha$.

Body sliding down rough plane at constant speed.

Figure 2

No acceleration so forces balance:
∥ to plane $\Rightarrow F = mg \sin \alpha$
⊥ to plane $\Rightarrow R = mg \cos \alpha$.

Body sliding down rough plane with acceleration.

Figure 3

No 'a' ⊥ to plane
$\Rightarrow R = mg \cos \alpha$.
Resultant force down plane is
$mg \sin \alpha - F$.
2nd law $\Rightarrow mg \sin \alpha - F = ma$.

1-D Particle Dynamics
Worked example, Guided example and Exam questions

 A train of total mass 300 tonnes *is travelling along a straight horizontal track at a constant speed of* 54 km/h. *The resistances to the motion are* 50 newtons *per tonne. The rear coach of mass* 50 tonnes *becomes detached but the tractive force of the engine remains the same. Calculate*

(a) *the acceleration of the rest of the train*

(b) *the distance the rear coach travels, after becoming detached, before it stops.*

Force diagram for complete train.

50 × 300
(resistive force) ◁———[300 × 10³ kg]———▷ T (tractive force)

Since speed is constant, $T = 50 \times 300$ N
i.e. $T = 15\,000$ N.

Force diagram for remainder of train.

50 × 250 ◁———[250 × 10³ kg]———▷ T = 15 000

Resultant accelerating force $= 15\,000 - 50 \times 250$ N
$\qquad = 2500$ N

Using Newton's 2nd law:
Accelerating force $=$ mass $\times$ acceleration
$\qquad 2500 = (250 \times 10^3) \times a$
$\qquad a = 0.01$ m s^{-2}, the acceleration.

The only force acting on the rear coach when it becomes detached is the resistance force.

Force diagram for rear coach:

50 × 50 ◁———[50 × 10³ kg]

Take right as positive.

Let f be the acceleration of the coach.
Newton's 2nd law gives:
$\qquad (-50 \times 50) = (50 \times 10^3) \times f$
$\Rightarrow \qquad f = -0.05$ m s^{-2} i.e. a retardation.

Now $s = ?$, $u = 54 \times \dfrac{5}{18}$ m s^{-1}, $t = ?$, $v = 0$, $a = -0.05$ m s^{-2}
Using $v^2 = u^2 + 2as$
$\qquad 0 = 15^2 + 2(-0.05)\,s$
$\Rightarrow \qquad s = 2250$ m
So the coach travel 2250 m before it stops.

 A lift of mass 500 kg *is descending with an acceleration of* 1.5 m s^{-2}. *A man of mass* 80 kg *is inside the lift. Calculate*
(a) *the tension in the cable connected to the lift,*
(b) *the force between the man and the floor of the lift.*

First consider the man and lift to be one mass subject to forces of T upwards (the tension in the cable) and the weight force downwards. Write down the equation of motion downwards. Next consider the force between the man's feet and the floor as (say), F. This force can be considered to be acting on either the man's feet upwards (if you consider forces on the man), or on the floor of the lift downwards (if you consider forces acting on the lift). Choose one of these only. Draw a force diagram for either the man or the lift and then write down the appropriate equation of motion. Hence find F.

 1 State Newton's Laws of Motion. A miniature engine of mass 110 kg is coupled to and pulls a miniature carriage of mass 30 kg along a horizontal track. The resistance to the motion of the engine is $\dfrac{1}{100}$ of its weight; the resistance to the motion of the carriage is $\dfrac{1}{150}$ of its weight. Given that the whole tractive force exerted by the engine is equal to the weight of 3 kg, find the tension in the coupling.
(W)

2 A constant force of 35 N, always acting in the same horizontal direction, causes a particle of mass 2 kg to move over a rough horizontal plane. The particle passes two points X and Y, 4 m apart, with speeds of 5 m/s and 10 m/s respectively. The frictional resistance to motion is constant. Calculate:
  (i) the acceleration of the particle;
  (ii) the magnitude of the frictional resistance;
  (iii) the distance of the particle from X, 4 s after it has passed X.
(A)

3 A water skier of mass 95 kg is towed by a horizontal rope behind a boat. His body is straight, and the thrust of the water acts along the line of his body. When moving with uniform velocity, he is leaning back at 10° from the vertical. Find the tension in the rope. The boat begins to accelerate, and the skier leans back at 15°. The tension in the rope now becomes 500 N. Find the acceleration of the boat.
(OLE)

4 A breakdown truck of mass 2000 kg is towing a car of mass 1000 kg by means of a rope, up an incline of 1 in 20. The resistances due to friction on each vehicle are proportional to the masses of the vehicles. The engine of the truck exerts a tractive force of 3600 N when moving up the hill at a steady speed of 18 km/h. Show that the tension in the rope is 1200 N. The rope breaks and the two vehicles continue to move up the hill. Calculate:
  (i) how much time elapses before the car comes momentarily to rest;
  (ii) how far the car travels in this time.
(OLE)

5 A lift, which is initially at rest, ascends for 10 s with a uniform acceleration until a speed of 2 m s^{-1} is reached. It continues to ascend for 5 s at this constant speed before decelerating to rest over a further 5 s. Calculate:
  (i) the initial acceleration of the lift;
  (ii) the total distance travelled by the lift.
A man of mass 60 kg is travelling in the lift. Calculate the reaction between the man and the floor of the lift over each stage of the three-stage journey.
(S)

6 A heavy particle is suspended by a spring balance from the ceiling of a lift. When the lift moves up with constant acceleration f m/s^2 the balance shows a reading 1.8 kg. When the lift descends with constant acceleration $\tfrac{1}{2}f$ m/s^2 the balance shows a reading 1 kg. Find the mass of the particle and the value of f.
(L)

7 When pulled by a horizontal force of 16 N, a particle of mass 2 kg moving on a rough horizontal plane has an acceleration of 4 m s^{-2}. Find the coefficient of friction. When the same plane is inclined at 23° to the horizontal and the force of 16 N no longer acts, the particle slides down with an acceleration of a m s^{-2}. Find a.
(O & C)

M6 Connected Particles

Problem solving, Common situations.

Problem solving

Two particles connected by a light inextensible string which passes over a fixed light smooth frictionless pulley are called **connected particles.**
The tension in the string is the same throughout its length, so each particle is acted upon by the same tension.

Problems concerned with connected particles usually involve finding the acceleration of the system and the tension in the string.

To solve problems of this type:
1. Draw a clear diagram showing the forces on each particle and the common acceleration.
2. Write down the equation of motion,
i.e. force = mass × acceleration
for each particle separately.
3. Solve the two equations to find the common acceleration, a, and/or the tension, T, in the string.

i *Two particles mass m_1 and m_2, with $m_1 > m_2$, are connected by a light inextensible string which passes over a fixed light smooth frictionless pulley. Find the common acceleration, a, of each mass and the tension, T, in the string when the system is moving freely.*

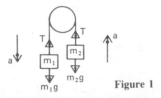

Figure 1

For m_1, with acceleration a ($\downarrow$), the equation of motion, i.e. force = mass × acceleration

is $\qquad m_1g - T = m_1a \qquad$ (1)

For m_2, with acceleration a ($\uparrow$), the equation of motion

is $\qquad T - m_2g = m_2a \qquad$ (2)

Adding (1) and (2) to eliminate T:

$$m_1g - m_2g = m_1a + m_2a$$

i.e. $\qquad a = \dfrac{(m_1 - m_2)}{(m_1 + m_2)}g$

Substituting for a in (1):

$$m_1g - T = m_1\frac{(m_1 - m_2)}{(m_1 + m_2)}g$$

Rearranging gives:

$$T = \frac{2m_1m_2}{(m_1 + m_2)}g$$

Common situations

The simplest situation in which connected particles occur is illustrated above. There are several other situations in which the motion of connected particles is considered. The most common are shown below.

One particle on a **smooth horizontal table** as shown.

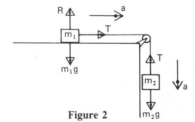

Figure 2

For m_1:
Resolving ⊥ to table: $\qquad R = m_1g$
Equation of motion: $\qquad T = m_1a$
For m_2:
Equation of motion: $m_2g - T = m_2a$

One particle on a **smooth inclined plane** as shown.

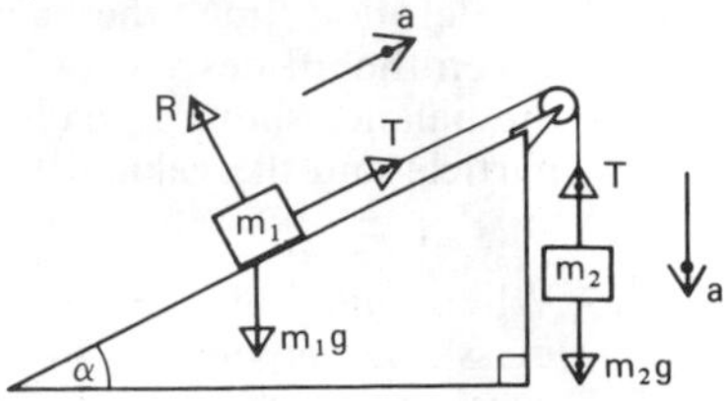

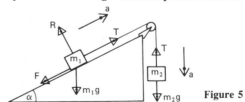

Figure 3

For m_1:
Resolving ⊥ to plane: $\qquad R = m_1g \cos \alpha$
Equation of motion: $T - m_1g \sin \alpha = m_1a$
For m_2:
Equation of motion: $\qquad m_2g - T = m_2a$

One particle on a **rough horizontal table** as shown.

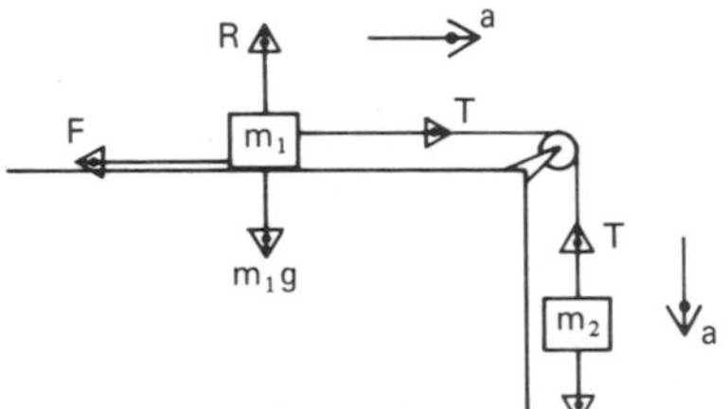

Figure 4

For m_1:
Resolving ⊥ to table: $\qquad R = m_1g$
Equation of motion: $T - F = m_1a$
For m_2:
Equation of motion: $m_2g - T = m_2a$

One particle on a **rough inclined plane** as shown.

Figure 5

For m_1:
Resolving ⊥ to plane: $\qquad R = m_1g \cos \alpha$
Equation of motion: $T - F - m_1g \sin \alpha = m_1a$
For m_2:
Equation of motion: $\qquad m_2g - T = m_2a$

Connected Particles
Worked example and Exam questions

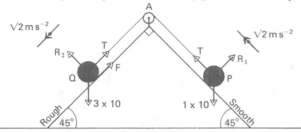

A smooth plane and a rough plane, both inclined at 45° to the horizontal, intersect in a fixed horizontal ridge. A particle P of mass 1 kg is held on the smooth plane by a light inextensible string which passes over a small frictionless pulley A on the ridge and is attached to a particle Q of mass 3 kg which rests on the rough plane. The plane containing P, Q and A is perpendicular to the ridge. The system is released from rest with the string taut. Given that the acceleration of each particle is of magnitude $\sqrt{2}$ m s^{-2}, find

(a) *the tension in the string,*

(b) *the coefficient of friction between Q and the rough plane,*

(c) *the magnitude and direction of the force exerted by the string on the pulley.* [*Take the value of g to be 10 m s^{-2}*]

Let T be the tension in the string,
and F be the frictional force on Q.
Let R_1 and R_2 be the normal reactions on P and Q respectively.

For P
Equation of motion:
$$T - 10 \cos 45° = 1 \times \sqrt{2}$$
$$\Rightarrow \quad T = 5\sqrt{2} + \sqrt{2}$$
i.e. $T = 6\sqrt{2}$ N, the tension in the string.

For Q
Resolving perpendicular to slope:
$$R_2 = 3 \times 10 \cos 45°,$$
$$\Rightarrow R_2 = 15\sqrt{2} \text{ N.}$$
Equation of motion:
$$3 \times 10 \cos 45° - T - F = 3 \times \sqrt{2}$$
$$\Rightarrow \quad F = 15\sqrt{2} - 3\sqrt{2} - 6\sqrt{2}$$
i.e. $F = 6\sqrt{2}$ N.

Since friction is limiting (particle is in motion)
$$F = \mu R_2, \quad \mu \text{ coefficient of friction.}$$
Hence $6\sqrt{2} = \mu 15\sqrt{2}$
$$\Rightarrow \mu = \frac{6\sqrt{2}}{15\sqrt{2}} = \frac{2}{5}, \text{ the coefficient of friction.}$$

Forces on the pulley have the same magnitude as the tensions in the strings:

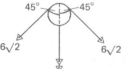

The resultant force on the pulley is
$6\sqrt{2} \cos 45° + 6\sqrt{2} \cos 45°$,
i.e.12 N vertically downwards.

1 Masses of 1 kg and 2 kg are attached to the ends of a long light string which passes over a light pulley supported by a frictionless horizontal axis. If the tension in the string is T newtons, write down the equation of motion of each mass, and hence find:
  (i) the tension in the string;
  (ii) the time taken for the heavier mass to fall from rest a distance of 1.5 m.   *(O & C)*

2 Two particles X and Y, of mass 150 g and 100 g respectively, are attached to the ends of a light inextensible string. The particle X is held on a rough horizontal table, with the string passing along the table and over a small smooth pulley which is fixed on the edge of the table. The string is in a plane perpendicular to the edge of the table and Y hangs freely. The coefficient of friction between X and the table is $\frac{1}{3}$. The particle X is released and after $1\frac{1}{2}$ s, before X reaches the edge of the table, the string breaks. Calculate:
(a) the acceleration with which X moves before the string breaks;
(b) the speed attained by X at the instant the string breaks;
(c) the total distance X moves before coming to rest, assuming it still has not reached the edge of the table.
         (A)

3 Two particles A and B, of masses $0 \cdot 4$ kg and $0 \cdot 3$ kg respectively, are connected by a light inextensible string. The particle A is placed near the bottom of a smooth plane inclined at 30° to the horizontal. The string passes over a small smooth light pulley which is fixed at the top of the inclined plane and B hangs freely. The system is released from rest, with each portion of the string taut and in the same vertical plane as a line of greatest slope of the inclined plane. Calculate:
(a) the common acceleration, in m/s^2, of the two particles;
(b) the tension, in N, in the string.
Given that A has not reached the pulley, find:
(c) the time taken for B to fall $6 \cdot 3$ m from rest;
(d) the speed that B has then acquired.
[Take the value of g to be 9.8 m s^{-2}]
         (L)

4 (In this question, you may assume that the strings are of such a length, and the pulley so positioned, that at no time during the motion is the pulley hit by either mass.) Masses of $3m$ and m are connected by a light inextensible string passing over a light smooth pulley. The system is released from rest with the string taut and with both masses at a height h above the ground.
Find:
  (i) the acceleration with which they both move;
  (ii) the tension in the string before the $3m$ mass hits the ground;
  (iii) the loss of kinetic energy at the impact of the $3m$ mass with the ground, (the $3m$ mass does not rebound from the ground);
  (iv) the greatest height reached by the smaller mass, and the total time taken to get there;
  (v) the speed with which the $3m$ mass leaves the ground again.
         (S)

5 A light inextensible string passes over a smooth light fixed pulley and masses of 3 kg and 7 kg are attached to its ends. The system is held at rest with the string taut, those parts not in contact with the pulley being vertical, and then released. Find the acceleration of each mass and the tension in the string, stating units. After the 7 kg mass has descended a distance of one metre it strikes an inelastic horizontal table. Show that the time taken for this to happen is 5/7 s from the start of the motion, assuming that the acceleration due to gravity is 9.8 m s^{-2}. Find the time during which the 7 kg mass is at rest on the table. (Assume throughout that the 3 kg mass does not reach the pulley.)
         (O & C)

M7 Work and Energy

Definitions, Hooke's law, Kinetic and potential energy, Mechanical energy, Conservation of mechanical energy.

Definitions

Work may be done by or against a force (often gravity). It is a **scalar**.

When a constant force F moves its point of application along a straight line from A to B, the **work done** by F is $|F|\cos\theta.|AB|$

SI unit of work is the **joule** (J).

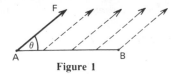

Figure 1

1 joule is the work done by a force of 1 N in moving its point of application 1 m in the direction of the force.

Energy is the capacity to do work. It is a scalar.
SI unit of energy is the **joule** (the same as work).
A body possessing energy can do work and lose energy. Work can be done on a body and increase its energy.
i.e. Work done = change in energy.

Hooke's law

Hooke's law for an elastic string or spring is $T=\dfrac{\lambda x}{l}$,

where T is the tension in string or spring,
λ is its **modulus of elasticity**,
l is its natural (unstretched) length,
x is the extension. (Note: a negative extension of a spring is a compression.)

Work done in stretching the string or spring is $\dfrac{\lambda x^2}{2l}$.

ℹ️ *An elastic string AB of natural length 3 m and modulus 12 N has its end A attached to a fixed point. A force of 4 N is applied to the end B. Calculate the work done by the force in producing the extension.*

Hooke's law, $T=\dfrac{\lambda x}{l}$, gives $4=\dfrac{12x}{3}$

$\Rightarrow x=1$ m, the extension.

Work done by the force $=\dfrac{12\times 1^2}{2\times 3}=2$ J.

Kinetic and potential energy

Kinetic energy and **potential energy** are types of **mechanical energy**.

(a) Kinetic energy (K.E.) is due to a body's motion. The K.E. of a body of mass m, moving with velocity v, is $\frac{1}{2}mv^2$.

(b) Potential energy (P.E.) is due to a body's position. Gravitational P.E. is a property of height.
The P.E. of a body of mass m at a distance h,
(i) above an initial level is mgh,
(ii) below an initial level is $-mgh$.

The initial level can be any level you choose and the P.E. at the initial level is zero.

Elastic P.E., a property of stretched elastic strings and springs or compressed springs, is $\dfrac{\lambda x^2}{2l}$, where λ is the modulus of the elasticity of the 'string', l is its natural length and x the extension (see Hooke's law).

ℹ️ A stone of mass 2 kg is thrown horizontally with speed 3 m s⁻¹. The initial K.E. of the moving stone is $\frac{1}{2}mv^2=\frac{1}{2}\times 2\times 3^2\,\text{J}=9\,\text{J}$.

ℹ️ A body of mass 2 kg is suspended 3 m above a floor. The P.E. of the body relative to:
(a) the floor is $mgh=2\times 10\times 3\,\text{J}=60\,\text{J}$.
(b) a table 1 m high is $mgh=2\times 10\times 2\,\text{J}=40\,\text{J}$.
(in both cases taking $g=10$ m s⁻².)

ℹ️ An elastic string of natural length 0.5 m and modulus 1 N is stretched to a length 0.75 m.

Elastic P.E. stored in the string $=\dfrac{\lambda x^2}{2l}=\dfrac{1\times 0.25^2}{2\times 0.5}\text{J}$

$=0.0625$ J

Mechanical energy

The **mechanical energy** (M.E.) of a particle (or body) = P.E. + K.E. of the particle (or body).

If a system includes one or more elastic strings, then:
total M.E. of the system = P.E. + K.E. + elastic P.E.

M.E. is lost (as heat energy or sound energy) when we have:
resistances (friction) or
impulses (collisions or strings jerking taut).

ℹ️ A particle of mass 3 kg is moving with a speed of 5 m/s, 0.5 m above ground level (P.E. = 0).
Total mechanical energy
= P.E. + K.E.
$= mgh + \frac{1}{2}mv^2$
$= 3\times 10\times 0.5+\frac{1}{2}\times 3\times 5^2=52.5$ J

ℹ️ A 5 kg mass, moving horizontally on a smooth table at 9 m/s, hits a vertical plane barrier and rebounds at 4 m/s.
Loss in K.E. $=\frac{1}{2}mv_1^2-\frac{1}{2}mv_2^2$
$=\frac{1}{2}\times 5\times 9^2-\frac{1}{2}\times 5\times 4^2=162.5$ J.

Conservation of mechanical energy

The total mechanical energy of a body (or system) will be **conserved** if
(a) no external force (other than gravity) causes work to be done, and
(b) none of the M.E. is converted to other forms.
Given these conditions: P.E. + K.E. = constant
or loss in P.E. = gain in K.E.
or loss in K.E. = gain in P.E.

ℹ️ *A particle falls freely from rest until its speed is 9 m s⁻¹. How far has it fallen? (Use $g=10$ m s⁻²)*

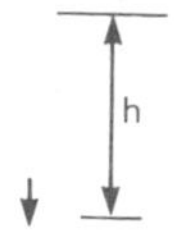

Figure 2

Initially, P.E. $=mgh$, K.E. $=0$.
So total M.E. $=mgh$.
Finally, P.E. $=0$, K.E. $=\frac{1}{2}m.9^2$.
So total M.E. $=\frac{1}{2}m.9^2$.

Total M.E. is conserved, so $mgh=\frac{1}{2}m9^2 \Rightarrow h=4.05$ m.

Work and Energy
Worked example, Guided example and Exam questions

WE (a) *A particle of mass m is projected directly up a rough plane of inclination α with velocity V. If μ is the coefficient of friction between the particle and the plane, calculate how far up the plane the particle travels before coming to rest.*

(b) *A light elastic string OA of natural length l and modulus 2mg has its end O fixed to a point on a ceiling. A particle of mass m is attached to the end A of the string and is held as close as possible to O. If the particle is released from rest, find the maximum length of OA in the subsequent motion.*

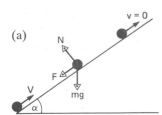

(a)

F = frictional force
N = normal reaction
Let l be the distance along the slope the particle travels.

Since the particle is moving along the plane, friction is limiting, so $F = \mu N$.
Resolving perpendicular to the plane:
$$N = mg \cos \alpha,$$
so frictional force $F = \mu mg \cos \alpha$.
At bottom of slope, total energy $= \frac{1}{2} mV^2$.
At top of slope, total energy $= mgl \sin \alpha$.
Work done against friction $= mgl \cos \alpha$.
Now,
initial total energy
= final total energy + work done against friction,
i.e. $\frac{1}{2}mV^2 = mgl \sin \alpha + mgl \cos \alpha$
$$\Rightarrow l = \frac{V^2}{2g(\sin \alpha + \mu \cos \alpha)}$$
and is the distance travelled by the particle along the slope before it comes to rest.

(b) Let L be the maximum length of OA.
OA will be a maximum when the particle comes to rest at its lowest point.
When the particle is at O,
$$P.E. = mgL$$
$$E.P.E. = 0$$
$$K.E. = 0.$$
So, total energy $= mgL$
When particle is at lowest point,
$$P.E. = 0$$
$$E.P.E. = \frac{2mg(L-l)^2}{2l}$$
$$K.E. = 0.$$
So, total energy $= \frac{2mg(L-l)^2}{2l}$
By conservation of mechanical energy,
$$mgl = \frac{2mg(L-l)^2}{2l}$$
$$\therefore L^2 - 2Ll = 0 \quad \text{i.e. } L(L - 2l) = 0$$
$$\Rightarrow L = 2l, \text{ the maximum length of } OA.$$

GE *The top of a chute whose length is 12 m is 3 m vertically above its lowest point. A parcel of mass 1.6 kg slides from rest from the top of the chute and reaches the lowest point with a speed of 5 m/s. Calculate, for the parcel,*
(i) *the gain in kinetic energy,*
(ii) *the loss in potential energy,*

(iii) *the work done in overcoming the frictional resistance,*
(iv) *the average value of this resistance.*

After reaching the lowest point of the chute, the parcel slides along a horizontal floor the resistance to motion being 4 N. Calculate how far the parcel travels before coming to rest.

(i) Find the kinetic energy at the top and bottom of the slope. Hence find gain.
(ii) Find the potential energy at the top and bottom of the slope. Hence find loss.
(iii) Find the loss of mechanical energy. (This is the difference between the total energy at the top and bottom of the slope.) Hence find work done.
(iv) Work done by the average resistance is $R \times 12$ m, where R is the average resistance. Equate this to work done calculated in (iii). Hence find R.
For final part, use
loss in K.E. = work done against 4 N resistive force
to find the distance travelled.

EX 1 A block of mass 6.5 kg is projected with a velocity of 4 m/s up a line of greatest slope of a rough plane. Calculate the initial kinetic energy of the block. The coefficient of friction between the block and the plane is $\frac{2}{3}$ and the plane makes an angle θ with the horizontal where $\sin \theta = \frac{5}{13}$. The block travels a distance of d m up the plane before coming instantaneously to rest. Express in terms of d:
(i) the potential energy gained by the block in coming to rest;
(ii) the work done against friction by the block in coming to rest.
Hence calculate the value of d.
(C)

2 A boy on a sledge slides down a hill of variable gradient. In so doing he travels a distance of 168 m, measured along the surface of the track, and descends a vertical distance of 30 m. The combined mass of the boy and the sledge is 80 kg. If the initial speed is 2 m s^{-1} and the final speed is 16 m s^{-1}, find in the same units:
(i) the increase in the kinetic energy of the combined mass of boy and sledge;
(ii) the work done by gravity.
Hence find the average resistance to motion (defined as the work done against the resisting forces divided by the distance travelled).
(O & C)

3 A fixed plane is inclined at an angle α to the horizontal, where $\tan \alpha = \frac{4}{3}$. A particle of mass m is projected, from the point A on the plane, up a line of greatest slope. The coefficient of friction between the particle and the plane is $\frac{1}{3}$. The particle has moved a distance d up the plane when it comes instantaneously to rest at the point B.
(i) Find the total work done against the external applied forces during the motion from A to B.
(ii) Find the speed of projection from A.
(iii) Find the total work done against the external applied forces during the motion from A to B and back to A again.
(iv) Find the kinetic energy of the particle when it has passed through A and moved a further distance $4d$ down the plane from A.
(C)

4 An elastic string, of natural length l and modulus of elasticity λ, is stretched to a length $l + x$. As a result, the tension in the string is mg and the energy stored in it is E. Find x and λ in terms of E, g, l and m.
(L)

M8 Power
Definitions, Moving vehicles, Common situations.

Definitions

Power is the rate at which a force does work.
It is a **scalar.**
SI unit of power is the **watt** (W).
1 watt (W) = 1 joule per second (J s⁻¹).
The **kilowatt** (1 kW = 1000 W) is often used.
When a body is moving in a straight line with velocity v m s⁻¹ under a tractive force F newtons, the power of the force is Fv watts.

ℹ️ *A pump raises water at a rate of* 500 kg *per minute through a vertical distance of* 3 m. *If the water is delivered at* 2.5 m s⁻¹, *find the power developed.*

The pump does work to create both P.E. and K.E.
P.E. created is $500 \times 10 \times 3 = 15\,000$ J per min.
K.E. created is $\frac{1}{2} \times 500 \times 2.5^2 = 1562.5$ J per min.
So, power developed is $(15\,000 + 1562.5) \div 60 \approx 276$ W.

Moving vehicles

The power of a moving vehicle is supplied by its engine. The **tractive force** of an engine is the pushing force it exerts.

To solve problems involving moving vehicles:

1. Draw a clear force diagram.
Note: 'non-gravitational resistance' means 'frictional force'.
2. Resolve forces perpendicular to the direction of motion.
3. If the velocity is:
   (a) constant (vehicle moving with steady speed), then resolve forces parallel to the direction of motion (Newton's first law),
   (b) not constant (vehicle accelerating), then find the resultant force acting and write down the equation of motion in the direction of motion.
4. Use Power = tractive force × speed.

ℹ️ *A train of total mass* 200 *tonnes is moving at a steady speed of* 72 km h⁻¹ *on a straight level track. If the non-gravitational resistance is* 10⁴ *newtons, at what rate is the engine working? Take* $g = 10$ m s⁻².

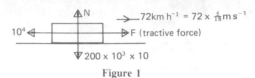

Figure 1

Resolve ($\uparrow$): $N = 200 \times 10^3 \times 10$
$\qquad = 2 \times 10^6$ newtons
Resolve ($\rightarrow$): $F = 10^4$ newtons
Power $= Fv$
$\qquad = 10^4 \times 72 \times \dfrac{5}{18} = 2 \times 10^5$ W $= 200$ kW

Common situations

The following illustrate some common situations which arise in problems.

1. Vehicles **on the level**
(a) moving with **steady speed** v

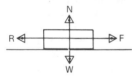

Figure 2

Resolve ($\uparrow$): $N = W$
Resolve ($\rightarrow$): $F = R$
Power: $P = Fv$

(b) moving with **acceleration** a and instantaneous speed v

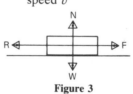

Figure 3

Resolve ($\uparrow$): $N = W$
Equation of motion:
$\qquad F - R = ma$
Power: $P = Fv$

Note: if the vehicle is retarding, i.e. $R > F$, then a will be in the opposite direction.

2. Vehicles **on a slope** of angle α
(a) moving with **steady speed** v
   (i) moving **up**

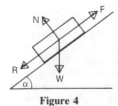

Figure 4

Resolve $\perp$ to plane:
$\qquad N = W \cos \alpha$
Resolve $\parallel$ to plane:
$\qquad F = R + W \sin \alpha$
Power: $P = Fv$

(b) moving with **acceleration** a and instantaneous speed v
   (ii) moving **up**

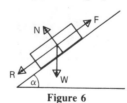

Figure 6

Resolving $\perp$ to plane:
$\qquad N = W \cos \alpha$
Equation of motion $\parallel$ to plane:
$\qquad F - R - W \sin \alpha = ma$
Power: $P = Fv$

Note: if the vehicle is moving up the plane but retarding, then $F < R + W \sin \alpha$.
   (ii) moving **down**

(ii) moving **down**

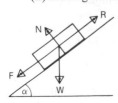

Figure 5

Resolve $\perp$ to plane:
$\qquad N = W \cos \alpha$
Resolve $\parallel$ to plane:
$\qquad F + W \sin \alpha = R$
Power: $P = Fv$

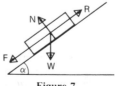

Figure 7

Resolve $\perp$ to plane:
$\qquad N = W \cos \alpha$
Equation of motion $\parallel$ to plane:
$\qquad F + W \sin \alpha - R = ma$
Power: $P = Fv$

Note: if the vehicle is retarding, using the engine for braking, then F acts up the plane and $F + R > W \sin \alpha$.

Power
Worked example and Exam questions

WE *A bus of mass 5 tonnes freewheels down a slope of inclination* $\sin^{-1}\left(\dfrac{1}{40}\right)$ *to the horizontal at constant speed. Assuming that the non-gravitational resistances remain the same, find the rate at which the engine must work in order to drive the bus up the same incline at a steady speed of 12 km/h. If the power is suddenly increased to 10 kW find, in* m/s², *the immediate acceleration of the bus.*

Stage 1, *bus freewheeling down slope.*
F is the non-gravitational resistance. Since speed is steady down the slope,
forces down slope = forces up slope

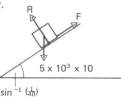

i.e. $5 \times 10^3 \times 10 \times \dfrac{1}{40} = F$

$\Rightarrow F = 1250$ N, the non-gravitational resistance.

Stage 2, *bus being driven up the slope at steady speed.*
T is the tractive force of the engine.
Since speed is steady,
forces up slope = forces down slope

i.e. $T = 1250 + 5 \times 10^3 \times 10 \times \dfrac{1}{40}$

$\qquad = 1250 + 1250$

So, $\qquad T = 2500$ N.

Now, power = Tv watts, v being the speed up the slope.

$v = 12 \times \dfrac{5}{18}$ m/s.

$\quad = \dfrac{10}{3}$ m/s

So, power = $2500 \times \dfrac{10}{3}$ watts

$\qquad = \dfrac{25}{3}$ kW

$\qquad = 8\tfrac{1}{3}$ kW.

When the power is suddenly increased to 10 kW, a new tractive force T_1 acts, but the speed at this instant is still $\dfrac{10}{3}$ m/s.

Using Power = Tv watts,

$10 \times 10^3 = T_1 \times \dfrac{10}{3}$

$\Rightarrow \qquad T_1 = 3 \times 10^3$ N.

Stage 3, *bus accelerating up the slope.*
We now have a resultant accelerating force acting up the slope equal to,

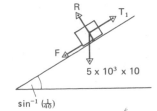

$T_1 - F - 5 \times 10^3 \times 10 \times \dfrac{1}{40}$

$= 3 \times 10^3 - 1250 - 1250$

$= 500$ N.

Using, resultant accelerating force = mass × acceleration, up the slope, we have,

$500 = 5 \times 10^3 \times a$, where a m/s² is the acceleration

$\Rightarrow \qquad a = \dfrac{500}{5 \times 10^3}$ m/s²

i.e. $\quad a = \dfrac{1}{10}$ m/s².

EX 1 The engine of a car is working at a constant rate of 6 kW in driving the car along a straight horizontal road at a constant speed of 54 km/h. Find, in N, the resistance to the motion of the car.

*(L)

2 A motor car of mass 800 kg is towing a trailer of mass 300 kg along a straight horizontal road, Resistances, which are constant, are 600 N for the car and 240 N for the trailer. Calculate the tractive force exerted by the motor and the tension in the coupling between the car and the trailer in each of the following cases:
  (i) when both are travelling at constant velocity;
  (ii) when both are accelerating at 2.5 m/s².
Calculate the power developed by the motor when the car and trailer are travelling at a constant velocity of 15 m/s.

*(C)

3 (Take g as 10 m s⁻².) The three parts of this question are all concerned with a car of mass 3000 kg.
  (i) The car will *just* run down a slope of inclination α (sin $\alpha = \frac{1}{20}$) under its own weight (i.e. the engine is *not* switched on). Find the resistance to motion in newtons.
  (ii) The car is driven along a level road, its engine exerting a constant tractive force of T newtons. Given that the force resisting motion is the same (in magnitude) as when the car just runs down the plane (Part (i)) and that, starting from rest, the car reaches a speed of 15 m s⁻¹ in a time of 5 minutes, calculate:
  (a) the acceleration of the car; (b) the value of T;
  (c) the power developed by the engine.
  (iii) When the car is driven *up* the slope of inclination α (sin $\alpha = \frac{1}{20}$) its engine exerts such a tractive force that the car travels at a constant speed of 40 km/hour. Given that the resistance to motion is the same, in magnitude, as in Parts (i) and (ii), calculate the rate of working in kW, giving your answer correct to two decimal places.

*(W)

4 A car of mass 1000 kg moves with its engine shut off down a slope of inclination α, where sin $\alpha = \frac{1}{20}$, at a steady speed of 15 m s⁻¹. Find the resistance, in newtons, to the motion of the car. Calculate the power delivered by the engine when the car ascends the same inclination at the same steady speed, assuming that resistance to motion is unchanged. [Take g as 10 m s⁻².]

(L)

5 The frictional resistance to the motion of a car of mass 1000 kg is kv newtons, where v m s⁻¹ is its speed and k is constant. The car ascends a hill of inclination arcsin($\frac{1}{10}$) at a steady speed of 8 m s⁻¹, the power exerted by the engine being 9.76 kW. Prove that the numerical value of k is 30. Find the steady speed at which the car ascends the hill if the power exerted by the engine is 12.8 kW.
When the car is travelling at this speed, the power exerted by the engine is increased by 2 kW. Find the immediate acceleration of the car. (Take 9.8 m s⁻² as the acceleration due to gravity.)

(O & C)

6 A car of mass 1.2 tonnes is travelling up a slope of 1 in 150 at a constant speed of 10 m s⁻¹. If the frictional and air resistances are 100 newtons, calculate the power exerted by the engine. The car descends the same slope working at a rate of 2 kW. What will be its acceleration when its speed is 20 m s⁻¹ if the resistances are the same? If the engine is shut off when the speed of the car is 25 m s⁻¹ as it descends the slope how long will it be before the car comes to rest?

(S)

M9 Impulse and Momentum

Definitions, Relation between impulse and momentum, Conservation of momentum, Problem solving, Impulses in strings.

Definitions

Impulse is the time effect of a force. It is a **vector**. For a **constant force** F, acting for time t,

$$\text{impulse} = Ft.$$

For a **variable force** F, acting for time T,

$$\text{impulse} = \int_0^T F\, dt.$$

SI unit of impulse is the **newton second** (N s).

The **momentum** of a moving body is the product of its mass m and velocity v, i.e. momentum $= mv$. It is a **vector** whose direction is that of the velocity. SI unit of momentum is the **newton second** (N s).

ⓘ *A constant force acts on a particle of mass* 0.5 kg *changing its speed from* 3 m s⁻¹ *to* 7 m s⁻¹, *the force acting in the direction of motion. What is its impulse?*

Impulse $I = Ft = mat$ since $F = ma$
$v = u + at \Rightarrow at = 7 - 3 = 4$
So, impulse $I = 0.5 \times 4 = 2$ N s

ⓘ *Find the momentum of a particle of mass* 1.5 kg *moving in a straight line at* 5 m s⁻¹.

Momentum $= 1.5 \times 5 = 7.5$ N s

Relation between impulse and momentum

The **impulse** of a force, constant or variable, is equal to the **change of momentum** it produces. If a force F acts for a time t on a body of mass m, changing its velocity from u to v, then

$$\text{impulse} = mv - mu.$$

ⓘ *A golf ball of mass* 0.06 kg *resting on a tee is given a horizontal impulse of* 1.8 N s. *Calculate the velocity* v *with which it moves off.*

Using impulse $=$ change of momentum
$$1.8 = 0.06\, v - 0.06 \times 0 \Rightarrow v = 30 \text{ m s}^{-1}.$$

Conservation of momentum

The **principle of conservation of momentum** states that the total momentum of a system is constant in any direction provided no external force acts in that direction,

i.e. initial momentum $=$ final momentum.

In this context a system is usually two bodies.

ⓘ *A pile driver of mass* 2 tonnes, *moving with velocity* 7 m s⁻¹ *before impact, hits a stationary pile of mass* 0.5 tonne. *Find their common velocity after impact.*

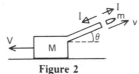

By conservation of momentum:
$$2000 \times 7 = 2000\, v + 500\, v$$
$$\Rightarrow \quad v = 5.6 \text{ m s}^{-1}.$$

Figure 1

Problem solving

Problems concerning impulse and momentum usually involve finding the impulse acting or the velocity or mass of a body in a system.

To find an impulse for such a system: write down the impulse equation for each body.

To find a velocity or mass for such a system: write down the equation of conservation of momentum.

ⓘ *A gun of mass* M, *whose barrel is at an angle of elevation* θ, *fires a shell of mass* m *and recoils horizontally with speed* V. *The shell travels at speed* v *relative to the barrel of the gun.*

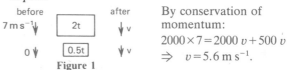

Figure 2   Velocity triangle for shell   Figure 3

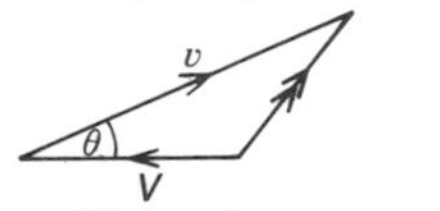

Velocity of shell, relative to the ground, as it leaves the barrel is the resultant of v and V.

For the gun $(\rightarrow)$: $-I\cos\theta = -MV$
For the shell $(\rightarrow)$: $I\cos\theta = m(v\cos\theta - V)$
For the shell $(\uparrow)$: $I\sin\theta = mv\sin\theta$
By conservation of momentum $(\rightarrow)$:
$$0 = m(v\cos\theta - V) - MV$$

Impulses in strings

When a string jerks taut, impulses, which are equal in magnitude but opposite in direction, act at the two ends. If two particles are attached by a string which jerks taut, then the two particles will experience the **equal and opposite impulses**.

Impulse problems for other connected particles may be solved in the same way if the string is considered to be straight and the particles move in a straight line

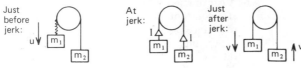

Figure 4

So this system is equivalent to that shown in ⓘ

ⓘ Consider this system involving two masses m_1 and m_2.

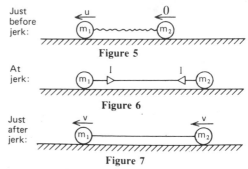

Figure 5

Figure 6

Figure 7

For mass m_1: $-I = m_1 v - m_1 u$
For mass m_2: $I = m_2 v - m_2 \times 0$
By conservation of momentum: $m_1 u = m_1 v + m_2 v.$

Impulse and Momentum
Worked example, Guided example and Exam questions

 A shell of mass 20 kg *is travelling horizontally at* 100 m s⁻¹ *when it suddenly explodes into three pieces A, B, C of masses* 12 kg, 6 kg *and* 2 kg *respectively. The diagram shows the direction of travel of the shell before the explosion and the directions of the three pieces A, B, C after the explosion.*

Before explosion

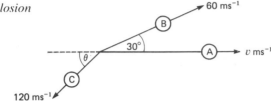

After explosion

Calculate
(a) the angle θ made by the direction of C with the backward horizontal direction,
(b) the speed of A.

Since no external impulse acts on the system, momentum is conserved in any chosen direction.
Using conservation of momentum at right angles to the original direction of travel, we have:

$$6 \times 60 \cos 60° - 2 \times 120 \sin \theta = 0$$
$$\Rightarrow \quad \sin \theta = \tfrac{3}{4}$$
$$\therefore \quad \theta = \sin^{-1}\left(\tfrac{3}{4}\right)$$

Using conservation of momentum parallel to the original direction of travel we have:

$$6 \times 60 \cos 30° + 12 \times v - 2 \times 120 \cos \theta = 20 \times 100$$
$$\therefore \quad v = 166\tfrac{2}{3} + 20 \cos \theta - 15\sqrt{3}$$

Since $\sin \theta = \tfrac{3}{4}$, $\cos \theta = \dfrac{\sqrt{7}}{4}$,

hence, $v = 166\tfrac{2}{3} + 5\sqrt{7} - 15\sqrt{3}$
i.e. $v \approx 154$ m s⁻¹.

 A pile driver of mass 3 tonnes *falls through a distance of* 5 m *onto a pile of mass* 1 tonne *without rebounding. If the pile is driven* 15 cm *into the ground find the average resistance of the ground and the time of penetration.*

Use conservation of momentum to find the common velocity of the pile and driver combination just after impact. Use constant acceleration formulae to find the value of the retardation over 15 cm. Write down the equation of motion for the pile and driver combination. (Remember that the accelerating force downwards will be $(4 \times 10^4 - R)$ newtons, where R newtons is the average resistance of the ground). Finally use constant acceleration formulae to find the time of penetration.

---

 1 A bullet of mass 50 g, moving horizontally, strikes a stationary target at 486 m/s and becomes embedded in it. The target is of mass 4 kg and is free to move. Calculate, ignoring the time taken by the bullet to become embedded in the target:
   (i) the speed at which the target and the embedded bullet move initially;
   (ii) the impulse imparted to the target by the bullet,
   (iii) the kinetic energy lost in the impact. *(A)*

2 A railway engine of mass 5300 kg, moving on horizontal rails at 0·4 m/s, strikes the buffers in a siding and is brought to rest from this speed in 0·2 s. Calculate:
   (a) the impulse, in N s, of the force exerted by the buffers on the engine in bringing the engine to rest;
   (b) the magnitude, in N, of this force, assuming it to be constant. *(L)*

3 Two particles A and B, of masses 3m and m respectively, are connected by a light inextensible string and are free to move on a smooth horizontal table. Initially, A is at rest and B has speed u in the direction AB. The first diagram shows the situation just before the string tightens. Find the impulse in the string at the instant when it tightens and the common speed of A and B afterwards.

Later, B is brought instantaneously to rest while A continues towards B. Immediately after the impact between the two particles, the speeds of A and B are x and y respectively, as indicated in the second diagram. In this impact, two-ninths of the kinetic energy of the system just before the impact is lost.

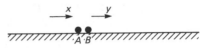

Prove that $3x + y = \tfrac{3}{4}u$ and that $3x^2 + y^2 = \tfrac{7}{48}u^2$. Hence determine the values of x and y in terms of u. *(C)*

4 When a body of mass 3m is moving in a straight line with speed u, it explodes. As a result it splits into two bodies A and B, of respective masses m and 2m, which move in the same straight line as before, but in opposite directions. Given that the extra energy created by the explosion is $3mu^2$, find the speeds of A and B. The body B then immediately strikes a body of mass M which is at rest and also free to move in the same straight line. If the impact is perfectly elastic, prove that B will subsequently strike A if $M > 6m$. *(OLE)*

5 A gun of mass 600 kg is free to move along a horizontal track and is connected by a light inelastic rope to an open truck containing sand whose total mass is 1490 kg. The truck is free to move along the same track as the gun. A shell of mass 10 kg is fired from the gun towards the truck and when it leaves the barrel has a horizontal velocity of 915 m s⁻¹ relative to the gun and parallel to the track. The shell lodges in the sand where it comes to relative rest before the rope tightens. Find:
   (i) the speeds of the gun and shell just after the shell leaves the barrel;
   (ii) the speed of the truck before the rope tightens when the shell is at relative rest inside the truck;
   (iii) the speed of the gun and truck just after the rope tightens;
   (iv) the loss in kinetic energy due to the rope tightening;
   (v) the magnitude of the impulsive tension in the rope. *(S)*

6 A particle of mass m, initially at rest, is subjected to an impulse I. In the ensuing motion the only force on the particle is a force directly opposing the motion of the particle and of magnitude k times the square of the velocity of the particle. Show that at time t after the impulse the

particle has velocity $v = \dfrac{mI}{Ikt + m^2}$. *(J)*

M10 Impact

Definitions, Direct impact of spheres, Direct impact with a wall, Oblique impact with a wall.

Definitions

If two bodies **rebound** on collision, then the impact is **elastic**.

If two bodies **coalesce** on collsion, then the impact is **inelastic**.

Newton's experimental law for an elastic impact of two bodies can be written as:

speed of separation after impact $= e \times$ speed of approach before impact

where e is the **coefficient of restitution**.

The value of e depends on the materials of the colliding bodies. For different materials $0 \leqslant e \leqslant 1$.

If $e = 0$, the impact is inelastic. If $e = 1$, the impact is perfectly elastic (not realisable in practice).

Direct impact of spheres

Direct impact takes place when **two similar spheres** moving along the same straight line collide.

To solve problems involving the direct impact of two smooth spheres of masses m_1 and m_2, moving with initial velocities u_1 and u_2 ($u_1 > u_2$) and final velocities v_1 and v_2 and coefficient of restitution e:

1. Draw a clear diagram.

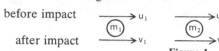

Figure 1

2. Use conservation of momentum in the chosen direction,

i.e. $\qquad m_1 u_1 + m_2 u_2 = m_1 v_1 + m_2 v_2$

3. Apply Newton's experimental law,

i.e. $\qquad v_2 - v_1 = e(u_1 - u_2)$

ⓘ *A sphere of mass 3 kg moving at 5 m s^{-1} strikes a similar sphere of mass 2 kg travelling in the opposite direction at 2 m s^{-1}. The coefficient of restitution is $\frac{2}{7}$. Find the velocities after impact.*

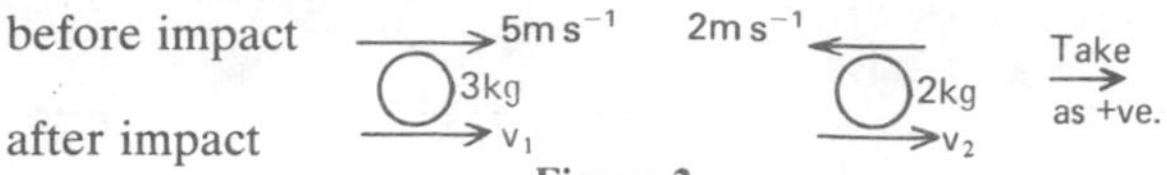

before impact → 5 m s^{-1} 3 kg   2 m s^{-1} 2 kg → Take as +ve.

after impact → v_1 → v_2

Figure 2

By the conservation of momentum:

$$(3 \times 5) + (2 \times -2) = 3v_1 + 2v_2$$

i.e. $\qquad 11 = 3v_1 + 2v_2 \qquad (1)$

By Newton's experimental law:

$$v_2 - v_1 = \tfrac{2}{7}(5 - (-2))$$

i.e. $\qquad v_2 - v_1 = 2 \qquad (2)$

Solving (1) and (2): $v_1 = 1.4 \text{ m s}^{-1}$, $v_2 = 3.4 \text{ m s}^{-1}$.

Direct impact with a wall

When a smooth sphere collides **directly with a smooth wall,** the sphere's direction of motion is perpendicular to the wall. The sphere receives an impulse perpendicular to the wall.

To solve problems involving the direct impact with a vertical wall of a smooth sphere of mass m moving with velocity u before impact and v after impact:

1. Draw a clear diagram.

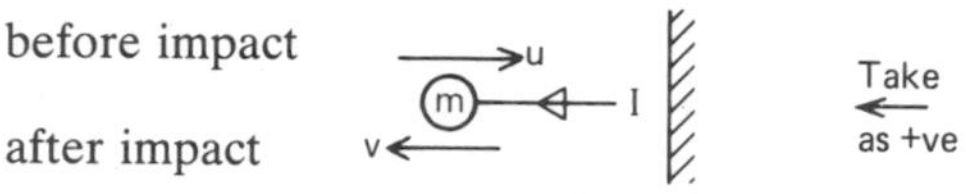

before impact → u

after impact v ← (m) ← I   Take ← as +ve

Figure 3

2. Apply Newton's experimental law,

i.e. $\qquad v = eu$

3. Use impulse = change in momentum if needed,

i.e. $I = mv - (-mu)$

ⓘ *A ball of mass 2 kg travelling along a horizontal floor at 5 m s^{-1} collides directly with a vertical wall. The coefficient of restitution is 0.3. Calculate the speed of the rebound and the impulse given to the ball in the collision.*

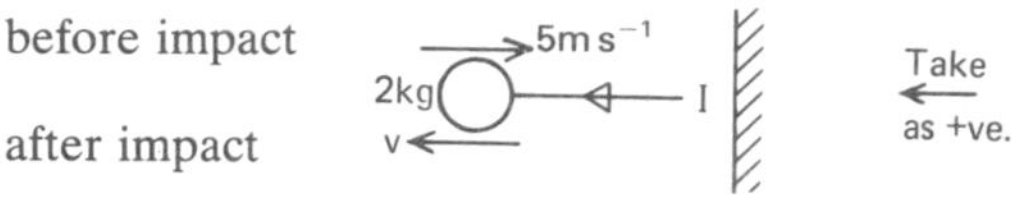

before impact → 5 m s^{-1} 2 kg ← I   Take ← as +ve.

after impact v ←

Figure 4

By Newton's experimental law:

$$v = 0.3 \times 5$$
$$= 1.5 \text{ m s}^{-1} \quad \text{the rebound speed.}$$

Using Impulse = change in momentum:

$$I = (2 \times 1.5) - (2 \times -5)$$
$$= 13 \text{ N s}$$

Oblique impact with a wall

When a smooth sphere collides **obliquely with a smooth wall,** the sphere's direction of motion is at an angle ($\neq 90°$) to the wall. The sphere receives an impulse perpendicular to the wall. The component of velocity parallel to the wall is unchanged since both surfaces are smooth.

To solve problems in which a smooth sphere mass m strikes a wall at an angle α with velocity u and rebounds at an angle β with velocity v:

1. Draw a clear diagram.

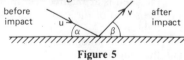

Figure 5

2. Equate components of velocity parallel to the wall,

i.e. $\qquad u \cos \alpha = v \cos \beta$

3. Use Newton's experimental law, perpendicular to the wall,

i.e. $\qquad v \sin \beta = eu \sin \alpha$

4. Use Impulse = change of momentum, perpendicular to the wall if needed,

i.e. $\qquad I = mv \sin \beta - (-mu \sin \alpha)$

ⓘ *A smooth sphere travelling along the ground at 3 m s^{-1} strikes a smooth wall at 60° and rebounds at 45°. Calculate the velocity after impact and the value of the coefficient of restitution.*

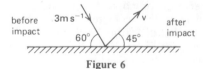

Figure 6

Equate components of velocity parallel to the wall:

$$3 \cos 60° = v \cos 45°$$
$$\therefore v = \frac{3\sqrt{2}}{2} \text{ m s}^{-1}$$

By Newton's experimental law, perpendicular to the wall

$$v \sin 45° = e \times 3 \sin 60°$$
$$\therefore e = \frac{1}{\sqrt{3}}$$

Impact
Worked example, Guided example and Exam questions

WE *Three smooth spheres A, B and C of masses 2m, 7m and 14m respectively and of equal size, are at rest on a smooth horizontal floor. The centres of the spheres lie in a straight line. The co-efficient of restitution between each pair of spheres is ½. Sphere A is projected towards B with speed u. Show that after two impacts B is at rest and A and C are each moving with equal speeds in opposite directions. Calculate the total kinetic energy of the spheres after the two impacts.*

(a) Diagram showing the first impact between A and B:

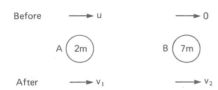

Before $\longrightarrow u$ $\longrightarrow 0$

A (2m) B (7m)

After $\longrightarrow v_1$ $\longrightarrow v_2$

(b) Conservation of momentum (take to the right as positive):
$$(2m \times u) + (7m \times 0) = 2m \times v_1 + 7m \times v_2$$
i.e. $\qquad 2u = 2v_1 + 7v_2$ $\qquad$ [1]
(c) Newton's experimental law:
$$v_2 - v_1 = \tfrac{1}{2}u$$ $\qquad$ [2]
[1] and [2] give $v_1 = -\tfrac{1}{6}u$ and $v_2 = \tfrac{1}{3}u$.

Sphere B now goes on to hit sphere C.

Before $\longrightarrow \tfrac{1}{3}u$ $\longrightarrow 0$

B (7m) C (14m)

After $\longrightarrow v_3$ $\longrightarrow v_4$

Conservation of momentum:
$$(7m \times \tfrac{1}{3}u) + (14m \times 0) = (7m \times v_3) + (14m \times v_4)$$
i.e. $\qquad u = 3v_3 + 6v_4$ $\qquad$ [3]
Newton's experimental law:
$$v_4 - v_3 = \tfrac{1}{2}(\tfrac{1}{3}u)$$
i.e. $6v_4 - 6v_3 = u$ $\qquad$ [4]

[3] and [4] give: $v_3 = 0$ and $v_4 = \tfrac{1}{6}u$.
So A and C are now each moving with speed $\tfrac{1}{6}u$ in opposite directions and B is at rest.
Total K.E. after two impacts is
$$\tfrac{1}{2}.2m(\tfrac{1}{6}u)^2 + \tfrac{1}{2}.(14m).(\tfrac{1}{6}u)^2 = \tfrac{2}{9}mu^2.$$

GE *A ball is thrown vertically upwards from the floor with velocity V. It rebounds from the ceiling, which is a height h above the floor, and then rebounds from the floor. After this second rebound, it just reaches the ceiling again.*
If the coefficient of restitution between the ball and ceiling is e, and between the ball and floor is f, prove that
$$V^2 = \frac{2gh(1 - f^2 + e^2f^2)}{e^2f^2}.$$

First treat the ball as a particle moving freely under gravity and calculate its velocity just before it hits the ceiling. Consider impact with ceiling knowing the initial velocity (just found) and find its velocity just as it comes off the ceiling. Now find the velocity of the ball just before it hits the floor. Use impact again to find the new upward velocity just as it begins to rise. The final velocity, since the ball just reaches the ceiling for a second time, is zero. Using the results you have obtained, derive the required equation.

EX 1 A railway truck A of mass 4000 kg travelling at 2 m/s collides with another truck B of mass 6000 kg travelling at 1 m/s in the same direction. The speed of truck A after the collision is 1·25 m/s in the same direction. Calculate the speed of truck B after the collision. A and B are now brought to rest by frictional forces which are in each case 50 N per 1000 kg mass. Calculate:
(i) for how long A and B are each in motion after the collision;
(ii) the final distance between them.
$\qquad\qquad$ *(C)

2 Two identical smooth spheres, S and T, moving in opposite directions with speeds u, 3u respectively, collide directly. The sphere T is reduced to rest. Find the coefficient of restitution between the spheres.
$\qquad\qquad$ (L)

3 A particle moving along a smooth horizontal floor hits a smooth vertical wall and rebounds in a direction at right angles to its initial direction of motion. The coefficient of restitution is e. Find, in terms of e, the tangent of the angle between the initial direction of motion and the wall. Prove that the kinetic energy after the rebound is e times the initial kinetic energy.
$\qquad\qquad$ (J)

4 (i) A sphere of mass m moving along a smooth horizontal table with speed V collides directly with a stationary sphere of the same radius and of mass 2m. Obtain expressions, in terms of V and the coefficient of restitution e, for the speeds of the two spheres after impact. Half of the kinetic energy is lost in the impact. Find the value of e.
(ii) A particle of mass m moving in a straight line with speed u receives an impulse of magnitude I in the direction of its motion. Show that the increase in kinetic energy is given by $I(I + 2mu)/(2m)$.
$\qquad\qquad$ (L)

5 Three beads A, B and C, of masses 3m, 2m and m respectively, are threaded in that order on a smooth horizontal straight wire. Initially, A, B and C are separated and at rest, and A is then projected towards B with speed 10V. The coefficient of restitution between A and B is ½. Show that the speed of B after the collision is 9V. Find the velocity of A after the collision and find also the kinetic energy lost in the collision. After A and B have collided, C is projected towards B with speed 6V. Given that the collision between B and C is perfectly elastic (e = 1), find the velocities of B and C after this collision.
$\qquad\qquad$ (C)

6 Two particles, A of mass 2m and B of mass m, moving on a smooth horizontal table in opposite directions with speeds 5u and 3u respectively, collide directly. Find their velocities after the collision in terms of u and the coefficient of restitution e. Show that the magnitude of the impulse exerted by B on A is $\dfrac{16}{3}mu(1+e)$. Find the value of e for which the speed of B after the collision is 3u. Moving at this speed B subsequently collides with a stationary particle C of mass km, and thereafter remains attached to C. Find the velocity of the combined particle and find the range of values of k for which a third collision will occur.
$\qquad\qquad$ (J)

141

M11 Projectiles
Definition, Analysis of motion, Standard results.

Definition

A **projectile** is a particle which is given an initial velocity and then moves freely under gravity. It is assumed that gravity is the only force acting on the particle, i.e. air resistance is negligible.
If its **initial velocity** is **vertical**, then the particle will move in a **straight line** under gravity.
If its **initial velocity** is **not vertical**, the particle will move in a **curve** (a parabola).

Analysis of motion

Consider a particle projected with initial velocity u at an angle α to the horizontal and has velocity v at time t.

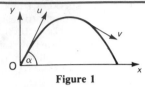

Figure 1

Its flight can be analysed by considering **horizontal** and **vertical motion separately** and using the **equations for uniform acceleration** in a straight line,

i.e. $v = u + at$
$s = ut + \frac{1}{2}at^2$
$v^2 = u^2 + 2as$

	horizontal motion	**vertical** motion
u	$u_x = u \cos \alpha$	$u_y = u \sin \alpha$
a	$\ddot{x} = 0$	$\ddot{y} = -g$
v	$v_x = u \cos \alpha$	$v_y = u \sin \alpha - gt$
s	$x = (u \cos \alpha)t$	$y = (u \sin \alpha)t - \frac{1}{2}gt^2$

ℹ️ *A particle is projected from ground level with speed 30 m s^{-1} at an angle of 30° to the horizontal. Calculate: (a) the time of flight, (b) the range.*

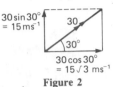

Figure 2

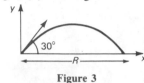

Figure 3

(a) Consider vertical motion:
When the particle reaches the ground $s = 0$.
$u = 15$, $v = ?$, $a = -10$, $s = 0$, $t = ?$

Using $s = ut + \frac{1}{2}at^2$
$0 = 15t + \frac{1}{2}(-10)t^2$

i.e. $5t(3 - t) = 0$
$\Rightarrow t = 0$ or 3 s
$t = 0$ is the starting time, $t = 3$ s is time of flight.

(b) The horizontal velocity $15\sqrt{3}$ m s^{-1} is constant. Since the particle travels for 3 s at this velocity, range $R = 15\sqrt{3} \times 3 = 45\sqrt{3}$ m.

Standard results

Time of flight
i.e. the time taken for the projectile to travel along its path from O to A.
Consider vertical motion:

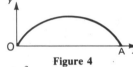

Figure 4

At any time t, $y = (u \sin \alpha)t - \frac{1}{2}gt^2$
At A, $y = 0 \therefore 0 = (u \sin \alpha)t - \frac{1}{2}gt^2$
$\Rightarrow t = 0$ (initial position)
or $t = \dfrac{2u \sin \alpha}{g}$ (time of flight)

Range
i.e. the horizontal distance OA travelled by the projectile.
Consider horizontal motion:

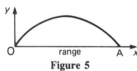

Figure 5

At any time t, $x = (u \cos \alpha)t$

When $t = \dfrac{2u \sin \alpha}{g}$, then $x = (u \cos \alpha)\dfrac{2u \sin \alpha}{g}$

i.e. $x = \dfrac{u^2 \sin 2\alpha}{g}$ (the range)

This is a maximum when $\sin 2\alpha = 1$, i.e. $\alpha = \dfrac{\pi}{4}$ or 45°.

So the maximum range is $\dfrac{u^2}{g}$.

Angle of projection for a given range

Let the range be $\dfrac{ku^2}{g}$.

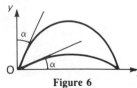

Figure 6

i.e. $\dfrac{u^2 \sin 2\alpha}{g} = \dfrac{ku^2}{g}$

$\Rightarrow \sin 2\alpha = k$
If $k = \sin \theta$, then $2\alpha = \theta$ or $\pi - \theta$,
i.e. $\alpha = \frac{1}{2}\theta$ or $\frac{1}{2}(\pi - \theta)$
So there are two possible angles of projection.

Greatest height
The projectile reaches its greatest height when the vertical velocity is zero.
Consider vertical motion:
using $v^2 = u^2 + 2as$

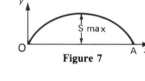

Figure 7

$0 = u^2 \sin^2 \alpha - 2gs$
$\Rightarrow s_{max} = \dfrac{u^2 \sin^2 \alpha}{2g}$ (greatest height)

Direction and velocity at any time
At any time the projectile is always moving along a tangent to its path.
Horizontal velocity: $u \cos \alpha$
Vertical velocity: $u \sin \alpha - gt$

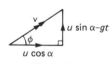

Figure 8

From the diagram: $v^2 = (u \cos \alpha)^2 + (u \sin \alpha - gt)^2$
$\tan \phi = \dfrac{(u \sin \alpha - gt)}{(u \cos \alpha)}$

Equation of the path of the projectile
Take x and y axes through the point of projection O.
If t is the time for the projectile to travel from O to $P(x, y)$, then:

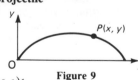

Figure 9

Horizontal distance: $x = (u \cos \alpha)t$
Vertical distance: $y = (u \sin \alpha)t - \frac{1}{2}gt^2$
Eliminating t between these equations gives:

$$y = x \tan \alpha - \dfrac{gx^2}{2u^2}\sec^2 \alpha$$

the equation of the path or trajectory of the projectile.

Projectiles
Worked example and Exam questions

A stone is thrown from a point O which is at the top of a cliff 50 m above a horizontal beach. The speed with which the stone is thrown is 40 m s^{-1} and it hits the beach at a point R which is at a horizontal distance of 200 m from O. If the stone was thrown at an angle of elevation α, show that one of the possible values of $\tan \alpha$ is $\frac{3}{5}$ and find the other possible value.

Given that $\tan \alpha = \frac{3}{5}$, calculate

(i) the time the stone was in the air,
(ii) the angle at which the stone hits the beach at R.

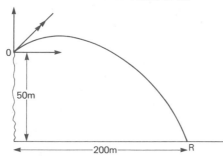

Consider the horizontal motion of the stone.
The horizontal velocity $40 \cos \alpha$ m s^{-1} is constant,
so, $40 \cos \alpha \times T = 200$ (T is the time of flight)
$\Rightarrow \qquad T = 5 \sec \alpha.$ [1]
Consider the vertical motion (take up as positive).
$s = -50, u = 40 \sin \alpha, a = -10, t = T$
Using $s = ut + \frac{1}{2}at^2$ gives
$\qquad -50 = 40 (\sin \alpha)T + \frac{1}{2}(-10)T^2,$
and substituting for T from [1] gives
$\qquad -50 = 200 \tan \alpha - 125 \sec^2 \alpha.$
So, $-2 = 8 \tan \alpha - 5(1 + \tan^2 \alpha)$
i.e. $5 \tan^2 \alpha - 8 \tan \alpha + 3 = 0$
i.e. $(5 \tan \alpha - 3)(\tan \alpha - 1) = 0$
$\Rightarrow \tan \alpha = \frac{3}{5}$ or 1.

(i) If $\tan \alpha = \frac{3}{5}$, $\sin \alpha = \frac{3}{\sqrt{34}}$ and $\cos \alpha = \frac{5}{\sqrt{34}}$.

Using [1],
$\qquad T = 5 \sec \alpha$
i.e. $T = 5 \cdot \dfrac{\sqrt{34}}{5},$

So $\qquad T = \sqrt{34}$ s — the time of flight.

(ii) To find the angle the stone hits the beach at R, we need to find the vertical component of velocity at R.

Consider the vertical motion (take up as positive).
$u = 40 \sin \alpha = \dfrac{60\sqrt{34}}{17}, v = ?, a = -10, t = T = \sqrt{34}$

Using $v = u + at$ gives,
$\qquad v = \dfrac{60\sqrt{34}}{17} + (-10)\sqrt{34}$
$\qquad = \dfrac{-110}{17}\sqrt{34}$ m s^{-1}.

Let θ be the angle to the horizontal at which the stone hits the beach then the vector triangle is

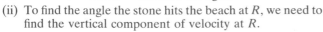

$\tan \theta = \dfrac{\frac{110}{17}\sqrt{34}}{\frac{100}{17}\sqrt{34}} = \dfrac{110}{100} = \dfrac{11}{10}$

i.e. the stone hits the beach at an angle $\tan^{-1}\left(\dfrac{11}{10}\right)$ to the horizontal.

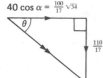

1 A body is projected upwards from a point on a horizontal plane, with a velocity of 40 m/s, at an angle of 60° to the horizontal. The point of projection is at a horizontal distance of 40 m from the foot of a vertical wall which is 10 m high, and the motion takes place in a plane perpendicular to the wall. Calculate:
  (i) the vertical height by which the body clears the wall;
  (ii) the greatest height above the horizontal plane reached by the body;
  (iii) the time of flight of the body;
  (iv) the horizontal distance beyond the wall at which the body strikes the plane.
  (A)

2 A ball was thrown from a balcony above a horizontal lawn. The velocity of projection was 10 m/s at an angle of elevation α, where $\tan \alpha = \frac{3}{4}$. The ball moved freely under gravity and took 3 s to reach the lawn from the instant when it was thrown. Calculate:
  (a) the vertical height above the lawn from which the ball was thrown;
  (b) the horizontal distance between the point of projection and the point A at which the ball hit the lawn;
  (c) the angle, to the nearest degree, between the direction of the velocity of the ball and the horizontal at the instant when the ball reached A.
  (L)

3 A batsman strikes a ball at a height of 1.5 m above the ground, giving it an initial speed of 29 m s^{-1} at an angle of 30° to the horizontal. What is the minimum distance of the boundary from the batsman if he scores a 'six' (i.e. the ball passes over the boundary line without first bouncing)? A fielder, who is capable of catching a ball at a height of 2.75 m or below, goes to the boundary line. What speed must the batsman give to the ball if he is to hit it at the same height and elevation as before and ensure that he will score a six and not be caught by the fielder?
  (S)

4 The muzzle speed of a gun is V and it is desired to hit a small target at a horizontal distance a away and at a height b above the gun. Show that this is impossible if $V^2(V^2 - 2gb) < g^2a^2$, but that, if $V^2(V^2 - 2gb) > g^2a^2$, there are two possible elevations for the gun. Show that, if $V^2 = 2ga$ and $b = \frac{3}{4}a$, there is only one possible elevation, and find the time taken to hit the target.
  (OLE)

5 A particle is projected from a point O with speed 5 m s^{-1} at an angle of elevation θ, where $\theta \neq \pi/2$, and moves freely under gravity. Taking the acceleration due to gravity to be 10 m s^{-2}, show that the equation of the path of the projectile referred to horizontal and upward vertical axes

Ox, Oy is $y = x \tan \theta - \dfrac{x^2}{5}(1 + \tan^2 \theta).$

By considering this equation as a quadratic equation in $\tan \theta$, show that there are two distinct values of θ for which the projectile passes through a given point (X, Y), where $X > 0$, provided that $20Y < 25 - 4X^2$.
Given that the two values of θ are α and β and that (X, Y) is a point whose co-ordinates satisfy this inequality, write down expressions for $\tan \alpha + \tan \beta$ and $\tan \alpha \tan \beta$ in terms of X and Y, and deduce an expression for $\tan (\alpha + \beta)$. If $Y = X$, show that $\alpha + \beta = 3\pi/4$.
  (J)

M12 Motion in a Horizontal Circle
Definitions, Problem solving, Common situations.

Definitions

Consider a particle P of mass m moving in a **horizontal circle**, centre O, radius r, with **constant speed** v.

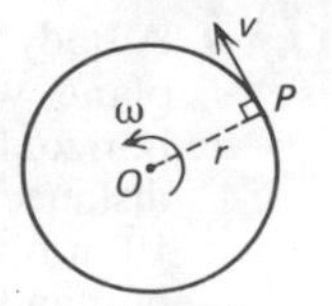

Figure 1

The **linear velocity** v of P is directed along the tangent to the circle at P.

The constant **angular velocity** ω of P is $\omega = \dfrac{v}{r}$.

ω is measured in **radians per second** (rad s^{-1}). There is no acceleration along the tangent since the particle moves with constant speed around the circle. The **acceleration** a of P is in the direction $\overrightarrow{PO}$, i.e. **towards the centre of the circle**, and $a = \dfrac{v^2}{r}$ or $r\omega^2$.

By Newton's 2nd law, this acceleration must be produced by a **force** which is also directed **towards the centre of the circle**.
So the **equation of motion** for the particle is:

$$\text{force} = \frac{mv^2}{r} \text{ or } mr\omega^2.$$

This force may be the tension in a string, a frictional force, a gravitational force, etc.

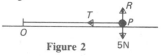

Find the velocity and acceleration of a particle moving in a horizontal circle, radius 20 cm, at a constant angular velocity of 30 revolutions per minute.

Angular velocity = 30 revolutions per minute

$$= 30 \times \frac{2\pi}{60} \text{ rad. s}^{-1} = \pi \text{ rad. s}^{-1}$$

Velocity $v = r\omega = 0.2 \times \pi \text{ m s}^{-1} \approx 0.628 \text{ m s}^{-1}$

Acceleration $a = r\omega^2 = 0.2 \times \pi^2 \text{ m s}^{-2} \approx 1.97 \text{ m s}^{-2}$

A particle of mass 0.5 kg is attached by a light inextensible string, length 2 m, to a fixed point O on the top of a smooth horizontal table. The particle is made to rotate in a horizontal circle with the string taut at a constant speed of 8 m s^{-1}. Calculate the tension in the string.

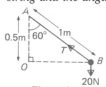

Figure 2

Equation of motion along PO: $T = 0.5 \times \dfrac{8^2}{2} = 16$ N.

Problem solving

When solving problems in which a particle P describes a horizontal circle, centre O, with constant speed or constant angular velocity:
1. Draw a clear force diagram.
2. Resolve vertically, (since the particle does not move up or down, forces must balance in this direction).
3. Write down the equation of motion along the radius $\overrightarrow{PO}$.

A conical pendulum consists of a particle of mass 2 kg attached to one end B of a light inextensible string AB of length 1 m. A is a fixed point. The particle describes a horizontal circle whose centre O is 0.5 m vertically below A. Calculate the tension in the string and the angular velocity of the particle.

Since $OA = 0.5$ m and $AB = 1$ m,

$O\hat{A}B = 60°$ and $OB = \dfrac{\sqrt{3}}{2}$ m.

Let ω be angular velocity.

Figure 3

Resolve ($\uparrow$): $T \cos 60° = 20 \Rightarrow T = 40$ N   (1)

Equation of motion along BO:

$$T \sin 60° = 2 \times \frac{\sqrt{3}}{2} \times \omega^2 \qquad (2)$$

From (1) and (2): $\omega^2 = 20 \Rightarrow \omega = 2\sqrt{5}$ rad. s^{-1}.

Common situations

The following illustrate some other common situations which arise in problems.
1. Particle P moving inside a **hollow cone**, with friction

(a) P about to move **up** cone ($\omega - a$ maximum)

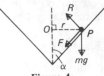

Figure 4

Resolve ($\uparrow$):
$$R \sin \alpha = mg + F \cos \alpha$$

Equation of motion along $\overrightarrow{PO}$:
$$R \cos \alpha + F \sin \alpha = \frac{mv^2}{r}$$

(b) P about to move **down** cone ($\omega - a$ minimum)

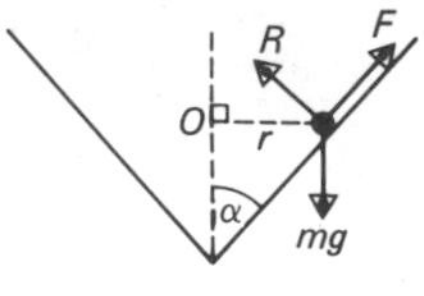

Figure 6

Resolve ($\uparrow$):
$$R \sin \alpha + F \cos \alpha = mg$$

Equation of motion along $\overrightarrow{PO}$:
$$R \cos \alpha - F \sin \alpha = \frac{mv^2}{r}$$

2. Car rounding a bend on a **banked track**

(a) car cornering at **maximum speed**

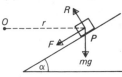

Figure 5

resolve ($\uparrow$):
$$R \cos \alpha = mg + F \sin \alpha$$

Equation of motion along $\overrightarrow{PO}$:
$$R \sin \alpha + F \cos \alpha = \frac{mv^2}{r}$$

(b) car cornering at **minimum speed**

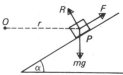

Figure 7

Resolve ($\uparrow$):
$$R \cos \alpha + F \sin \alpha = mg$$

Equation of motion along $\overrightarrow{PO}$:
$$R \sin \alpha - F \cos \alpha = \frac{mv^2}{r}$$

Motion in a Horizontal Circle
Worked example, Guided example and Exam questions

WE *Two rigid light rods AB, BC each of length $\frac{1}{2}$ m are smoothly* **EX**
jointed at B and the rod AB is smoothly jointed at A to a fixed
smooth vertical rod. The joint at B has a particle of mass 2 kg
attached. A small ring, of mass 1 kg is smoothly jointed to BC at
C and can slide on the vertical rod below A. The ring rests on a
smooth horizontal ledge fixed to the vertical rod at a distance
$\frac{\sqrt{3}}{2}$ *m below A. The system rotates about the vertical rod with*

constant angular velocity 6 *radians per second.*
Calculate
(a) the forces in the rods AB and BC,
(b) the force exerted by the ledge on the ring.

Notice that the angles at A and C are 30°.
Force diagram for the system.

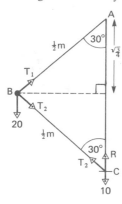

Let T_1 and T_2 be the forces in
the rods AB and BC
respectively.
Let R be the force exerted on
the ring by the ledge.
Resolving vertically for C:
$T_2 \cos 30° + R = 10$ [1]
Resolving vertically for B:
$T_1 \cos 30° = T_2 \cos 30° + 20$ [2]
Equation of motion for B:
$T_1 \cos 60° + T_2 \cos 60°$
       $= 2 \times \frac{1}{4} \times 6^2$ [3]

Solving [2] and [3] gives

$T_1 = 18 + \dfrac{20\sqrt{3}}{3}$ N and $T_2 = 18 - \dfrac{20\sqrt{3}}{3}$ N.

Substituting for T_2 into [1] gives
$R = (20 - 9\sqrt{3})$ N.

GE *A body of mass M moves in a circle of radius R under a force*
kM which is directed towards the centre, k being constant.
Show that the velocity of the body is of constant magnitude and
that T, the time for a revolution, is given by

$$T = 2\pi \sqrt{\left(\frac{R}{k}\right)}.$$

The gravitational attraction of the earth on a satellite of mass M
in a circular orbit of radius R about the centre of the earth is
gMr^2/R^2, *where r is the radius of the earth. If its time of*
revolution is T, show that

$$R^3 = g\left(\frac{rT}{2\pi}\right)^2.$$

A satellite's orbit keeps it always vertically above a fixed point on
the equator. Given that the radius of the earth is 6.378×10^6 m
and that the earth takes 8.616×10^4 s *to turn on its axis, show that*
the height of the satellite above the surface of the earth is
approximately 3.58×10^7 m.
(Take the acceleration due to gravity to be 9.8 m/s².)

Write down the equation of motion using $\dfrac{v^2}{R}$ for the

acceleration. Hence show v is constant. Use $v = R\omega$ to find ω.

$T = \dfrac{2\pi}{\omega}$ gives required result for T. For the second part, use

$k = \dfrac{gr^2}{R^2}$ in the expression obtained for T. Hence get the

required expression for R^3. The final part of the answer is
obtained by using the given values for r and T to find R. Height
of the satellite above the earth's surface is $R - r$.

1 In a conical pendulum the inelastic string is of length $1\frac{1}{2}$m
and a particle of mass M kg is attached to the end of the
string. When the string makes an angle of 60° with the
vertical the tension in the string is 10 N. Calculate the value
of M. The string will break if the tension in it exceeds 48 N.
Calculate the greatest number of revolutions per minute
the particle can attain.   *(A)*

2 (a) A small smooth ring P of mass m is threaded on to a
light inextensible string of length $2a$, whose ends are tied to
fixed points A and B where A is distant a vertically above B.
Show that it is not possible for the particle to move in a
horizontal circle at constant speed with AP and BP equally
inclined to the vertical, but that it can move in a horizontal
circle with BP horizontal and find its speed in this case.

(b) A smooth hollow right circular cone with vertex
downwards is rotating with angular velocity ω about its axis
which is vertical. A particle is at relative rest on the inside
of the cone at a vertical height h above the vertex. Prove
that $\omega = \sqrt{(g/h)} \cot \alpha$ where α is the semi-vertical angle of
the cone.   *(S)*

3 Prove that the acceleration of a point moving in a fixed
circle of radius r with constant angular speed ω is directed
towards the centre of the circle and has magnitude $\omega^2 r$.

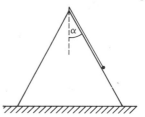

One end of a light inextensible string of length l is attached
to the vertex of a smooth cone of semi-vertical angle α. The
cone is fixed to the ground and its axis is vertical. The other
end of the string is attached to a particle of mass m which
can rotate in a horizontal circle in contact with the outer
surface of the cone, as shown in the diagram. Given that the
angular speed of the particle is ω, find an expression for the
tension in the string. Find an expression for the greatest
value of ω for which the motion as described can occur.
   (C)

4 A light inextensible string of length $5a$ has one end fixed at a
point A and the other end fixed at a point B which is
vertically below A and at a distance $4a$ from it. A particle P
of mass m is fastened to the midpoint of the string and
moves with speed u, and with the parts AP and BP of the
string both taut, in a horizontal circular path whose centre
is the midpoint of AB. Find, in terms of m, u, a and g, the
tensions in the two parts of the string, and show that the
motion described can take place only if $8u^2 \geqslant 9ga$.
   (J)

5 An artificial satellite of mass m moves under the action of a
gravitational force which is directed towards the centre, O,
of the earth and is of magnitude F. The orbit of the satellite
is a circle of radius a and centre O. Obtain an expression for
T, the period of the satellite, in terms of m, a and F.
Show that, if the gravitational force acting on a body of
mass m at a distance r from O is $m\mu/r^2$, where μ is a
constant, then $T^2\mu = 4\pi^2 a^3$.
Assuming that the radius of the earth is 6400 km and that
the acceleration due to gravity at the surface of the earth is
10 m s⁻², show that $\mu = (6.4)^2 10^{13}$ m³ s⁻².
Hence, or otherwise, find the period of revolution, in hours
to 2 decimal places, of the satellite when it travels in a
circular orbit 600 km above the surface of the earth.
   (L)

M13 Motion in a Vertical Circle
Definitions, Types of motion, Problem solving, Simple pendulum.

Definitions

When a particle P, of mass m, is moving in a **vertical circle**, centre O, radius r, its **speed** v is **variable**.
The particle P has an **acceleration** a in the direction $\overrightarrow{PO}$, i.e. **towards the centre of the circle**, given by $a = \dfrac{v^2}{r}$ or $r\omega^2$. So this **acceleration** is **variable** too.

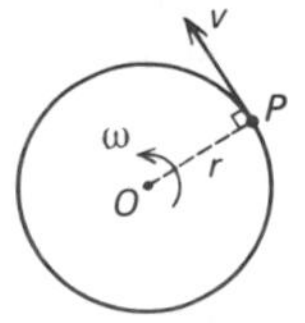

Figure 1

(Note: The tangential acceleration need not be considered at this level.) By Newton's 2nd law, the acceleration towards O must be produced by a **force** which is also directed **towards O**.

So the **equation of motion** for the particle along the radius $\overrightarrow{PO}$ is: force $= \dfrac{mv^2}{r}$ or $mr\omega^2$.

This variable force will be the resultant of the weight force mg and at least one other force.

Types of motion

The **two main types** of motion in a vertical circle for a particle with initial speed u are described below.

1. The particle **cannot leave the circular path**, e.g. a bead threaded on a vertical wire.

The particle can do one of these three things.

(i) **Complete the circle** if $v > 0$ at top

(ii) Come to **rest** at top if $v = 0$ at top

(iii) **Oscillate** if $v = 0$ for $0 < \theta < \pi$

  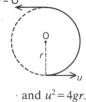

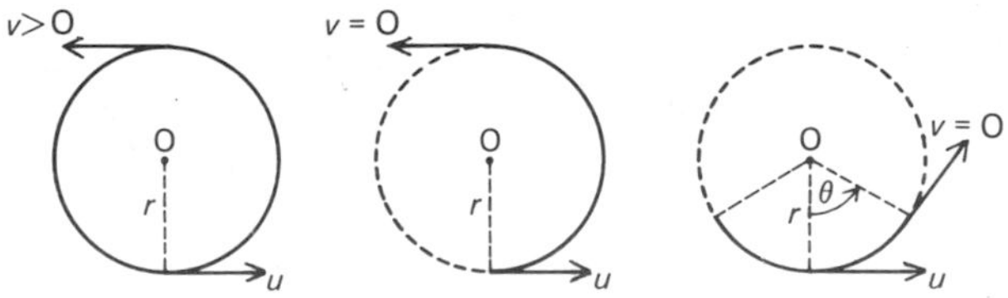

and $u^2 > 4gr$. and $u^2 = 4gr$. and $u^2 < 4gr$.

Figure 2

2. The particle **can leave the circular path** and become a projectile, e.g. a particle attached to a string.
The particle can do one of these three things.
(T is the tension in the string or a normal reaction)

(i) **Complete the circle** if $T \geq 0$ for all values of θ

(ii) Become a **projectile** if $T = 0$ for $\pi/2 < \theta \leq \pi$

(iii) **Oscillate** if $v = 0$ for $\theta \leq \pi/2$

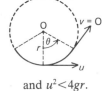

and $u^2 \geq 5gr$. and $2gr < u^2 < 5gr$. and $u^2 \leq gr$.

Figure 3

Problem solving

When solving problems in which a particle P describes a vertical circle, centre O:
1. Draw a clear force diagram.
2. Use conservation of mechanical energy, i.e. Initial (P.E. + K.E.) = (P.E. + K.E.) at any point.
3. Write down the equation of motion for the particle along the radius $\overrightarrow{PO}$.

Note: The given conditions of the problem will indicate whether the particle completes a circle, oscillates, becomes a projectile, etc. (see 'Types of motion' above).

ℹ️ *A particle of mass m is suspended from a fixed point O by a light inextensible string of length l. When the particle is hanging freely in equilibrium it is given a horizontal speed of $\sqrt{3gl}$. Find the tension T in the string when the angle between the string and the downward vertical is 60°.*

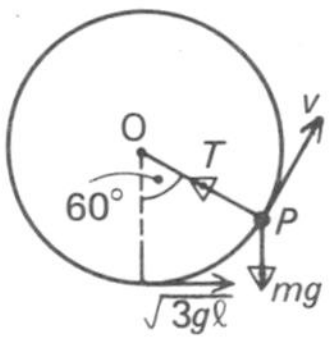

Figure 4

By conservation of M.E.:
$$\tfrac{1}{2}m(\sqrt{3gl})^2 = \tfrac{1}{2}mv^2 + mgl(1 - \cos 60°)$$

Equation of motion along $\overrightarrow{PO}$:
$$T - mg\cos 60° = \frac{mv^2}{l}$$

Eliminating v gives $T = \tfrac{5}{2}mg$.

Simple pendulum

A **simple pendulum** is a special case of a particle making **small oscillations** in a vertical circle.
When the pendulum has swung through an angle θ from the downward vertical, $v = l\dot{\theta}$.

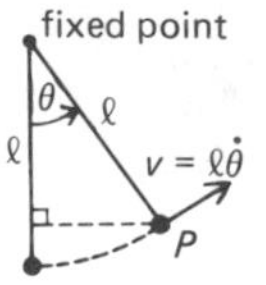

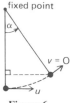

Figure 5

By conservation of M.E. at P:
$$mg(l - l\cos\theta) + \tfrac{1}{2}m(l\dot{\theta})^2 = \text{constant}$$
Differentiating with respect to time gives:
$$(mgl\sin\theta)\dot{\theta} + ml^2\dot{\theta}\ddot{\theta} = 0$$
i.e. $\ddot{\theta} = -\dfrac{g}{l}\sin\theta$

Since θ is small, $\sin\theta \approx \theta$, so approximately
$$\ddot{\theta} = -\frac{g}{l}\theta$$

Compare this with the basic S.H.M. equation $(\ddot{x} = -\omega^2 x)$.

So the motion is **angular S.H.M.** with period $2\pi\sqrt{\dfrac{l}{g}}$.

ℹ️ *A simple pendulum consists of a particle of mass m making small oscillations on the end of a light inextensible string of length l attached to a fixed point. When hanging in equilibrium, the particle is given a small horizontal speed u. Calculate α, the maximum angular displacement.*

Figure 6

By conservation of M.E.:
$$\tfrac{1}{2}mu^2 = mg(l - l\cos\alpha)$$
$$\Rightarrow \cos\alpha = 1 - \frac{u^2}{2gl}$$

For small u, α will be small and $\cos\alpha \approx 1 - \tfrac{1}{2}\alpha^2$

So $1 - \tfrac{1}{2}\alpha^2 \approx 1 - \dfrac{u^2}{2gl}$

$$\Rightarrow \alpha \approx \frac{u}{\sqrt{gl}}.$$

Motion in a Vertical Circle
Worked example, Guided example and Exam questions

A particle of mass m is suspended from a fixed point O by a light inextensible string of length l. The particle is hanging freely in equilibrium when it is given a horizontal speed of $\sqrt{(3gl)}$. Find the height of the particle above its equilibrium position when the string becomes slack.

First draw a diagram showing the forces on the particle P when OP makes an angle θ with the downward vertical.
Let T be the tension in the string and v be the speed of the particle at P.

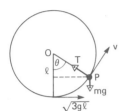

Conservation of energy gives:
$$\tfrac{1}{2}m(\sqrt{3gl})^2$$
$$= \tfrac{1}{2}mv^2 + mg(l - l\cos\theta)$$
i.e. $3gl = v^2 + 2gl(1 - \cos\theta)$ [1]

Equation of motion along PO:
$$T - mg\cos\theta = m\frac{v^2}{l} \qquad [2]$$

When the string goes slack, $T = 0$. Use this in [2] to get:
$$v^2 = -gl\cos\theta.$$
Use this value of v^2 in [1]:
$$3gl = -gl\cos\theta + 2gl - 2gl\cos\theta$$
$$\Rightarrow \qquad \cos\theta = -\frac{1}{3}.$$

The height of the particle when the string becomes slack is
$$l - l\cos\theta = l + \frac{1}{3}l = \frac{4}{3}l.$$

A smooth sphere with centre O and radius a is fixed with a point B of its surface in contact with a vertical wall. A particle P of mass m rests at the highest point A of the sphere. It is slightly disturbed so that it moves from rest towards the wall in the plane OAB. If at any instant in the subsequent motion the line OP makes an angle θ with the line OA and the particle is still in contact with the sphere, find expressions for the velocity of P at this instant and for the reaction of the sphere upon it in terms of m, g, a and θ.

Prove that the particle leaves the sphere when $\cos\theta = \dfrac{2}{3}$ and that its speed is then $\sqrt{(2ga/3)}$.
Show that P hits the wall at a height $\tfrac{1}{8}a(5\sqrt{5} - 9)$ above B.

Draw a clear force diagram. Use conservation of energy (take OB as the initial level for P.E. and consider the initial velocity of P to be zero).
Write down the equation of motion along PO. Particle leaves sphere when the reaction is zero. When particle leaves sphere, consider it to be a projectile moving freely under gravity (see unit M11).

---

1 A heavy particle connected to a fixed point O by a light inelastic string of length a is moving in a vertical circle about O. Its speed when at the lowest point of the circle is $(\tfrac{5}{2}ga)^{\frac{1}{2}}$. Find the inclination of the string to the vertical when it becomes slack, and show that the speed of the particle is then $(\tfrac{1}{2}ga)^{\frac{1}{2}}$. Find also the maximum height above O reached by the particle.

(OLE)

2 A particle P is projected horizontally with speed u from the lowest point A of the smooth inside surface of a fixed hollow sphere of internal radius a.
  (i) In the case when $u^2 = ga$ show that P does not leave the surface of the sphere. Show also that, when P has

moved halfway along its path from A towards the point at which it first comes to rest, its speed is
$$\sqrt{\{ga(\sqrt{3} - 1)\}}.$$
  (ii) Find u^2 in terms of ga in the case when P leaves the surface at a height $\dfrac{3a}{2}$ above A, and find, in terms of a and g, the speed of P as it leaves the surface.

(J)

3 A particle of mass m slides down the smooth outside surface of a fixed sphere of radius a. At the top of the sphere its velocity is horizontal and of magnitude u. If θ is the angle that the radius to the particle makes with the upward vertical, show that the reaction between the particle and the sphere is $mg(3\cos\theta - 2) - mu^2/a$. Show that the particle, when just displaced from rest at the top, leaves the surface when $\theta = \cos^{-1}\tfrac{2}{3}$, and find its speed at that instant.

(W)

4 A small bead is free to move on a smooth circular wire of radius a which is fixed in a vertical plane. The bead is projected with speed $(4ag)^{\frac{1}{2}}$ from the lowest point of the wire. Prove that the radius from the centre of the wire to the bead makes an angle θ with the vertical at time t after the instant of projection, where
$t = (a/g)^{\frac{1}{2}} \ln(\sec\tfrac{1}{2}\theta + \tan\tfrac{1}{2}\theta)$, and the reaction between the wire and the bead vanishes when $\theta = \pi - \cos^{-1}(\tfrac{2}{3})$.

(OLE)

5 One end of a light inextensible string of length a is attached to a particle of mass m. The other end is attached to a fixed point O which is at a height $\tfrac{5}{2}a$ above the horizontal ground. Initially the string is taut and horizontal. The particle is then projected vertically downward with velocity $(2ag)^{\frac{1}{2}}$. When the string has turned through an angle θ ($<\pi$) find the velocity v of the particle and show that the tension in the string is $mg(2 + 3\sin\theta)$.
(a) If the string can withstand a tension of at least 5mg, prove that the string will not break.
(b) If the string can withstand a tension of at most $\tfrac{7}{2}mg$, find the values of θ and v when the string breaks. In this case find the time to reach the vertical through O. Hence show that the particle strikes the ground at the point vertically below O.

(O & C)

6 Show that small oscillations of a simple pendulum of length l are simple harmonic with period $2\pi\sqrt{l/g}$. A pendulum clock beats seconds (i.e. one half-period = 1 second) at a point where $g = 9.812$ m s^{-2}. Find the length of the pendulum correct to 3 significant figures. If the clock is moved to a place where $g = 9.921$ m s^{-2}, will the clock gain or lose? Find how much it would gain or lose during one day. To what length should the pendulum be altered if it is to register correctly?

(S)

7 A small bead P of mass m is threaded on a smooth circular wire, with centre O and radius r, which is fixed in a vertical plane. Initially the bead is at rest at the highest point of the wire. If the bead is slightly displaced from this position, determine an expression for the speed of the bead when the line OP has turned through an angle θ. Show that the magnitude of the force exerted by the wire on the bead in the direction of OP is $mg(3\cos\theta - 2)$. State the direction of this force when θ increases beyond the value $\cos^{-1}(\tfrac{2}{3})$.

(J)

M14 Variable Forces

Introduction, Force as a function of time, Force as a function of velocity, Force as a function of displacement.

Introduction

If the **force** acting on a body of constant mass is **variable**, then the **acceleration** of the body will also be **variable**. This is a consequence of Newton's second law of motion which states that:

force = mass × acceleration.

Under these conditions the **acceleration** of the body must be expressed as a **function of time or velocity or displacement** and calculus used to solve the problem.

Force as a function of time

The **force** or **acceleration** may be given as a **function of time** t.

To find v in terms of t:

use $a = \dfrac{dv}{dt}$.

To find s in terms of t:
(a) find v in terms of t,

(b) use $v = \dfrac{ds}{dt}$.

ⓘ *A particle of mass 8 kg is acted upon by a force $4(1-e^{-\frac{t}{6}})$ N. If the body is initially at rest, find the velocity of the particle after 3 s.*

Use $a = \dfrac{dv}{dt}$ for acceleration.

The equation of motion ($F = ma$) gives:

$$4(1-e^{-\frac{t}{6}}) = 8\frac{dv}{dt}$$

i.e. $\dfrac{dv}{dt} = \frac{1}{2}(1-e^{-\frac{t}{6}})$

Integrating gives: $v = \frac{1}{2}(t+6e^{-\frac{t}{6}})+c$
When $t=0$, $v=0$, so $0=\frac{1}{2}(6)+c \Rightarrow c=-3$
Hence, $v=\frac{1}{2}(t+6e^{-\frac{t}{6}})-3$
After 3 s, $v=\frac{1}{2}(3+6e^{-\frac{1}{2}})-3 \approx 0.32$ m s^{-1}.

Force as a function of velocity

The **force** or **acceleration** may be given as a **function of the velocity** v.

To find v in terms of t:

use $a = \dfrac{dv}{dt}$.

To find v in terms of s:

use $a = v\dfrac{dv}{ds}$.

ⓘ *A particle of unit mass moves from rest along a straight line under the action of a force $(2-0.1\,v)$ N. where v is the velocity in m s^{-1}. Find the displacement when the velocity is 10 m s^{-1}.*

Use $a = v\dfrac{dv}{ds}$ for acceleration.

The equation of motion ($F = ma$) gives:

$$(2-0.1v) = 1 \cdot v\frac{dv}{ds}$$

So $\displaystyle\int ds = \int \frac{v\,dv}{(2-0.1v)}$

i.e. $\displaystyle\int ds = \int \left(-10+\frac{20}{(2-0.1v)}\right)dv$

$$s = -10v - 200\ln|2-0.1v|+c$$

When $s=0$ and $v=0$, then $c=200\ln 2$.

Hence, $s=200\ln\left|\dfrac{2}{2-0.1v}\right|-10v$.

When $v=10$, $s=200\ln 2-100 \approx 38.6$ m.

Force as a function of displacement

The **force** or **acceleration** may be given as a **function of the displacement** s.

To find v in terms of s:

use $a = v\dfrac{dv}{ds}$.

To find s in terms of t:
(a) find v in terms of s,

(b) use $v = \dfrac{ds}{dt}$.

ⓘ *A particle of unit mass, moving in a straight line, is acted upon by a force equal to $(-4x)$ N, where x m is the displacement of the particle from a fixed point O in the line. If initially the particle is at rest when $x=3$ m, find the velocity when $x=1$ m.*

Use $a = v\dfrac{dv}{dx}$ for acceleration.

The equation of motion ($F = ma$) gives:

$$1 \cdot v\frac{dv}{dx} = -4x$$

So $\displaystyle\int v\,dv = -4\int x\,dx$

$$\tfrac{1}{2}v^2 = -2x^2+c$$

When $x=3$, $v=0$, so $c=18$.
Hence, $v^2=4(9-x^2)$.
When $x=1$, $v^2=4.8 \Rightarrow v=\pm 2\sqrt{2}$ m s^{-1}.

Variable Forces
Worked example, Guided example and Exam questions

WE *A particle of unit mass falls from rest under gravity through the air. The resistance of the air is kv^2 where k is a constant and v is the speed of the particle after it has fallen for time t. Calculate the time taken for the particle to acquire a speed V.*

Equation of motion for the particle is

$$\frac{dv}{dt} = g - kv^2.$$

Rearranging this differential equation we have,

$$\int \frac{dv}{g - kv^2} = \int dt$$

i.e. $\dfrac{1}{g} \displaystyle\int \dfrac{dv}{1 - \dfrac{k}{g}v^2} = \int dt$

Let $\dfrac{k}{g} = w^2$, then $1 - \dfrac{k}{g}v^2 = 1 - w^2v^2 = (1 + wv)(1 - wv)$.

Using partial fractions we have

$$\frac{1}{2g} \int \left[\frac{1}{1 + wv} + \frac{1}{1 - wv} \right] dv = \int dt$$

i.e. $\dfrac{1}{2gw} \ln \left| \dfrac{1 + wv}{1 - wv} \right| = t + c$, c is a constant of integration.

When $t = 0$, $v = 0 \Rightarrow c = 0$.

So, $t = \dfrac{1}{2gw} \ln \left| \dfrac{1 + wv}{1 - wv} \right|$.

But $w = \sqrt{\dfrac{k}{g}}$, so the time taken for the particle to acquire a speed of V is, say, T where,

$$T = \frac{1}{2\sqrt{kg}} \ln \left| \frac{\sqrt{g} + V\sqrt{k}}{\sqrt{g} - V\sqrt{k}} \right|.$$

GE *A body of mass m falls from rest under gravity through a resisting medium. The resistance is kv^2 per unit mass where k is constant and v is the velocity when the body has fallen a distance x.*

(i) *Given that u is the limiting value of the velocity, i.e. the velocity for which there would be zero acceleration, establish the differential equation*

$$v \frac{dv}{dx} = k(u^2 - v^2).$$

(ii) *By solving this differential equation obtain an expression for v in terms of x.*

(iii) *Show that the work done by the resistance when the body has fallen a distance x is*

$$\frac{mu^2}{2} (2kx + e^{-2kx} - 1).$$

(i) Set up the equation of motion for the particle using $v\dfrac{dv}{dx}$ as the expression for acceleration. As acceleration approaches zero i.e. $v\dfrac{dv}{dx} \to 0$, velocity approaches u

i.e. $g - ku^2 \to 0$.

Hence get the required differential equation.

(ii) Solve the equation using the method of variables separable.

(iii) The resistance is a variable force so use

$$\text{Work done} = \int_0^x F dx \text{ where } F = kv^2$$

i.e. Work done $= \displaystyle\int_0^x mkv^2\, dx$.

Use the expression found for v in terms of x (from (ii)) in the integral to obtain the work done.

EX

1 A particle of mass m, subject to a resistance mk times the square of its speed, is projected vertically downwards with speed w, where $kw^2 < g$. Find the speed of the particle when it has descended a distance x.

(J)

2 Show that the acceleration of an object moving along a straight line may be written as $v\dfrac{dv}{ds}$. A vehicle of mass 2500 kg moving on a straight course is subject to a single resisting force in the line of motion of magnitude kv newtons, where v metres per second is the velocity and k is constant. At 100 km/h this force is 2000 N.
The vehicle is slowed down from 100 km/h to 50 km/h. Find:
 (i) the distance travelled;
 (ii) the time taken.

(A)

3 A particle, of mass m, moves in a horizontal straight line under the action of a resisting force of magnitude mkv^2, where v is the velocity and k is a positive constant. When $t = 0$, $v = U$ and $x = a$, where x is the displacement from the origin at time t. Find expressions for:
 (i) v in terms of x;
 (ii) v in terms of t;
 (iii) x in terms of t.

(C)

4 At time t a particle is moving vertically downwards with speed v in a medium which exerts a resistance to the motion proportional to the square of the speed of the particle. If its terminal velocity is V, prove that the equation of motion of the particle is $\dfrac{dv}{dt} = g\left(1 - \dfrac{v^2}{V^2}\right)$, and write down the equation of motion when the particle is moving vertically upwards. A particle is projected vertically upwards in the medium with speed equal to the terminal velocity V. Prove that when it returns to the point of projection its speed is $V/\sqrt{2}$.

(OLE)

5 The motion of a particle is such that its speed v at time t is given by $\dfrac{dv}{dt} = \dfrac{1}{2}(v - v^2)$ and $v = 0.2$ when $t = 0$. By solving the differential equation:
 (i) find the value of t when $v = 0.5$, giving your answer correct to two decimal places;
 (ii) express v in terms of t.
By considering the differential equation in the form $v\dfrac{dv}{dx} = \dfrac{1}{2}(v - v^2)$, or otherwise, where x is the distance travelled when the speed is v, and $x = 0$ when $v = 0.2$, show that the value of x when $v = 0.8$ is double its value when $v = 0.6$.

(J)

6 A particle of mass m is projected vertically upwards under gravity with speed u in a medium in which the resistance is mk times the speed. If the particle reaches its greatest height H in a time T, show that $u = gT + kH$. If the particle returns to its original position with speed w after a further time T', show that $w = gT' - kH$. Find the particle's speed as a function of time during the upward motion and show that $kT = \log_e(1 + ku/g)$.

(W)

M15 Simple Harmonic Motion
Definitions, Equations, Forces producing S.H.M.

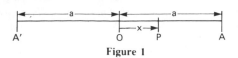

Figure 1

Definitions

Simple Harmonic Motion (S.H.M.) is a special type of oscillation.

In linear S.H.M. a particle oscillates in a straight line with a **linear acceleration** which is **proportional to the linear displacement from a fixed point** and always **directed towards that fixed point.**

Consider a particle P, oscillating with S.H.M. along the line AA', as shown in the diagram.

O is a fixed point, the **centre** or **mean position.**

a is the **amplitude** of the S.H.M., i.e. the maximum distance of the particle from the centre O.

Note:

At O, where $x=0$,
 (a) the speed is a maximum $(=na)$,
 (b) the acceleration is zero.

At A and A', where $x=\pm a$,
 (a) the speed is zero,
 (b) the acceleration is maximum $(=\omega^2 a)$.

Equations

The **basic equation of S.H.M.** is:

$$\frac{d^2x}{dt^2} = -\omega^2 x \text{ where } \omega \text{ is a constant.}$$

From it can be derived:

$$v^2 = \left(\frac{dx}{dt}\right)^2 = \omega^2(a^2 - x^2)$$

$$x = a \sin \omega t, \text{ if } x=0 \text{ when } t=0$$

$$x = a \cos \omega t, \text{ if } x=a \text{ when } t=0$$

The **period**, T, of the S.H.M. is the time for a complete oscillation, i.e. to travel a total distance $4a$. The **frequency**, f, of the S.H.M. is the number of oscillations made per unit time.

$$T = \frac{2\pi}{\omega} = \frac{1}{f}$$

Note: T and f are independent of the amplitude a.

ⓘ *A particle is executing S.H.M. with period $\pi/4$ s and amplitude 0.5 m. Calculate:*
(a) the speed when the displacement is 0.25 m,
(b) the magnitude of the acceleration when the displacement is 0.1 m.

(a) $T = \dfrac{2\pi}{\omega} \Rightarrow \omega = \dfrac{2\pi}{T} = \dfrac{2\pi}{\pi/4} = 8$

Using $v^2 = \omega^2(a^2 - x^2)$
$$= 8^2[(0.5)^2 - (0.25)^2] = 12$$
$$\therefore v = \sqrt{12} \approx 3.46 \text{ m s}^{-1}$$

(b) Using acceleration $= -\omega^2 x$
$$= -8^2(0.1) = -6.4 \text{ m s}^{-2}$$
$\therefore$ the magnitude of the acceleration is 6.4 m s^{-2}.

Forces producing S.H.M.

A force directed towards a fixed point and **proportional to the displacement from that point** produces S.H.M.

A simple example of a force producing S.H.M. is the tension in a stretched elastic string or spring.

To show that the motion produced is S.H.M.:

1. Draw a clear force diagram showing the particle in equilibrium.

2. Use Hooke's law to find the static extension.

3. Draw a diagram showing the particle at a point between the equilibrium position and an extreme.

4. Write down the equation of motion measuring displacement from the equilibrium position.

5. Compare this equation with the basic equation of S.H.M., i.e. $\dfrac{d^2x}{dt^2} = -\omega^2 x$.

Once a motion has been shown to be S.H.M. then the equations of S.H.M. can be used to find ω, v, a, etc.

If only part of the motion of a particle is S.H.M., then each part of the motion must be dealt with separately. The motion of a particle on an elastic string, for example, is S.H.M. only while the string is in tension. When the string becomes slack the only force acting on the particle is its weight. So the particle moves in a vertical line under gravity, its initial speed being obtained from $v^2 = \omega^2(a^2 - x^2)$.

ⓘ *A particle of mass m hanging on the end of an elastic string of natural length l and modulus λ is pulled down a distance a ($<mgl/\lambda$) below its equilibrium position and then released. Prove that the subsequent oscillations are simple harmonic, find the period of oscillations and state the amplitude.*

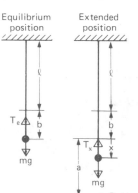

Figure 2

In equilibrium position:
b is the static extension.

By Hooke's law: $T_e = \dfrac{\lambda b}{l}$

Resolve ($\uparrow$): $T_e = mg$

So $mg = \dfrac{\lambda b}{l}$ \quad (1)

In extended position:
By Hooke's law:
$$T_x = \frac{\lambda(b+x)}{l} \quad (2)$$

Equation of motion:
$$mg - T_x = m\frac{d^2x}{dt^2} \quad (3)$$

Equations (1), (2) and (3) give $\dfrac{d^2x}{dt^2} = \dfrac{-\lambda}{ml}x$.

This is of the form $\dfrac{d^2x}{dt^2} = -\omega^2 x$ with $\omega = \sqrt{\dfrac{\lambda}{ml}}$,

i.e. S.H.M. about the static equilibrium position.

Period of oscillations $T = \dfrac{2\pi}{\omega} = 2\pi\sqrt{\dfrac{ml}{\lambda}}$.

Amplitude is a.

Simple Harmonic Motion
Worked example, Guided example and Exam questions

 A particle is executing simple harmonic motion with amplitude 2 metres *and period* 12 seconds. *Calculate the maximum speed of the particle.*
Initially, the particle is moving at maximum speed. Show that the distance moved by the particle until its speed is half the maximum value is $\sqrt{3}$ metres *and find the time taken by the particle to travel this distance.*
(Standard formulae relating to simple harmonic motion may be quoted without proof.)

Using $T = \dfrac{2\pi}{\omega}$, we have

$$12 = \frac{2\pi}{\omega} \Rightarrow \omega = \frac{\pi}{6}.$$

Now, $v^2 = \omega^2(a^2 - x^2)$

so, $v^2 = \dfrac{\pi^2}{36}(4 - x^2)$, since $a = 2$ m.

v is a maximum when $x = 0$,

i.e. $v_{\max} = \dfrac{\pi}{3}$ m s^{-1} is the maximum speed.

When $v = \dfrac{1}{2}v_{\max}$ i.e. $v = \dfrac{\pi}{6}$ m s^{-1},

we have, $\left(\dfrac{\pi}{6}\right)^2 = \dfrac{\pi^2}{36}(4 - x^2)$,

i.e. $x^2 = 3$

$\Rightarrow \qquad x = \sqrt{3}$ m — the distance travelled.

To find the time taken to travel this distance,

use, $\qquad x = a \sin \omega t$,

i.e. $\sqrt{3} = 2 \sin \left(\dfrac{\pi}{6}t\right)$

$\Rightarrow \qquad \dfrac{\pi}{6}t = \dfrac{\pi}{3}$

$\Rightarrow \qquad t = 2$ seconds.

 One end of an elastic string of modulus mg and natural length a is attached to a fixed point O. To the other end A are attached two particles P and Q, P having mass 2m and Q having mass m. The particles hang down in equilibrium under gravity. If Q falls off, show that P subsequently performs simple harmonic motion and state the period and amplitude of this motion. If on the other hand P falls off, find the distance from O of the highest point reached by Q.

First use Hooke's Law for the elastic string attached to a particle of mass $3m$ to find the total length OA. Now use Hooke's Law for a particle of mass $2m$ to find a new length OA. The difference between the two lengths will be the amplitude of the oscillations.
Consider the $2m$ particle to be moving and displaced x metres from its equilibrium position. Write down the equation of motion and show this is an equation of simple harmonic motion. Hence ω and T. For the last part of the question, use conservation of energy (*see* unit M5).

---

 1 A particle P of mass 8 kg describes simple harmonic motion with O as centre and has a speed of 6 m/s at a distance of 1 m from O and a speed of 2 m/s at a distance of 3 m from O.
  (i) Find:
    (a) the amplitude of the motion;
    (b) the period of the motion;
    (c) the maximum speed of P;
    (d) the time taken to travel from O directly to one extreme point B of the motion.

  (ii) Determine the magnitude of:
    (a) the acceleration of P when at a distance of 2 m from O;
    (b) the force acting on P when at a distance of 2 m from O;
  (iii) Write down an expression for the displacement of P from O at any time t, given that P is at O at $t = 0$. Hence, or otherwise, find the time taken to travel directly from O to a point C between O and B and at a distance of 1 m from O. Find also the time taken to go directly from C to the point D between O and B and at a distance of 2 m from O. [Answers may be left in a form involving inverse trigonometric functions.]

(A)

2 A particle moves on the line Ox so that after time t its displacement from O is x, and $\dfrac{d^2x}{dt^2} = -9x$.

When $t = 0$, $x = 4$ and $dx/dt = 9$. Find:
 (i) the position and velocity of the particle when $t = \pi/6$;
 (ii) the maximum displacement of the particle from O.

(J)

3 A particle of mass m is attached to one end of a light elastic string of length a and modulus $\frac{3}{2}mg$. The other end of the string is attached to a fixed point O and the particle hangs in equilibrium under gravity at the point E. Find the distance OE. If the particle is a *further* distance x below E show that the resultant force acting on the particle is proportional to x. The particle is pulled down to the point at a distance a below E and released from rest. Show that, in the subsequent motion and while the string is taut, the particle executes Simple Harmonic Motion and that its distance below E at time t after being released is

$$a \cos \left\{\left(\frac{3g}{2a}\right)^{\frac{1}{2}} t\right\}$$

$(O \,\&\, C)$

4 (Take g as 10 m s^{-2} in this question.) A light elastic spring has natural length a and modulus of elasticity λ. Prove that the energy stored in the spring when it is stretched is $\lambda x^2/(2a)$, where x is the extension. A light elastic spring of natural length $0 \cdot 2$ m and modulus of elasticity 50 N hangs vertically with one end attached to a fixed point and with a particle of mass 2 kg attached to the lower end.
 (i) Calculate the extension of the spring when the particle is in equilibrium.
 (ii) The particle is pulled down below its equilibrium position until the *total* extension of the spring is $0 \cdot 2$ m and it is then released from rest in this position. Calculate the speed of the particle when it passes the equilibrium position, and find the maximum compression of the spring in the resulting motion.

(C)

5 A mass rests on a horizontal platform which is moving horizontally to and fro with simple harmonic motion of amplitude 0.5 m, making twenty complete oscillations per minute. If the mass remains at rest relative to the platform throughout the motion, show that the coefficient of friction must not be less than 0.224 approximately. If $\mu = \frac{1}{2}$, the mass is 10 kg, and the platform is stopped abruptly when 0.3 m from its mean position, write down the equation describing the subsequent motion of the mass, and derive the relation that holds between the kinetic energy of the mass and the work done against friction during that motion. How far will the mass slide before coming to rest?

(W)

M16 Vectors in Dynamics

Displacement, Velocity, Acceleration, Force, Momentum, Impulse, Kinetic energy, Work, Power.

Displacement, velocity, acceleration

The **position vector** r of a point $P(x, y, z)$ referred to the origin O can be written as:

$$r = x\mathbf{i} + y\mathbf{j} + z\mathbf{k} \text{ or } r = \begin{pmatrix} x \\ y \\ z \end{pmatrix} \text{ in three dimensions;}$$

$$r = x\mathbf{i} + y\mathbf{j} \text{ or } r = \begin{pmatrix} x \\ y \end{pmatrix} \text{ in two dimensions.}$$

The **velocity** v of P is $\dfrac{d\mathbf{r}}{dt}$, sometimes written as $\dot{\mathbf{r}}$.

The acceleration a of P is $\dfrac{d\mathbf{v}}{dt}$ or $\dfrac{d^2\mathbf{r}}{dt^2}$,

sometimes written as $\ddot{\mathbf{r}}$.
SI unit for $\mathbf{r}$ is the **metre** (m); for v the **metre per second** (m s^{-1}); for a the **metre per second squared** (m s^{-2}).

$\boxed{i}$ *A particle moves so that its position vector r in metres at time t in seconds is $r = 5\mathbf{i} + t^3\mathbf{j} + t^2\mathbf{k}$. Find the velocity and acceleration of the particle at time t and its speed after 3 seconds.*

At time t: $\mathbf{v} = \dfrac{dr}{dt} = 3t^2\mathbf{j} + 2t\mathbf{k}$

$$\mathbf{a} = \dfrac{d\mathbf{v}}{dt} = 6t\mathbf{j} + 2\mathbf{k}$$

Speed is the magnitude of the velocity, i.e. $|\mathbf{v}|$.
$$|\mathbf{v}| = \sqrt{[(3t^2)^2 + (2t)^2]}$$
$$= t\sqrt{(9t^2 + 4)}$$
When $t = 3$, $\quad |\mathbf{v}| = 3\sqrt{85} \approx 27.7 \text{ m s}^{-1}$

Force

Newton's second law of motion:
i.e. **force = mass × acceleration**
can be given in vector form as
$$\mathbf{F} = m\mathbf{a}$$
or $\quad \mathbf{F} = m\ddot{\mathbf{r}}$.
SI unit for force is the **newton** (N).

$\boxed{i}$ *Find the force acting on a mass of 2 kg with position vector $r = t^3\mathbf{i} + 2t^2\mathbf{j} + 3\mathbf{k}$ at time t.*

$$\mathbf{r} = t^3\mathbf{i} + 2t^2\mathbf{j} + 3\mathbf{k}$$
$$\dot{\mathbf{r}} = 3t^2\mathbf{i} + 4t\mathbf{j}$$
$$\ddot{\mathbf{r}} = 6t\mathbf{i} + 4\mathbf{j}$$

So $\mathbf{F} = m\ddot{\mathbf{r}} = 2(6t\mathbf{i} + 4\mathbf{j}) = 12t\mathbf{i} + 8\mathbf{j}$

Momentum

The momentum of a particle mass m, velocity $\mathbf{v}$ is given by:

$$\text{momentum} = m\mathbf{v}$$
SI unit for momentum is the **newton second** (N s).

$\boxed{i}$ *Find the momentum of a particle mass 5 kg and velocity $v = 2i - j$.*

$$\text{momentum} = 5(2\mathbf{i} - \mathbf{j}) = 10\mathbf{i} - 5\mathbf{j} \text{ Ns.}$$

Impulse

The **impulse** $\mathbf{I}$ produced by a force $\mathbf{F}$ acting for time T is defined as:

$$\mathbf{I} = \int_0^T \mathbf{F}\,dt.$$

SI unit for impulse is the **newton second** (N s).
Since $\mathbf{F} = m\mathbf{a}$,

$$\mathbf{I} = \int_0^T m\mathbf{a}\,dt = m\int_0^T \dfrac{d\mathbf{v}}{dt}\,dt.$$

$$= m(\mathbf{v} - \mathbf{u}) \text{ i.e. change in momentum.}$$

$\boxed{i}$ *Find the impulse produced by a force given by $F = \sin t\,i + \cos t\,j$ acting for the time interval $0 \leqslant t \leqslant \pi/2$.*

$$\text{Impulse} = \mathbf{I} = \int \mathbf{F}\,dt = \int_0^{\frac{\pi}{2}} (\sin t\,\mathbf{i} + \cos t\,\mathbf{j})\,dt$$

$$= \left[-\cos t\,\mathbf{i} + \sin t\,\mathbf{j} \right]_0^{\frac{\pi}{2}}$$

$$= (\mathbf{j}) - (-\mathbf{i}) = \mathbf{i} + \mathbf{j}$$

Kinetic energy

The **kinetic energy**, K.E., of a particle mass m, velocity $\mathbf{v}$ is

$$\tfrac{1}{2}m\mathbf{v} \cdot \mathbf{v} = \tfrac{1}{2}mv^2$$
SI unit for kinetic energy is the **joule** (J).

$\boxed{i}$ *Find the K.E. of a particle of mass 4 kg and velocity $v = 3i + 2j$.*

K.E. $= \tfrac{1}{2} \cdot 4(3\mathbf{i} + 2\mathbf{j}) \cdot (3\mathbf{i} + 2\mathbf{j}) = 26$ J

Work

The **work** done by a force $\mathbf{F}$ is defined as $\int \mathbf{F} \cdot \mathbf{v}\,dt$.
SI unit for work is the **joule** (J).

Since $\mathbf{F} = m\dfrac{d\mathbf{v}}{dt}$,

the work done is $m\int \mathbf{v} \cdot \dfrac{d\mathbf{v}}{dt}\,dt$

$$= \tfrac{1}{2}mv^2 - \tfrac{1}{2}mu^2 \text{ i.e. increase in K.E.}$$

$\boxed{i}$ *Find the work done by a force $F = 2t\,i + 4\,j$ on a particle with velocity $v = 5i - tj$ in the time interval $0 \leqslant t \leqslant 2$.*

Work done $= \displaystyle\int_0^2 \mathbf{F} \cdot \mathbf{v}\,dt = \int_0^2 (2t\mathbf{i} + 4\mathbf{j}) \cdot (5\mathbf{i} - t\mathbf{j})\,dt$

$$= \int_0^2 6t\,dt = \left[3t^2 \right]_0^2 = 12 \text{ J}$$

Power

The **power** exerted by a force $\mathbf{F}$ is the rate at which $\mathbf{F}$ does work.

So power is $\dfrac{d}{dT}\left(\displaystyle\int_0^T \mathbf{F} \cdot \mathbf{v}\,dt \right) = \mathbf{F} \cdot \mathbf{v}$

SI unit for power is the **watt** (W).

$\boxed{i}$ *Find the power exerted by a force $F = 5t^2\,i + 2t\,j$ on a particle with velocity $v = t\,i - 2t^2\,j$ at time t.*

Power $= \mathbf{F} \cdot \mathbf{v} = (5t^2\mathbf{i} + 2t\mathbf{j}) \cdot (t\mathbf{i} - 2t^2\mathbf{j})$
$$= 5t^3 - 4t^3 = t^3$$

Vectors in Dynamics
Worked example and Exam questions

In this question the units of mass, length and time are the kilogram, metre and second respectively.
A particle of unit mass moves so that its position vector $\mathbf{r}$ at time t is
$\mathbf{r} = \cos t\,\mathbf{i} + \sin t\,\mathbf{j} + \tfrac{1}{2}t^2\,\mathbf{k}$.
Find (a) *the momentum at time t,*
    (b) *the kinetic energy at time t,*
    (c) *the work done on the particle in the time interval $t = 0$ to $t = 4$,*
    (d) *the force acting on the particle at time t,*
    (e) *the power exerted by this force at time t.*

Since $\mathbf{r} = \cos t\,\mathbf{i} + \sin t\,\mathbf{j} + \tfrac{1}{2}t^2\,\mathbf{k}$,
    $\dot{\mathbf{r}} = -\sin t\,\mathbf{i} + \cos t\,\mathbf{j} + t\,\mathbf{k}$,
and $\ddot{\mathbf{r}} = -\cos t\,\mathbf{i} - \sin t\,\mathbf{j} + \mathbf{k}$.

(a) The momentum at time t is $m\dot{\mathbf{r}}$ so,
momentum $= -\sin t\,\mathbf{i} + \cos t\,\mathbf{j} + t\,\mathbf{k}$ N s.

(b) The kinetic energy at time t is $\tfrac{1}{2}mv^2 = \tfrac{1}{2}m\dot{\mathbf{r}}.\dot{\mathbf{r}}$ so, kinetic energy
$= \tfrac{1}{2}(-\sin t\,\mathbf{i} + \cos t\,\mathbf{j} + t\,\mathbf{k}).(-\sin t\,\mathbf{i} + \cos t\,\mathbf{j} + t\,\mathbf{k})$
$= \tfrac{1}{2}(\sin^2 t + \cos^2 t + t^2)$
$= \tfrac{1}{2}(1 + t^2)$ joules.

(c) The work done on the particle in the time interval $t = 0$ to $t = 4$ is $\int_0^4 \mathbf{F}.\mathbf{v}\, dt$, so

Work done
$= \int_0^4 (-\cos t\,\mathbf{i} - \sin t\,\mathbf{j} + \mathbf{k}).(-\sin t\,\mathbf{i} + \cos t\,\mathbf{j} + t\,\mathbf{k})\,dt$
$= \int_0^4 (\sin t \cos t - \sin t \cos t + t)\,dt$
$= \left[\dfrac{t^2}{2}\right]_0^4$
$= 8$ joules.

(d) The force acting on the particle at time t is $\mathbf{F} = m\ddot{\mathbf{r}}$, so
Force $= -\cos t\,\mathbf{i} - \sin t\,\mathbf{j} + \mathbf{k}$ N

(e) The power exerted by the force at time t is $\mathbf{F}.\mathbf{v}$, so
Power $= (-\cos t\,\mathbf{i} - \sin t\,\mathbf{j} + \mathbf{k}).(-\sin t\,\mathbf{i} + \cos t\,\mathbf{j} + t\,\mathbf{k})$
       $= (\sin t \cos t - \sin t \cos t + t)$
       $= t$ watts.

---

1 A particle initially at rest at the point $(2, 2)$ has acceleration $\begin{pmatrix} t \\ 3 \end{pmatrix}$ in m s^{-2} after t seconds. Find vector expressions for its velocity and position after t seconds.
Find its change in position in the first $\frac{1}{100}$ second. After how many seconds is it moving in a direction inclined at 45° to the x-axis?   *(O & C)*

2 A force $\mathbf{F}_1 = (4\mathbf{i} + 2\mathbf{j})$ N. State the magnitude of $\mathbf{F}_1$.
A second force $\mathbf{F}_2$ has magnitude $8\sqrt{5}$ N and acts in a direction given by the vector $\mathbf{i} + 2\mathbf{j}$. State the force vector $\mathbf{F}_2$. Hence calculate the resultant force $\mathbf{F}_R$ of these two forces and the unit vector in the direction of this resultant. What is the acceleration that this resultant would produce on a mass of 3 kg? The mass was initially at rest at the point with position vector $2\mathbf{i} - 4\mathbf{j}$. If the two forces continue to act on the mass, show that the point with position vector $18\mathbf{i} + 20\mathbf{j}$ lies on the path traced out by the mass.   *(S)*

3 In this question distances are measured in metres and time in seconds. At time $t = 0$ two particles P and Q are set in motion in the x-y plane. Initially P is at $A(1, 0)$ and Q is at $B(0, 8)$. The particle P moves with a constant speed of 5 m/s parallel to the line $3y = 4x$ and Q moves with a constant speed of 4 m/s parallel to the line $y = -\lambda x$, the sense of motion of both P and Q being that in which x is increasing. Given that $\mathbf{i}$ and $\mathbf{j}$ are the unit vectors in the directions of x increasing and y increasing, respectively, show that the unit vectors in the directions of motion of P and Q are $\dfrac{3}{5}\mathbf{i} + \dfrac{4}{5}\mathbf{j}$ and $\dfrac{1}{\sqrt{1+\lambda^2}}\mathbf{i} - \dfrac{\lambda}{\sqrt{1+\lambda^2}}\mathbf{j}$ respectively.
Determine, in the form $a\mathbf{i} + b\mathbf{j}$:
(i) the velocities of P and Q;
(ii) the vectors $\overrightarrow{AP}$, $\overrightarrow{BQ}$ and $\overrightarrow{PQ}$ at time t.
Show that, if P and Q meet, λ must satisfy the equation
$$7(1 + \lambda^2)^{\frac{1}{2}} = 8 - \lambda.$$
Verify that $\lambda = -\frac{3}{4}$ is a solution of this equation and for this value of λ find the time when P and Q meet.   *(A)*

4 In this question $\mathbf{i}$ and $\mathbf{j}$ are vectors of magnitude 1 km in directions E and N respectively. Units of time and speed are hours and kilometres per hour. A and B move in a horizontal plane, A with constant velocity $4\mathbf{i} + 4\mathbf{j}$ and B with constant acceleration $2\mathbf{i} + 2\mathbf{j}$. At time $t = 0$, A is at the point with position vector $\mathbf{i} + 4\mathbf{j}$ and B is at $4\mathbf{i} + \mathbf{j}$ moving with velocity $2\mathbf{j}$.
(i) Find the position vectors of A and B at time t and hence show that $\mathbf{AB} = (t^2 - 4t + 3)\mathbf{i} + (t^2 - 2t - 3)\mathbf{j}$.
(ii) Find the time when B will be due S of A and the distance AB at that moment.
(iii) Show that A and B subsequently collide and give the time at which this happens.
(iv) Find the magnitude and direction of the velocity of B just before the collision occurs.   *(S)*

5 At time t the position vector $\mathbf{r}$ of the point P with respect to the origin O is given by $\mathbf{r} = (a \sin pt)\mathbf{i} + a\mathbf{j}$, where a and p are constants. Show that the vector $\dfrac{d^2\mathbf{r}}{dt^2} + p^2\mathbf{r}$ is constant during the motion.   *(L)*

6 A particle of mass m moves in a horizontal plane Oxy with speed v along the x-axis in the positive direction. It is subjected to a horizontal impulse $\mathbf{I}$ which turns its direction of motion through 30° in an anticlockwise sense and reduces its speed to $v/\sqrt{3}$. Find the vector $\mathbf{I}$. At the same instant an impulse $-\mathbf{I}$ is applied to a particle of mass $3m$ which is at rest. Find the magnitude and direction of the resultant velocity of this particle.   *(J)*

7 At time t a particle is in motion with velocity $\mathbf{v}$ and is being acted upon by a variable force $\mathbf{F}$. Write down expressions for (i) the power at time t, (ii) the work done by $\mathbf{F}$ during the time interval $0 \leqslant t \leqslant T$.
The particle, of mass m, moves in a plane where $\mathbf{i}$ and $\mathbf{j}$ are perpendicular unit vectors so that its position vector at time t is given by $\mathbf{r} = 2a \cos 2t\,\mathbf{i} + a \sin 2t\,\mathbf{j}$, where a is a positive constant. Derive expressions for the velocity $\mathbf{v}$ and the force $\mathbf{F}$ at time t. Obtain an expression in terms of t for the power at time t and show that the work done by $\mathbf{F}$ during the interval $0 \leqslant t \leqslant T$ is $3ma^2(1 - \cos 4T)$. If T varies, find the maximum value of the work done by $\mathbf{F}$ and determine also the smallest value of T for which this maximum value is reached.   *(J)*

M17 Coplanar Concurrent Forces

Definitions, Resultant of two forces, Resolving a force, Resultant of a system of forces.

Definitions

Coplanar forces are forces whose lines of action all lie in the same plane.
Concurrent forces act at the same point. If forces act on a particle, then they must be concurrent.

Resultant of two forces

If two forces **p** and **q** are **concurrent** then they act at a point, O say. Their **resultant r** may be found by **vector addition** using the **triangle law**, i.e. $\mathbf{p}+\mathbf{q}=\mathbf{r}$.

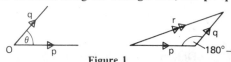

Figure 1

The **magnitude** of **r** is given by the cosine rule:
i.e. $r=\sqrt{p^2+q^2+2pq\cos\theta}$
since $\cos(180°-\theta)=-\cos\theta$.
The resultant r also acts at the point O as shown.
The **direction** of **r** is given by the sine rule:

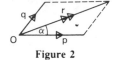

Figure 2

i.e. $\sin\alpha=\dfrac{q}{r}\sin\theta$

If **p** and **q** are at right angles, then $\theta=90°$ and

$r=\sqrt{p^2+q^2}$ and $\tan\alpha=\dfrac{q}{p}$.

i *A particle is acted upon by forces in a horizontal plane.* 6 newtons *in a direction* NE, 7 newtons *in a direction* S26°E. *Find the resultant force.*

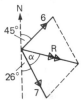

Figure 3

The magnitude R of the resultant force is given by:

$$R=\sqrt{[6^2+7^2+(2\times6\times7\cos109°)]}$$
$$=\sqrt{[36+49-27.35]}$$
$$=\sqrt{57.65}$$
$$\Rightarrow R\approx7.59 \text{ newtons}$$

If α is the angle between the direction of the resultant and the 7 newton force, then

$$\sin\alpha\approx\frac{6}{7.59}\sin109°$$
$$\approx0.7474$$
$$\Rightarrow\alpha\approx48.4°$$

Resolving a force

A single force can be split into two **components** or **resolutes** by the converse of the triangle law for vector addition. This process is called **resolving the force**.

i

Figure 4

$\mathbf{a}=\mathbf{b}+\mathbf{c}$
a is resolved into components **b** and **c**.

Although a force may be resolved in an infinite number of ways, the most useful way is when the two components are perpendicular to each other.

i

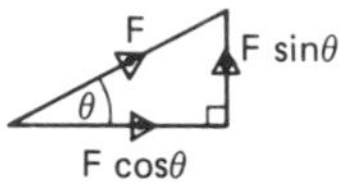

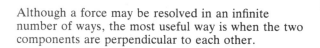

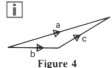

Figure 5

F is resolved into perpendicular components **F** $\cos\theta$ and **F** $\sin\theta$.

In problem solving it is often necessary to resolve a force in one or more directions, e.g. horizontally, vertically, parallel to a plane, perpendicular to a plane, etc.

i A particle is acted upon by the coplanar concurrent forces **W**, **R** and **F** as shown. The table gives the resolutes of the forces in four directions.

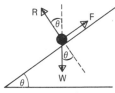

Figure 6

In diagrams it is conventional to mark the magnitudes of a force and its resolutes.

Direction / Force	Vertical	Horizontal	∥ to slope	⊥ to slope
W	W	0	$W\sin\theta$	$W\cos\theta$
R	$R\cos\theta$	$R\sin\theta$	0	R
F	$F\sin\theta$	$F\cos\theta$	F	0

Resultant of a system of forces

To find the **resultant of a system** of coplanar concurrent forces:

1. Resolve each force in a stated direction and find the sum of the resolutes, **p** say, in that direction.
2. Resolve each force in a direction perpendicular to the first stated direction and find the sum of these resolutes, **q** say.
3. Find the resultant **r** of these two concurrent forces **p** and **q** by vector addition using the triangle law.

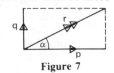

Figure 7

$$r=\sqrt{p^2+q^2} \text{ and } \tan\alpha=\frac{q}{p}$$

i *Find the single force which is equivalent to the given system of forces.*

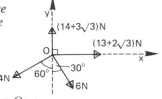

Figure 8

Total resolute in direction Ox
$=(13+2\sqrt{3})-4\cos30°+6\cos60°=16$ N

Total resolute in direction Oy
$=(14+3\sqrt{3})-4\cos60°-6\cos30°=12$ N

Figure 9

$R=20$ N(3:4:5△)
$\theta=\arctan0.75$

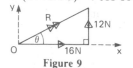

Coplanar Concurrent Forces
Worked example, Guided example and Exam questions

WE *PQRS is a square. Calculate the resultant of the following forces:*
5 N *acting along PQ,*
$3\sqrt{2}$ N *acting along PR,*
3 N *acting along PS.*
Find also the angle the resultant makes with PQ.

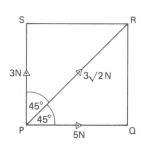

Let X and Y be the components of the resultant force in the directions of PQ and PS.

$X = (5 + 3\sqrt{2} \cos 45°)$ N

$\quad = \left(5 + 3\sqrt{2} . \dfrac{1}{\sqrt{2}}\right)$ N

$\quad = 8$ N,

and

$Y = (3 + 3\sqrt{2} \cos 45°)$ N

$\quad = \left(3 + 3\sqrt{2} . \dfrac{1}{\sqrt{2}}\right)$ N

$\quad = 6$ N.

Hence, the resultant force **R** has magnitude R where,

$R = \sqrt{(X^2 + Y^2)}$

$\quad = \sqrt{(8^2 + 6^2)}$

$\quad = 10$ N.

R makes an angle $\tan^{-1}\left(\dfrac{Y}{X}\right)$ with PQ,

i.e. **R** makes an angle $36°\ 52'$ with PQ.

GE *The medians of an equilateral triangle PQR intersect at G. Forces of magnitude 2, 2 and 4 N act along GQ, GR and GP respectively. Calculate the magnitude and direction of the resultant force.*

Choose two directions at right angles along which to resolve, say, RQ and GP.
Find the resolutes, say, X and Y of the resultant force in the two chosen directions.
Calculate $R = \sqrt{(X^2 + Y^2)}$, the magnitude of the resultant force.
State the direction of the resultant force.

EX 1 A horizontal force **R** is of magnitude 12 N and acts due east from a point O. The horizontal forces **P** and **Q** act from O in the directions 030° and due south respectively. Given that **P** + **Q** = **R**, calculate the magnitudes of **P** and **Q**.
(L)

2 The following horizontal forces pass through a point O: 5 N in a direction 000°, 1 N in a direction 090°, 4 N in a direction 225° and 6 N in a direction 315°. Find the magnitude and direction of their resultant. Two further horizontal forces are introduced to act at O: P N in a direction 135° and Q N in a direction 225°. If the complete set of forces is now in equilibrium calculate the value of P and of Q.
(C)

3 The resultant of a force $2P$ N in a direction 060° and a force 10 N in a direction 180° is a force of $\sqrt{3}P$ N. Calculate the value of P and the direction of the resultant. A third force of 25 N, concurrent with the other two and in the same plane, is added so that the resultant of the system is in the direction 180°. Find the direction in which the third force is applied and find the magnitude of the resultant.
(C)

4 (i) Find the resultant of the system of coplanar forces shown in the figure, giving its magnitude and the angle it makes with the 400 N force.

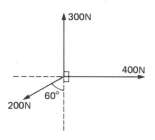

(ii) Two forces, P and Q, which are inclined at an angle of 120°, have a resultant of magnitude $P\sqrt{7}$. Calculate the magnitude of Q in terms of P.
(O & C)

5 Three forces act through the point with position vector $3\mathbf{i} + 2\mathbf{j}$.
$\mathbf{F}_1$ has magnitude 15 newtons and acts in the direction given by $3\mathbf{i} + 4\mathbf{j}$.
$\mathbf{F}_2$ has magnitude $3\sqrt{2}$ newtons and acts in the direction given by $\mathbf{i} - \mathbf{j}$.
$\mathbf{F}_3$ has magnitude $4\sqrt{5}$ newtons and acts in the direction given by $2\mathbf{i} + \mathbf{j}$.
Express the three forces in terms of the unit vectors $\mathbf{i}$ and $\mathbf{j}$. Hence find the resultant $\mathbf{F}_R$ of these three forces in terms of the unit vectors. If $\mathbf{i}$ and $\mathbf{j}$ are the unit vectors in the directions of the x and y axes, the unit of length being the metre, illustrate the resultant $\mathbf{F}_R$ graphically. Using the graph, calculate the magnitude of the moment of $\mathbf{F}_R$ about the origin.
(S)

6 (a) In the regular hexagon $ABCDEF$, $\overrightarrow{AB} = \mathbf{a}$ and $\overrightarrow{BC} = \mathbf{b}$. Express, in terms of $\mathbf{a}$ and $\mathbf{b}$, the vectors:
(i) $\overrightarrow{AC}$; (ii) $\overrightarrow{AD}$; (iii) $\overrightarrow{AE}$; (iv) $\overrightarrow{AF}$.
(b) The origin O, the point A with position vector $4\mathbf{i} + 3\mathbf{j}$ and the point C with position vector $3\mathbf{i} - 4\mathbf{j}$ are three vertices of a square $OABC$. Calculate the position vector of B. Forces of magnitudes 5 N, $10\sqrt{2}$ N and 10 N act along $\overrightarrow{OA}$, $\overrightarrow{OB}$ and $\overrightarrow{CO}$ respectively. Express each of these forces as a vector in terms of $\mathbf{i}$ and $\mathbf{j}$. Hence show that the resultant of these forces acts along $\overrightarrow{OA}$ and calculate the magnitude of this resultant.
(A)

M18 Moments and Couples
Moment of a force, Resultant moment, Principle of moments, Parallel forces, Couple

Moment of a force

When a force acts on a rigid body it may cause the body to turn about an axis. This **turning effect** is measured by the moment of the force about this axis.

The **moment of a force about an axis** is defined as the product of the magnitude of the force and the perpendicular distance of the line of action of the force from the axis. It is usual to refer simply to the **moment 'about a point'** instead of using the more correct description 'about an axis through a point . . .'.

The moment of force F about O is Fd.

The moment of force F about X is zero.

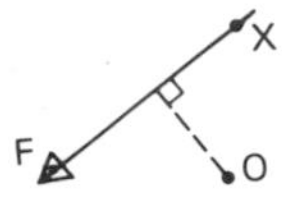

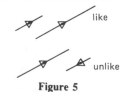

Figure 1

SI unit of moment is the newton-metre (Nm). Anticlockwise ↺ moments are usually taken as positive, clockwise ↻ moments as negative.

ℹ A heavy rod AB is acted upon by the coplanar forces X, Y, W and P as shown. The table gives the moments of the forces about A, B and G.

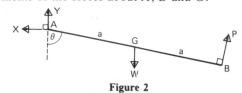

Figure 2

Force / Point	X	Y	W	P
A	0	0	$-W.a \sin \theta$	$P.2a$
B	$X.2a \cos \theta$	$-Y.2a \sin \theta$	$W.a \sin \theta$	0
G	$X.a \cos \theta$	$-Y.a \sin \theta$	0	$P.a$

Resultant moment

When a set of coplanar forces acts on a body, the **resultant moment** about a point in the plane is the algebraic sum of the moments of the individual forces about that point.

ℹ *Forces act along the sides of a square $ABCD$ of side 1 m as shown. Find the resultant moment about A.*

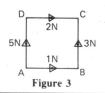

Figure 3

Resultant moment about A is:
$(1 \times 0) + (3 \times 1)$
$+ (-2 \times 1) + (-5 \times 0)$
$= 1 \, \text{Nm}$

Principle of moments

The **principle of moments** states that:
the resultant moment of a set of coplanar forces about a point is equal to the moment of their resultant about the same point.

ℹ *Forces of magnitude 4 N and 3 N act along the sides AB and AD respectively of a square $ABCD$ of side 2 m. Find the perpendicular distance d of the line of action of their resultant R from O, the midpoint of DC.*

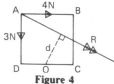

Figure 4

$R = \sqrt{3^2 + 4^2} = 5 \, \text{N}$

Moment of R about O is $-5d$
Resultant moment of forces about O is:
$(3 \times 1) - (4 \times 2) = -5.$

By the principle of moments:
$$-5 = -5d \Rightarrow d = 1 \, \text{m}$$

Parallel forces

Like parallel forces act in the same direction.

Unlike parallel forces act in opposite directions.

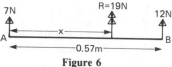

Figure 5

The **resultant** of a set of parallel forces is parallel to the original forces. Its magnitude is the algebraic sum of the magnitudes of the individual forces.
The location of the resultant may be found using the principle of moments.

ℹ *In the given diagram, find the distance x of the resultant R from the point A.*

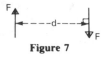

Figure 6

Moment of R about A is $19x$.

Resultant moment of 7 N and 12 N forces about A is:
$(7 \times 0) + (12 \times 0.57) = 6.84$
By the principle of moments:
$$6.84 = 19x \Rightarrow x = 0.36 \, \text{m}$$

Couple

A **couple** is formed by two equal unlike parallel forces which are non-collinear.

Figure 7

It has zero resultant but is does have a moment.
The **moment of the couple** shown is Fd. This is constant about any point in the plane of the couple.

ℹ *The diagram shows a uniform rod AB, pivoted at A and held horizontally by a couple of moment G. Find G.*

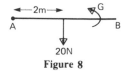

Figure 8

Moments about A give: $G = 20 \times 2 = 40 \, \text{Nm}$.

Moments and Couples
Worked example, Guided example and Exam questions

 Calculate the turning effect about O of the force $F_1 = 3i + j$ acting at the point $r_1 = i + j$ and the force $F_2 = 2i - 5j$ acting at the point $r_2 = 2i - j$.

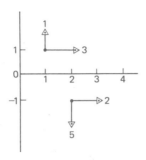

Total clockwise moment
about O
$= (3 \times 1) + (5 \times 2)$
$= 13$ Nm.

Total anticlockwise moment
about O
$= (1 \times 1) + (2 \times 1)$
$= 3$ Nm.

Resultant moment about $O = -13 + 3$
$= -10$ Nm,
i.e. a clockwise moment of 10 Nm.

 A uniform plank AB, 3 m long, of mass 10 kg, is supported in a horizontal position by two vertical strings attached at distances 1 m and 2 m from end A. Calculate the mass which should be placed at the end A of the plank so that
(i) the tension in the string nearer end B just vanishes,
(ii) the tension in the string nearer A is three times that in the string nearer B.

Draw a diagram showing the forces acting on the plank. These will be the two tensions in the strings, the weight force of the plank and the unknown weight at A.
(i) Let the tension in the string nearer B be zero. Find the unknown weight by taking moments about the point where the other string is attached to the plank.
(ii) Use tensions $3T$ and T say. Resolve vertically and take moments once to find the unknown weight this time.

---

 1 Two forces F_1 and F_2 of magnitudes $3\sqrt{5}$ N and $\sqrt{5}$ N act through the point with position vector $2i + j$ in directions $i + 2j$ and $i - 2j$ respectively. Calculate F_1 and F_2 and hence state F_R the resultant of these forces. Draw a clear diagram to illustrate F_R in component form and hence calculate the magnitude of the moment of F_R about the point with position vector i. What do you deduce from this result? (Take the unit of length to be 1 metre.)

(S)

2 A uniform rod AB, of length 150 mm and mass 50 g, has a load of X grams attached at a point C of the rod such that $AC = 30$ mm. The rod rests horizontally on a smooth support placed at a point D where $AD = 60$ mm. Calculate the numerical value of X. A second smooth support is now placed at B and the load of X grams is removed. A new load of 60 g is attached to the rod at a point E such that $EB = 35$ mm. If the rod still rests in a horizontal position, calculate the thrust on each support.

(A)

3 A uniform bar AB of length 6 m and mass 15 kg lies horizontally on supports C and D where $AC = 1$ m and $DB = 2$ m. Find the magnitudes of the vertical forces at C and D.
(i) Find the value of the downward vertical force which, when applied at A, would just cause the bar to tilt.
(ii) Find the distance from A at which an upward vertical force of 60 N should be applied to cause the bar just to tilt about D.

(C)

4 A thin non-uniform beam AB, of length 6 m and mass 50 kg, is in equilibrium resting horizontally on two smooth supports which are respectively 2 m and 3.5 m from A. The thrusts on the two supports are equal. Find the position of the centre of gravity of the beam. The original supports are removed and a load of 10 kg is attached to the beam at B. The loaded beam rests horizontally on two new smooth supports at A and C, where C is a point on the beam 1 m from B. Calculate the thrusts on each of the new supports.

(A)

5 A straight uniform rigid rod AB is of length 8 m and mass 10 kg. The rod is supported at the point X, where $AX = 5$ m, and, when downward vertical forces of magnitudes P and $4P$ newtons are applied at A and B respectively, the rod rests in equilibrium with AB horizontal. Calculate:
(a) the value of P;
(b) the force, in N, exerted on the support at X.

(L)

6 A uniform rod AGB of weight w N rests horizontally on two supports C and D. $AG = GB = 6$ cm. The support C can be placed in any position from A to G, and the support D can be placed in any position from G to B. The reactions at the supports C and D are P N and Q N respectively. Denoting AC by x cm and DB by y cm, express P and Q in terms of x, y and w. Given that $P = 2Q$:
(i) show that $2x - y = 6$;
(ii) find the value of x when the support D is placed at B.

(C)

7 A uniform straight plank AB, of mass 12 kg and length 2 m, rests horizontally on two supports, one at C and the other at D, where $AC = CD = 0.6$ m. A particle P of mass X kg is hung from B and the plank is on the point of tilting:
(a) Find the value of X.
The particle P is removed from B and hung from A.
(b) Find, in N, the magnitude of the force exerted on the plank at each support.

(L)

8 The figure shows a light horizontal beam AB, of length 9 m, supported at its ends by a force S acting vertically and a force R acting at an angle of α to the line of the beam. A force of 30 N is applied to the beam, at an angle of $30°$, 3 m from B. If the beam is in equilibrium, calculate:
(a) S; (b) α; (c) R.
Calculate the magnitude and sense of the necessary moment that would have to be applied at A to reduce the reaction at B to zero.

(S)

9 A non-uniform rod AB of length $6a$ rests in a horizontal position on two pegs distant a from each end. (Draw your diagram with B to the right of A.) The rod will just tilt if a weight W is attached to A or a weight $2W$ is attached to B. Find the weight of the rod and the distance of its centre of gravity from A. When the rod is resting on the pegs (with neither of the weights attached) a clockwise couple of moment Wa is applied to the rod in the vertical plane containing the rod. Find the magnitudes of the reactions of the pegs on the rod.

(S)

157

M19 Equilibrium

Particle in equilibrium, Rigid body in equilibrium, Conditions for equilibrium.

Particle in equilibrium

When a particle is in equilibrium under a system of coplanar concurrent forces the following condition is satisfied:
the total resolute of all the forces in any direction must be zero.

When solving problems about particles in equilibrium:

1. Draw a clear force diagram.

2. Choose a direction for resolving, remembering that the resolute of a force in a direction perpendicular to itself is zero.

3. Resolve the forces acting in this chosen direction and equate the total resolute to zero.

4. If necessary, resolve the forces acting in another suitable direction and equate the total resolute to zero.

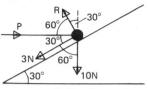

A particle on a slope is subject to the forces shown in the diagram and is in equilibrium. Find the forces R and P.

Figure 1

Resolving vertically (to eliminate force P):
$$R \cos 30° - 10 - 3 \cos 60° = 0$$
i.e. $R = \dfrac{23\sqrt{3}}{3}$ N

Resolving parallel to slope (to eliminate force R):
$$P \cos 30° - 3 - 10 \cos 60° = 0$$
i.e. $P = \dfrac{16\sqrt{3}}{3}$ N

Rigid body in equilibrium

When a rigid body is in equilibrium under a system of coplanar forces, the following two conditions are satisfied:

1. the total resolute of all the forces in any direction must be zero,

2. the total moment of all the forces about any point in the plane must be zero.

When solving problems about rigid bodies in equilibrium:

1. Draw a clear force diagram.

2. Choose two directions at right angles for resolving, remembering that the resolute of a force in a direction perpendicular to itself is zero.

3. Resolve the forces acting in the two chosen directions and equate each total resolute to zero.

4. Take moments about a suitable point in the plane, remembering that the moment of a force about a point on the line of action of the force is zero.

A uniform ladder 5 m long, weight 200 N, rests on rough horizontal ground and against a smooth vertical wall. It is inclined at an angle of 30° to the vertical. Find the normal reactions at each end of the ladder.

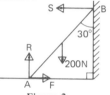

Ladder AB.
R – normal reaction at A.
S – normal reaction at B.
F – frictional force.

Figure 2

Moments about A give:
$$S \times 5 \cos 30° = 200 \times 2.5 \cos 60°$$
i.e. $S = \dfrac{100\sqrt{3}}{3}$ N

Resolving vertically gives:
$$R - 200 = 0 \Rightarrow R = 200 \text{ N}$$

Conditions for equilibrium

If a system of coplanar forces is in equilibrium, then:

1. no resultant force must act (or the system would have an acceleration), and

2. no resultant turning effect must exist, i.e. it must not reduce to a couple.

Three sets of necessary and sufficient conditions for equilibrium are given below. Any of these may be used to test the equilibrium of a system of forces.

Set I
A system of coplanar forces is in equilibrium if:

1. the total resolutes of the forces in two perpendicular directions are each zero, and

2. the resultant moment about any point in the plane is zero.

Set II
A system of coplanar forces is in equilibrium if:

1. the resultant moments about any two points in the plane, P and Q say, are each zero, and

2. the total resolute of the forces in one direction, not perpendicular to PQ, is zero.

Set III
A system of coplanar forces is in equilibrium if:
the resultant moments about three non-collinear points are each zero.

ABCD is a square of side 2 m. Forces of magnitude 7, 3, 3, 7 and $4\sqrt{2}$ N act along $\overrightarrow{BA}$, $\overrightarrow{BC}$, $\overrightarrow{DC}$, $\overrightarrow{DA}$, and $\overrightarrow{AC}$ respectively. Show that this system of forces is in equilibrium.

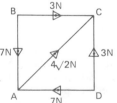

Figure 3

To show that this system of coplanar forces is in equilibrium it is necessary and sufficient to show that the resultant moments of the forces about three non-collinear points are each zero.

Moments about A give:
$$(3 \times 2) - (3 \times 2) = 0$$
Moments about B give:
$$(3 \times 2) - (7 \times 2) + (4\sqrt{2} \times \sqrt{2}) = 0$$
Moments about C give:
$$(7 \times 2) - (7 \times 2) = 0$$

Hence, the system of forces is in equilibrium.

Equilibrium
Worked example, Guided example and Exam questions

 The diagram shows a uniform rod AB of weight W and length 2l which is smoothly hinged at its midpoint to a fixed pivot M. A particle of weight 2W is attached to the rod at A. The other end B has a light string attached which is fastened to a fixed point C. The rod is in equilibrium with AB making an angle θ with the horizontal, where $\cos\theta = \frac{3}{4}$. The angle ABC is 90°. The points A, B and C are all in the same vertical plane.

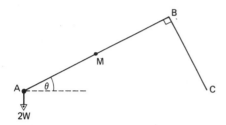

Calculate, in terms of W,
(i) the tension in the string,
(ii) the magnitude of the resultant force exerted by the pivot on the rod.

Draw a diagram showing the forces acting on the rod AB.

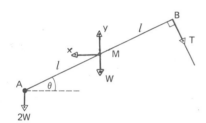

$$\cos\theta = \frac{3}{4}, \text{ so } \sin\theta = \frac{\sqrt{7}}{4}.$$

Let T be the tension in the string.
Let X and Y be the horizontal and vertical components of the reaction at the pivot.

(i) Moments about M:
$$Tl = 2Wl\cos\theta$$
$$\Rightarrow \quad T = \frac{3}{2}W \text{ — the tension in the string.}$$

(ii) Resolving vertically:
$$Y = 2W + W + T\cos\theta$$
i.e. $\quad Y = 3W + \frac{3}{2}W \cdot \frac{3}{4}$
$$\Rightarrow \quad Y = 4\tfrac{1}{8}W.$$
Resolving horizontally:
$$X = T\sin\theta$$
$$\Rightarrow \quad X = \frac{3\sqrt{7}}{8}W.$$

Magnitude of the force at the pivot is
$$\left[\left(4\tfrac{1}{8}\right)^2 + \left(\frac{3\sqrt{7}}{8}\right)^2\right]^{\frac{1}{2}} W = W3\sqrt{2}.$$

 A smooth circular cylinder of weight 150 N rests on level ground DL, touching a vertical wall LM, as shown in the diagram. The axis of the cylinder is parallel to the ground and the wall.

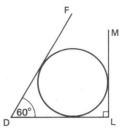

A uniform rod DF of weight 100 N and length 1.5 m, smoothly hinged at D so as to move in a vertical plane perpendicular to the axis of the cylinder, rests at an angle of 60° to the horizontal, touching the cylinder at a point 0.5 m from the end F. Calculate the magnitude of the forces on the cylinder at the points where it touches the rod, the ground and the wall.

First draw *two* separate force diagrams:
(i) Showing the forces acting on the cylinder,
(ii) Showing the forces acting on the rod.
Resolve horizontally and vertically for the cylinder. Take moments about D for the rod.
Solve the three equations to find the three required forces.

 1 A light inextensible string *ABCDE* has its ends *A* and *E* fixed at two points in the same horizontal line and has loads attached at the points *B*, *C* and *D*. If *AB*, *BC*, *CD* and *DE* make angles of 45°, 30°, 30° and 60° respectively with the horizontal and the load at the lowest point *C* is 3 kg, calculate, assuming the string and the loads are in equilibrium:
(i) the tension in each of the four portions of the string,
(ii) the loads at *B* and at *D*. *(A)*

2 A uniform rod *AB*, of length 4*a* and weight *W*, is smoothly hinged to a fixed point at *A*. The rod is held at 60° to the horizontal with *B* above *A* by a horizontal force **F** acting at *B*. Calculate, in terms of *W*:
(a) the magnitude of **F**;
(b) the magnitude of the force exerted by the hinge on the rod and find, to the nearest degree, the direction of this force. The horizontal force acting at *B* is removed and the rod is held in the same position by resting against a fixed smooth peg at *C*, where *AC* = 3*a*.
(c) Calculate, in terms of *W*, the magnitude of the force exerted by the peg on the rod.
(d) Find, to the nearest degree, the direction of the force exerted by the hinge on the rod. *(L)*

3 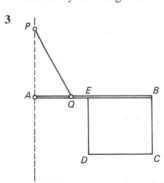 The figure shows a shop-sign consisting of a uniform metal bar *AB* weighing 10 kg and a uniform rectangular plate *BCDE* weighing 20 kg, the whole being supported by a light stay *PQ*. The joints at *P*, *Q* and *A* are smooth hinges. The dimensions are *AB* = 1.5 m, *AQ* = 0.5 m, *AE* = 0.7 m, *PQ* = 1 m.

Write down the equation of moments about *A*, and hence calculate the tension in the stay *PQ* in newtons. Find also the horizontal and vertical thrusts on the hinge at *A*.
(O & C)

M20 Three Force Problems

Three forces in equilibrium, Triangle of forces, Lami's theorem, Useful formulae.

Three forces in equilibrium

When a body is in equilibrium under a system of three coplanar forces only, several special results apply which make these 'three force problems' easier to solve.

The first special result is:
If a body is in equilibrium under the action of three coplanar forces, then these forces are either:

    (a) parallel

or (b) concurrent.

Spotting this in questions often makes their solution much easier.

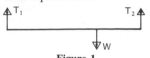 This horizontal bar held by two vertical strings is in equilibrium.

Three parallel coplanar forces.

Figure 1

This bar in contact with rough ground and held by a string is in equilibrium

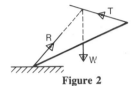

Three concurrent coplanar forces.

Figure 2

Triangle of forces

The second special result is:
If a body is in equilibrium under the action of three concurrent coplanar forces, then these forces can be represented by the sides of a triangle taken in order, since their vector sum must be zero.

Force diagram   Triangle of forces

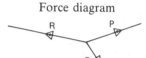

Figure 3

The sides of the triangle must be parallel to the forces they represent, and equal in length to the magnitudes of the forces.

A particle of weight W is supported by two light strings as shown. Find the tensions T_1 and T_2.

Force diagram   Triangle of forces

Figure 4

From the triangle of forces: $T_1 = W \cos \alpha$

$$T_2 = W \sin \alpha$$

Notice how the arrows 'chase each other round' in the triangle of forces, showing zero resultant, i.e. particle in equilibrium.

Lami's theorem

The third special result is Lami's theorem which is a version of the sine rule.

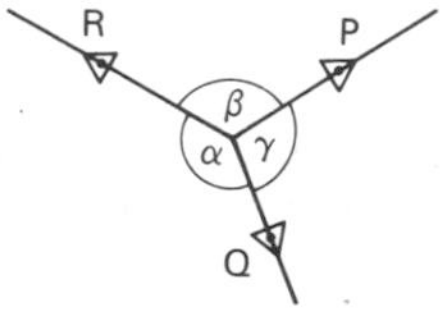

Figure 5

If three concurrent coplanar forces P, Q and R are in equilibrium and the angles between Q and R, R and P, P and Q are α, β and γ respectively as shown, then Lami's theorem states that:

$$\frac{P}{\sin \alpha} = \frac{Q}{\sin \beta} = \frac{R}{\sin \gamma}$$

This is particularly useful when one of the forces and the angles between pairs of forces are known.
It may also be used to solve the triangle of forces when this has been sketched.

The diagram shows a uniform ladder AB of weight 200 N resting in equilibrium with its foot on horizontal rough ground and its upper end against a rough vertical wall. Find R and S, the total reactions at A and B.

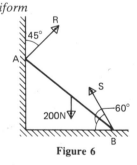

Figure 6

The ladder is in equilibrium under three non-parallel forces R, S and 200 N, so the forces are concurrent.

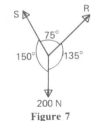

Figure 7

Lami's theorem gives:

$$\frac{200}{\sin 75°} = \frac{R}{\sin 150°} = \frac{S}{\sin 135°}$$

$$R = \frac{\sin 30°}{\sin 75°} \times 200 \approx 104 \text{ N}$$

$$S = \frac{\sin 45°}{\sin 75°} \times 200 \approx 146 \text{ N}$$

Useful formulae

The following **trigonometrical formulae** are often useful.

When D divides AB in the ratio $m:n$ then:

$$(m+n) \cot \theta = n \cot A - m \cot B$$
$$(m+n) \cot \theta = m \cot \alpha - n \cot \beta$$

When D is the midpoint of AB, then

$$2 \cot \theta = \cot A - \cot B = \cot \alpha - \cot \beta$$

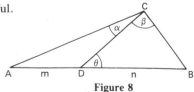

Figure 8

Three Force Problems
Worked example, Guided example and Exam questions

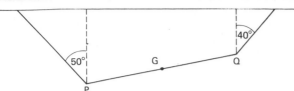

The diagram shows a uniform rod PQ of mass 10 kg *which is held in equilibrium by two strings attached at the ends P and Q of the rod. The strings are inclined to the vertical as shown. Calculate:*
(a) the tensions in the strings,
(b) the angle made by PQ with the vertical.

Draw the force diagram showing the forces acting on the rod PQ. θ is the angle of inclination of PQ to the vertical.

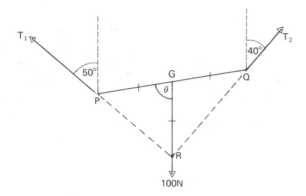

The rod is in equilibrium under the action of the three forces which pass through a common point, say, R.
Draw the triangle of forces.

From the triangle,
$$T_1 = 100 \cos 50° \text{ N},$$
$$T_2 = 100 \cos 40° \text{ N}.$$

Since G is the midpoint of PQ and $\angle ABC = 90°$, P, Q and R must all lie on a circle (angle at the centre is 90°). Hence $GP = GQ = GR$ so $\angle GPR = 50°$. Hence $\theta = 80°$ is the angle of inclination of PQ to the vertical.

 A smooth uniform sphere of radius 18 cm *and weight* 24 N *rests against a smooth vertical wall and is supported by an inextensible wire* 12 cm *long tied to the wall and the surface of the sphere. Calculate the tension in the wire and the reaction of the wall on the sphere.*

Sketch a diagram showing the three forces acting on the sphere. (They must be concurrent.)
Sketch the triangle of forces. One force, 24 N, is known.
Use the triangle to calculate the other two forces.

 1 The figure shows a uniform heavy bar AB of length 1 m and mass 8 kg which is freely hinged at A to a vertical wall. The bar rests in equilibrium with AB in contact with a smooth

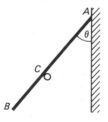

peg at C and makes an angle θ with the vertical where $\sin \theta = 0.6$. The distance AC is 60 cm. Draw a figure showing the forces acting on the bar. Calculate:
(i) the magnitude of the reaction at C;
(ii) the angle which the reaction at A makes with the horizontal. *(C)*

2

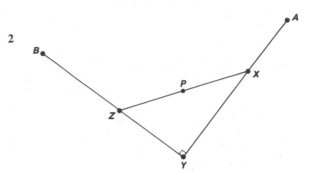

The diagram represents a uniform plane triangular lamina XYZ of weight 50 N and the angles YXZ and XYZ are 34° and 90° respectively. The lamina is suspended in equilibrium by two light strings AX and BZ. AXY and BZY are straight lines. If P is the mid-point of XZ, show that $PX = PY = PZ$. Why must PY be vertical? Hence calculate (i) the angle which XZ makes with the horizontal; (ii) the tensions in the strings.
(O & C)

3 A uniform rod XY of mass 10 kg rests in a vertical plane with the end X in contact with a smooth vertical wall. The end Y is below X. The rod is inclined at 60° to the vertical and is held in equilibrium by a light string attached to Y and to a point Z in the wall vertically above X. Show, in a diagram, the forces acting on the rod and hence that the distance ZX is half the length of the rod.
Find (i) the inclination of the string to the vertical; and (ii) the tension in the string.
(W)

4 Two light rings can slide on a rough horizontal rod. The rings are connected by a light inextensible string of length a to the midpoint of which is attached a weight W. Show that the greatest distance between the rings consistent with equilibrium is $\mu a/(1+\mu^2)^{\frac{1}{2}}$ where μ is the coefficient of friction between either ring and the rod.

5 A uniform body is in the form of a thick hemispherical shell having internal and external radii $2a$ and $3a$. Show that the distance of the centre of mass from the centre of the plane face is $\frac{195}{152} a$.

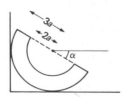

The body rests, as shown (in cross-section), on a fixed horizontal surface and against a fixed vertical surface, with its axis in a vertical plane perpendicular to both surfaces. The vertical surface is smooth and the coefficient of friction between the body and the horizontal surface is $\frac{1}{4}$. Given that the body is in limiting equilibrium, find the value of $\sin \alpha$, where α is the inclination of the plane face to the horizontal. *(C)*

M21 Friction
Force of friction, Angle of friction, Problem solving.

Force of friction

When one body slides or attempts to slide over another, **forces of friction** usually exist between the two surfaces in contact.

Forces of friction act between **rough** surfaces in contact. **Smooth** surfaces in contact are frictionless. The following **experimental laws** describe the behaviour of frictional forces.

1. A frictional force only exists when one body slides or tries to slide over another.

2. A frictional force always **opposes** the tendency of one body to slide over another.

3. The magnitude of a frictional force may vary, always being just sufficient to prevent motion, until it reaches a **maximum value** called the **limiting value**.

4. The **limiting value** of the frictional force is μR, where μ is called the **coefficient of friction** and R is the normal reaction for the surfaces in contact. μ is a measure of the degree of roughness of the two surfaces in contact and is different for different pairs of surfaces.

5. When one body slides over another, the frictional force between them equals the limiting value μR.
A consequence of laws (3) and (4) is that the frictional force F obeys the relation $F \leq \mu R$.

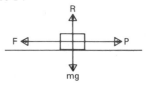

i A body, mass m, is resting on a rough horizontal plane and is being acted upon by a horizontal force P.

Figure 1

As the magnitude of P is gradually increased from zero, the magnitude of the frictional force F will also increase from zero in an attempt to prevent motion. When motion begins F has reached its maximum, called the limiting value μR, and cannot increase any more to prevent motion. So the frictional force remains constant, i.e. $F = \mu R$, whatever the increase in P.

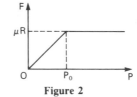

For:
$0 \leq P < P_0$ body stationary and $F < \mu R$.
$P = P_0$ limiting equilibrium and $F = \mu R$.
$P > P_0$ body accelerates and $F = \mu R$.

Figure 2

Angle of friction

The **resultant** S of the frictional force F and the normal reaction R is called the **total reaction**.

It makes an angle θ with the normal, where $\tan \theta = \dfrac{F}{R}$.

The normal reaction R is constant, but the frictional force F may vary.

As the frictional force F increases from zero to its maximum value F_L, the limiting value μR, the angle θ increases from zero to a maximum value λ, called the **angle of friction**.

$$\tan \lambda = \frac{\mu R}{R} = \mu$$

i.e. $\lambda = \tan^{-1} \mu$

When the frictional force has reached its limiting value F_L:

the **direction** of the total reaction S_L is at an angle λ to the normal reaction R,
the **magnitude** of the total reaction is $\sqrt{(R^2 + \mu^2 R^2)}$
$= R\sqrt{(1 + \mu^2)} = R \sec \lambda$.

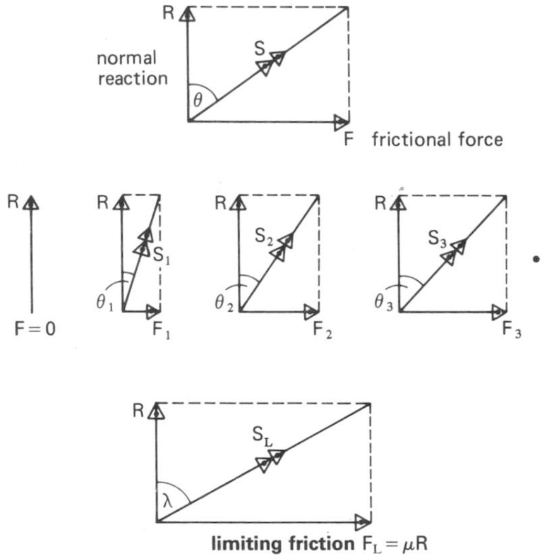

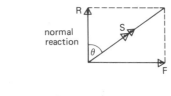

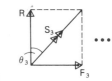

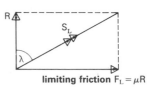

limiting friction $F_L = \mu R$

Figure 3

Problem solving

The following points are important when solving problems involving a frictional force F.

1. Draw a clear force diagram. Show the frictional force as F, do not use μR. Remember: F tends to oppose motion.

2. In general $F \leq \mu R$. If F has reached its limiting value, then $F = \mu R$ may be used in the solution.

3. 'Limiting equilibrium' indicates that the body is at rest but on the point of moving and that $F = \mu R$.

4. If the body is in equilibrium, then the equations of equilibrium (see p. 144) and $F \leq \mu R$ are used.

5. If λ is given, not μ, then it is often easier to solve the problem by considering the total reaction, rather than F and R separately. This is often the case in three force problems (see p.146).

i *Find the least force P required to just prevent this particle from sliding down this inclined plane.*

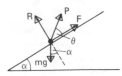

Figure 4

Resolve ∥ to slope: $P \cos \theta + F - mg \sin \alpha = 0$
$\Rightarrow F = mg \sin \alpha - P \cos \theta$
Resolve ⊥ to slope: $R + P \sin \theta - mg \cos \alpha = 0$
$\Rightarrow R = mg \cos \alpha - P \sin \theta$
Limiting friction, so $F = \mu R$
$\quad mg \sin \alpha - P \cos \theta = \mu(mg \cos \alpha - P \sin \theta)$

Using $\mu = \tan \lambda$, $P = \dfrac{mg \sin(\alpha - \lambda)}{\cos(\theta + \lambda)}$

P is a minimum when $\cos(\theta + \lambda)$ is a maximum, i.e. 1.
Hence, minimum $P = mg \sin(\alpha - \lambda)$.
This occurs when $(\theta + \lambda) = 0$, i.e. $\theta = -\lambda$.

Friction
Worked example, Guided example and Exam questions

A uniform ladder of length 7 m leans against a vertical wall at an angle of 45° to the horizontal ground. The coefficients of friction between the ladder and the wall and the ladder and the ground are $\frac{1}{3}$ and $\frac{1}{2}$ respectively. How far up the ladder can a man, whose weight is half that of the ladder, ascend before the ladder slips?

Assume that the man has climbed to such a position that the ladder is about to slip.
This diagram shows the forces acting on the ladder AB. M is the man.

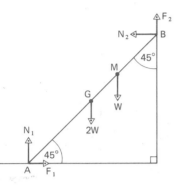

Let $AM = x$ metres.
$AG = GB = 3\frac{1}{2}$ metres.
F_1 and F_2 are the frictional forces.
N_1 and N_2 are the normal reactions.

Since ladder is about to slip
$F_1 = \frac{1}{2}N_1$ and $F_2 = \frac{1}{3}N_2$.
Resolving vertically:
$N_1 + F_2 = 3W$.
Resolving horizontally:
$\quad F_1 = N_2$.

These four equations give,
$N_1 = \frac{18}{7}W,\ F_1 = \frac{9}{7}W,\ N_2 = \frac{9}{7}W,\ F_2 = \frac{3}{7}W$.

Moments about A:
$2W \times 3\frac{1}{2} \cos 45° + W \times x \cos 45° = N_2 \times 7 \sin 45° + F_2 \times 7 \cos 45°$,
so, $7W + xW = 9W + 3W$
i.e. $x = 5$ metres — the distance up the ladder the man can safely climb.

A particle P of weight W rests in limiting equilibrium on a rough plane which is inclined at an angle α to the horizontal. Prove that the coefficient of friction between the particle and the plane is $\tan \alpha$.

(a) Figure (a) shows a horizontal force H, which is applied to P and acts in the vertical plane containing the line of greatest slope of the inclined plane which passes through P. If equilibrium is limiting with P on the point of moving up the plane, find H in terms of W and α.

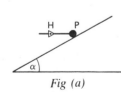

Fig (a)   Fig (b)

(b) Figure (b) shows a force Q which is applied to P in the vertical plane containing the line of greatest slope through P. The force is inclined at an angle θ to this line. If equilibrium is limiting with P on the point of moving up the plane show that

$$Q = \frac{W \sin 2\alpha}{\cos (\theta - \alpha)}.$$

Hence find, in terms of α, the value of θ for which Q is least.

Draw a diagram showing the three forces acting on P. Since equilibrium is limiting, $F = \mu N$. Hence find μ.
(a) Copy Figure (a) and add the missing three forces to it. (Remember friction will act *down* the plane.)
Resolve parallel and perpendicular to the plane. Use $\mu = \tan \alpha$. Hence find H.

(b) Copy Figure (b) and add the missing three forces to it. Use resolution in two directions at right angles and $\mu = \tan \alpha$. Hence find Q. Q will be a minimum when $\cos (\theta - \alpha)$ is a maximum, i.e. 1. Hence state the value of θ for $\cos (\theta - \alpha) = 1$.

---

1 A particle P, of mass $7m$, is placed on a rough horizontal table, the coefficient of friction between P and the table being μ. A force of magnitude $2mg$, acting upwards at an acute angle α to the horizontal, is applied to P and equilibrium is on the point of being broken by the particle sliding on the table. Given that $\tan \alpha = \dfrac{5}{12}$, find the value of μ.

(L)

2 A block of mass 1.5 kg lying on a rough inclined plane is prevented from slipping down the plane by a string attached at one end to a point of the block and, at the other end, to a fixed point. The string is parallel to a line of greatest slope of the plane. The angle of inclination of the plane to the horizontal is α, where $\tan \alpha = \frac{4}{3}$, and the coefficient of friction between the block and the plane is 0.5. Calculate the tension of the string in newtons. If the string is cut, find the acceleration with which the block slides down the plane.

(O & C)

3 The foot of a uniform ladder, of length l and weight W, rests on rough horizontal ground, and the top of the ladder rests against a smooth vertical wall. The ladder is inclined at 30° to the vertical. Find the magnitude of the force exerted by the ladder on the wall. Given that the coefficient of friction between the ladder and the ground is $\frac{1}{4}\sqrt{3}$, show that a man of weight $4W$ cannot climb to the top of the ladder without the ladder slipping, and find the least weight which when placed on the foot of the ladder would enable the man to climb to the top of the ladder.

(L)

4 A fixed hollow hemisphere has centre O and is fixed so that the plane of the rim is horizontal. A particle A of mass m can move on the inside surface of the hemisphere. The particle is acted on by a horizontal force of magnitude P, whose line of action is in the vertical plane through O and A. The diagram shows the situation when A is in equilibrium, the line OA making an acute angle θ with the vertical.

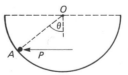

(i) Given that the inside surface of the hemisphere is smooth, find $\tan \theta$ in terms of P, m and g.
(ii) Given instead that the inside surface of the hemisphere is rough, with coefficient of friction μ between the surface and A, and that the particle is about to slip downwards, show that $\tan \theta = \dfrac{P + \mu mg}{mg - \mu P}$.

(C)

M22 Bodies in Contact
Force diagrams, Problem solving.

Force diagrams

Bodies in contact may be either simply **touching** each other or connected together with a **hinge**.

In both cases, if the bodies in contact are in **equilibrium** under a set of coplanar forces, then:

(a) the **complete system** is in **equilibrium**,

(b) each **separate body** is in **equilibrium**.

The complete system may be treated as if it were a single 'body'. Its force diagram must show the forces which act on this 'body' and originate from outside it, e.g. weight force, reactions and frictional forces between the 'body' and its surroundings.

Force diagrams for each separate body must show the forces which act on that body, e.g. weight force, reactions and any frictional forces at all points of contact.

Note: The force acting at a smooth hinge is usually shown resolved into its horizontal and vertical components in the force diagram.

i A rough cylinder of weight W rests in equilibrium on rough horizontal ground with its axis horizontal. A uniform rod of weight w is smoothly hinged at its lower end to a point on the ground and rests in contact with the cylinder such that its upper end is above the point of contact, the plane containing the rod being perpendicular to the axis of the cylinder.

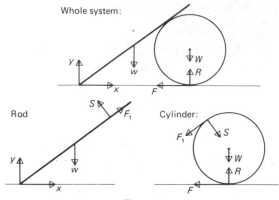

Figure 1

Problem solving

When solving problems involving bodies in contact:

1. Draw a clear force diagram for the complete system, i.e. treat the complete system as if it were a single 'body'.

2. Calculate any external forces required which act on the complete system by resolving and taking moments.

3. Draw individual force diagrams for the separate bodies which make up the system.

4. Resolve and take moments as necessary to calculate any required reactions.

Note: The **maximum number of independent equations** which can be obtained for a system consisting of n separate bodies is $3n$. In practice this maximum number of equations is usually not needed to solve a problem.

i *Two uniform rods AB and BC, each of length $2a$ and of mass 2 kg and 3 kg respectively are smoothly hinged at B. The ends A and C are each smoothly hinged to two points in the same horizontal straight line and distance $2a$ apart. Find the horizontal and vertical components of the reactions at each hinge.*

For the whole system:

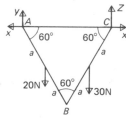

Figure 2

By symmetry the horizontal reactions at A and C must be equal.

Let X and Y be the horizontal and vertical components of the reaction at A.

Let X and Z be the horizontal and vertical components of the reaction at C.

Resolve ($\uparrow$): $Y + Z = 50$ (1)

Moments about A: $Z.2a = 20.\frac{1}{2}a + 30.\frac{3}{2}a$

$$\Rightarrow Z = 27.5 \text{ N}$$

From (1) $Y = 22.5$ N

For separate bodies:

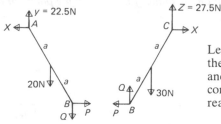

Figure 3

Let P and Q be the horizontal and vertical components of reaction at B.

Moments about B for BC:

$$30.\frac{1}{2}a + X.2a.\frac{\sqrt{3}}{2} = Z.2a.\frac{1}{2} \Rightarrow X \approx 7.22 \text{ N}$$

Resolve ($\rightarrow$) for BC: $P = X \approx 7.22$ N

Resolve ($\uparrow$) for AB: $Q = 30 - Z = 2.5$ N.

Bodies in Contact
Worked example, Guided example and Exam questions

WE *A rough circular cylinder is fixed with its axis horizontal. A uniform rod AB of length 2l and weight W is placed in contact with the cylinder at a point C, where A, B and C all lie in the same vertical plane. When a horizontal force P is applied at B which just prevents the rod from slipping downwards, the inclination of AB to the horizontal is θ and the midpoint of AB is at a distance x from C. If μ(= tan λ) is the coefficient of friction between the rod and the cylinder, prove that,*

(a) $P = W \tan(\theta - \lambda)$,

(b) $\mu < \tan \theta$,

(c) $x = l \sin \theta \sin(\theta - \lambda) \sec \lambda$.

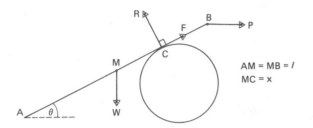

$$AM = MB = l$$
$$MC = x$$

The force diagram shows the forces acting on AB.
R is the normal reaction at C, F is the frictional force acting at C.

(a) Since AB is about to slip,
$$F = \mu R = (\tan \lambda) R \qquad [1]$$
Resolving parallel to AB:
$$F + P \cos \theta = W \sin \theta \qquad [2]$$
Resolving perpendicular to AB:
$$R = W \cos \theta + P \sin \theta. \qquad [3]$$
[1] and [2] give,
$$(\tan \lambda) R = W \sin \theta - P \cos \theta,$$
[3] × tan λ gives,
$$(\tan \lambda) R = W \tan \lambda \cos \theta + P \tan \lambda \sin \theta.$$
Eliminating R gives,
$$P(\cos \theta + \tan \lambda \sin \theta) = W(\sin \theta - \tan \lambda \cos \theta)$$
i.e. $P \cos(\theta - \lambda) \sec \lambda = W \sin(\theta - \lambda) \sec \lambda$
$$\Rightarrow \qquad P = W \tan(\theta - \lambda).$$

(b) If $\theta < \lambda$, $\tan(\theta - \lambda) < 0 \Rightarrow P < 0$; equilibrium impossible.
If $\theta = \lambda$, $\tan(\theta - \lambda) = 0 \Rightarrow P = 0$; not true.
Hence $\theta > \lambda \Rightarrow \tan \theta > \tan \lambda$
i.e. $\mu < \tan \theta$.

(c) Moments about C give:
$$Wx \cos \theta = P(l - x) \sin \theta.$$
Using the value of P obtained we get,
$$x \cos \theta = (l - x) \sin \theta \tan(\theta - \lambda)$$
i.e. $l \sin \theta \tan(\theta - \lambda) = x(\sin \theta \tan(\theta - \lambda) + \cos \theta)$
$$\Rightarrow \quad l \sin \theta \sin(\theta - \lambda) = x(\sin \theta \sin(\theta - \lambda) + \cos \theta \cos(\theta - \lambda))$$
$$= x \cos(\theta - (\theta - \lambda))$$
$$= x \cos \lambda$$
$$\Rightarrow \qquad x = l \sin \theta \sin(\theta - \lambda) \sec \lambda.$$

GE *Two equal rough cylinders are lying in contact with each other, with their axes parallel and horizontal, on a rough horizontal plane. A third equal cylinder is placed symmetrically on top of the other two. If equilibrium is about to be broken by the upper cylinder slipping between the other two, prove that the coefficient of friction between any two cylinders is $2 - \sqrt{3}$.*

Draw two force diagrams, one showing the forces acting on the top cylinder and the other showing the forces acting on one of

the lower cylinders. (By symmetry, the forces acting on the other lower cylinder will be the same.)
Take moments about the point of contact of the lower cylinder with the horizontal plane. If the top cylinder is about to slip, the normal reaction between the two lower cylinders will be zero. Put this force equal to zero in the moments equation. Use '$F = \mu R$' for the forces acting at the point of contact of the upper and lower cylinders to obtain the required value of 'μ'.

EX

1 Two uniform rods AB and BC of the same thickness and material, and of length 4 metres and 3 metres respectively, are freely hinged together and rest in a vertical plane with the ends A and C on a rough horizontal plane. The system is in limiting equilibrium when the angle ABC is $90°$. Determine how equilibrium will be broken when the angle ABC is slightly increased beyond $90°$ and show that the coefficient of friction between the rods and the ground is $\frac{84}{163}$. (W)

2 Two uniform rods, AB and AC, each of length $2a$ and weighing $3W$ and W respectively, are freely jointed at A and rest in a vertical plane with B and C on a rough horizontal floor. The coefficient of friction between either rod and the floor is μ. In limiting equilibrium,
   (i) will slipping first occur at B or at C?
   (ii) what will be the reaction at A (giving both magnitude and direction)?
   (iii) at what angle to the horizontal will the rods be inclined? (S)

3 A uniform sphere of radius a and weight $W/\sqrt{3}$ rests on a rough horizontal table. A uniform rod AB of weight $2W$ and length $2a$ is freely hinged at A to a fixed point on the table and leans against the sphere so that the centre of the sphere and the rod lie in a vertical plane. The rod makes an angle of $60°$ with the horizontal. Show that the frictional force between the rod and the sphere is $\frac{1}{3}W$. The coefficient of friction at each point of contact is μ. What is the smallest value of μ which makes equilibrium possible? (O & C)

4

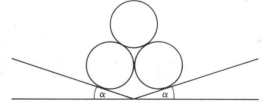

Two smooth uniform right circular cylinders, each of mass m and radius a, are placed symmetrically in contact with each other and with two planes, each inclined at angle α to the horizontal. The axes of the cylinders lie in the same horizontal plane, and are parallel to the line of intersection of the two inclined planes. Another smooth uniform circular cylinder, of mass $2m$ and of radius a, is placed symmetrically on top of the other two. If the two lower cylinders are forced apart, show that $\tan \alpha < 1/(2\sqrt{3})$. (OLE)

5 A uniform rigid rod AB of length $2a$ and weight W, is smoothly jointed at A to a uniform rigid rod AC of length $2a\sqrt{3}$ and weight W'. The rods rest in a vertical plane with B and C on a smooth horizontal plane, equilibrium being maintained by a light inextensible string of length $4a$, joining B and C. Prove that the tension in the string is
$$\frac{\sqrt{3}}{8}(W + W').$$

Prove further that the reaction at A on the rod AC makes an angle of $\tan^{-1}\dfrac{3W' - W}{(W + W')\sqrt{3}}$ with the horizontal.

M23 Equivalent Systems of Forces
Equivalence, Reduction to a force or a couple, Reduction to a force and a couple.

Equivalence

Systems of coplanar forces which produce exactly the same linear and turning effects on a rigid body are **equivalent**.

To establish that two coplanar force systems are equivalent, show that:

1. the total resolutes in two perpendicular directions are the same in both systems, and
2. the resultant moment about a point in the plane containing the forces is the same in both systems.

A known system of coplanar forces may be replaced by an equivalent, often simpler, system using (1) and (2).

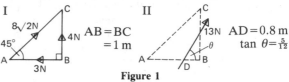 These two systems of forces are equivalent:

Figure 1

	System I	System II
Resolve ∥ AB	$8\sqrt{2}\sin 45° - 3 = 5$	$13\sin\theta = 5$
Resolve ⊥ AB	$8\sqrt{2}\cos 45° + 4 = 12$	$13\cos\theta = 12$
Moments (A)	$4\times 1 = 4$	$13\times 0.8\sin\theta = 4$

Reduction to a force or a couple

The **resultant** of a system of coplanar forces, which is not in equilibrium, is either a **single force or a couple**. This resultant is equivalent to the original system of coplanar forces.

A system **reduces to a single force** if: one or both of the total resolutes in two perpendicular directions is non-zero.
To locate the position of the line of action of the resultant force, take moments about any point in the plane and use the principle of moments.
A system **reduces to a couple** if one of the following sets of conditions is satisfied.

Set I
1. The total resolutes in two perpendicular directions are are each zero, and
2. The resultant moment about any point in the plane is non-zero.

Set II
The resultant moments about three non-collinear points are each non-zero.

  ABC is an isosceles triangle with $AB = AC = 5$ cm and $BC = 6$ cm. M is the midpoint of BC. Forces of 15, 12, 5 and 8 N act along $\vec{AB}, \vec{BC}, \vec{CA}, \vec{MA}$ respectively.
Show that this system of forces is equivalent to a couple and find its moment.

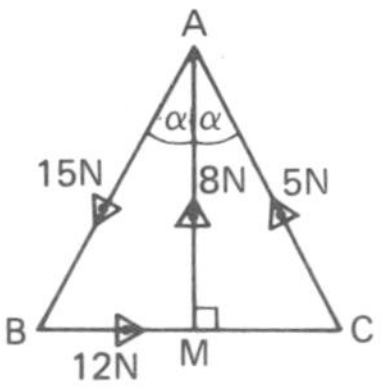

Figure 2

$AB = AC = 5$ cm $= 0.05$ m
$BM = MC = 3$ cm $= 0.03$ m
so $AM = 4$ cm $= 0.04$ m.

Let $\angle MAB = \angle MAC = \alpha$,
so $\sin\alpha = \frac{3}{5}$
$\cos\alpha = \frac{4}{5}$

Resolve ∥ to BC:
$$12 - 15\sin\alpha - 5\sin\alpha = 12 - 15\times\tfrac{3}{5} - 5\times\tfrac{3}{5} = 0.$$

Resolve ⊥ to BC:
$$8 - 15\cos\alpha - 5\cos\alpha = 8 - 15\times\tfrac{4}{5} - 5\times\tfrac{4}{5} = 0$$

Moments about A:
$$12\times 0.05\cos\alpha = 0.48 \text{ N m}$$
Hence,
the system of forces ≡ couple of moment 0.48 N m.

Reduction to a force and a couple

Any system of coplanar forces acting on a rigid body may be replaced by an equivalent system which consists of a **single force**, acting at a particular point in the plane of the forces, **together with a couple**.

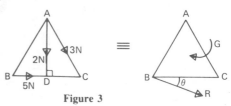 Forces 3 N and 5 N act along the sides $\vec{AC}$ and $\vec{BC}$ of an equilateral triangle, side a metres. A force of 2 N acts along the altitude $\vec{AD}$. Find the force at B and the couple which together are equivalent to this system.

Figure 3

Let R be the required single force at angle θ to BC and G be the moment of the required couple.

Resolve along BC for original system: $5 + 3\cos 60°$
for new system: $R\cos\theta$
So $\qquad R\cos\theta = 5 + 3\cos 60° \qquad (1)$
Resolve ⊥ to BC for original system: $2 + 3\cos 30°$
for new system: $R\sin\theta$
So $\qquad R\sin\theta = 2 + 3\cos 60° \qquad (2)$
Solving (1) and (2) gives $R \approx 7.96$ N and $\theta \approx 35.3°$.

Moments about B: $(2\times\tfrac{1}{2}a) + (3\times a\sin 60°) = G$

i.e. $\qquad\qquad G = \left(\dfrac{1 + 3\sqrt{3}}{2}\right) a$ Nm

Equivalent Systems of Forces
Worked example, Guided example and Exam questions

WE *ABCD is a square of side* 2 m. *Forces of magnitudes* 3 N, 5N, 7 N *and* 2 N *act along the sides DA, AB, BC and CD respectively. Calculate:*

(a) *the magnitude of the resultant of the forces and the angle made by the resultant with AD,*

(b) *the sum of the moments of the forces about A,*

(c) *the distance from A of the point where the line of action of the resultant of the forces cuts DA produced.*

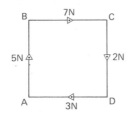

(a) Let X and Y be the resolutes of the resultant force in the directions AD and AB respectively.

$X = (7-3)$ N $= 4$ N
$Y = (5-2)$ N $= 3$ N
Hence, $R = \sqrt{(4^2+3^2)}$ N $= 5$ N
at an angle $\theta = \tan^{-1}\left(\frac{3}{4}\right)$ to AD.

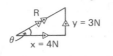

(b) Moments about A for the system of forces gives
$G = (7 \times 2) + (2 \times 2)$ Nm
$\quad = 18$ Nm, in a clockwise sense.

(c) Let $\mathbf{R}$, the resultant of the forces, cut DA produced at P.
Let $AP = x$ metres.

Moments about A for the resultant force gives $G = 5 \sin\theta \times x$.

Since the moments G must be equal,
$5 \sin\theta \times x = 18$

$\Rightarrow \quad x = \dfrac{18}{5 \cdot \dfrac{3}{5}} = 6$ m $\left(\text{since } \sin\theta = \dfrac{3}{5}\right)$.

Hence, the resultant of the forces cuts DA produced at 6 m from A.

GE *A regular hexagon ABCDEF has sides of length* 2 m. *Forces of magnitude* 4, R, 2, 3, 6 *and* 5 newtons *act along the sides AB, BC, DC, DE, EF and AF respectively. A seventh force of magnitude S newtons acts along EB. The directions of the forces are indicated by the order of the letters. Calculate R and S when the given system of forces is equivalent to*

(a) *a single force of magnitude* 6 N *in a direction parallel to EB,*

(b) *a couple,*

In (b) *calculate also the moment of the couple.*

(a) Find the sum of the resolutes of the forces
 (i) parallel to EB and equate to 6 N,
(ii) perpendicular to EB and equate to zero.
Solve the two resulting equations to find R and S.

(b) Repeat (a) (ii) but and (a) (i) but equate the forces to zero. Solve the resulting equations to find the new values for R and S.
To find the moment of the couple, take moments about the centre of the hexagon for the total system of forces.

EX 1 Forces of 5 N and 3 N act along the sides $\vec{AB}$, $\vec{AC}$ respectively of an equilateral triangle ABC of side 12 m. Find the magnitude and direction of their resultant. The line of action of the resultant intersects BC at D. By taking moments about D, or otherwise, find the length of BD.
(C)

2 A rectangle is defined by the four points $A(0, 0)$, $B(5, 0)$, $C(5, 3)$ and $D(0, 3)$, distances being measured in metres. Forces of magnitude 6 N, 8 N, 4 N, and 2 N act along AB, BC, CD and DA respectively in directions indicated by the letters. Calculate:
(a) the magnitude of the resultant of this system of forces;
(b) the angle between the line of action of the resultant and the x-axis.
The line of action of this resultant cuts the x-axis at $(a, 0)$.
(c) Find a value for a by consideration of moments about A. Hence determine the equation of the line of action of this resultant.
(S)

3 The square $ABCD$ has each side of length 6 m. Forces of magnitude 1, 2, 8, 5, $5\sqrt{2}$ and $2\sqrt{2}$ N act along AB, BC, CD, DA, AC and DB respectively, in the directions indicated by the order of the letters. Prove that these forces are equivalent to a couple. Calculate the magnitude and sense of this couple.
(A)

4 $OABC$ is a square of side 1 m. Forces of magnitude 2, 3, 4 and $5\sqrt{2}$ newtons act along OA, AB, CB and AC respectively in directions indicated by the order of the letters and a couple of moment 7 N m acts in the plane of the square in the sense $OCBA$. Find the magnitude and direction of the resultant of the system and the equation of its line of action referred to OA and OC as axes. What is the magnitude and direction of the least force introduced at A if the resultant of the original system and this new force is to pass through O?
(S)

5 A rectangle $ABCD$ has $AB = 3$ cm and $BC = 4$ cm. Forces, all measured in newtons and of magnitudes 2, 4, 6, 8 and k, act along AB, BC, CD, DA and AC respectively, the direction of each force being shown by the order of the letters. The resultant of the five forces is parallel to BD. Find k and show that the resultant has magnitude $\frac{8}{5}$ newtons. Find the distance from A of the line of action of the resultant.
(O & C)

6 A rigid rectangular lamina $ABCD$, with $AB = 4a$ and $BC = 3a$, is subject to forces of magnitudes $10P$, P, $2P$, $3P$ acting along CA, AD, DC, CB respectively in the directions indicated by the order of the letters.
 (i) Find the magnitude of the resultant of the four forces.
 (ii) Find the tangent of the acute angle between the line of action of the resultant and the edge AB of the lamina.
(iii) Find the distance from A of the point where the line of action of the resultant meets AB.
(iv) Indicate clearly on a diagram the line of action and the direction of the resultant.
 (v) Find the magnitude and sense of the couple G which, if added to the system, would cause the resultant force to act through E, the midpoint of CD.
(vi) In the case when G is *not* applied, find forces S along AB, T along AD and U along BC which, when added to the system, would produce equilibrium.
(J)

M24 Centre of Mass
Definitions, System of particles, Symmetry, Standard results, Composite bodies.

Definitions

The **centre of mass** of a body is the point at which the mass of the body may be considered to be acting.
The **centre of gravity** of a body is the point through which the line of action of its weight acts.
The **centroid** of a body is at its geometric centre.
The centre of mass and centre of gravity of a body coincide in a uniform gravitational field.
The centre of mass and the centroid of a body coincide in a uniform body.
A **uniform body** has uniform density.

System of particles

For a **set of particles** of masses $m_1, m_2, m_3, \ldots$ at the points $(x_1, y_1), (x_2, y_2), (x_3, y_3), \ldots$ in the x-y plane, the centre of mass $(\bar{x}, \bar{y})$ is given by

$$\bar{x} = \frac{m_1 x_1 + m_2 x_2 + m_3 x_3 + \ldots}{m_1 + m_2 + m_3 + \ldots} = \frac{\Sigma m_i x_i}{\Sigma m_i}$$

and $\bar{y} = \dfrac{m_1 y_1 + m_2 y_2 + m_3 y_3 + \ldots}{m_1 + m_2 + m_3 + \ldots} = \dfrac{\Sigma m_i y_i}{\Sigma m_i}$

⒤ *Particles of masses 5, 3 and 8 kg are at (0, 0), (3, 4) and (6, 0) respectively. Find $(\bar{x}, \bar{y})$, their centre of mass.*

$$\left. \begin{array}{l} \bar{x} = \dfrac{5(0) + 3(3) + 8(6)}{5 + 3 + 8} = \dfrac{57}{16} \\[2mm] \bar{y} = \dfrac{5(0) + 3(4) + 8(0)}{5 + 3 + 8} = \dfrac{3}{4} \end{array} \right\}$$ So $(\bar{x}, \bar{y})$ is $\left(\dfrac{57}{16}, \dfrac{3}{4} \right)$.

Symmetry

The centre of mass of a **uniform body** lies on every line or plane of **symmetry** of the body. It is at the point where any two lines, or three planes of symmetry intersect.
By symmetry the centres of mass of the following lie at their geometric centres:
uniform rod, circular lamina, rectangular lamina, sphere, cuboid.

Standard results

uniform body	centre of mass
triangular lamina	intersection of medians
circular arc, radius a, angle at centre 2α	$\dfrac{a \sin \alpha}{\alpha}$ from centre
circular sector, radius a, angle at centre 2α	$\dfrac{2a \sin \alpha}{3\alpha}$ from centre
solid hemisphere, radius a	$\dfrac{3a}{8}$ from plane face
hollow hemisphere, radius a	$\dfrac{a}{2}$ from plane face
solid cone, height h (tetrahedron, pyramid)	$\dfrac{h}{4}$ from base
hollow cone, no base, height h	$\dfrac{h}{3}$ from 'base'

⒤
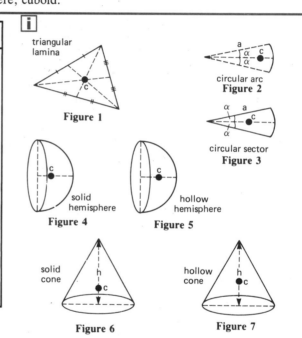

Figure 1 — triangular lamina

Figure 2 — circular arc

Figure 3 — circular sector

Figure 4 — solid hemisphere

Figure 5 — hollow hemisphere

Figure 6 — solid cone

Figure 7 — hollow cone

Composite bodies

A **composite body** is one made from two or more parts (usually standard).

To find the centre of mass of a composite body
(a) Draw a clear diagram.
(b) Mark any lines of symmetry.
(c) Choose two axes at right angles to each other. If a line of symmetry exists choose this as an axis.
(d) Divide the body into known (standard) bodies.
(e) Tabulate the 'masses' and 'distances of centres of masses from the chosen axes'.
Note: In a uniform lamina, mass $\propto$ area.
In a uniform solid, mass $\propto$ volume.
(f) Take moments about the chosen axes.
(g) Use the principle of moments:
Moment of total mass about an axis = sum of moments of separate masses about same axis.

This method can also be used to deal with a body from which a part has been removed.

⒤
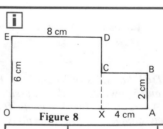

Figure 8

Find the centre of mass of this uniform lamina referred to OA and OE as axes.

Divide the lamina into two rectangles $OXDE$ and $XABC$.

shape	mass (M is mass/unit area)	distance of centre of mass	
		from OE	from OA
$OXDE$	$(6 \times 8)M = 48M$	4	3
$XABC$	$(4 \times 2)M = 8M$	$(8+2) = 10$	1
$OABCDE$	$56M$	$\bar{x}$	$\bar{y}$

Moments about OE give: $48M \times 4 + 8M \times 10 = 56M \times \bar{x}$
$$\Rightarrow \bar{x} = 4\tfrac{6}{7} \text{ cm}$$
Moments about OA give: $48M \times 3 + 8M \times 1 = 56M \times \bar{y}$
$$\Rightarrow \bar{y} = 2\tfrac{5}{7} \text{ cm}$$

$\therefore$ Centre of mass is at a point which is $4\tfrac{6}{7}$ cm from OE and $2\tfrac{5}{7}$ cm from OA.

Centre of Mass
Worked example, Guided example and Exam questions

WE *A uniform right circular solid cylinder has a radius r and length 4r. A solid hemisphere of radius r is cut from one end of the cylinder, the plane face of which is one of the plane faces of the cylinder. The hemisphere so removed, is now attached by its plane face to the uncut plane face of the cylinder thus forming a new solid. Find the position of the centre of mass of the new solid.* **EX**

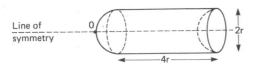

Let O be the point on the line of symmetry at the extreme end of the solid.
Let $\bar{x}$ be the distance of the centre of mass of the 'new solid' from O.

Shape		Mass	Distance of c of m from O
(1)		$4\pi r^3$	$r + 2r = 3r$
(2)		$\frac{2}{3}\pi r^3$	$\frac{5}{8}r$
(3)		$\frac{2}{3}\pi r^3$	$r = 4r - \frac{3}{8}r = \frac{37}{8}r$
(4)		$4\pi r^3$	$\bar{x}$

Notice that if we put together shapes (1) and (2) we get the same shape as we do by putting together shapes (3) and (4). We use this to write down our moments equation.
Moments about O give:

$$\left(4\pi r^3 \times 3r\right) + \left(\frac{2}{3}\pi r^3 \times \frac{5}{8}r\right) = \left(\frac{2}{3}\pi r^3 \times \frac{37}{8}r\right) + \left(4\pi r^3 \times \bar{x}\right)$$

$$\Rightarrow \bar{x} = \frac{7}{3}r.$$

GE *A uniform lamina is formed by removing a circular disc of radius r from a circular disc of radius 2r as shown. Find the position of the centre of gravity of the lamina with respect to the two axes Ox and Oy as shown.*

Notice that Ox is an axis of symmetry.
Tabulate:

(a) The masses of
    (i) the original circular disc,
    (ii) the small circular disc which was removed,
    (iii) the lamina.
(b) The distances of the centres of mass from O along Ox.

Use the principle of moments, putting together shapes (ii) and (iii) to make (i). Hence find the position of the centre of mass of the lamina.

1 A uniform rectangular lamina $ABCD$ is of mass $3M$; $AB = DC = 4$ cm and $BC = AD = 6$ cm. Particles, each of mass M, are attached to the lamina at B, C and D. Calculate the distance of the centre of mass of the loaded lamina: (a) from AB, (b) from BC.   *(L)*

2 (a) The figure below shows a plate of uniform thickness, circular in shape, which has two circular holes drilled through it. The radius of the plate is 80 mm and AOB, COD are perpendicular axes of the plate.

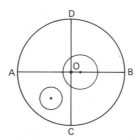

One hole, of radius 20 mm, has its centre on OB at a distance of 5 mm from O; the other, of radius 10 mm, has its centre at a distance of 40 mm from OA and 20 mm from OC. Show that the centre of mass of the plate is located on the axis COD and find its distance from O.
(b) Masses p, q and r are placed at the points whose cartesian co-ordinates are respectively $(0, 0)$, $(20, 0)$ and $(0, 16)$. If $p:q:r = 1:4:3$, find the co-ordinates of the centre of mass of the three masses.   *(W)*

3 A can in the form of a circular cylinder, without a lid, is made of thin metal sheeting of uniform thickness and with a mass per unit area of 1 g/cm². The radius of the can is 10 cm and its height is 20 cm. The can is placed with its base on a horizontal plane and is half-filled with a liquid of density 1.5 g/cm³. Calculate the height of the centre of gravity of the can together with the liquid, above the base of the can.   *(A)*

4 The diagram shows a square $OABC$ of side a. The midpoint of BC is D. Show that, with respect to OA and OC as axes, the coordinates of the centroid F of the triangular region ABD are $(\frac{5}{6}a, \frac{2}{3}a)$. Find the coordinates of the centre of mass of a uniform lamina in the form of the figure $OADC$.   *(J)*

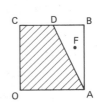

5 A uniform solid right circular cone has its top removed by cutting the cone by a plane parallel to its base, leaving a truncated cone of height h, the radii of its ends being r and $4r$. Show that the distance of the centre of gravity of the truncated cone from its broader end is $\frac{9}{28}h$.   *(O & C)*

6 Prove that the centre of gravity of a uniform circular arc subtending an angle 2θ at the centre of a circle of radius a is $a \sin\theta/\theta$ from the centre. Deduce that the centre of gravity of a uniform sector bounded by that arc and the radii to its extremities is $\frac{2}{3}a \sin\theta/\theta$ from the centre. Show also that the centre of gravity of a segment of a circular lamina cut off by a chord subtending a right angle at the centre of the circle is $\frac{2}{3}\sqrt{2}a/(\pi - 2)$ from the centre.   *(W)*

Suspended bodies, Toppling bodies.

Suspended bodies

When a body is **freely suspended** from a frictionless pivot, P, it will rest in equilibrium with its centre of mass, M, directly below the point of suspension on the vertical through P.
For equilibrium: the reaction R and the weight W act in opposite directions along the same vertical line, and $R = W$.

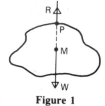

Figure 1

Problems concerned with freely suspended bodies in equilibrium often require you to find the angle made by a line in the body with the vertical. This angle is called the angle of inclination to the vertical.

To solve problems of this type
(a) Draw a clear diagram.
(b) Find the position of the centre of mass, M, of the body.
(c) Draw in the line through the point of suspension, P, and the centre of mass, M. This line will be vertical when the body is freely suspended from P. Your original diagram need not be redrawn.
(d) Obtain an expression for the angle of inclination to the vertical using the position of the centre of mass and geometry or trigonometry from the diagram.

ℹ️ *A uniform rectangular plate ABCD of weight $2W$ has dimensions $AB = DC = 2a$ and $AD = BC = 2b$. A particle of weight W is attached to the plate at C. When the lamina, with the particle attached, is freely suspended from D, DC makes an angle θ with the downward vertical. Show that $\tan \theta = \dfrac{b}{2a}$.*

First find the centre of gravity, $G(\bar{x}, \bar{y})$, for the plate and particle.
Choose DC and DA as axes for 'moments'.

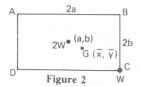

Figure 2

Consider the weight $2W$ of the plate to be at (a, b). The particle of weight W is at $(2a, 0)$.

Moments about DA give:
$$2W \times a + W \times 2a = 3W\bar{x} \Rightarrow \bar{x} = \frac{4a}{3}$$

Moments about DC give:
$$2W \times b + W \times 0 = 3W\bar{y} \Rightarrow \bar{y} = \frac{2b}{3}$$

Now show the vertical line through G and D, the point of suspension.

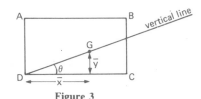

Figure 3

Since DC makes an angle θ with the vertical,
$$\tan \theta = \frac{\bar{y}}{\bar{x}} = \frac{2b}{3} \bigg/ \frac{4a}{3} = \frac{b}{2a}.$$

Toppling bodies

When a body rests in equilibrium on a plane, it will be **stable** provided the line of action of the weight force lies within the extreme points of contact between the body and the plane.

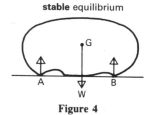

Figure 4

The body will **topple** if the line of action of the weight force lies outside one of these extreme points of contact. It will topple about the point of contact nearest to the line of action of the weight.

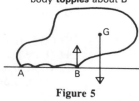

Figure 5

If the body is on a rough inclined plane, it will **topple** if the line of action of the weight force lies outside the lower point of contact of the body with the plane.
On an inclined plane the equilibrium of a body may be broken by sliding rather than toppling.

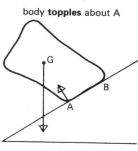

Figure 6

ℹ️ *ABCD is a uniform square lamina, of side a, from which EBC is removed. Find the least length of AE which will allow the lamina AECD to stand in a vertical plane with AE on a horizontal surface.*

Figure 7

First find the distance, $\bar{x}$, of the centre of gravity of $AECD$ from AD.
Let $AE = x$ and let w be the weight per unit area.

shape	weight	distance of c. of g. from AD
$ABCD$	a^2w	$\frac{1}{2}a$
EBC	$\frac{1}{2}a(a-x)w$	$x + \frac{2}{3}(a-x) = \frac{1}{3}(2a+x)$
$AECD$	$\frac{1}{2}a(a+x)w$	$\bar{x}$

Moments about AD give:
$$a^2w \times \tfrac{1}{2}a = \tfrac{1}{2}a(a-x)w \times \tfrac{1}{3}(2a+x) + \tfrac{1}{2}a(a+x)w \times \bar{x}$$
$$\Rightarrow \bar{x} = \frac{a^2 + ax + x^2}{3(a+x)}$$

For no toppling about E:
$\bar{x} \leqslant AE$,
i.e. $\dfrac{a^2 + ax + x^2}{3(a+x)} \leqslant x$.

Figure 8

$\Rightarrow x \geqslant \tfrac{1}{2}a(\sqrt{3}-1)$.
So the least value of x for equilibrium is $\tfrac{1}{2}a(\sqrt{3}-1)$.

Suspending and Toppling
Worked example, Guided example and Exam questions

WE *A toy is constructed as follows.*
A particle of weight W is attached to one end of a light rod of length 3r. The other end of the rod is attached to the centre of the plane face of a uniform solid hemisphere of weight w and radius r, the angle between the rod and the plane face of the hemisphere being 90°. Find, in terms of W, the least value of w such that when the toy is knocked over on a horizontal surface it will always return to an upright position.

We first find the position of the centre of gravity of the toy.

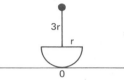

Shape	Weight	Height of c. of g. above O
	$W+w$	$\bar{h}$
	W	$4r$
	w	$\dfrac{5}{8}r$

Moments about O give:
$$(W+w)\bar{h} = 4rW + \frac{5}{8}rw$$
$$\Rightarrow \qquad \bar{h} = \frac{r}{8}\left[\frac{32W+5w}{W+w}\right]$$

Now consider the toy to be knocked over.

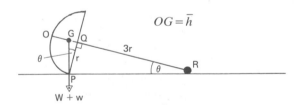
$$OG = \bar{h}$$

Let θ be the angle between the rod and the horizontal. If the toy is to return to the vertical position, the line of action of the weight force must lie to the left of P, the point of contact between the horizontal plane and the hemisphere.

In $\triangle PQR$, $\tan\theta = \dfrac{r}{3r} = \dfrac{1}{3}$.

In $\triangle PQG$, $\tan\theta = \dfrac{r-\bar{h}}{r}$.

So, $\dfrac{r-\bar{h}}{r} = \dfrac{1}{3}$, $\Rightarrow \bar{h} = \dfrac{2r}{3}$.

Hence, $\dfrac{2r}{3} = \dfrac{r}{8}\left[\dfrac{32W+5w}{W+w}\right]$

i.e. $w = 48W$.

So, the least value of w such that the toy always returns to an upright position is $48W$.

GE *A thin uniform plate is formed by a square of side 6 cm being surmounted by an isosceles triangle of vertical height 3 cm, as shown below.*

(a) State the distance of the centre of gravity of the triangle BCD from its side BD.

(b) Calculate the distance of the centre of gravity of the whole plate from sides AB and AE.

(c) If the plate is freely suspended from A, find the inclination of AE to the horizontal.

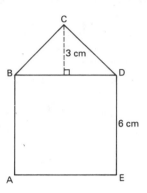

(a) Do as the question says — state.

(b) Notice the shape has a line of symmetry.
Use this line of symmetry as one axis. Use AE as the other axis. Draw the lamina $ABCDE$.
Tabulate the weights of the triangle, square and plate and the distances of their centres of gravity from AE.
Use the principle of moments to find the centre of gravity of the lamina.

(c) Mark the centre of gravity G of the lamina on your drawing.
Put in the 'vertical' through A and G. Mark as θ the angle between AE and the 'vertical'. Use trigonometry to find θ. The inclination of AE to the horizontal is $90° - \theta$.

EX **1** A uniform lamina of mass M is in the shape of a circular disc, centre O. Two points A and B on the circumference of the disc are such that the angle AOB is a right angle. A particle of mass kM is attached to the disc at B. When the loaded disc is in equilibrium suspended freely from A, AO is inclined to the downward vertical at an angle α, where $\tan\alpha = 0\cdot4$. Calculate the value of k.

(A)

2 A uniform lamina $ABCD$ has the shape of a trapezium with DC parallel to AB and $\widehat{BAD} = 90°$, $AB = 3a$, $CD = 2a$ and $AD = 2b$. Find the distances of its centre of gravity from AB and AD. The lamina is freely pivoted at B to a fixed point and hangs down in equilibrium. If $a = 7$ cm, $b = 13$ cm, find the inclination of AB to the vertical.

(O & C)

3 A toy consists of a solid hemisphere of radius a to which is glued a solid circular cylinder of radius a and height $2a$ so that the plane end of the hemisphere is in complete contact with a plane end of the cylinder. The cylinder is made of uniform material of density ϱ, and the hemisphere is made of uniform material of density $k\varrho$. The toy is designed so that if placed on a horizontal table with the hemisphere downwards and then tilted to one side, it will return to the vertical position. Show that $k > 8$. The toy is placed on a desk of slope α where $\sin\alpha = \frac{1}{8}$, sufficiently rough to prevent slipping. It rests in equilibrium with the hemisphere in contact with the desk. Find an expression giving the (acute) angle β made by its axis of symmetry with the vertical. Hence deduce that $k \geqslant 13\frac{1}{2}$.

(O & C)

MECHANICS QUESTION BANK

Answers are given on pages 178–189. **A** and **AS** denote A-level and AS-level, respectively.

1 A   12 mins
At time $t = 0$ a particle is projected vertically upwards from a point O with speed 19.6 m s^{-1} and, two seconds later, a second particle is projected vertically upwards from O with the same speed. Assuming that the only force acting is that due to gravity, express the heights above O of both particles in terms of t and hence, or otherwise, find the value of t when they collide.

Find the speeds of the particles at the instant of collision.

(W)

2 AS   24 mins
(a) A particle moves along a straight line ABC. It starts from rest at A and moves with constant acceleration 2 m s^{-2} until it reaches B. It then moves from B to C with constant acceleration 1 m s^{-2}. The times taken to travel from A to B and from B to C are each equal to T seconds. Show that $5AB = 2BC$.

Given that the distance AC is 56 m, calculate T.

(b) A small ball is released from rest and falls on to a horizontal platform which is descending vertically with a constant speed of 7 m s^{-1}. Given that the ball is 12 m above the platform at the instant of release, calculate the time that elapses before the ball hits the platform.

[Take $g = 10$ m s^{-2}.]

(C)

3 A/AS   15 mins
A rocket is fired vertically upwards. Ignition and liftoff occur at time $t = 0$. Burnout occurs after 30 seconds and the rocket then continues moving vertically as a projectile. The acceleration of the rocket is recorded by on-board accelerometers which give the following trace:

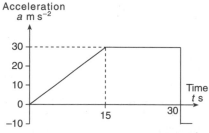

From the trace determine expressions for the acceleration for each of the two periods $0 \le t \le 15$ and $15 < t \le 30$. From the first of these expressions find an expression in terms of t for the speed v of the rocket during the first 15 seconds of flight, assuming that v is initially zero. Hence find the rocket's speed when $t = 15$. From the second expression for acceleration find an expression for the additional speed gained during the period $15 < t \le 30$. Hence find the speed of the rocket at burnout.

(O & C)

4 A/AS   7 mins
A car starts from rest at time $t = 0$ seconds and moves with a uniform acceleration of magnitude 2.3 m s^{-2} along a straight horizontal road. After T seconds, when its speed is V m s^{-1}, it immediately stops accelerating and maintains this steady speed until it hits a brick wall when it comes instantly to rest. The car has then travelled a distance of 776.25 m in 30 s.

(a) Sketch a speed–time graph to illustrate this information.
(b) Write down an expression for V in terms of T.
(c) Show that
$$T^2 - 60T + 675 = 0.$$

(L)

5 A   22 mins
At 1.00 p.m. a battleship is travelling on a bearing of $\theta°$ (i.e. $\theta°$ east of north) at 30 knots (1 knot = 1 nautical mile per hour) relative to the sea, when it sights a submarine which is moving due north at 10 knots relative to the sea. When first sighted, the submarine is 12 nautical miles north-east of the battleship.

If the vessels continue sailing with the above velocities,
(i)   draw a diagram of the above situation at 1.00 p.m.;
(ii) calculate the value of the angle θ if the battleship steers in order to intercept the submarine;
(iii) calculate the time of interception, and the distance apart of the two vessels at 1.15 p.m.

Describe any simplifying assumption you have made concerning the surface of the ocean in the neighbourhood of the vessels.

(N)

6 A   25 mins
11(a) An aircraft flies in a straight line from A to B, where AB = 500 km and B is due north of A. The speed of the aircraft in still air is 250 km h^{-1} and the wind is blowing from the direction 290° at 30 km h^{-1}. Find
(i) the course set by the pilot of the aircraft,
(ii) the time taken, in minutes, for the journey from A to B.
(b) A wind is blowing at 24 km h^{-1} from the direction 270°. Find the magnitude and direction of the velocity of the wind relative to a cyclist travelling at 16 km h^{-1} in the direction 030°.

(C)

7 AS   24 mins
A man of mass 80 kg stands on the floor of a lift which is ascending vertically. Given that the reaction of the floor on the man is 830 N, calculate the acceleration of the lift.

Given that the lift starts from rest at ground level and ascends with this acceleration for 8 s, show that the lift attains a speed of 3 m s^{-1}.

When the speed of the lift reaches 3 m s^{-1} it begins to slow down and the reaction of the floor on the man drops to a constant value of 760 N. Calculate the retardation of the lift, and the height, above ground level, which it reaches before coming to rest.

[Take $g = 10$ m s^{-2}.]

(C)

8 A   25 mins
[In this question take the value of g to be 10 m s^{-2}.]

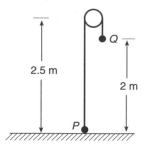

Two particles P and Q, of mass 0.3 kg and 0.7 kg respectively, are attached to the ends of a light inextensible string. The string passes over a small, smooth pulley fixed at a height of 2.5 m above horizontal ground. Initially both parts of the string are taut and vertical, with P resting on the ground and Q held at a height of 2 m above the ground (see diagram). At time $t = 0$, Q is released from rest and the system then moves freely under gravity with the string taut. Find the tension in the string.

Show that, when $t = 0.5$ s, Q has fallen a distance of 0.5 m.

At the instant when $t = 0.5$ s, part of Q becomes detached, leaving a particle Q' of mass 0.2 kg attached to the string and with unchanged velocity.

Find (i) the minimum height above the ground reached by Q',
  (ii) the speed of P just before it hits the ground.

When P hits the ground, it rebounds vertically with a speed of 2 m s^{-1}. Find the impulse exerted on the ground by P.

(C)

9 AS   10 mins

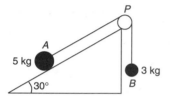

The diagram shows a particle A, of mass 5 kg, resting on a smooth plane which is inclined at 30° to the horizontal. A light inextensible string connects A to a second particle B, of mass 3 kg, which hangs freely. The string passes over a small smooth pulley P fixed at the top of the inclined plane, and the portion AP of the string is parallel to a line of greatest slope of the plane. The system is released from rest with the string taut and the hanging part vertical.
(a) Calculate, in m s^{-2} to 2 decimal places, the acceleration of A.
(b) Calculate, in N to 2 decimal places, the tension in the string.

(L)

10 A   22 mins

A team from a dangerous sports club decide that one of their members will drop from the span of a bridge connected to it by an elastic rope. The team has a number of ropes available, all of natural length a. The member chosen has weight W and the distance from the span of the bridge to the water below is $3a$. Determine the stiffness k of the rope if the rope stops her just above the surface of the water.

On the journey to the bridge the chosen member falls ill and is replaced by another member of the team who has weight $3W/2$. Unwisely the team do not think it is necessary to change the rope and he drops from the bridge with initial zero speed. Find the speed with which he hits the water.

The team member enters the water and returns to the surface with zero speed. If he remains connected to the rope
(i) find the net force on the team member
    (a) just before entering the water,
    (b) just after leaving the water.
(ii) Show that the string just slackens in the subsequent motion.

(You may assume that the team member may be modelled as a particle and ignore the effects of surface tension.)

(OLE)

11 AS   24 mins

[In this question take g to be 10 m s^{-1}.]
(a) A weightlifter lifts a weight of mass 100 kg from the floor to height of 2 m above the floor. Calculate the work done on the weight by the weightlifter.
The weightlifter then allows the weight to fall back to the floor. State the loss in potential energy of the weight, and hence calculate the speed of the weight on impact with the floor.
(b) Water flows over a waterfall where there is a vertical drop of 80 m. The water at the top of the waterfall is flowing at a speed of 3 m s^{-1}. By considering the potential and kinetic energy of 1 kg of water, or otherwise, find the speed of the water after it has fallen 80 m.
Water flows over the waterfall at a rate of 200 m^3 s^{-1} and 1 m^3 of water has a mass of 1000 kg. Assuming that 40% of the energy of the water at the bottom of the waterfall can be converted into electricity by suitable generators, calculate the power, in kilowatts, that could be developed.

(C)

12 A   22 mins

Define *power* and state whether it is a scalar or a vector.
A lift cage whose mass together with the occupants must not exceed 2000 kg is drawn up and down a shaft by an engine using an inextensible cable. The velocity–time (v–t) graph below represents the motion of the lift's ascent.

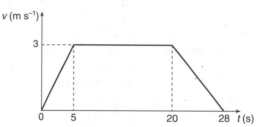

(a) If the lift is fully loaded:
    (i) show that the power generated by the engine during the time when the lift has constant velocity is 60 kW;
    (ii) determine the maximum power generated during the lift's ascent.
(b) Having reached the top of the shaft the lift descends, again fully loaded. Find the maximum power that the engine will need to develop in order that the lift's motion should have the same v–t graph when descending.

(OLE)

13 AS   12 mins

A car of mass 900 kg travelling on a straight level stretch of motorway accelerates uniformly from 36 to 108 km h^{-1} in 10 seconds. The car engine provides a constant driving force, F newtons, and the total resistance to the forward motion of the car is constant and equal to R newtons. Given that when the car is travelling at 50 km h^{-1} the power being used to provide the driving force is 40 kW, find the value of F. Hence calculate the value of R.

(J)

Mechanics Question Bank

14 A 9 mins
(a) A shell of mass 50 kg is fired horizontally at 600 m s^{-1} from a gun of mass 4000 kg.
Calculate
  (i) the initial recoil velocity of the gun,
  (ii) the value of the uniform horizontal force required for the distance of recoil to be 1.25 m.
                                               (C)

15 A/AS 5 mins
A small ball, of mass 0.3 kg, moving with velocity $(5\mathbf{i} - 3\mathbf{j})$ m s^{-1} receives an impulse $(-1.2\mathbf{i} + 5.7\mathbf{j})$ N s. Find the speed of the ball immediately afterwards.
                                               (L)

16 A 27 mins
Two small smooth spheres A and B of equal radius, but of masses m and km respectively, are at rest on a smooth horizontal floor. The centres of the spheres lie on a line perpendicular to a smooth vertical wall with B lying between A and the wall. Sphere B is at a distance of 3 m from the wall. The coefficient of restitution for all collisions is 0.2. Sphere A is then projected directly towards sphere B with speed u m s^{-1}. Find, in terms of u and k, the velocities of the spheres immediately after their first collision.
(a) Given that $k = 3$ find
  (i) the distance between A and B when B hits the wall,
  (ii) the distance from the wall to the point at which the spheres next collide.
(b) Given that $k \neq 3$ find the least value of k so that the spheres do not collide after B hits the wall.
                                               (W)

17 AS 10 mins
A small ball B, of mass 120 g, moving with speed 14 m s^{-1} collides directly with a small ball C, of mass 100 g, moving with speed 16 m s^{-1} in the opposite direction. The coefficient of restitution between B and C is e. Immediately after the collision the speed of C is v m s^{-1}
(a) Show that
$$v = \frac{1}{11}(180e + 4).$$
(b) Show that
$$\tfrac{4}{11} \leq v \leq 16\tfrac{8}{11}.$$
(c) Find, in terms of e, the velocity of B.
(d) Given that B is brought to rest by the collision, find the value of e.
                                               (L)

18 A 15 mins

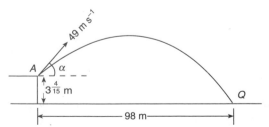

A golf ball is projected with speed 49 m s^{-1} at an angle of elevation α from a point A on the first floor of a golf driving range. Point A is at a height of $3\tfrac{4}{15}$ m above horizontal ground. The ball first strikes the ground at a point Q which is at a horizontal distance of 98 m from the point A as shown in the diagram.
(a) Show that
$$6\tan^2 \alpha - 30\tan \alpha + 5 = 0.$$
(b) Hence find, to the nearest degree, the two possible angles of elevation.
(c) Find, to the nearest second, the smallest possible time of direct flight from A to Q.
                                               (L)

19 A 25 mins
A particle P is projected from a point O on a horizontal plane with speed 40 m s^{-1} at an angle θ to the horizontal, where $\tan \theta = \frac{4}{3}$. Find
(i) the time taken for P to return to the plane,
(ii) the maximum height attained by P,
(iii) the range of P,
(iv) the speed of P after 2.2 seconds.
A second particle Q is projected from the same point O with speed v m s^{-1} at an angle ϕ to the horizontal, where $\tan \phi = \frac{8}{15}$. Given that Q attains the same maximum height as P, find
(v) the value of v,
(vi) the range of Q.
                                               (C)

20 A 22 mins

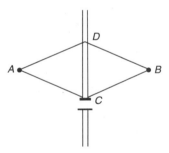

The mechanism shown is designed to regulate the flow of steam from a boiler. It consists of four light rigid rods each of length $2a$ together with small particles at A and B of mass m. AD, BD are smoothly jointed to a smooth vertical spindle at D. A small ring of mass m is smoothly jointed to AC and BC at C and can slide on the spindle below D. A, B, C, D are in the same vertical plane with CD vertical. When the valve is open the ring rests on a smooth horizontal ledge fixed to the spindle at a distance $2a$ below D.
The system rotates around the axis CD with angular velocity ω, find
(a) (i) the tension or thrust in the rods AC and BC;
    (ii) the force exerted by the ledge on the ring.
(b) Show that if $a\omega^2 > 2g$, then the ring rises.
                                           (OLE)

21 AS 20 mins
A particle P of mass m is attached to one end of a light inextensible string of length l. The other end of the string is attached to a fixed support A at a height h ($<l$) above a smooth horizontal surface.
The particle moves at a constant angular speed ω on a horizontal circular path, at a height y ($<h$) above the surface.

Express y in terms of h, g and ω and show that

$$\omega^2 > \frac{g}{h}.$$

Now suppose that P describes a circle on the surface at a constant angular speed ω_1 and with the string taut. Find, in terms of m, g, h and ω_1, the magnitude of the force exerted by P on the surface.

(J)

22 A   13 mins

A particle P of mass m is released from rest at a point A on the surface of a fixed smooth sphere of centre O. The radius OA is inclined at an angle of 30° to the upward vertical. Show that, while the particle remains in contact with the sphere, the reaction on the particle is

$$mg\left(3\cos\theta - \sqrt{3}\right),$$

where θ is the angle between OP and the upward vertical. Find, to the nearest degree, the value of θ when the particle leaves the surface of the sphere.

(J)

23 AS   16 mins

A small bead P, of mass m, is threaded on a smooth thin wire, in the form of a circle of radius a and centre O, which is fixed in a vertical plane. The bead is projected along the wire with speed u from the lowest point A. The bead comes to instantaneous rest at the point where $\angle POA = 120°$.
Show that

$$u = \sqrt{(3ag)}.$$

Find, in terms of a, the height of P above A at the instant when the reaction of the wire on the bead is zero.

(J)

24 A   25 mins

In a test facility, a rocket-powered sled, initially stationary, accelerates uniformly at 20 m s^{-2} along a straight horizontal track from time $t = 0$ to time $t = 10$ (where t is measured in seconds). What is its velocity at time $t = 10$ and how far has it travelled from rest?
From time $t = 10$ to time $t = 12$, the sled decelerates *non-uniformly* so that during this period the velocity v of the sled satisfies

$$\frac{dv}{dt} = -\frac{v^2}{1200}.$$

Prove that the velocity of the sled at time $t = 12$ is 150 m s^{-1}.
Show that the distance travelled by the sled from time $t = 10$ to time $t = 12$ is given by

$$s = -1200\int_{200}^{150} \frac{1}{v}\,dv.$$

Find s.
At time $t = 12$ an ejection seat on the sled is fired by charges which give it a vertical impulse of 6000 N s. If the seat has mass 150 kg, show that the maximum height reached by the seat is 80 m and that it reaches this height at time $t = 16$.
[Take the acceleration due to gravity to be 10 m s^{-2}.]

(O & C)

25 AS   14 mins

A particle of mass 3 kg moves on a smooth horizontal table under the action of a variable horizontal force whose value at time t seconds is

$$6\cos t\mathbf{i} - 3e^{-t}\mathbf{j} \text{ newtons.}$$

When $t = 0$ the particle has velocity $\mathbf{j}$ m s^{-1} and is at the point with position vector $(3\mathbf{i} - \mathbf{j})$ metres.
Find
(i) the momentum of the particle at time t,
(ii) the position vector, $\mathbf{r}$, of the particle at time t.
Show that, for large values of t,

$$\mathbf{r} \approx (5 - 2\cos t)\mathbf{i}.$$

Describe, briefly, what an observer would see the particle doing when t is large.

(J)

26 A   25 mins

The three points O, B, C lie, in that order, on a straight line l on a smooth horizontal plane with $OB = 0.3$ m, $OC = 0.4$ m. A particle P describes simple harmonic motion with centre O along the line l.
At B the speed of the particle is 12 m s^{-1} and at C its speed is 9 m s^{-1}. Find
(a) the amplitude of the motion;
(b) the period of the motion;
(c) the maximum speed of P;
(d) the time to travel from O to C.
This simple harmonic motion is caused by a light elastic spring attached to P, the other end of the spring is fixed at a point A on l where A is on the opposite side of O to B and C and $AO = 2$ m. Given that P has mass 0.2 kg, find the modulus of the spring and the energy stored in it when $AP = 2.4$ m.

(A)

27 A   18 mins

A body of mass 3 kilograms moves under the action of gravity and a force $\mathbf{F}$ newtons. At time t seconds,

$$\mathbf{F} = 3\mathbf{i} + 6t\mathbf{j} + 6\mathbf{k},$$

where the unit vector $\mathbf{k}$ is directed vertically upwards.
Taking $g = 10$ m s^{-2}, find the acceleration of the body at t.
Given that the velocity of the body is $(3\mathbf{i} - 11\mathbf{j} + 15\mathbf{k})$ m s^{-1} when $t = 0$, find
(i) the speed of the body when $t = 3$,
(ii) the angle, to the nearest degree, between the velocity of the body when $t = 3$ and the resultant force acting on the body at this time.

(J)

28 AS   18 mins

A particle of mass 4 kg moves under the action of a force $\mathbf{F}$. At time t the momentum of the particle is $8\cos t\mathbf{i} - 12\sin t\mathbf{j}$.
(i)   Find $\mathbf{F}$ in terms of t.
(ii) Write down the velocity of the particle at time t, and find the smallest positive value of t for which the particle is moving in the direction of the vector $\mathbf{j}$.
(iii) Given that when $t = 0$ the position vector of the particle is $(\mathbf{i} - \mathbf{j})$, find its position vector and its distance from the origin when $t = \frac{\pi}{2}$.

(J)

29 A   5 mins

Three forces $(3\mathbf{i} + 5\mathbf{j})$ N, $(4\mathbf{i} + 11\mathbf{j})$ N, $(2\mathbf{i} + \mathbf{j})$ N act at a point. Given that $\mathbf{i}$ and $\mathbf{j}$ are perpendicular unit vectors find
(a) the resultant of the forces in the form $a\mathbf{i} + b\mathbf{j}$,
(b) the magnitude of this resultant,

(c) the cosine of the angle that the resultant makes with the unit vector **i**.

(A)

30 AS   24 mins

The points A, B and C of a horizontal plane have coordinates $(4, 3)$, $(-4, 0)$ and $(4, -3)$, respectively, these dimensions being in metres. A particle P on the plane is subject to three forces which are directed towards A, B and C.

(a) When P is at the origin the forces directed towards A, B and C have magnitudes 4 N, 2 N and 4 N, respectively, as shown in the diagram.

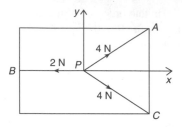

Calculate the magnitude of the resultant of the three forces, and state its direction.

(i) Given that the plane is rough, and that P is in equilibrium at the origin, state the magnitude and direction of the frictional force of P.

(ii) Given that the plane is smooth and that the mass of P is 0.1 kg, calculate the acceleration of P when it is at the origin.

(b) When P is at the point $(-4, 3)$ the force directed towards B is zero, and the forces directed towards A and C have magnitudes 10 N and 14 N, respectively. Calculate the magnitude and direction of the resultant of the two non-zero forces.

(C)

31 A   25 mins

A uniform straight rod AB has mass M and length $2a$. The end A is smoothly hinged at a fixed point so that the rod can turn freely in a vertical plane. Horizontal and vertical forces of magnitudes Mg and $\frac{3}{10}Mg$ respectively are applied to the end B. These forces and the weight of the rod are shown below.

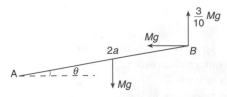

The rod rests in equilibrium at an angle θ to the horizontal.

(a) By taking moments about A, find the value of $\tan \theta$.

(b) Calculate the magnitude, in terms of M and g, and the direction, to the nearest degree, of the force exerted by the hinge on the rod AB.

The forces at B are removed from the system and a particle of mass $2M$ is stuck to the rod at B. A counter-clockwise couple of magnitude $2Mga$ is applied to the rod and acts in the vertical plane containing AB. In the new equilibrium position the rod is at an angle α to the horizontal, as shown in the following diagram.

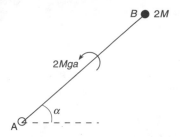

(c) Calculate the value of α giving your answer to the nearest degree.

(d) Calculate, in terms of M and g, the magnitude of the force exerted by the hinge on AB and state the direction of this force.

32 A/AS   15 mins

A tower crane consists of a vertical framework of square cross section of width a (the tower) upon which rests a uniform horizontal framework of mass M and length $10a$ (the gantry). A counterweight is fixed at the end of the shorter overhang of the gantry and a trolley of mass $M/10$, from which a lifting hook is suspended, can run along the longer overhang of the gantry. The crane is modelled in the diagram below.

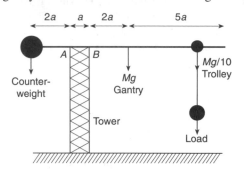

The counterweight is such that the gantry does not quite overbalance backwards about A before the trolley is fitted. Find the mass of the counterweight.

The maximum load that the crane can safely lift is such that the gantry does not quiet overbalance forwards about B when the trolley and lifting hook are at the far end of the gantry. Find this maximum load.

(O & C)

33 A   25 mins

A uniform ladder of length $4l$ and mass M rests with one end A on rough horizontal ground and the other end B against a smooth vertical wall. The vertical plane containing AB is at right angles to the wall. The coefficient of friction between the ladder and the ground is $\frac{1}{5}$. A particle of mass $2M$ is attached to the ladder at C where $AC = 3l$.

Given that equilibrium is limiting, show that the ladder is inclined at an angle $\tan^{-1}\left(\frac{10}{3}\right)$ to the horizontal. The ladder is moved to a similar position where the wall is rough. The ladder rests at an angle $\tan^{-1}\left(\frac{10}{3}\right)$ to the horizontal and the coefficients of friction between the ladder and the wall and the ladder and the ground are both $\mu\left(\neq \frac{1}{5}\right)$. The particle of mass $2M$ is moved to the top of the ladder. Given that equilibrium is limiting, show that $\mu^2 + 20\mu - 5 = 0$.

(L)

34 A 25 mins

(a) A particle of mass 1.5 kg rests on a rough plane inclined at 45° to the horizontal. It is maintained in equilibrium by a horizontal force of P N. Given that the coefficient of friction between the particle and the plane is $\frac{1}{4}$, calculate the value of P when the particle is on the point of moving
   (i) down the plane,   (ii) up the plane.

(b)

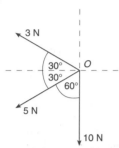

The diagram shows three coplanar horizontal forces acting on a particle at O. Calculate the magnitude and direction of the additional force which, acting on the particle, will result in equilibrium.

35 A 22 mins

The arrangement shown in the diagram is one that you may have used in a mechanics experiment. It consists of two fixed smooth light pulleys over which passes a long light inelastic string carrying weights P and Q at its ends. A third weight R is attached to the string as shown. When the system is in equilibrium α and β are the angles made with the vertical by the two portions of the string attached to R.

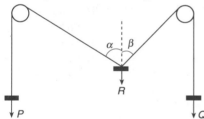

(a) If $P = 2$ N, $Q = 3$ N and $R = 4$ N find the values of $\cos\alpha$ and $\cos\beta$.
Give reasons why the values of both α and β must be less than $\frac{1}{2}\pi$ if $R > 0$.

(b) Show that $\cos\alpha = \dfrac{R^2 + P^2 - Q^2}{2RP}$ and write down a similar expression for $\cos\beta$.

(c) If $P = 2$ N, $Q = 3$ N and $R = 2$ N use the expressions to calculate $\cos\alpha$ and $\cos\beta$.
Is the configuration illustrated possible for these given values of P, Q and R? Give reasons.

(OLE)

36 AS 12 mins

A uniform beam AB of mass 20 kg and length 2 m is attached to a vertical wall by means of a smooth hinge at A. The beam is maintained in the horizontal position by means of a light inextensible string, one end of which is attached to the beam at B and the other end is attached to the wall at a point in the wall 2 m vertically above A.

(a) Calculate the tension in the string, in N, to 3 significant figures.
A particle of mass M kg is now attached to the beam at B. Given that the string is about to break, and that the breaking tension of the string is 400 N,

(b) Find the value of M to 3 significant figures.

(L)

37 A 12 mins

A particle of mass m is in equilibrium on a rough plane inclined at an angle θ to the horizontal. When a force of magnitude mg, in the sense up a line of greatest slope, is applied to the particle it is just about to move up the plane. When a force of magnitude $mg/2$, in the sense down a line of greatest slope, is applied to the particle it is just about to move down the plane. Find $\sin\theta$ and the coefficient of friction between the particle and the plane.

(W)

38 A/AS 15 mins

(a) (i) Draw a diagram showing the forces acting on an inclined ladder which is standing on a horizontal floor and leaning against a vertical wall.
  (ii) Explain why the ladder cannot be in equilibrium if the floor is frictionless, even if the wall is rough.

(b) A uniform ladder of length 8 m and mass 20 kg is inclined at 60° to the horizontal against a smooth vertical wall. A 60 kg man is standing on the ladder x m from its lower end. The horizontal floor has coefficient of friction 0.4 with the base of the ladder. The ladder is about to slip.
  (i) Show that the frictional force on the ladder is $32g$ N.
  (ii) Find the reaction of the wall on the ladder.
  (iii) By taking moments about the base of the ladder, or otherwise, show that x is about 6.06 m.

(O & C)

39 A 20 mins

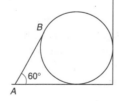

The diagram shows a uniform circular cylinder resting on rough horizontal ground and against a smooth vertical wall; the axis of the cylinder is horizontal and parallel to the wall. A uniform rod AB of weight W rests at right angles to the axis of the cylinder, with one end A on the ground and the other end B on the cylinder. AB is a tangent to the cylinder at B and makes an angle of 60° with the ground. The contact between the cylinder and the rod is smooth.

(i) Show that the reaction between the cylinder and the rod is of magnitude $\frac{1}{4}W$.
(ii) Show that the frictional force between the cylinder and the ground is zero.
(iii) Find the magnitude of the reaction between the cylinder and the wall.
(iv) Find the least value of the coefficient of friction between the rod and the ground required to prevent the rod from slipping.

(J)

Mechanics Question Bank

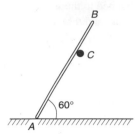

The diagram shows a uniform plank AB of weight W and length $4a$, whose lower end A rests on rough horizontal ground. The plank is inclined at $60°$ to the horizontal and rests in equilibrium supported by a smooth peg at C, where $AC = 3a$.
Find, in terms of W,
(a) the force exerted on the plank by the peg at C,
(b) the vertical and horizontal components of the force exerted on the plank by the ground at A.
Given that the equilibrium is limiting,
(c) find the coefficient of friction between the plank and the ground.

(L)

41 A 12 mins

$ABCD$ is a rectangle with sides AB and CD 3 m long and sides BC and AD 4 m long. Forces of magnitude 11 N, 3 N, 15 N and 7 N act along BA, BC, CA and CD respectively, the sense of the force being that indicated by the order of the letters.
Find the moment of this system of forces about C and the components parallel to BA and BC of the single resultant force to which this system can be reduced.
Find the distance from C of the point at which this resultant intersects BC.

(W)

42 A 8 mins

A composite body B is formed by joining, at the rims of their circular bases, a uniform solid right circular cylinder of radius a and height $2a$ and a uniform right circular cone of radius a and height $2a$. Given that the cylinder and the cone have masses M and λM respectively, find
(a) the distance of the centre of mass of B from the common plane face when $\lambda = 1$,
(b) the value of λ such that the centre of mass of B lies in the common plane face.

(A)

43 A 15 mins

A uniform rectangular lamina, $ABCD$, where AB is of length a and BC of length $2a$, has a mass $10m$. Further point masses m, $2m$, $3m$ and $4m$ are fixed to the points A, B, C and D, respectively.
Find the centre of mass of the system relative to x- and y-axes along AB and AD, respectively.
If the lamina is suspended from the point A find the angle that the diagonal AC makes with the vertical.
To what must the mass at point D be altered if this diagonal is to hang vertically?

(O & C)

44 AS 18 mins

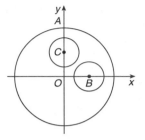

The diagram shows a uniform circular lamina, centre O, radius $4r$. Two circular pieces, each of radius r, with centres at $B(2r, 0)$ and $C(0, 2r)$ are removed to create a new lamina L.
(a) Calculate, in terms of r, the coordinates of the centre of mass, G, of L.
The point A has coordinates $(0, 4r)$. The lamina L is now freely suspended from A and hangs at rest.
(b) Find, in radians to 2 significant figures, the angle that AO makes with the downward vertical.

(L)

Question Bank Answers

1 A

Take up as positive. For both particles $g = -9.8$ m s^{-2}, $u = 19.6$ m s^{-1}, height at time of collision $= s$
1st particle, time of collision t ∴ $s = 19.6t - 4.9t^2$
2nd particle, time of collision $t - 2$
∴ $s = 19.6\,(t - 2) - 4.9\,(t - 2)^2$

Equating $19.6t - 4.9t^2 = 19.6(t - 2) - 4.9(t - 2)^2 \Rightarrow t = 3$ s
so particles collide 3 s after first particle was projected.
1st particle: $v = u + at \Rightarrow v = -9.8$ m s^{-1} (downwards)
2nd particle: $v = u + at \Rightarrow v = 9.8$ m s^{-1} (upwards)

2 AS

(a) From A to B: $u = 0$ m s^{-1}, $a = 2$ m s^{-2}, $t = T$
$s = ut + \frac{1}{2}at^2 \Rightarrow s = T^2$ and $v = u + at \Rightarrow v = 2T$

From B to C: $u = 2T$ m s^{-1}, $a = 1$ m s^{-2}, $t = T$
$s = ut + \frac{1}{2}at^2 \Rightarrow s = \frac{5T^2}{2}$

Thus $\frac{AB}{BC} = \frac{T^2}{5T^2/2} \Rightarrow 5AB = 2BC$

If $AC = 56$ m, $AB = 16$ m and $T = \sqrt{16} = 4$ s
(b) Take down as positive.
Let x be distance moved by platform before collision.

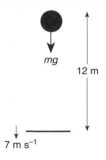

Consider ball: $u = 0$ m s^{-1}, $a = 10$ m s^{-2}, $s = 12 + x$

Using $s = ut + \frac{1}{3}at^2 \Rightarrow x = 5t^2 - 12$

Consider platform: $u = 7$ m s^{-1}, $a = 0$ m s^{-2}, $s = x$
$\Rightarrow x = 7t$

Equating values of x: $5t^2 - 12 = 7t \Rightarrow t = 2.4$ s
(+ve t only)

3 A/AS

$0 \leq t \leq 15$, $a = 2t$ m s^{-2} (from gradient of graph)

$15 < t \leq 30$, $a = 30$ m s^{-2}

Velocity = area under graph $\therefore v = \frac{1}{2}t \times 2t \Rightarrow v = t^2$

When $t = 15$ s, $v = 225$ m s^{-1}

For $15 < t \leq 30$, constant acceleration, so $v = u + at$, and time at this acceleration is $t - 15$. Thus speed gain, $v - u = (t - 15)$.

When $t = 15$ s, $u = 225$ m s^{-1}, so at $t = 30$ s, $v = 675$ m s^{-1}

4 A/AS

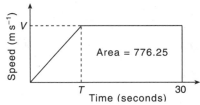

(a) Total distance travelled is given by area under speed–time graph.

(b) Acceleration = $\dfrac{\text{change in speed}}{\text{time taken}}$

$\Rightarrow 2.3 = \dfrac{V - 0}{T} \Rightarrow V = 2.3T$

(c) $\left(\frac{1}{2}TV\right) + (30 - T)V = 776.25$

$\Rightarrow \left(\frac{1}{2}T \times 2.3T\right) + (30 - T)2.3T = 776.25$

$\Rightarrow T^2 - 60T + 675 = 0$

5 A

(i) Initial situation at 1.00 p.m.

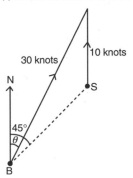

(ii) Imagine you are in the submarine. The battleship will appear to move directly towards you.

$$_B v_S = v_B - v_S$$

[Notation: $_B v_S$ is the velocity of the battleship relative to the submarine; v_B and v_S are the velocities of the battleship and submarine, respectively, relative to the sea.]

Velocity triangle.

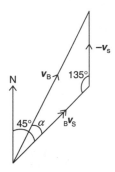

Using sine rule $\dfrac{v_B}{\sin 135°} = \dfrac{v_S}{\sin \alpha} \Rightarrow \sin \alpha = \dfrac{10 \sin 135°}{30}$

$\Rightarrow \alpha = 13.6°$, so the battleship must steer N 31.4° E

(iii) Using cosine rule, magnitude of $_B v_S$ is

$$\sqrt{\left[10^2 + 30^2 - 2 \times 10 \times 30 \times \cos 31.4°\right]} = 22.088 \text{ knots (3d.p.)}$$

Time of interception = $\dfrac{\text{initial distance apart}}{_B v_S}$

$$= \dfrac{12}{22.088} \text{ hours} = 32.6 \text{ min (1d.p.)}$$

So they intercept at 1.33 p.m.

At 1.15, the battleship has travelled for 15 min at a relative speed of 22.088 knots, so they are $12 - (0.25 \times 22.088) = 6.5$ nautical miles apart (1d.p.).

Simplifying assumptions:

1   The wind does not affect the vessels.
2   There are no currents in the sea.
3   No large waves on the surface.
4   The curvature of the earth can be ignored.

6 A

(a) Let velocity of aircraft over the ground = v_A, velocity of wind = $v_W = 30$ km h^{-1}

$$_A v_W = v_A - v_W = 250 \text{ km h}^{-1}$$

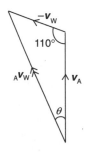

(i) By sine rule $\sin \theta = \dfrac{v_W \sin 110°}{_A v_W} \Rightarrow \theta = 6.5°$

Pilot must set a course of 353.5°

By cosine rule

$v_A{}^2 = 250^2 + 30^2 - 2.250.30 \cos 63.5°$

$\Rightarrow v_A = 238.14$ km h^{-1}

(ii) Plane flies a distance of 500 km, so time to complete journey is $(500/238.14) \times 60 = 126$ minutes.

(b) $_w\textbf{v}_C = \textbf{v}_w - \textbf{v}_C$

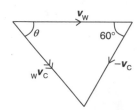

By cosine rule

$_w\textbf{v}_C^2 = 24^2 + 16^2 - 2.24.16\cos 60° \Rightarrow {}_w\textbf{v}_C = 21.16$ km h^{-1}

By sine rule $\sin\theta = \dfrac{16\sin 60°}{21.16} \Rightarrow \theta = 40.9°$

So velocity and direction of wind relative to cyclist are 21.16 km h^{-1} and 130.9°

7 AS

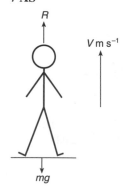

Equation of motion for the man: $R - mg = ma$

$\Rightarrow 830 - 800 = 80a \Rightarrow a = \frac{3}{8}$ m s^{-2}

Since $u = 0$ m s^{-1}, $t = 8$ s then $v = u + at \Rightarrow v = 3$ m s^{-1}

If $R = 760$ N, $760 - 800 = 80a \Rightarrow a = -\frac{1}{2}$ m s^{-2} (retardation)

During acceleration $\quad s = \dfrac{v^2 - u^2}{2a} = \dfrac{9 - 0}{\frac{3}{4}} = 12$ m

During retardation $\quad s = \dfrac{v^2 - u^2}{2a} = \dfrac{0 - 9}{-1} = 9$ m

So height of lift above ground is 21 m.

8 A

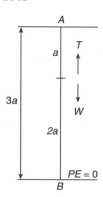

$m_P = 0.3$ kg, $m_Q = 0.7$ kg
Equation of motion for P:
$T - m_P g = m_P a \Rightarrow T - 3 = 0.3a \qquad [1]$

where a is the common acceleration of the particles.
Equation of motion for Q:
$m_Q g - T = m_Q a \Rightarrow 7 - T = 0.7a \qquad [2]$

Adding [1] and [2] gives $a = 4$ m s^{-2} and from [1] $T = 4.2$ N
Consider Q: $u = 0$, $a = 4$ m s^{-2}, $t = 0.5$ s
Using $s = ut + \frac{1}{2}at^2$ gives $s = 0.5$ m

(i) Equation of motion for Q': $2 - T = 0.2a \qquad [3]$
Adding [1] and [3] gives new acceleration $= -2$ m s^{-2}
(retardation)
Q' will come to rest at minimum height $\therefore v = 0$

Initial speed of $Q' = 0.5 \times 4 = 2$ m s^{-1}

Thus, using $v^2 = u^2 + 2as$, $0 = 4 - 4s \Rightarrow s = 1$ m

So Q' will reach a height of 0.5 m above ground.
(ii) P will begin to fall 1.5 m above ground.
Using $v^2 = u^2 + 2as$
$\Rightarrow v^2 = 0 + 6 \Rightarrow v = \sqrt{6}$ m s^{-1} just before P hits the ground.

Impulse $= mv - mu = 0.3(2 + \sqrt{6}) = 1.33$ N

9 AS

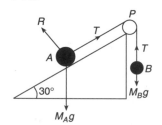

Equation of motion for A:
$T - 5g\sin 30° = 5a \Rightarrow T - 24.5 = 5a \quad [1]$

Equation of motion for B:

$3g - T = 3a \Rightarrow 29.4 - T = 3a \quad [2]$

(a) Adding [1] and [2] gives

$\quad 8a = 4.9 \Rightarrow a = 0.61$ m s^{-2} (2 d.p.)

(b) From [1] $T = 5a + 24.5 \Rightarrow T = 27.56$ N (2 d.p.)

10 A

Diagram showing points A, a, T, 3a, W, 2a, PE = 0, B.

At $A \quad$ P.E. $= mgh = 3aW$ J, K.E. $= 0$ J, E.P.E. $= 0$ J
At $B \quad$ P.E. $= 0$ J, K.E. $= 0$ J, E.P.E. $= \frac{1}{2}kx^2 = 2a^2k$

By principle of conservation of energy $3aW = 2a^2k \Rightarrow \dfrac{3W}{2a} = k$

If weight is now $\dfrac{3W}{2}$

At $A \quad$ P.E. $= \dfrac{9aW}{2}$ J, K.E. $= 0$ J, E.P.E. $= 0$ J

At B P.E. $= 0$ J, K.E. $= \frac{1}{2}mv^2 = \frac{3Wv^2}{4g}$ J, E.P.E. $= 3aW$ J

By principle of conservation of energy

$$\frac{9aW}{2} = \frac{3Wv^2}{4g} + 3aW \Rightarrow v = \sqrt{2ag}\ \text{ms}^{-1}$$

(i) (a) Before entering water, resultant force $= \frac{3W}{2} - T$,

      but $T = kx = 3W$ (by Hooke's law)

      $\Rightarrow$ resultant force $= -\frac{3W}{2}$ N (upwards)

   (b) After leaving water conditions are exactly the same,

      so resultant force is $\frac{3W}{2}$ N upwards.

(ii) Let C be position where man momentarily comes to rest $(v = 0)$.

At B P.E. $= 0$ J, K.E. $= 0$ J, E.P.E. $= 3aW$ J

At C P.E. $= \frac{3W}{2}(2a - x)$ J, K. E. $= 0$ J, E.P.E $= \frac{3Wx^2}{4a}$ J

By principle of conservation of energy

$$\frac{3Wx^2}{4a} + \frac{3W}{2}(2a - x) = 3aW \Rightarrow x^2 - 2ax = 0$$

$$\Rightarrow x = 0,\ x = 2a$$

Thus string just slackens when $x = 0$.

11 AS

(a) Work done $= Fs = 100g \times 2 = 2000$ J

At maximum height   P.E. $= mgh = 2000$ J, K.E. $= 0$ J

At floor   P.E. $= 0$ J, K.E. $= \frac{1}{2}mv^2 = 50v^2$

Loss in potential energy is 2000 J

$\therefore$ K.E. at floor $= 2000$ J (by conservation of energy)

and $v = 2\sqrt{10}$ ms^{-1}

(b)

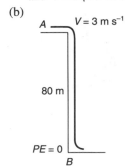

Consider 1 kg of water.

At A P.E. $= mgh = 800$ J, K.E. $= \frac{1}{2}mv^2 = 4.5$ J

At B P.E. $= 0$, K.E. $= \frac{1}{2}v^2$

By principle of conservation of energy $v = 40.1$ ms^{-1}

Total energy per second at $B = 804.5 \times 200 \times 1000$

                       $= 160\ 900$ kJ s^{-1}

Power generated $= 40\% \times 160\ 900 = 64\ 360$ kW

12 A

Power is the rate at which a force does work. It is a scalar.

(a)

(i) Resolve $\uparrow$: $T = 2000g = 20\ 000$ N

Power $= Fv \Rightarrow F = \dfrac{P}{v} \Rightarrow T = \dfrac{P}{v}$

From graph $v = 3$ m s^{-1} when lift is at constant velocity,

so $P = 60\ 000$ W $\Rightarrow$ Power generated is 60 kW

(ii) Equation of motion for lift: $T - mg = ma$

$$\Rightarrow \frac{P}{v} - 20000 = 2000a$$

$$\Rightarrow P = 2000(a + 10)v$$

Maximum power occurs with maximum a and v so, from the graph,

$$P_{max} = 2000\left(\tfrac{3}{5} + 10\right)3 = 63600\ \text{W} = 63.6\ \text{kW}$$

(b)

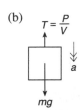

$T = \dfrac{P}{V}$

Equation of motion: $2000g - T = 2000a$

$$\Rightarrow P = 2000(10 - a)v$$

Maximum power now occurs at minimum a.

Thus $P = 2000\left(10 - \left(-\tfrac{3}{8}\right)\right)3 = 62250\ \text{W} = 62.25\ \text{kW}$

13 AS

$$36\ \text{km h}^{-1} = \frac{36 \times 1000}{60 \times 60} = 10\ \text{m s}^{-1}$$

$$108\ \text{km h}^{-1} = \frac{108 \times 1000}{60 \times 60} = 30\ \text{m s}^{-1}$$

$$50\ \text{km h}^{-1} = \frac{50 \times 1000}{60 \times 60} = \frac{125}{9}\ \text{m s}^{-1}$$

Equation of motion: $F - R = ma$

Now $a = \dfrac{v - u}{t} = 2\ \text{m s}^{-2}$ $\therefore F - R = 900 \times 2 = 1800$ N

$$P = Fv \Rightarrow F = \frac{P}{v}$$

$P = 40\ \text{kW} = 40\ 000\ \text{W}$ when $v = 50\ \text{km h}^{-1} = \dfrac{125}{9}\ \text{m s}^{-1}$

$$\Rightarrow F = \frac{40\ 000}{\frac{125}{9}} = 2880\ \text{N}$$

Thus $R = 2880 - 1800 = 1080$ N

14 A

(a)

4000 kg	50 kg

$v \longleftarrow$ $\longrightarrow$ 600 m s^{-1}

Initial momentum $= 0$

Momentum $= 4000v - (50 \times 600)$ $\therefore 4000v - 30\ 000 = 0$

                     $\Rightarrow v = 7.5$ m s^{-1}

(b) $s = 1.25$ m

$F = ma$. Using $v^2 = u^2 + 2as \Rightarrow 0 = 7.5^2 + 2.5a$

                         $\Rightarrow a = -22.5$ m s^{-2}

and $F = 4000 \times -22.5 = 90\ 000$ N in opposite direction to recoil of gun.

Mechanics Question Bank: Answers

15 A/AS

Before impulse, momentum $= m\mathbf{u} = 1.5\mathbf{i} - 0.9\mathbf{j}$

Impulse $= m\mathbf{v} - m\mathbf{u}$

$\Rightarrow (-1.2\mathbf{i} + 5.7\mathbf{j}) = 0.3(\mathbf{v}) - (1.5\mathbf{i} - 0.9\mathbf{j})$

$\Rightarrow \mathbf{v} = \mathbf{i} + 16\mathbf{j}$

So speed of particle is $|\mathbf{v}| = \sqrt{1^2 + 16^2} = 16.03$ m s^{-1}

16 A

Before impact

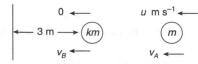

After impact

By conservation of momentum

$mu + 0 = mv_A + kmv_B \Rightarrow u = v_A + kv_B$ [1]

By Newton's experimental law

$v_B - v_A = 0.2(u - 0) \Rightarrow 0.2u = v_B - v_A$ [2]

Adding [1] and [2]

$1.2u = (1+k)v_B \Rightarrow v_B = \dfrac{6u}{5(1+k)}$ and $v_A = \dfrac{(5-k)u}{5(1+k)}$

(a) (i) $k = 3 \Rightarrow v_B = \dfrac{3u}{10}$ and $v_A = \dfrac{u}{10}$

Time taken for B to reach wall $t = \dfrac{3}{v_B} = \dfrac{10}{u}$ s

Distance moved by A in this time $s = \dfrac{10}{u} \cdot \dfrac{u}{10} = 1$ m

So distance between A and B is 2 m.

(ii)

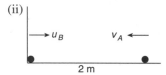

By Newton's experimental law $u_B = 0.2\, v_B = \dfrac{3u}{50}$

If B travels d m till collision, A travels $2 - d$ m

So, equating t for A and B

$\dfrac{50d}{3u} = \dfrac{10(2-d)}{u} \Rightarrow d = 0.75$ m

The particles collide again 0.75 m from the wall.

(b) For the spheres not to collide, v_A must be directed away from the wall (i.e. k > 5), and be greater than, or equal to, the speed of B after hitting the wall.

$\therefore v_A \geq u_B \Rightarrow \dfrac{-(5-k)u}{5(1+k)} \geq \dfrac{6u}{25(1+k)} \Rightarrow -5 + k \geq \dfrac{6}{5}$

$\Rightarrow k \geq \dfrac{31}{5}$ i.e. minimum $k = \dfrac{31}{5}$

17 AS

(a) Before impact   → 14 m s^{-1} 16 m s^{-1} ←

      (B)   (C)

After impact   → u → v

By principle of conservation of momentum

$(0.12 \times 14) + (0.1 \times -16) = 0.12u + 0.1v$

$\Rightarrow 0.08 - 0.1v = 0.12u$ [1]

Applying Newton's experimental law $v - u = 30e$ [2]

Eliminating u from [1] and [2] gives $v = \dfrac{1}{11}(180e + 4)$

(b) Using $v = \dfrac{1}{11}(180e + 4)$

$e = 0 \Rightarrow v = \dfrac{4}{11}$

$e = 1 \Rightarrow v = 16\dfrac{8}{11}$

$\therefore \dfrac{4}{11} \leq v \leq 16\dfrac{8}{11}$

(c) Eliminating v from [1] and [2] gives $u = \dfrac{1}{11}(4 - 150e)$

(d) If B comes to rest $\dfrac{1}{11}(4 - 150e) = 0 \Rightarrow e = \dfrac{2}{75}$

18 A

(a) Horizontal motion: $u_x = 49\cos\alpha$ and $x = 49t\cos\alpha$

Vertical motion: $a_y = -g$, $u_y = 49\sin\alpha$ (up positive)

Using $s = ut + \frac{1}{2}at^2 \Rightarrow y = 49t\sin\alpha - \frac{1}{2}gt^2$

At Q, $x = 98$ m $\Rightarrow t = \dfrac{2}{\cos\alpha}$

$y = -3\frac{4}{15} = 49\left(\dfrac{2}{\cos\alpha}\right)\sin\alpha - \frac{1}{2}g\left(\dfrac{2}{\cos\alpha}\right)^2$

$\Rightarrow 98\tan\alpha - 2g\sec^2\alpha + \dfrac{49}{15} = 0$

$\Rightarrow 6\tan^2\alpha - 30\tan\alpha + 5 = 0$

(b) Let $X = \tan\alpha$ in expression

$\Rightarrow 6X^2 - 30X + 5 = 0$

$X = \dfrac{30 \pm \sqrt{(30)^2 - 120}}{12} = \tan\alpha$

$\Rightarrow \alpha = 10°$ or $\alpha = 79°$ (to the nearest degree)

(c) At Q, $x = 98 \Rightarrow t = \dfrac{2}{\cos\alpha}$

For minimum time, choose $\alpha = 10°$

$\therefore t = \dfrac{2}{\cos 10°} \Rightarrow t = 2$ s (to nearest second)

19 A

$\tan\theta = \frac{4}{3} \Rightarrow \sin\theta = \frac{4}{5}$, $\cos\theta = \frac{3}{5}$

(i) Consider vertical motion:

$a = -10\,\text{ms}^{-2}$, $u = 40\sin\theta = 32\,\text{ms}^{-1}$, $s = 0$

Using $s = ut + \frac{1}{2}at^2$ gives $32t - 5t^2 = 0$

$\Rightarrow t = 0$ or $t = 6.4$ s

(ii) Consider vertical motion, using $v^2 = u^2 + 2as$ with $v = 0$ at maximum height:

$0 = 32^2 - 20s \Rightarrow s = 51.2\,\text{m}$

(iii) Consider horizontal motion, range at $t = 6.4$ s (when height is zero):

$u = 40\cos\theta = 24\,\text{ms}^{-1}$, $a = 0 \therefore R = ut = 153.6$ m

(iv) Using $v = u + at$ with $t = 2.2$ s.

Vertical speed $v_y = 32 - 22 = 10\,\text{ms}^{-1}$

Horizontal speed $v_x = 24\,\text{ms}^{-1}$

Speed of particle $= \sqrt{24^2 + 10^2} = 26$ ms^{-1}

(v) For Q: $\tan\phi = \frac{8}{15} \Rightarrow \sin\phi = \frac{8}{17}$, $\cos\phi = \frac{15}{17}$

Consider vertical motion:

maximum height $= 51.2$ m,

Using $v^2 = u^2 + 2as$

gives $0 = v^2 \sin^2\phi + 2as \Rightarrow v = 68\text{ms}^{-1}$

(vi) Consider vertical motion:

range will be reached at $t = 6.4$ s (as for P).

Consider horizontal motion: $R_Q = v\cos\phi \times 6.4 = 384\text{m}$

20 A

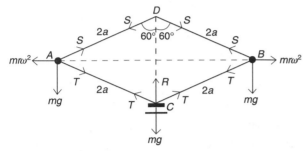

(a) System is symmetrical, so forces in AC and BC are equal, as are the forces in AD and BD.

Consider point A.

Resolve vertically:

$mg + T\cos 60° = S\cos 60° \Rightarrow S = 2mg + T$

Equation of motion for A: $S\sin 60° = T\sin 60° = mr\omega^2$

Substitute for S and $r = \sqrt{3}a$

$\Rightarrow \sqrt{3}mg + \sqrt{3}T = \sqrt{3}ma\omega^2$

$\Rightarrow T = m(a\omega^2 - g)$

(ii) Resolve vertically at C:

$2T\cos 60° + R = mg \Rightarrow R = m(2g - a\omega^2)$

(b) Ring is in contact only if $R \geq 0 \Rightarrow m(2g - a\omega^2) \geq 0$

$\Rightarrow 2g \geq a\omega^2$

Thus the ring will rise if $a\omega^2 > 2g$.

21 AS

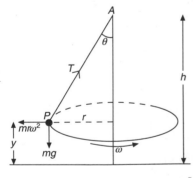

Resolve vertically: $T\cos\theta = mg$ [1]

Equation of motion for P: $T\sin\theta = mr\omega^2$ [2]

Dividing [2] by [1] gives $\tan\theta = \dfrac{r\omega^2}{g}$

but $\tan\theta = \dfrac{r}{h-y} \therefore \dfrac{g}{\omega^2} = h - y \Rightarrow y = h - \dfrac{g}{\omega^2}$

Now $y > 0 \therefore h - \dfrac{g}{\omega^2} > 0 \Rightarrow \omega^2 > \dfrac{g}{h}$

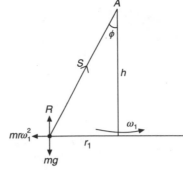

Force on surface $\equiv R$

Resolve vertically: $S\cos\phi + R = mg \Rightarrow S\cos\phi = mg - R$ [3]

Equation of motion for P: $S\sin\phi = mr_1\omega_1^2$ [4]

Dividing [4] by [3] $\tan\phi = \dfrac{mr_1\omega_1^2}{mg - R}$

but $\tan\phi = \dfrac{r_1}{h} \therefore \dfrac{r_1}{h} = \dfrac{mr_1\omega_1^2}{mg - R} \Rightarrow R = m(g - h\omega_1^2)$

22 A

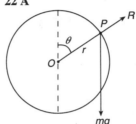

Equation of motion along OP: $mg\cos\theta - R = \dfrac{mv^2}{r}$ [1]

Taking P.E. = 0 where P falls off the sphere.

Initially P.E. = mgh, K.E. = 0, $h = r\cos 30° - r\cos\theta$

At fall off point P.E. = 0, K.E. $= \frac{1}{2}mv^2$

By principle of conservation of energy

$\frac{1}{2}mv^2 = mgr(\cos 30° - \cos\theta) \Rightarrow v^2 = 2gr\left(\dfrac{\sqrt{3}}{2} - \cos\theta\right)$

Substitute in equation [1] $R = mg(3\cos\theta - \sqrt{3})$

When particle leaves surface

$R = 0 \Rightarrow 3\cos\theta - \sqrt{3} = 0 \Rightarrow \theta = 55°$ (to nearest degree)

23 AS

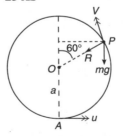

At A P.E. = 0, K.E. $= \frac{1}{2}mu^2$

At P P.E. $= mg(a + a\cos 60°)$

$= \dfrac{3mga}{2}$, K.E. = 0 (since $v = 0$)

By principle of conservation of energy $\frac{1}{2}mu^2 = \dfrac{3mga}{2} \Rightarrow u$

$= \sqrt{3ga}$

Mechanics Question Bank: Answers

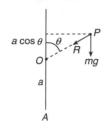

Equation of motion along OP: $R + mg\cos\theta = \dfrac{mv^2}{a}$

If $R = 0$ then $v^2 = ga\cos\theta$

and, by principle of conservation of energy,

$$mg(a + a\cos\theta) + \frac{mv^2}{2} = \frac{3mga}{2}$$

Substituting for v^2: $mg(a + a\cos\theta) + \dfrac{mga\cos\theta}{2} = \dfrac{3mga}{2}$

$$\Rightarrow 3\cos\theta = 1 \Rightarrow \theta = 70.5°$$

and height above A is then $\dfrac{4a}{3}$.

24 A

$u = 0\,\mathrm{ms^{-1}}$, $t = 10\mathrm{s}$, $a = 20\,\mathrm{ms^{-2}}$ $\therefore v = u + at \Rightarrow v = 200\,\mathrm{ms^{-1}}$

and $s = ut + \frac{1}{2}at^2 \Rightarrow s = 1000\,\mathrm{m}$

$$\frac{dv}{dt} = \frac{-v^2}{1200} \Rightarrow -\int \frac{1200}{v^2}dv = \int dt \Rightarrow \frac{1200}{v} = t + C$$

At $t = 10\mathrm{s}$, $v = 200\,\mathrm{ms^{-1}} \Rightarrow C = -4 \therefore v = \dfrac{1200}{t-4}$

When $t = 12\mathrm{s}$, $v = \dfrac{1200}{8} = 150\ \mathrm{ms^{-1}}$

Now $\dfrac{dv}{dt} = v\dfrac{dv}{ds} \Rightarrow \dfrac{dv}{ds} = \dfrac{-v}{1200}$ and $t = 10\mathrm{s}$, $v = 200\,\mathrm{ms^{-1}}$

$\phantom{Now \dfrac{dv}{dt} = v\dfrac{dv}{ds} \Rightarrow \dfrac{dv}{ds} = \dfrac{-v}{1200} and}$ $t = 12\mathrm{s}$, $v = 150\,\mathrm{ms^{-1}}$

so $\displaystyle\int_{200}^{150} \frac{-1200}{v}dv = \int ds \Rightarrow s = -1200\int_{200}^{150}\frac{1}{v}dv$

$\Rightarrow s = -1200[\ln v]_{200}^{150} \Rightarrow s = 345\mathrm{m}$ (3 s.f.)

Consider vertical motion of ejection seat. Impulse = $mv - mu$

$\Rightarrow 6000 = 150v - 0 \Rightarrow v = 40\,\mathrm{ms^{-1}}$

In flight $a = -10\ \mathrm{ms^{-2}}$, $u = 40\ \mathrm{ms^{-1}}$,

at maximum height h, $v = 0$

$v = u + at \Rightarrow 0 = 40 - 10t \Rightarrow t = 4\ \mathrm{s}$

$s = ut + \frac{1}{2}at^2 \Rightarrow h = 160 - 80 \Rightarrow h = 80\ \mathrm{m}$

Thus maximum height is 80 m, reached when $t = 12 + 4 = 16\mathrm{s}$

25 AS

(i) $\mathbf{a} = \dfrac{\mathbf{F}}{m} = (2\cos t)\mathbf{i} - (\mathrm{e}^{-t})\mathbf{j}$

$\mathbf{v} = \displaystyle\int \mathbf{a}\,dt = (2\sin t)\mathbf{i} + (\mathrm{e}^{-t})\mathbf{j} + c_1$

At $t = 0$, $\mathbf{v} = \mathbf{j} = \mathbf{j} + c_1 \Rightarrow c_1 = 0 \therefore \mathbf{v} = (2\sin t)\mathbf{i} + (\mathrm{e}^{-t})\mathbf{j}$

Momentum $= m\mathbf{v} = (6\sin t)\mathbf{i} + (3\mathrm{e}^{-t})\mathbf{j}$

(ii) $\mathbf{r} = \displaystyle\int \mathbf{v}\,dt = (-2\cos t)\mathbf{i} - (\mathrm{e}^{-t})\mathbf{j} + c_2$

At $t = 0$ $\mathbf{r} = 3\mathbf{i} - \mathbf{j} = -2\mathbf{i} - \mathbf{j} + c_2 \Rightarrow c_2 = 5\mathbf{i}$

$\therefore \mathbf{r} = (5 - 2\cos t)\mathbf{i} - (\mathrm{e}^{-t})\mathbf{j}$

For large t, $\mathrm{e}^{-t} \approx 0$ $\therefore \mathbf{r} \approx (5 - 2\cos t)\mathbf{i}$

An observer would see the particle describing simple harmonic motion with an amplitude of 2 m about the point $5\mathbf{i}$.

26 A

$$O \quad\underset{0.3\,\mathrm{m}}{\bullet}\quad \overset{12\ \mathrm{ms^{-1}}}{B}\ \underset{0.1\,\mathrm{m}}{\overset{9\ \mathrm{ms^{-1}}}{\bullet}}\ C$$

(a) $v^2 = \omega^2(a^2 - x^2)$

At B $\ 144 = \omega^2(a^2 - 0.09) \Rightarrow \omega^2 = \dfrac{144}{a^2 - 0.09}$

At C $\ 81 = \omega^2(a^2 - 0.16) \Rightarrow \omega^2 = \dfrac{81}{a^2 - 0.16}$

Equating expressions for ω^2:

$$144(a^2 - 0.16) = 81(a^2 - 0.09) \Rightarrow a = 0.5$$

(b) $\omega^2 = \dfrac{144}{0.25 - 0.09} \Rightarrow \omega = 30$

$T = \dfrac{2\pi}{\omega} \Rightarrow T = \dfrac{\pi}{15}$

(c) $v_{\max}$ occurs at $x = 0$ $\therefore v_{\max} = a\omega = 15\,\mathrm{ms^{-1}}$

(d) Let $t = 0$ at O, then $x = a\sin \omega t$ and $x = OC = 0.4\,\mathrm{m}$

$\therefore \sin \omega t = \dfrac{0.4}{0.5} \Rightarrow \omega t = 0.927 \Rightarrow t = 0.03\mathrm{s}$

$$A \quad\underset{2\,\mathrm{m}}{\bullet}\quad \overset{T \leftarrow}{\underset{O}{\bullet}}\quad P$$
$$\longleftarrow 2.4\ \mathrm{m} \longrightarrow$$

$T = \dfrac{\lambda x}{l} \Rightarrow T = 0.2\lambda$

Equation of motion: $T = -m\dfrac{d^2x}{dt^2} = -0.2\omega^2 x = -72$

Equating expressions for T gives $\lambda = 360$

E.P.E. $= \dfrac{\lambda x^2}{2l} = \dfrac{360 \times 0.4^2}{4} = 14.4\ \mathrm{J}$

27 A

$\mathbf{F} - mg\mathbf{k} = m\ddot{\mathbf{r}} \Rightarrow \ddot{\mathbf{r}} = \mathbf{i} + 2t\mathbf{j} - 8\mathbf{k}$

$\dot{\mathbf{r}} = \displaystyle\int \ddot{\mathbf{r}}\,dt = t\mathbf{i} + t^2\mathbf{j} - 8t\mathbf{k} + c_1$

Initially $t = 0$, $\dot{\mathbf{r}} = 3\mathbf{i} - 11\mathbf{j} + 15\mathbf{k} \Rightarrow c_1 = 3\mathbf{i} - 11\mathbf{j} + 15\mathbf{k}$

Thus $\dot{\mathbf{r}} = (t + 3)\mathbf{i} + (t^2 - 11)\mathbf{j} + (15 - 8t)\mathbf{k}$

and when $t = 3\ \mathrm{s}$, $\dot{\mathbf{r}} = 6\mathbf{i} - 2\mathbf{j} - 9\mathbf{k}$

so speed of particle is $|\dot{\mathbf{r}}| = \sqrt{6^2 + (-2)^2 + 9^2} = 11\mathrm{m}\ \mathrm{s^{-1}}$

(ii) When $t = 3\ \mathrm{s}$, $\ddot{\mathbf{r}} = \mathbf{i} + 6\mathbf{j} - 8\mathbf{k}$

Scalar (dot) product $\ddot{\mathbf{r}}.\dot{\mathbf{r}} = 6 - 12 + 72 = 66$

and $|\ddot{\mathbf{r}}| = 10.05$

$\cos\theta = \dfrac{\ddot{\mathbf{r}}.\dot{\mathbf{r}}}{|\dot{\mathbf{r}}||\ddot{\mathbf{r}}|} = \dfrac{66}{11 \times 10.05} \Rightarrow \theta = 53°$ (to nearest degree)

28 AS

(i) $m\dot{\mathbf{r}} = (8\cos t)\mathbf{i} - (12\sin t)\mathbf{j}$
    $\mathbf{F} = m\ddot{\mathbf{r}} = (-8\sin t)\mathbf{i} - (12\cos t)\mathbf{j}$

(ii) Since $m = 4$, $\dot{\mathbf{r}} = (2\cos t)\mathbf{i} - (3\sin t)\mathbf{j}$
    For particle to be moving in direction of vector $\mathbf{j}$,
    $2\cos t = 0 \Rightarrow t = \frac{\pi}{2}$ s

(iii) $\mathbf{r} = \int \dot{\mathbf{r}} dt = (2\sin t)\mathbf{i} + (3\cos t)\mathbf{j} + c$
    When $t = 0$, $\mathbf{r} = \mathbf{i} - \mathbf{j} \Rightarrow c = \mathbf{i} - 4\mathbf{j}$
    thus $\mathbf{r} = (2\sin t + 1)\mathbf{i} + (3\cos t - 4)\mathbf{j}$
    When $t = \frac{\pi}{2}$, $\mathbf{r} = 3\mathbf{i} - 4\mathbf{j}$ and $|\mathbf{r}| = 5$ m

29 A

(a) Resultant $= (3\mathbf{i} + 5\mathbf{j}) + (4\mathbf{i} + 11\mathbf{j}) + (2\mathbf{i} + \mathbf{j}) = (9\mathbf{i} + 17\mathbf{j})$ N

(b) Magnitude of resultant $= \sqrt{9^2 + 17^2} = 19.2$ N (3 s.f.)

(c)

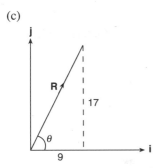

$\cos\theta = \dfrac{9}{|\mathbf{R}|} = 0.469$ (3 s.f.)

30 AS

(a) Resolve $\rightarrow$: $\left(4 \times \frac{4}{5}\right) + \left(4 \times \frac{4}{5}\right) - 2 = 4.4$ N

(Resultant in x-direction)

Resolve $\uparrow$: $\left(4 \times \frac{3}{5}\right) - \left(4 \times \frac{3}{5}\right) = 0$ N

(Resultant in y-direction)
Resultant force $= 4.4$ N in the x-direction.
(i) Frictional force $= 4.4$ N in the negative x-direction
(ii) $F = ma \Rightarrow ma = 4.4 \Rightarrow a = 44$ m s^{-2}

(b)

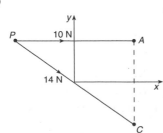

Resolve $\rightarrow$: $10 + \left(14 \times \frac{4}{5}\right) = 21.2$ N

Resolve $\uparrow$: $\left(-14 \times \frac{3}{5}\right) = -8.4$ N

Magnitude of resultant $= \sqrt{(21.2)^2 + (-8.4)^2} = 22.8$ N

Direction of resultant $= \tan^{-1}\left(\dfrac{-8.4}{22.8}\right) = -20.22°$ to PA

31 A

(a) Moments about A:

    $(Mg \times a\cos\theta) = (Mg \times 2a\sin\theta) + \left(\frac{3}{10}Mg \times a\cos\theta\right)$

    $\Rightarrow \frac{4}{10}\cos\theta = 2\sin\theta \Rightarrow \tan\theta = \frac{2}{10} = \frac{1}{5}$

(b) Resolve $\rightarrow$: Mg
    Resolve $\uparrow$: $Mg - \frac{3}{10}Mg = \frac{7}{10}Mg$

    Reaction has magnitude $\sqrt{(Mg)^2 + \left(\frac{7}{10}Mg\right)^2} = \dfrac{\sqrt{149}}{10}Mg$

    Direction to horizontal $= \tan^{-1}\dfrac{\frac{7}{10}Mg}{Mg} = 35°$

(c)

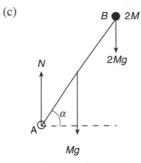

Moments about A:
$(Mg \times a\cos\alpha) + (2Mg \times 2a\cos\alpha) = 2Mga$
$\Rightarrow \cos\alpha = \frac{2}{5} \Rightarrow \alpha = 66°$

(d) Resolve $\rightarrow$: $N\sin\gamma = 0$ since couple has no resultant
    $\Rightarrow \gamma = 0$ and N has magnitude $3Mg$, acting upwards.

32 A/AS

Let M_c be mass of counterweight.
Moments about A: $M_c \times 2a = M \times 3a \Rightarrow M_c = \frac{3}{2}M$
Let M_L be maximum load.

Moments about B: $\frac{3}{2}M \times 3a = M \times 2a + \left(\frac{1}{10}M + M_L\right) \times 7a$

    $\Rightarrow \dfrac{9M}{2} = \dfrac{27M}{10} + 7M_L \Rightarrow M_L = \dfrac{9M}{35}$

33 A

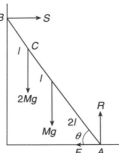

Resolve $\uparrow$: $R = 3Mg$
Moments about B:
$(2Mg \times l\cos\theta) + (Mg \times 2l\cos\theta) + (F \times 4l\sin\theta) = (R \times 4l\cos\theta)$
$\Rightarrow 4F\sin\theta = (4R - 4Mg)\cos\theta \Rightarrow \tan\theta = \dfrac{R - Mg}{F}$

In limiting equilibrium $F = \mu R = \dfrac{R}{5} = \dfrac{3Mg}{5}$ $\therefore \theta = \tan^{-1}\left(\frac{10}{3}\right)$

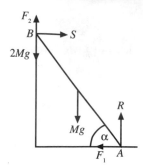

$$\alpha = \tan^{-1}\left(\frac{10}{3}\right)$$

In limiting equilibrium the forces F_1 and F_2 will be:

$F_1 = \mu R$, $F_2 = 1\mu S$

Resolve →: $S = F_1 \Rightarrow S = \mu R$

Resolve ↑: $R + F_2 = 3Mg$

$\Rightarrow \quad R + \mu^2 R = 3Mg$

$\Rightarrow \quad R(1 + \mu^2) = 3Mg$ [1]

Moments about B:

$Mg \times 2l\cos\alpha + F_1 \times 4l\sin\alpha = R \times 4l\cos\alpha$

$\Rightarrow Mg + 2\mu R\tan\alpha = 2R$

$\Rightarrow Mg = 2R - \frac{20}{3}\mu R$ [2]

Eliminating Mg from [1] and [2]

$\frac{R}{3}(1 + \mu^2) = R\left(2 - \frac{20}{3}\mu\right)$

$\Rightarrow 1 + \mu^2 = 6 - 20\mu$

$\Rightarrow \mu^2 + 20\mu - 5 = 0$

34 A

(i)

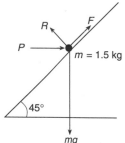

Limiting equilibrium $\therefore F = \mu R \Rightarrow F = \frac{R}{4}$

Resolve parallel to plane: $mg\sin 45° - F - P\cos 45° = 0$

$\Rightarrow \frac{15}{\sqrt{2}} - \frac{R}{4} - \frac{P}{\sqrt{2}} = 0$

Resolve perpendicular to plane:

$R - mg\cos 45° - P\sin 45° = 0 \Rightarrow R - \frac{15}{\sqrt{2}} - \frac{P}{\sqrt{2}} = 0$

Eliminating R gives $15 + P = 60 - 4P \Rightarrow P = 9$ N

(ii)

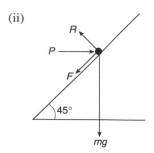

Resolve parallel to plane: $mg\sin 45° + F - P\cos 45° = 0$

$\Rightarrow \frac{15}{\sqrt{2}} + \frac{R}{4} - \frac{P}{\sqrt{2}} = 0$

Resolve perpendicular to plane:

$R - mg\cos 45° - P\sin 45° = 0 \Rightarrow R - \frac{15}{\sqrt{2}} - \frac{P}{\sqrt{2}} = 0$

Eliminating R gives $4P - 60 = 15 + P \Rightarrow P = 25$ N

(b) Resolve →: $(3\cos 30° + 5\cos 30°) = 4\sqrt{3}$ N

Resolve ↑: $10 + 5\sin 30° + 3\sin 30° = 11$ N

Thus additional force has magnitude

$$\sqrt{\left(4\sqrt{3}\right)^2 + (11)^2} = 13 \text{ N}$$

and direction $\tan^{-1}\left(\frac{11}{4\sqrt{3}}\right)$ to $OX = 57.8°$ to OX.

35 A

(NOTE – you can also use Lami's theorem for this problem but this method is more concise)

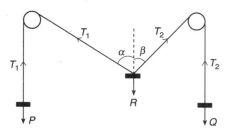

(a) $P = 2$ N , $Q = 3$ N, $R = 4$ N

Resolve ↑ for P: $T_1 = 2$ N

Resolve ↑ for Q: $T_2 = 3$ N

Thus problem can be reduced to a three-force problem. The system is in equilibrium, so forces form a triangle.

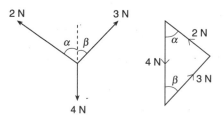

Using cosine rule:

$$\cos\alpha = \frac{4^2 + 2^2 - 3^2}{2 \times 4 \times 2} = \frac{11}{16}, \quad \cos\beta = \frac{4^2 + 3^2 - 2^2}{2 \times 4 \times 3} = \frac{7}{8}$$

If $R > 0$, R must be below the level of the pulleys to provide upward forces to balance R, hence $\alpha \le \frac{\pi}{2}$ and $\beta \le \frac{\pi}{2}$.

(b) In general, using cosine rule and a triangle of forces as above,

$$\cos\alpha = \frac{R^2 + P^2 - Q^2}{2RP} \quad \text{and} \quad \cos\beta = \frac{R^2 + Q^2 - P^2}{2RQ}$$

(c) $\cos\alpha = -\frac{1}{8}, \cos\beta = \frac{3}{4}$

$\cos\alpha$ is negative, therefore $\alpha > \frac{1}{2}\pi$, so the configuration is not possible.

36 AS

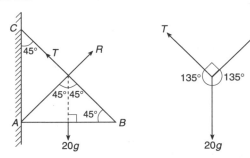

Since $\triangle ABC$ is isosceles, $\hat{B} = \hat{C} = 45°$.
Other angles follow from similar triangles.
(a) Using Lami's theorem:

$$\frac{20g}{\sin 90°} = \frac{T}{\sin 135°} \Rightarrow T = 139 \text{ N (3 s.f.)}$$

(b)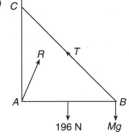

Moments about A:
$$196 + 3Mg = 400 \times 2 \sin 45°$$
$$\Rightarrow 196 + 19.6M = 565.69 \Rightarrow M = 18.9 \text{ kg (3 s.f.)}$$

37 A

(i)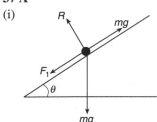

Resolve parallel to plane: $F_1 + mg \sin\theta = mg$
In limiting equilibrium $F_1 = \mu R \Rightarrow \mu R = mg(1 - \sin\theta)$ [1]

(ii)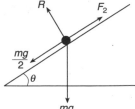

Resolve parallel to plane: $\dfrac{mg}{2} + mg\sin\theta = F_2$

In limiting equilibrium $F_2 = \mu R \Rightarrow \mu R = mg(\frac{1}{2} + \sin\theta)$ [2]

From [1] and [2] $mg(1 - \sin\theta) = mg(\frac{1}{2} + \sin\theta) \Rightarrow \sin\theta = \frac{1}{4}$

From [1] $\mu R = \dfrac{3mg}{4}$

Resolve perpendicular to plane: $R = mg\cos\theta$

thus $\mu mg\cos\theta = \dfrac{\sqrt{15}}{4}\mu mg = \dfrac{3}{4}mg \Rightarrow \mu = \dfrac{3}{\sqrt{15}}$

38 A/AS
(a) (i)   Diagram to show forces acting on ladder.

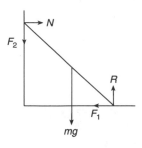

(ii)   Resolve $\rightarrow$: $N = F_1$
If floor is frictionless $F_1 = 0$, but $N \neq 0$,
so the ladder would slip.

(b)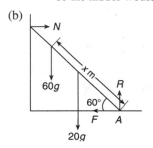

(i) $F = \mu R$ Resolve $\uparrow$: $R = 20g + 60g = 80g$ N
$$\therefore F = 0.4 \times 80g = 32g \text{ N}$$
(ii)   Resolve $\rightarrow$: $N = F \Rightarrow N = 32g$ N
(iii)   Moments about A:
$$(20g \times 4\cos 60°) + (60g \times x\cos 60°) = (N \times 8\sin 60°)$$
$$\Rightarrow 40 + 30x = 221.7025 \Rightarrow x = 6.06\,\text{m}$$

39 A
Forces acting on the system.

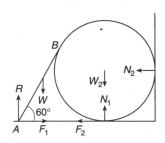

(i)   Consider forces acting on rod.

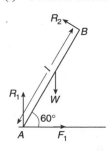

Taking moments about A:
$$W \times \tfrac{1}{2}l\cos 60° = R_2 \times l \Rightarrow R_2 = \dfrac{W}{4}$$

(ii) Consider forces acting on cylinder.

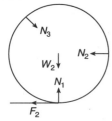

Taking moments about centre: $F_2 \times r = 0 \Rightarrow F_2 = 0$, since $r \neq 0$

(iii) Resolve $\rightarrow$: $N_3 \sin 60° = N_2$, but $N_3 = R_2 = \dfrac{W}{4}$

$$\therefore N_2 = \frac{\sqrt{3}W}{8}$$

(iv) Consider rod.
Resolve $\rightarrow$: $F_1 = R_2 \sin 60° \Rightarrow F_1 = \dfrac{\sqrt{3}W}{8}$

Resolve $\uparrow$: $R_1 + R_2 \cos 60° = W \Rightarrow R_1 = \dfrac{7W}{8}$

In limiting equilibrium, $F_1 = \mu R_1 \Rightarrow \mu = \dfrac{\sqrt{3}}{7}$

40 AS

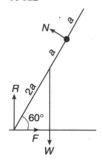

(a) Moments about A: $W \times 2a \cos 60° = N \times 3a \Rightarrow N = \dfrac{W}{3}$

(b) Resolve $\uparrow$: $R + N \cos 60° = W \Rightarrow R = \dfrac{5W}{6}$

Resolve $\rightarrow$: $F = N \sin 60° \Rightarrow F = \dfrac{\sqrt{3}W}{6}$

(c) Equilibrium is limiting so $F = \mu R \Rightarrow \mu = \dfrac{\sqrt{3}}{5}$

41 A

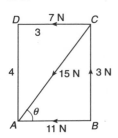

Moments about C: $G = 11 \times 4 = 44$ N m
Resolve parallel to BA: $X = 11 + 7 + 15 \cos \theta = 27$ N
Resolve parallel to BC: $Y = 3 - 15 \sin \theta = -9$ N
Magnitude of resultant $= \sqrt{27^2 + (-9)^2} = 28.46$

Direction of resultant, $\alpha = \tan^{-1} \dfrac{27}{9} \Rightarrow \alpha = 71.5°$

Let R cross BC x from C.

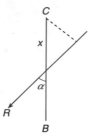

Moments about C: $Rx \sin \alpha = G = 44$

$$\Rightarrow x = \frac{44}{28.46 \sin 71.5°} = 1.63\text{m}$$

42 A

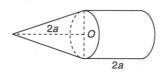

Shape	Mass	Distance of centre of mass from O
cylinder	M	a
cone	λM	$a/2$
combined	$M + \lambda M$	$\bar{x}$

Moments about O: $\dfrac{\lambda Ma}{2} + (M + \lambda M)\bar{x} = Ma$

(a) If $\lambda = 1$, $\dfrac{Ma}{2} + 2M\bar{x} = Ma \Rightarrow \bar{x} = \dfrac{a}{4}$

(b) For $\bar{x} = 0$, $\dfrac{\lambda Ma}{2} = Ma \Rightarrow \lambda = 2$

43 A

Lamina is uniform, so mass acts from centre.

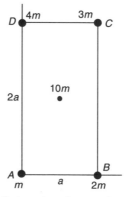

Let centre of mass of new body be $(\bar{x}, \bar{y})$

$$\bar{x} = \frac{\sum m_i x_i}{\sum m_i} = \frac{m(0) + 2m(a) + 3m(a) + 4m(0) + 10m(\frac{a}{2})}{m + 2m + 3m + 4m + 10m}$$

$$\Rightarrow \bar{x} = \frac{10ma}{20m} = \frac{a}{2}$$

$$\bar{y} = \frac{\sum m_i y_i}{\sum m_i} = \frac{m(0) + 2m(0) + 3m(2a) + 4m(2a) + 10m(a)}{m + 2m + 3m + 4m + 10m}$$

$$= \frac{24ma}{20m} = \frac{6a}{5}$$

∴ Centre of mass has position $\left(\dfrac{a}{2}, \dfrac{6a}{5}\right)$.

Let centre of mass be M.

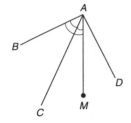

$B\hat{A}C = \arctan 2 \Rightarrow B\hat{A}C = 63.43°$

$B\hat{A}M = \arctan \frac{12}{5} \Rightarrow B\hat{A}M = 67.38°$

$\therefore C\hat{A}M = B\hat{A}M - B\hat{A}C = 3.95°$ (3 s.f.)

For AC vertical,

$\bar{y} = a \Rightarrow \dfrac{10ma + 6ma + 2an}{20m} = a \Rightarrow n = 2m$

$\therefore$ A mass of $2m$ would need to be hung at D.

44 AS

(a) Uniform lamina ∴ mass ∝ area. Let M be mass per unit area.

	Mass	Distance of centre of mass from OX	Distance of centre of mass from OY
Original shape	$16\pi r^2 M$	0	0
B	$\pi r^2 M$	0	$2r$
C	$\pi r^2 M$	$2r$	0
New shape	$14\pi r^2 M$	$\bar{x}$	$\bar{y}$

Moments about OY: $\pi r^2 M \times 2r + 14\pi r^2 M \times \bar{x} = 0 \Rightarrow \bar{x} = \dfrac{-r}{7}$

Moments about OX: $\pi r^2 M \times 2r + 14\pi r^2 M \times \bar{y} = 0 \Rightarrow \bar{y} = \dfrac{-r}{7}$

New centre of mass is $\left(-\frac{r}{7}, -\frac{r}{7}\right)$.

(b)

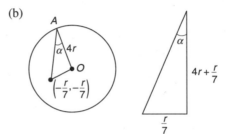

$\tan \alpha = \dfrac{r}{7} \bigg/ \dfrac{29r}{7} = \dfrac{1}{29} \Rightarrow \alpha = 0.034$ radians (2 s.f.)

S1
core

Pictorial Representation
Categorical data, Bar chart, Pie chart, Isotype diagram.

Categorical data

Information which can be put into categories is called **categorical data.**

Categorical data may be represented pictorially by **bar charts, pie charts** and **isotype diagrams** (or **pictograms**).

ℹ️ Table showing a man's annual expenditure.

Item	Expenditure (£)
House	3000
Food	2000
Fuel	800
Travel	800
Others	1100

Here the categories are the items of expenditure, e.g. House, etc.

Bar chart

In a **bar chart** data are represented by a series of parallel bars of equal width. The length of each bar is proportional to the frequency of the category it represents. The distance between adjacent bars should be equal.

Bars may be drawn horizontally or vertically but all must start from the same base line. If drawn vertically, the diagram is often called a **column graph**.

ℹ️ For the data above a suitable scale is $1\,\text{cm} \leftrightarrow £500$.

The length of the bar representing 'House' is $\dfrac{3000}{500}\,\text{cm}$
$$= 6\,\text{cm}$$

The lengths of the other bars, working down the table, are 4 cm, 1.6 cm, 1.6 cm and 2.2 cm.

Bar chart showing a man's annual expenditure

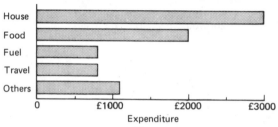

Figure 1

Pie chart

In a **pie chart,** the total data is represented by the area of a circle which is divided into sectors, one sector for each category.

Each sector angle is a fraction of 360° and may be found from:

$$\text{sector angle} = \frac{\text{category value}}{\text{sum of category values}} \times 360°.$$

Since the 'sum of the category values' is represented by the complete circle, the sum of the sector angles must be 360°. This is a useful calculation check.

A pie chart should not contain too many sectors (less than eight is usual). Each sector should be clearly labelled.

ℹ️ For the data above the 'sum of category values' is £7700.

The sector angle for 'House' is $\dfrac{3000}{7700} \times 360° = 140.3°$

The sector angles for the other sectors, in order, are 93.5°, 37.4°, 37.4° and 51.4°.

Pie chart showing a man's annual expenditure

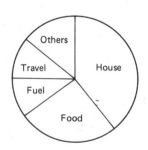

Figure 2

Isotype diagram (or pictogram)

In an **isotype diagram** (or **pictogram**) data are represented by symbols (usually pictures). A symbol is used to represent a stated number of units of the data. Appropriate fractions of the symbol are used to represent fractions of the basic number of units.

The symbol used is often associated in some way with the data it represents.

ℹ️ For the data above a suitable symbol would be

🪙 to represent £500.

Figure 3

Isotype diagram showing a man's annual expenditure

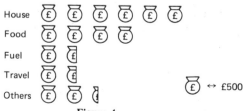

Figure 4

190

Pictorial Representation
Worked example and Exam questions.

 The approximate expenditure in the United Kingdom during an academic year on various sectors of education is given below:

Sector	Expenditure (millions of £)
Primary	523
Secondary	608
Special	46
Adult	260
Teacher training	57
Universities	258

Illustrate these data by a pie chart, showing clearly any necessary calculations.

Total expenditure is £1752 millions

Thus £1752 millions $\longleftrightarrow 360°$

$$£1 \text{ million} \longleftrightarrow \left(\frac{360}{1752}\right)°$$

and $£523$ millions $\longleftrightarrow \left(\frac{360 \times 523}{1752}\right)° = 107\cdot5°$, to the nearest half-degree.

Replacing 523 by the other entries in the table in turn and tabulating the appropriate sector angles gives the following table.

Sector	Sector angle in pie chart
Primary	107.5°
Secondary	125.0°
Special	9.5°
Adult	53.5°
Teacher training	11.5°
Universities	53.0°

The total of the sector angles is 360° as required.

The appropriate pie chart is shown below.

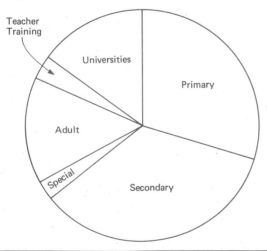

1 The table below, adapted from a magazine article, shows the approximate total number of deaths in England and Wales in 1975 from preventable external causes.

Cause	Number of deaths
Smoking	100 000
Traffic Accidents	6 000
Alcohol	5 000
Falls	4 000
Others	2 000

Represent this information on a pie chart, stating the size of the angles. Suggest briefly how the pie chart might be displayed on a poster to achieve immediate visual impact.

*(A)

2 In 1977, the group sales of ICI by geographical region were:

United Kingdom	£1 868 000 000
The rest of Western Europe	£865 000 000
The Americas	£628 000 000
Australasia	£505 000 000
Others	£807 000 000

Display this information on a pie chart, showing clearly any necessary calculations.

*(A)

3 The cash flow of BP during 1977 was reported as follows:

'Where the funds came from.'

Income before UK tax	£769 million
Depreciation	£304 million
Other	£19 million
Total	£1092 million

'How they were used.'

Capital investment	£721 million
UK tax	£35 million
Additional working capital	£65 million
Dividends	£78 million
Repayment of borrowings	£193 million
Total	£1092 million

Represent these data diagrammatically.

*(A)

4 Five companies form a group. The sales of each company during the year ending 5th April, 1978, are shown in the table below

Company	A	B	C	D	E
Sales (in £1000s)	55	130	20	35	60

Draw a pie chart of radius 5 cm to illustrate this information. For the year ending 5th April, 1979, the total sales of the group increased by 20% and this growth was maintained for the year ending 5th April, 1980. If pie charts were drawn to compare the total sales for each of these years with the total sales for the year ending 5th April, 1978, what would be the radius of each of these pie charts? If the sales of company E for the year ending 5th April, 1980, were again £60 000, what would be the angle of the sector representing them?

*(C)

5 Answer any TWO of the following:
(a) Explain the meaning of 'correlation'. Referring to your projects, discuss briefly two correlation coefficients which you have studied, and compare their uses.
(b) Discuss three methods of representing data diagrammatically, explaining the advantages and disadvantages of each method.
(c) You wish to study the prevalence of five different grass types on a very large grassy hillside. Explain the principles which would guide you in collecting random samples and, assuming that a table of random numbers is available, how this table could be used for the collection.

(L)

Frequency Distributions

Definition, Class limits and class boundaries, Histogram, Frequency polygon and frequency curve.

Definition

When repeated observations are made on a variable the result is a **frequency distribution**. The variable may be discrete or continuous.

A frequency distribution is recorded in a **frequency table**. The values of the variable are often grouped into classes. The frequency table gives the possible values or **class intervals** of the variable and the corresponding frequencies (f).

ⓘ The marks of 40 students in a test (discrete data)

Mark	–9	10–19	20–29	30–39	40–49
Frequency (f)	4	8	17	9	2

Estimated UK population in 1930 (continuous data)

Age (years)	0–4	5–14	15–29	30–59	60–
Number (millions)	3.5	7.6	11.9	17.7	5.3

Class limits and class boundaries

For a **grouped frequency distribution** (continuous or discrete) the **lower** and **upper class limits** are the extreme values of each class in the frequency table. Open classes have no well-defined class limits. They may be closed at arbitrary but convenient points.

For a continuous frequency distribution, the **lower class boundary** (l.c.b.) and **upper class boundary** (u.c.b.) are the smallest and largest values respectively that an item in the class can (theoretically) have.

For a grouped discrete frequency distribution the class boundaries are adjusted because of the continuous nature of the variable scale. They may be found using:

$\frac{1}{2}$ (u.c. limit of one class + l.c. limit of next class).

The **class width** or **class interval** is the difference between the two class boundaries, i.e. (u.c.b.–l.c.b.).

The **class midpoint** or **mid-value** is half-way between the two class boundaries, i.e. $\frac{1}{2}$(l.c.b. + u.c.b.). It is often used to represent the class interval.

ⓘ In the discrete data above, the open class '–9' may be closed at 0 (the lowest possible mark). It becomes '0–9' with lower and upper class limits of 0 and 9.

In the continuous data above, the open class '60–' may be closed at 109 (a possible maximum age!).

ⓘ For the class '15–29' in the continuous data above: If the ages were measured 'to the nearest year', then the l.c.b. is 14.5 and the u.c.b. is 29.5, the class width is (29.5 − 14.5) = 15, the class mid-value is $\frac{1}{2}$(14.5 + 29.5) = 22.

Note: If the ages were measured as 'age in years last birthday', then the real class interval would be '15– less than 30', with class width 15.

For the class '10–19' in the discrete data above: l.c.b. is $\frac{1}{2}$(9 + 10) = 9.5 and u.c.b. is $\frac{1}{2}$(19 + 20) = 19.5, the class width is (19.5 − 9.5) = 10, the class mid-value is $\frac{1}{2}$(9.5 + 19.5) = 14.5.

Histogram

A **histogram** illustrates a frequency distribution. It consists of rectangles drawn on a continuous base. The area of each rectangle is proportional to the frequency of the class it represents. The rectangles do not have to be of equal width but their bases must be proportional to the class widths, i.e. the extremes of the base of each rectangle are at the l.c.b. and u.c.b. of the class it represents.

The ratio of the heights of each rectangle may be found using $\frac{\text{class frequency(cf)}}{\text{class width(cw)}}$ for each class. A suitable scale is selected for the vertical axis which should be labelled as shown.

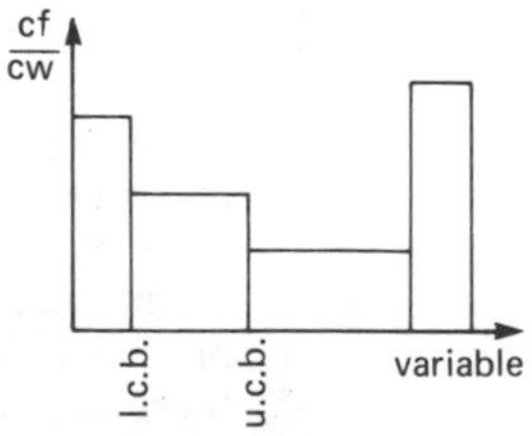

Figure 1

Note: Since the base is continuous, there must be no space between rectangles. The u.c.b. of one class must coincide with the l.c.b. of the next.

ⓘ *Draw a histogram for the continuous data above, given that the ages are 'to the nearest year'.*

class widths:	4.5	10	15	30	50
$\frac{\text{class frequency}}{\text{class width}}$ (to 2 d.p.)	0.78	0.76	0.79	0.59	0.11

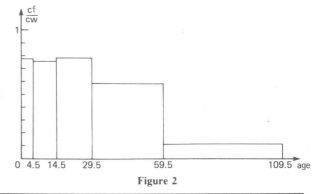

Figure 2

Frequency polygon and frequency curve

A **frequency polygon** is a line graph which may be drawn by joining the midpoints of the tops of the rectangles which would form a histogram.

It is extended to the next lower and higher classes, these having zero frequency.

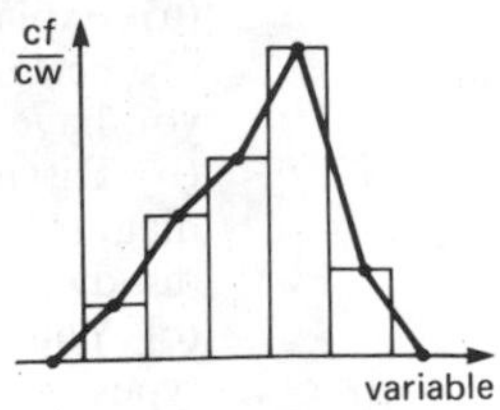

Figure 3

A smooth **frequency curve** may be drawn through the midpoints if the number of classes is large.

ⓘ Some commonly occurring frequency curves

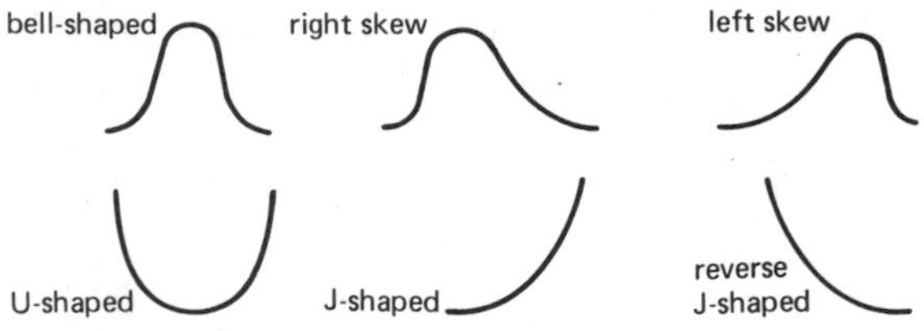

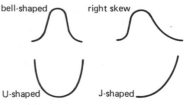

bell-shaped   right skew   left skew

U-shaped   J-shaped   reverse J-shaped

Figure 4

Frequency Distributions

Stem and leaf diagrams.
Worked example, Guided example and Exam question.

Stem and leaf diagrams

This is a quick way to picture the distribution of a data set. It is a way of finding the **median** (see S4) and the **skewness** (see S6) of the distribution. You may need to identify gaps in the stem and individual observations that lie far outside the overall pattern of the data, and then look for an explanation for these unusual observations.

To create a **stem and leaf diagram**:

(a) Separate each observation into a **stem**, consisting of one or more of the leading digits, and a **leaf**, which consists of the remaining digits.
(b) Stem values are listed vertically in increasing order from top to bottom. A vertical line is drawn to the right of the stem.
(c) Leaves are added to the right of the line corresponding to the particular stem, and are listed in increasing order from left to right.

 Construct a stem and leaf diagram for the following set of data. Choose a suitable stem and locate the median.

116	118	125	104	134	159	141	136	125	109
117	133	134	128	134	155	113	119	120	143
152	139	140	151	160	131	129			

Suitable stems are 10, 11, 12, 13, 14, 15, 16.

10	4 9
11	3 6 7 8 9
12	0 5 5 8 9
13	1 3 4 4 4 6 9
14	0 1 3
15	1 2 5 9
16	0

The median is 133.

WE *In 1959 the age distribution of the population of the United Kingdom was as follows:*

Age (years)	0–	20–	30–	40–	50–	60–	80–100
Number (in millions)	15.6	6.6	7.4	6.9	6.8	7.7	1.0

Draw a histogram for these data.

Let the linear scale for the age axis be 1 cm to 10 years. The calculation of the histogram column heights is set out in the table below.

Class	Class width	Freq.	Histogram col. width (cm)	Class freq. / Class width	Histogram col. height (cm)
0–	20	15.6	2	0.78	7.8
20–	10	6.6	1	0.66	6.6
30–	10	7.4	1	0.74	7.4
40–	10	6.9	1	0.69	6.9
50–	10	6.8	1	0.68	6.8
60–	20	7.7	2	0.385	3.85
80–100	20	1.0	2	0.05	0.5

The appropriate histogram is shown below.

Note: the column class frequency/class width gives the ratio of the column heights in the histogram, by taking the scale as 10 cm to one unit on the corresponding axis gives a set of column heights of reasonable dimensions.

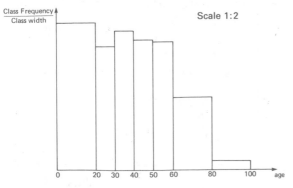

GE *Draw a frequency polygon for the frequency distribution (see next column) which gives the distribution of life of 300 electric light bulbs.*

Life (hours)	Frequency	Life (hours)	Frequency
950–	20	1500–	29
1200–	28	1550–	28
1300–	44	1600–	46
1400–	27	1700–	28
1450–	29	1800–2100	21

Since a frequency polygon is obtained by erecting ordinates at the centre of each class interval, the calculation procedure is almost identical with that for a histogram. Appropriate table headings together with the first row of the table completed are shown below.

Class	Class width	Class midpoint	Freq.	Freq. poly interval width (cm)	Class freq. / Class width	Freq. poly ordinate height (cm)
950–	250	1075	20	2.5	0.08	0.8

The scales used are 1 cm to 100 hours for the horizontal (life) axis and 10 cm to 1 unit for the vertical (class freq./class width) axis, giving rise to the frequency polygon shown below.

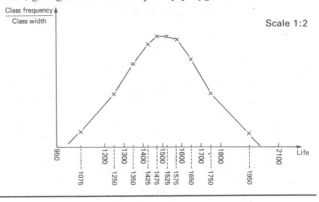

EX **1** The number of passengers on a certain regular weekday train service on each of 50 occasions was

165	141	163	153	130	158	119	187	185	209
177	147	166	154	159	178	187	139	180	143
160	185	153	168	189	173	127	179	163	182
171	146	174	149	126	156	155	174	154	150
210	162	138	117	198	164	125	142	182	218

Choose suitable class intervals and reduce these data to a grouped frequency table. Plot the corresponding frequency polygon on squared paper using suitable scales. *(A)*

S3
core

Mode and Means
Mode, Arithmetic mean, Weighted mean, Geometric mean, Harmonic mean.

Mode

The **mode** of a set of values is that value which occurs most frequently.

The **modal class** of a grouped frequency distribution is the class with the greatest frequency.

The value of the mode within the modal class may be estimated from the histogram of the distribution as shown in the diagram.

To calculate the value of this mode use:

$$\text{mode} = L + \left(\frac{\Delta_1}{\Delta_1 + \Delta_2}\right) c$$

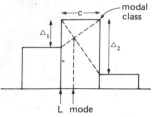

Figure 1

where L = lower boundary of modal class

Δ_1 = modal class $f - f$ of next lower class

Δ_2 = modal class $f - f$ of next higher class

c = width of modal class

> ℹ️ The mode of 2, 3, 3, 1, 3, 2, 4, 5, 6, 3, 2, 4, 4, 3 is 3 since the value 3 has the largest frequency.

> ℹ️ *Calculate the mode of this distribution*:

Class	10–	15–	20–	25–	30–	35–40
f	2	12	27	41	30	7

For this distribution use: $\text{mode} = L + \left(\dfrac{\Delta_1}{\Delta_1 + \Delta_2}\right) c$

The modal class is '25–'.

So $L = 25$

$\Delta_1 = 41 - 27 = 14$

$\Delta_2 = 41 - 30 = 11$

$c = 5$

$\therefore \text{mode} = 25 + \left(\dfrac{14}{14 + 11}\right) 5 = 27.8$

Arithmetic mean

The **arithmetic mean** of the n values $x_1, x_2, \ldots, x_n$ is

$$\text{A.M.} = \bar{x} = \frac{(x_1 + x_2 + \ldots + x_n)}{n} = \frac{\Sigma x}{n}$$

For n values with respective frequencies $f_1, f_2, \ldots f_n$,

$$\bar{x} = \frac{(f_1 x_1 + f_2 x_2 + \ldots + f_n x_n)}{(f_1 + f_2 + \ldots + f_n)} = \frac{\Sigma f x}{\Sigma f}$$

If a is a **working mean** and **deviation** $d_r = a - x_r$, then

$$\bar{x} = a + \frac{\Sigma f d}{\Sigma f}$$

For a grouped frequency distribution (continuous or discrete), the mean is given by:

$$\bar{x} = \frac{\Sigma f x}{\Sigma f}$$

where the class mid-value represents each class.

If a is a working mean and either the class intervals are of equal width c or the deviations d_r have a common factor c such that $d_r = c u_r$, then

$$\bar{x} = a + c \frac{\Sigma f u}{\Sigma f}$$

> ℹ️ *Calculate the arithmetic mean of the discrete data given in this frequency distribution.*

x	1	2	3	4	5	6
f	1	3	5	3	1	1

Tabulating with a working mean 3 gives

x	f	d	fd
1	1	−2	−2
2	3	−1	−3
3 = a	5	0	0
4	3	1	3
5	1	2	2
6	1	3	3
	$\Sigma f = 14$		$\Sigma fd = 3$

$\therefore \text{arithmetic mean} = 3 + \dfrac{3}{14} = 3.21$ (2 d.p.)

Weighted mean

If the numbers $x_1, x_2, \ldots, x_n$ are given the weights $w_1, w_2, \ldots, w_n$, then **the weighted mean** is

$$\bar{x}_w = \frac{(w_1 x_1 + w_2 x_2 + \ldots + w_n x_n)}{(w_1 + w_2 + \ldots + w_n)} = \frac{\Sigma w x}{\Sigma w}$$

> ℹ️ A pupil's marks in four tests are 38%, 67%, 43%, 72%.
> The weights for the tests are 1, 2, 2, 3 respectively.
> $$\bar{x}_w = \frac{38 \times 1 + 67 \times 2 + 43 \times 2 + 72 \times 3}{1 + 2 + 2 + 3} = 59.25\%$$

Geometric mean

The **geometric mean** of the n values $x_1, x_2, \ldots, x_n$ is

$$\text{G.M.} = \sqrt[n]{(x_1 \times x_2 \times \ldots \times x_n)}$$

For n values with respective frequencies $f_1, f_2, \ldots, f_n$,

$$\text{G.M.} = \sqrt[\Sigma f]{(x_1^{f_1} \times x_2^{f_2} \times \ldots \times x_n^{f_n})}$$

> ℹ️ The geometric mean of this distribution is:
>
> | x | 1 | 2 | 3 | 4 | 5 | 6 |
> |-----|---|---|---|---|---|---|
> | f | 2 | 3 | 5 | 3 | 4 | 2 |
>
> $\text{G.M.} = \sqrt[19]{(1^2 \times 2^2 \times 3^5 \times 4^3 \times 5^4 \times 6^2)}$
> $= \sqrt[19]{(2.80 \times 10^9)} = 3.14$

Harmonic mean

The **harmonic mean** of the n values $x_1, x_2, \ldots, x_n$ is $n / \Sigma(1/x)$

For n values with respective frequencies $f_1, f_2, \ldots, f_n$, harmonic mean is $n / \Sigma(f/x)$

> ℹ️ The harmonic mean of the 5 values 2, 4, 5, 6, 9 is:
> $$\text{H.M.} = \frac{5}{\frac{1}{2} + \frac{1}{4} + \frac{1}{5} + \frac{1}{6} + \frac{1}{9}} = 4.07$$

Mode and Means
Worked examples, Exercises and Exam questions.

 (a) (i) *Obtain the arithmetic mean of the numbers* 1, 2, 3, 4, 5, 6, 7, 8.

(ii) *Hence show that the geometric mean of the numbers* $9, 9^2, 9^3, 9^4, 9^5, 9^6, 9^7, 9^8$ *is* 3^9.

(b) *Given that* $p > q > 0$, *use the expansion of* $(\sqrt{p} - \sqrt{q})^2$ *to show that the arithmetic mean of p and q is greater than their geometric mean.*

(a) (i) Let the arithmetic mean be $\bar{x}$,

$$\bar{x} = \frac{1+2+3+4+5+6+7+8}{8} = \frac{36}{8} = \frac{9}{2}$$

(ii) Let the geometric mean be g

$$g = \sqrt[8]{9^1 \times 9^2 \times 9^3 \times 9^4 \times 9^5 \times 9^6 \times 9^7 \times 9^8}$$

$$= 9^{\frac{1+2+3+4+5+6+7+8}{8}}$$

$$= 9^{\bar{x}} = 9^{\frac{9}{2}} = (3^2)^{\frac{9}{2}} = 3^9$$

(b) Since $p > q$, $\sqrt{p} > \sqrt{q}$

$\therefore \sqrt{p} - \sqrt{q} > 0$

and $(\sqrt{p} - \sqrt{q})^2 > 0$

$\therefore (\sqrt{p})^2 + (\sqrt{q})^2 - 2\sqrt{p}\sqrt{q} > 0$

$$\frac{p+q}{2} > \sqrt{pq}$$

But $\frac{p+q}{2} = (\text{A.M.})_{pq}$ and $\sqrt{pq} = (\text{G.M.})_{pq}$

$\therefore (\text{A.M.})_{pq} > (\text{G.M.})_{pq}$

WE *The following distribution gives the estimated total population of the UK for the year 1977, in millions. Find the mean age.*

Age	0–	10–	20–	30–	40–	50–	60–	70–	80–
Frequency	10·1	9·3	7·9	7·6	6·7	6·7	6·0	3·8	1·2

For the following tabular calculation note the points below:
(1) the last class has been closed at 90 years.
(2) the working mean a is 45 years.
(3) d is the deviation of the mid-class value from a.
(4) $c (= 10)$ is the scale factor for the mid-class deviations.

Class	Class mid-value	Frequency f	Deviation from a, d	$u = \dfrac{d}{c}$	fu
0–	5	10.1	−40	−4	−40.4
10–	15	9.3	−30	−3	−27.9
20–	25	7.9	−20	−2	−15.8
30–	35	7.6	−10	−1	−7.6
40–	45 = a	6.7	0	0	0
50–	55	6.7	10	1	6.7
60–	65	6.0	20	2	12.0
70–	75	3.8	30	3	11.4
80–	85	1.2	40	4	4.8
90					
		$\Sigma f = 59.3$			$\Sigma fu = -91.7 + 34.9$
					$= -56.8$

$$\bar{x} = a + \frac{c\Sigma fu}{\Sigma f} = 45 - \frac{10 \times 56.8}{59.3} = 35.42 \text{ years}$$

---

 1 The wing spans of 1000 specimens of a type of insect were measured accurately and the results are summarised in the table below.

Wing span (cm)	Frequency
0–	0
1–	5
2–	20
3–	90
4–	215
5–	265
6–	240
7–	120
8–	35
9–	10
10–	0

Calculate the mean wing span. *

2 The percentage marks of 100 candidates in an examination are given in the table below.

Mark per cent	Frequency
0-19	6
20-29	4
30-39	9
40-49	27
50-59	22
60-69	18
70-79	8
80-99	6

Calculate the mean percentage mark. *

3 The atmospheric pressure at a weather station was measured once each day for a year. The results are recorded below.

Pressure (millibars)	Number of days
920-	3
980-	14
990	44
1000-	77
1010-	150
1020-	63
1030-1040	14

Find the mean pressure. *

4 (a) Calculate: (i) the arithmetic mean; (ii) the geometric mean of the numbers 1, 2, 3, 4, 5, 6.
(b) Show, by means of clearly labelled sketches, the shape of the frequency curve of a distribution when it is: (i) skew with the mode less than the mean; (ii) bi-modal. *(A)

5 (a) For a set of positive real numbers $x_1, x_2, \ldots, x_n$, give the formula for: (i) their arithmetic mean; (ii) their geometric mean. Show that the arithmetic mean of two different positive real numbers x_1 and x_2 is always greater than their geometric mean.
(b) Define the mode of a frequency distribution and give a real-life example of a multimodal distribution. *(A)

6 The arithmetic mean of the positive numbers a_1, a_2, a_3, is $\bar{a}$ and their geometric mean is A. Similarly the arithmetic mean of the positive numbers b_1, b_2, b_3, is $\bar{b}$ and their geometric mean is B. Find in terms of $\bar{a}$ and $\bar{b}$ only the arithmetic mean of:
(i) $(a_1 + b_1)$, $(a_2 + b_2)$, $(a_3 + b_3)$;
(ii) $a_1, b_1, a_2, b_2, a_3, b_3$;
(iii) $(100 + 10a_1 + b_1)$, $(100 + 10a_2 + b_2)$, $(100 + 10a_3 + b_3)$.
Find in terms of A and B only the geometric mean of:
(iv) $a_1 b_1, a_2 b_2 a_3 b_3$;
(v) $a_1^2 b_1^3, a_2^2 b_2^3, a_3^2 b_3^3$. *(A)

7 (a) (i) Obtain the arithmetic mean of the numbers: 1, 2, 3, 4, 5, 6, 7, 8, 9.
(ii) Hence, or otherwise, show that the geometric mean of the numbers: $4, 4^2, 4^3, 4^4, 4^5, 4^6, 4^7, 4^8, 4^9$, is 2^{10}.
(b) Given that $a > b > 0$, use the expansion of $(\sqrt{a} - \sqrt{b})^2$ to show that the arithmetic mean of a and b is greater than their geometric mean. *(A)

S4
core

Medians and Quantiles
Definitions, Median for a discrete variable, Median and quantiles for grouped data.

Definitions

The **median** is that value of the variable which divides the distribution into two equal parts with equal frequencies.

Associated with the median are the quartiles, deciles and percentiles. These are called the **quantiles**.

The **quartiles** divide the distribution into four equal parts. The three corresponding values of the variable being denoted by Q_1, Q_2 and Q_3.

The **deciles**, $D_1, D_2, \ldots, D_9$, divide the distribution into ten equal parts.

The **percentiles**, $P_1, P_2, \ldots, P_{99}$, divide the distribution into one hundred equal parts.

If M is the median, $M = Q_2 = D_5 = P_{50}$.

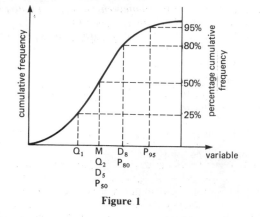

Figure 1

Median for a discrete variable

To find the median for a set of discrete variables

(a) Arrange the distribution in order of magnitude:
$$x_1, x_2, x_3, \ldots, x_n$$

(b) If n is odd, the median is the middle item, i.e. the $\frac{1}{2}(n+1)$th item.

(c) If n is even, the median is the arithmetic mean of the middle two items, i.e. the $\frac{1}{2}n$th and $\frac{1}{2}(n+2)$th items.

ⓘ *Find the median of (a) 3, 7, 4, 1, 2, 3, 6, 9, 8, (b) 9, 3, 1, 5, 8, 5, 7, 4, 8, 4, 7, 6*

(a) In order: 1, 2, 3, 3, 4, 6, 7, 8, 9
The median is 4.

(b) In order: 1, 3, 4, 4, 5, 5, 6, 7, 7, 8, 8, 9.
The median is $\frac{1}{2}(5+6) = 5.5$.

Median and quantiles for grouped data

For grouped data of a discrete or continuous variable the following **graphical method** can be used to **estimate the median and quantiles**.

(a) Form the **cumulative frequency distribution.** The cumulative frequency for any class is the sum of frequencies of that class and lower classes.

(b) Plot each cumulative frequency against the upper limit of the corresponding class interval.

(c) Join these points with either straight line segments to form the **cumulative frequency polygon** or a smooth curve to form the **cumulative frequency curve** (or **ogive**).

(d) The middle number of the distribution is located on the cumulative frequency axis and the corresponding value of the variable is the median. The quantiles can be found in a similar way.

A more accurate value of the median may be found using the formula:

$$\text{median} = L + \left(\frac{\frac{1}{2}N - (\Sigma f)_L}{f_{\text{median}}} \right) c$$

where

L = lower boundary of median class
N = total frequency
$(\Sigma f)_L$ = sum of frequencies below median class
f_{median} = frequency of median class
c = width of median class

ⓘ *The table below is the frequency distribution of marks obtained in a test by 200 students.*

mark	10–	20–	30–	40–	50–	60–	70–	80–90
f	18	34	58	42	24	10	6	8

Draw a cumulative frequency polygon to illustrate the data. Estimate the median from the graph and by calculation.

How many students would fail if the pass mark is 40? If the top 10% of students are to be given a grade I, what is the lowest mark which will achieve this?

The cumulative frequency distribution is:

mark	10–	20–	30–	40–	50–	60–	70–	80–90
cf	18	52	110	152	176	186	192	200

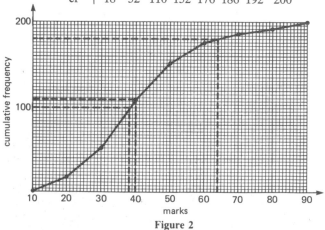

Figure 2

From the graph: $M \approx 38$ marks

By calculation: $M = 30 + \dfrac{(\frac{1}{2}(200) - 52)10}{58} = 38.3$

From the graph : 110 students fail,
64 is the lowest mark for grade I.

Median and Quantiles
Worked example and Exam questions.

The lives of 80 circuit components were recorded in hours to the nearest hour and grouped as follows:

Life (hours)	Frequency
660-669	3
670-679	7
680-689	10
690-699	15
700-709	24
710-719	12
720-729	5
730-739	4

(i) *State the limits between which the actual life of each component in the first group must lie.*

(ii) *Construct the cumulative frequency and draw the cumulative frequency curve.*

(iii) *Use the curve to estimate (a) the median, (b) the 90th percentile.*

(i) The true limits for the first class are $659.5 - 669.5$, since the life is recorded to the nearest hour.

(ii)

Life	660–669	670–679	680–689	690–699	700–709	710–719	720–729	730–739
f	3	7	10	15	24	12	5	4
cf	3	10	20	35	59	71	76	80

The appropriate cumulative frequency curve is shown below.

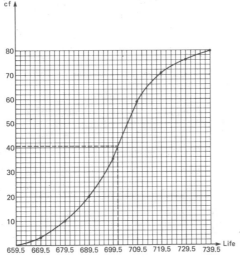

(iii) Since there are 80 observations the median corresponds to the 40.5th observation; from the graph the median value is estimated to be 701.5 hours.

The 90th percentile corresponds to the $\frac{90}{100} \times 80\text{th} = 72\text{nd}$ observation; from the graph this value is estimated to be 720.5 hours.

1 The table shows the marks, collected into groups, of 400 candidates in an examination. The maximum mark was 99.

Marks	No. of candidates
0–9	10
10–19	26
20–29	42
30–39	66
40–49	83
50–59	71
60–69	52
70–79	30
80–89	14
90–99	6

Compile the cumulative frequency table and draw the cumulative frequency curve. Use your curve to estimate: (i) the median; (ii) the 20th percentile. If the minimum mark for Grade A was fixed at 74, estimate from your curve the percentage of candidates obtaining Grade A. *(C)*

2 The table below shows the average productivity of coal miners in Great Britain over a 12-month period, measured in tonnes per manshift.

Productivity	Miners (thousands)
0–1	14
1–1.5	31
1.5–2.0	51
2.0–2.5	62
2.5–3.0	44
3.0–3.5	11
3.5–5.0	20

(a) Illustrate these data by drawing a histogram;
(b) Find, in thousands, the total number of miners;
(c) Draw a cumulative frequency polygon on a separate sheet;
(d) Estimate, from your graph, the median productivity;
(e) Estimate the total coal produced per shift.

(O & C)

3 On a particular date (30 June 1968), the age distribution of the population of the United Kingdom is given to have been as follows:

Age range	0–9	10–14	15–19	20–59	60–64	65–104
Millions of people	7.7	4.6	4.4	28.4	2.9	8.0

The categories are such that, for example, 10–14 consists of all people who have had their 10th birthday, but not their 15th birthday, and thus spans a range of 5 calendar years.
(i) Display the data on a histogram.
(ii) Estimate the median age, giving your answer to the nearest year.
(iii) Calculate an estimate of the mean age of the population of the United Kingdom on that date, showing your working clearly. *(C)*

4 An inspection of 34 aircraft assemblies revealed a number of missing rivets as shown in the following table.

Number of rivets missing	Frequency
0–2	4
3–5	9
6–8	11
9–11	6
12–14	2
15–17	1
18–20	0
21–23	1

Draw a cumulative frequency curve. Use this curve to estimate the median and the quartiles of the distribution. *(O & C)*

5 30 specimens of sheet steel are tested for tensile strength, measured in kN m^{-2}. The table gives the distribution of the measurements.

Tensile strength	Number of specimens
405–415	4
415–425	3
425–435	6
435–445	10
445–455	5
455–465	2

Draw a cumulative diagram of this distribution. Estimate the median and the 10th and 90th percentiles. *(O & C)*

S5 core
Measures of Dispersion
Range, Semi-interquartile range, Mean deviation, Variance and standard deviation.

Range

The **range** is the difference between the largest and smallest items of the distribution,

i.e.   largest item − smallest item.

ⓘ *Calculate the range for this distribution.*

x	1	2	3	4	5	6
f	1	3	9	2	1	1

The range is $(6-1)=5$.

Semi-interquartile range

The **semi-interquartile range** $= \frac{1}{2}(Q_3 - Q_1)$ where Q_1 and Q_3 are the first and third quartiles (see Median and Quantiles p. 138).

ⓘ *Calculate the semi-interquartile range for the distribution with $Q_1 = 29.41$ and $Q_3 = 49.52$.*

Semi-interquartile range $= \frac{1}{2}(49.52 - 29.41) = 10.05$.

Mean deviation

The **mean deviation** can be measured from the arithmetic mean, median, mode or any other specified value.
It is usually measured from the arithmetic mean.

The mean deviation from the mean of the n values $x_1, x_2, \ldots, x_n$ is:

$$\text{M.D.} = \frac{\Sigma|x - \bar{x}|}{n}$$

The mean deviation from the mean of a **frequency** distribution is:

$$\text{M.D.} = \frac{\Sigma f|x - \bar{x}|}{\Sigma f}$$

This formula is also used for continuous and grouped discrete frequency distributions but the class mid-value is used to represent each class.

ⓘ *Calculate the mean deviation from the mean of this distribution.*

x	10–	15–	20–	25–	30–	35–40
f	2	12	27	41	30	7

$\bar{x} = \dfrac{\Sigma fx}{\Sigma f} = \dfrac{3207.5}{119} = 26.95$ (to 2 d.p.)

x	mid-value	f	$|x-\bar{x}|$	$f|x-\bar{x}|$
10–	12.5	2	14.45	28.90
15–	17.5	12	9.45	113.40
20–	22.5	27	4.45	120.15
25–	27.5	41	0.55	22.55
30–	32.5	30	5.55	166.50
35–40	37.5	7	10.55	73.85
		$\Sigma f = 119$		$\Sigma f|x-\bar{x}| = 525.35$

mean deviation $= \dfrac{525.35}{119} = 4.41$ (2 d.p.)

Variance and standard deviation

Variance is denoted by σ^2 for a population and by s^2 for a sample.

The variance of the n values $x_1, x_2, \ldots, x_n$ is

$$\sigma^2 = \frac{\Sigma(x - \bar{x})^2}{n} \quad \text{(definition)}$$

$$= \frac{\Sigma x^2}{n} - \bar{x}^2 \quad \text{(computational form— easier for calculation)}$$

The variance of a frequency distribution is

$$\sigma^2 = \frac{\Sigma f(x - \bar{x})^2}{\Sigma f} \quad \text{(definition)}$$

$$= \frac{\Sigma fx^2}{\Sigma f} - \bar{x}^2 \quad \text{(computational form)}$$

These formulae are also used for continuous and grouped discrete frequency distributions but the class mid-value is used to represent each class.

If a is a working mean and either the class intervals are of equal width c or the deviations d_r from a have a common factor c such that $d_r = cu_r$, then

$$\sigma^2 = \frac{c^2 \Sigma fu^2}{\Sigma f} - b^2 \text{ where } b = \bar{x} - a.$$

Standard deviation is simply the positive square root of the variance, i.e. $\sqrt{\text{variance}}$.
It is denoted by σ for a population
         and by s for a sample.

ⓘ *Calculate the variance and standard deviation for this distribution of the test results of 200 students.*

mark	10–	20–	30–	40–	50–	60–	70–	80–90
f	18	34	58	42	24	10	6	8

class	mid-value x	f	fx	d	u ($c=10$)	u^2	fu^2
10–	15	18	270	−30	−3	9	162
20–	25	34	850	−20	−2	4	136
30–	35	58	2030	−10	−1	1	58
40–	45 = a	42	1890	0	0	0	0
50–	55	24	1320	10	1	1	24
60–	65	10	650	20	2	4	40
70–	75	6	450	30	3	9	54
80–90	85	8	680	40	4	16	128
			$\Sigma fx = 8140$				$\Sigma fu^2 = 602$

$\bar{x} = \dfrac{\Sigma fx}{\Sigma f} = \dfrac{8140}{200} = 40.7$

Let $a = 45$, so $b = \bar{x} - a = 40.7 - 45 = -4.3$

$\text{Variance} = \dfrac{c^2 \Sigma fu^2}{\Sigma f} - b^2 = \dfrac{100 \times 602}{200} - (-4.3)^2$

$= 301 - 18.49$

$= 282.51$

Standard deviation $= \sqrt{282.51} = 16.81$

Measures of Dispersion
Worked example and Exam questions.

 The table below gives the frequency distribution of the speeds of 95 cars passing a check point.

Speed (km/h)	30 –	40–	50–	55–	60–	70–
Frequency	0	20	30	35	10	0

Calculate the mean speed and the standard deviation. It is later found that the recording instrument gave a reading of 5 km/h below the true speed. Find the new mean and standard deviation.

Close the last class at 80.
Let the working mean be $a = 52.5$ km/h, d the deviation of the mid-class value from a and c $(= 2.5)$ the scale factor for the deviation of the mid-class values.

Tabulating the results:

Class	Class mid-value	Frequency f	Deviation from a, d	$u = \dfrac{d}{c}$	fu	fu^2
30–	35	0	−17.5	−7	0	0
40–	45	20	−7.5	−3	−60	180
50–	52.5 = a	30	0	0	0	0
55–	57.5	35	5	2	70	140
60–	65	10	12.5	5	50	250
70–	75	0	22.5	9	0	0
80						
		$\Sigma f = 95$			$\Sigma fu = 60$	$\Sigma fu^2 = 570$

Let the mean speed be $\bar{v}$, then

$$\bar{v} = a + \frac{c\Sigma fu}{\Sigma f} = 52.5 + \frac{2.5 \times 60}{95} = 54.1 \text{ km/h}$$

Let s_v be the standard deviation of $\bar{v}$, then

$$s_v^2 = \frac{c^2 \Sigma fu^2}{\Sigma f} - b^2, \text{ where } b = \bar{v} - a = 54.1 - 52.5 = 1.6$$

So $s_v^2 = \dfrac{2.5^2 \times 570}{95} - 1.6^2 = 34.94$

$\therefore s_v = 5.9$ km/h

Let $V = v + 5$ (i.e. V is the true speed), then $\bar{V} = \bar{v} + 5$
$= 59.1$ km/h

and $s_V = s_v = 5.9$ km/h

 1 The figures below are the yields to the nearest kilogram of a certain root crop obtained from 32 plots of equal size.

21	23	19	22	21	23	20	22
17	26	20	19	18	20	20	24
25	21	22	20	24	18	22	20
19	23	21	17	25	24	26	18

Draw up a table showing the frequencies of the various yields. Using your table and an assumed mean, estimate the mean yield and the standard deviation.   *(C)*

2 A zoologist weighs 200 eggs and records the weights in the following grouped frequency table.

Weight (g)	24–	30–	36–	42–	48– 54
No. of eggs	22	45	72	43	18

Find the mean and standard deviation, correct to two decimal places.
He later discovers that his scales were incorrectly set and that each egg was underweighed by 4 g. Determine the corrected mean and standard deviation.   *(S)*

3 The sum of 20 numbers is 320 and the sum of their squares is 5840. Calculate the mean of the 20 numbers and the standard deviation:
 (i) Another number is added to these 20 so that the mean is unchanged. Show that the standard deviation is decreased.
 (ii) Another set of 10 numbers is such that their sum is 130 and the sum of their squares is 2380. This set is combined with the original 20 numbers. Calculate the mean and standard deviation of all 30 numbers.
    (C)

4 Show, from the basic definition, why the standard deviation of a set of observations $x_1, x_2, x_3, \ldots\ldots, x_i, \ldots\ldots, x_n$ with

mean $\bar{x}$ may be found by evaluating $\sqrt{\dfrac{\Sigma x_i^2}{n} - \bar{x}^2}$

(a) Find, showing your working clearly and not using any pre-programmed function on your calculator, the standard deviation of the following frequency distribution:

x	25	26	27	28
f	2	0	15	1

(b) The average height of 20 boys is 160 cm, with a standard deviation of 4 cm. The average height of 30 girls is 155 cm, with a standard deviation of 3.5 cm. Find the standard deviation of the whole group of 50 children.
    (S)

5 Suppose that the values of a random sample taken from some population are $x_1, x_2, \ldots\ldots, x_n$. Prove the formula

$$\sum_{i=1}^{n} (x_i - \bar{x})^2 = \sum_{i=1}^{n} x_i^2 - n\bar{x}^2.$$

Parplan Opinion Polls Ltd. conducted a nationwide survey into the attitudes of teenage girls. One of the questions asked was "What is the ideal age for a girl to have her first baby?" In reply, the sample of 165 girls from the Northern zone gave a mean of 23.4 years and a standard deviation of 1.6 years. Subsequently, the overall sample of 384 girls (Northern plus Southern zones) gave a mean of 24.8 years and a standard deviation of 2.2 years. Assuming that no girl was consulted twice, calculate the mean and standard deviation for the 219 girls from the Southern zone.
    (A)

6 The following table summarises the masses, measured to the nearest gram, of 200 animals of the same species.

Mass (g)	Frequency
70–79	7
80–84	30
85–89	66
90–94	57
95–99	27
100–109	13

Calculate estimates of the median and upper quartile of the distribution.
Estimate the number of animals whose actual masses are less than 81 g.
Calculate estimates of the mean and the standard deviation of the distribution.
    (A)

S6 core

Comparing Frequency Distributions
Mean, Measures of spread, Box and whisker diagrams, Skewness.

Mean

The arithmetic average or **mean** (see Unit S3) is the most common measure of the centre of a distribution.

The weakness of the mean as a measure of centre is its insensitivity to the influence of **outliers,** which are unusually small or large observations. We say that the mean is **not a resistant measure** of the centre.

It follows that the median (see Unit S4) is a **resistant measure** since its value does not respond strongly to changes in a few observations, no matter how large they may be.

> **i** *Calculate the sample mean for the following two sets of data:*
>
> | Set 1: | 3 | 6 | 11 | 16 | 19 | 33 | 94 |
> | Set 2: | −18 | 6 | 11 | 16 | 19 | 33 | 94 |
>
> For the first set of data:
> $$\bar{x} = \frac{3+6+11+16+19+33+94}{7} = 26.$$
> For the second set of data
> $$\bar{x} = \frac{-18+6+11+16+19+33+94}{7} = 23.$$
> Notice that the median for both sets of data is 16.

Measures of spread

The spread or variability of a distribution can be indicated by the **interquartile range**, IQR, where

$$\text{IQR} = Q_3 - Q_1 \text{ (See Unit S4.)}$$

This is a resistant measure of spread and is most useful as a description of symmetric distributions.

A more common measure of the spread of a distribution is the **variance** (see Unit S5). The variance, s^2, of n observations $x_1, x_2 \ldots x_n$ is given by

$$s^2 = \frac{(x_1 - \bar{x})^2 + (x_2 - \bar{x})^2 + \ldots + (x_n - \bar{x})^2}{n} = \frac{\sum x_i^2}{n} - \bar{x}^2$$

This is not a resistant measure. The variance measures the spread about the mean and should be used when the mean is employed as the measure of centre.

The **standard deviation** s is the square root of the variance s^2, and is also used to indicate the spread of a distribution. Note that the variance is never negative; it is large if the observations are widely spread about the mean, and small if they are clustered about the mean. The standard deviation has the same units as the original observations.

> **i** *Calculate the standard deviation of the following measurements of the speed of cars passing a fixed point on a motorway in miles per hour (mph). Also find the median and the interquartile range.*
>
> 60.1 74.3 59.6 89.2 70.9 69.8 71.3 73.5
> $$\sum x^2 = 41026.09, \quad \sum x = 568.7, \quad n = 8.$$
> $$\bar{x} = \frac{568.7}{8} = 71.088$$
> $$s^2 = \frac{41026.09}{8} - (71.088)^2$$
> Hence the standard deviation $s = 8.65$ mph.
>
> Ordering the data from lowest to highest value gives
> 59.6 60.1 69.8 70.9 71.3 73.5 74.3 89.2
>
> The median $M = \dfrac{70.9 + 71.3}{2} = 71.1$ mph
>
> The lower quartile $Q_1 = \dfrac{60.1 + 69.8}{2} = 64.95$ mph
>
> The upper quartile $Q_3 = \dfrac{73.5 + 74.3}{2} = 73.9$ mph
>
> Hence $\text{IQR} = Q_3 - Q_1 = 8.95$ mph.

Box and whisker diagrams

Box and whisker diagrams are used to describe the most prominent features of a data set, and include the median or centre of the distribution, its spread and the extent and nature of any departure from symmetry and the identification of outliers. They are particularly suited to comparing distributions.

To draw a box and whisker diagram:
(a) Construct a measurement axis.
(b) Find Q_1 and Q_3 on the axis. Draw a box so that its 'ends' are at Q_1 and Q_3. Its length represents the interquartile range.
(c) Mark the median by a vertical line within the box.
(d) Extend two lines (or **whiskers**) from each side of the box to the smallest and largest observations.

> **i** *The data below show the actual blood pressure measurements in mmHg of 9 randomly selected people.*
>
> 138.4 130.0 113.7 122.0 108.3 131.5 118.6
> 133.2 127.4
>
> *Correct the blood pressures to the nearest 5 mmHg. Find the median M of the reported blood pressures and construct a box and whisker diagram.*
> Arranging the data in increasing reported values gives:
> 110 115 120 120 125 130 130 135 140
> Thus $M = 125$, $Q_1 = 117.5$ and $Q_3 = 132.5$ mmHg.
>
> 100 105 110 115 120 125 130 135 140 145 150
> Blood pressure mm Hg

Skewness

Skewness refers to the symmetry or lack of symmetry in the shape of a frequency distribution. It is useful for measuring the centrality of a distribution.

A distribution is **symmetrical** if the areas to the left and right of the centre are mirror images of each other.

A **positive skew** (right) has a right tail (higher values) much longer than the left tail (lower values).

A **negative skew** (left) has a left tail longer than the right.

Quartiles can be used to show the skewness of a distribution. If Q_1 is closer to the median than Q_3 the distribution is positively skewed. If Q_3 is closer to the median than Q_1 the distribution is negatively skewed.

> **i** *Decide the skewness of the following data:*
>
> | x | 1 | 2 | 3 | 4 | 5 | 6 | 7 | 8 | 9 |
> |---|---|---|---|---|---|---|---|---|---|
> | Frequency | 2 | 7 | 14 | 10 | 6 | 5 | 5 | 3 | 1 |
>
> The cumulative frequency distribution is:
>
> | x | −1 | −2 | −3 | −4 | −5 | −6 | −7 | −8 | −9 |
> |---|---|---|---|---|---|---|---|---|---|
> | Cum. freq. | 2 | 9 | 23 | 33 | 39 | 44 | 49 | 52 | 53 |
>
> Therefore $M = 4$, $Q_1 = 3$ and $Q_3 = 6$.
> The box and whisker diagram shows the distribution to be positively skewed.
>
>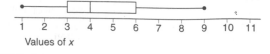
>
> 1 2 3 4 5 6 7 8 9 10 11
> Values of x

Comparing Frequency Distributions
Worked examples, Exercise and Exam questions.

 A biologist records the number of laid born beetle eggs he collects over a 130-day period. The frequency distribution of the eggs collected is shown below.

No. of eggs	10	11	12	13	14	15	16	17	18	19	20
Frequency (days)	1	2	4	5	8	11	16	22	29	23	9

What is the median number of eggs collected per day?
Decide if the distribution is positively or negatively skewed.

The cumulative frequency distribution is:

No. of eggs	–10	–11	–12	–13	–14	–15	–16	–17	–18	–19	–20
Cum. freq. (days)	1	3	7	12	20	31	47	69	98	121	130

The median observation corresponds to the $\dfrac{(65+66)}{2}$th observation, which falls in the class of 17 eggs per day.

Median value M = 17 eggs per day

$Q_1 = \dfrac{(32+33)}{2}$th observation = 16 eggs per day

$Q_3 = \dfrac{(97+98)}{2}$th observation = 18 eggs per day

So, $M - Q_1 = 1$ and $Q_3 - M = 1$.
The distribution is not skewed.

 In an experiment to compare the yields of two types of bean (A and B), some pods of each type of bean were opened and the number of beans in each pod counted. Compare the two types of bean given the following sets of data.

No. of beans per pod	1	2	3	4	5	6
Frequency A	22	34	41	21	0	0
Frequency B	9	33	46	40	9	8

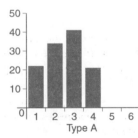 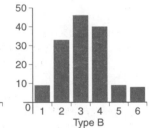

The cumulative frequency tables are:

No. of beans per pod	1	2	3	4	5	6
Cum. freq. A	22	56	97	118	118	118
Cum. freq. B	9	42	88	128	137	145

For distribution A:
The mean = $\bar{x}_A$ = 2.52 beans per pod
The median = M_A = 59.5th observation = 3 beans per pod
The mode = m_A = 3 beans per pod

For distribution B:
The mean = $\bar{x}_B$ = 3.21 beans per pod
The median = M_B = 73rd observation = 3 beans per pod
The mode = m_B = 3 beans per pod

The frequency diagrams show that, generally, type B bean gives more beans per pod than type A bean. The only measure of position which makes this fact apparent is the mean, since the median and the mode are all equal to 3 beans per pod for both of the distributions.

For distribution A:
Q_{A1} = 30th observation = 2 beans per pod
Q_{A3} = 89th observation = 3 beans per pod
$M_A - Q_{A1} = 1$ and $Q_{A3} - M_A = 0$.
Therefore distribution A is negatively skewed.

For distribution B:
Q_{B1} = 37th observation = 2 beans per pod
Q_{B3} = 110th observation = 4 beans per pod
$M_B - Q_{B1} = 1$ and $Q_{B3} - M_B = 1$.
Therefore distribution B is not skewed.

 1 Compare and comment upon the 1992 based population projections for the United Kingdom:

Age range	1992 estimated population ('000s)	2030 estimated population ('000s)
0 – <15	11 198	10 626
15 – < 30	12 773	10 686
30 – < 45	12 213	11 680
45 – < 60	9 813	10 982
60 – < 75	7 970	11 685
75+	4 043	6 626

2 In an experiment to compare the yields of two types of pea (A and B), some pods of each type were opened and the number of peas in each pod counted. Compare the two types of pea given the following sets of data.

No. of peas per pod	0	1	2	3	4	5	6
Frequency A	3	10	24	31	18	9	3
Frequency B	5	9	22	28	21	7	2

3 Compare and comment upon the age structure for males and females in Wales, based on early results from the 1991 Census.

Age (years)	Population ('000s)	
	Males	Females
0 – 4	99	94
5 – 14	187	177
15 – 24	203	193
25 – 34	205	203
35 – 44	194	195
45 – 59	242	244
60 – 64	74	80
65 – 74	128	157
75 – 84	60	104
85+	12	35

(J)

S7
core
Probability
Definitions, Addition rule, Conditional probability, Multiplication rule.

Definitions

An experiment has a finite number of outcomes, called the **outcome set** S.

An **event** E of an experiment is defined to be a subset of the outcome set S.

The **complement** of E, $\bar{E}$, is the subset of S where E does not occur.

Two events of the same experiment are **mutually exclusive** if they cannot occur simultaneously.

Two events are **independent** if the occurrence of one has no effect on the occurrence of the other.

If an experiment has $n(S)$ equally likely outcomes and $n(E)$ of them are the event E, then the **theoretical probability** of event E occurring is

$$P(E) = \frac{n(E)}{n(S)}$$

Note: $0 \leqslant P(E) \leqslant 1$
$P(E) = 0$ means that E is an **impossibility**.
$P(E) = 1$ means that E is a **certainty**.

If the outcome S has only n different possible events $E_1, E_2, \ldots, E_n$, then

$$P(E_1) + P(E_2) + \ldots + P(E_n) = \sum_{i=1}^{n} P(E_i) = 1$$

and $P(\bar{E}) = 1 - P(E)$

Venn diagram showing outcome set S and its subsets E and $\bar{E}$.

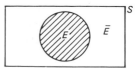
Figure 1

ℹ️ If a fair die is thrown once, then two different scores, e.g. 2 and 3, cannot occur simultaneously, so they are mutually exclusive events. If the die is thrown again, the second score is independent of the first.

ℹ️ *A fair die is thrown. List the possible outcomes. What is the probability of scoring:*
(a) a multiple of 3, (b) not a multiple of 3?

$S = \{$possible scores with a die$\} = \{1, 2, 3, 4, 5, 6\}$

(a) $E = \{$'multiple of 3' scores$\} = \{3, 6\}$

$$P(E) = \frac{n(E)}{n(S)} = \frac{2}{6} = \frac{1}{3}$$

$P(\bar{E}) = \{$'not multiple of 3' scores$\}$
$\quad = 1 - P(E) = 1 - \frac{1}{3} = \frac{2}{3}$

Addition rule

If E_1 and E_2 are two events of the same experiment, then the **probability of E_1 or E_2 or both** occurring is given by:

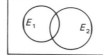
Figure 2

$P(E_1 \text{ or } E_2) = P(E_1) + P(E_2) - P(E_1 \text{ and } E_2)$
or $P(E_1 \cup E_2) = P(E_1) + P(E_2) - P(E_1 \cap E_2)$

If E_1 and E_2 are mutually exclusive, then $P(E_1 \cap E_2) = 0$
and so: $P(E_1 \text{ or } E_2) = P(E_1 \cup E_2) = P(E_1) + P(E_2)$

Figure 3

ℹ️ *What is the probability of drawing a club or an eight from a pack of cards?*

$S = \{$pack of cards$\}$, $n(S) = 52$
$E_1 = \{$clubs$\}$, $n(E_1) = 13$, $P(E_1) = \dfrac{13}{52}$

$E_2 = \{$eights$\}$, $n(E_2) = 4$, $P(E_2) = \dfrac{4}{52}$

E_1 and $E_2 = \{$clubs and eights$\} = \{$eight of clubs$\}$,

$n(E_1 \text{ and } E_2) = 1$, $P(E_1 \text{ and } E_2) = \dfrac{1}{52}$

$\therefore P(E_1 \text{ or } E_2) = P(E_1) + P(E_2) - P(E_1 \text{ and } E_2)$

$$= \frac{13}{52} + \frac{4}{52} - \frac{1}{52} = \frac{16}{52} = \frac{4}{13}$$

Conditional probability

If E_1 and E_2 are two events (not necessarily from the same experiment), then the **conditional probability that E_1 will occur given that E_2 has occurred** is

$$P(E_1|E_2) = \frac{P(E_1 \text{ and } E_2)}{P(E_2)} = \frac{n(E_1 \text{ and } E_2)}{n(E_2)}$$

If E_1 and E_2 are mutually exclusive, then $P(E_1|E_2) = 0$.

Two events E_1 and E_2 are **independent**, if $P(E_1) = P(E_1|E_2)$ and $P(E_2) = P(E_2|E_1)$.

ℹ️ *A card is drawn from a normal pack of 52 cards. Calculate $P(club|black\ suit)$*

$$P(club|black\ suit) = \frac{n(\text{club and black suit})}{n(\text{black suit})} = \frac{13}{26} = \frac{1}{2}$$

Multiplication rule

If E_1 and E_2 are any two events, then the **probability that both E_1 and E_2 occur** is

$P(E_1 \text{ and } E_2) = P(E_1 \cap E_2) = P(E_2) \times P(E_1|E_2)$
$\qquad\qquad\qquad\qquad = P(E_1) \times P(E_2|E_1)$

If E_1 and E_2 are independent, then
$P(E_1 \text{ and } E_2) = P(E_1 \cap E_2) = P(E_1) \times P(E_2)$

ℹ️ *A coin is tossed and a die thrown. Find the probability that a head and a score less than 3 result.*

These are independent events.
If $E_1 = \{$head$\}$ and $E_2 = \{$score less than 3$\}$, then
$\quad P(E_1 \text{ and } E_2) = P(E_1) \times P(E_2) = \frac{1}{2} \times \frac{2}{6} = \frac{1}{6}$

Probability
Worked examples and Exam questions.

Tree diagrams

A **tree diagram** can be used to find probabilities for **combined events**. The diagram is built up in stages. Each stage is about one activity.

Probabilities for *single events* are written on the 'branches'. (Branches from a point cover *all* possible outcomes for an activity, so their probabilities must *add up to* 1. After the 1st stage, probabilities may be conditional.)

Each 'route' along branches 'leads' to a combined event. To find its probability, *multiply* the probabilities along the route.

To find the probability for *one or other* of the combined events, *add* their probabilities.

 This probability tree diagram is about tossing a fair coin and die. H is 'get a Head', T is 'get a Tail', F is 'get a Five', $\bar{F}$ is 'get not a Five'.

tossing a coin	tossing a die	combined event	probability

H $\frac{1}{2}$ — F $\frac{1}{6}$ — $F \cap H$ — $\frac{1}{2} \times \frac{1}{6} = \frac{1}{12}$

$\bar{F}$ $\frac{5}{6}$ — $\bar{F} \cap H$ — $\frac{1}{2} \times \frac{5}{6} = \frac{5}{12}$

T $\frac{1}{2}$ — F $\frac{1}{6}$ — $F \cap T$ — $\frac{1}{2} \times \frac{1}{6} = \frac{1}{12}$

$\bar{F}$ $\frac{5}{6}$ — $\bar{F} \cap T$ — $\frac{1}{2} \times \frac{5}{6} = \frac{5}{12}$

WE *At Roundway petrol station 30% of customers buy 4-star petrol, 60% buy unleaded petrol and the remainder buy diesel. When a customer buys 4-star petrol there is a 25% chance that he/she will fill the tank. Customers buying unleaded petrol have an 80% chance of not filling the tank. Of those buying diesel, 70% fill their tank.*
(a) Draw a probability tree diagram to illustrate this situation.
(b) What is the probability that when a car leaves the petrol station it does not have a full tank?
(c) Given that a car leaving the petrol station has a full tank, what is the probability that the tank contains unleaded petrol?

Let E_1, E_2 and E_3 be the events 'buys 4-star petrol', 'buys unleaded petrol' and 'buys diesel' respectively.

Let event F be 'fills the tank' and event $\bar{F}$ be 'does not fill the tank'.

(a) Here is the probability tree diagram for this situation with the probabilities given as decimal fractions.

		combined event	probability

E_1 0.3 — 0.25 F — $F \cap E_1$ — $0.3 \times 0.25 = 0.075$

0.75 $\bar{F}$ — $\bar{F} \cap E_1$ — $0.3 \times 0.75 = 0.225$

E_2 0.6 — 0.2 F — $F \cap E_2$ — $0.6 \times 0.2 = 0.12$

0.8 $\bar{F}$ — $\bar{F} \cap E_2$ — $0.6 \times 0.8 = 0.48$

E_3 0.1 — 0.7 F — $F \cap E_3$ — $0.1 \times 0.7 = 0.07$

0.3 $\bar{F}$ — $\bar{F} \cap E_3$ — $0.1 \times 0.3 = 0.03$

(b) $P(\bar{F}) = P(E_1 \text{ and } \bar{F}) + P(E_2 \text{ and } \bar{F}) + P(E_3 \text{ and } \bar{F})$
$= 0.225 + 0.48 + 0.03$
$= 0.735$

(c) $P(E_2 | F) = \dfrac{P(E_2 \text{ and } F)}{P(F)} = \dfrac{0.12}{0.075 + 0.12 + 0.07}$
$= \dfrac{0.12}{0.265} = 0.453$ (3 d.p.)

WE *Mass-produced ceramic tiles are inspected for defects. The probability that a tile has air bubbles is 0.0015. If a tile has air bubbles the probability that it is also cracked is 0.55 while the probability that a tile free from air bubbles is cracked is 0.0055. What is the probability that a tile selected at random is cracked? The probability that a tile is discoloured is 0.0065.*
Given that discoloration is independent of the other two defects, find the probability that a tile selected at random has no defects.

Let A be the event 'the tile has air bubbles'
Let B be the event 'the tile is cracked'

Let C be the event 'the tile is discoloured'
$P(A) = 0.0015, \ P(\bar{A}) = 0.9885$
$P(C) = P(A \text{ and } C \text{ or } \bar{A} \text{ and } C)$
$= P(A \text{ and } C) + P(\bar{A} \text{ and } C)$
$= P(A)P(C|A) + P(\bar{A})P(C|\bar{A})$
$= 0.0015 \times 0.55 + 0.9985 \times 0.0055$
$= 0.000825 + 0.0054918$
$= 0.00632$ (3 s.f.)
$P(\text{no defects}) = P(\bar{A} \text{ and } \bar{C} \text{ and } \bar{D})$
$= P(\bar{A}) \times P(\bar{C}) \times P(\bar{D})$
$= 0.9985 \times 0.9945 \times 0.9935$
$= 0.987$ (3 s.f.)

EX

1 Ten cards, bearing the letters P, R, O, P, O, R, T, I, O, N, are placed in a box. Three cards are drawn out at random without replacement. Calculate the probability that:
  (i) the first two cards bear the same letter,
  (ii) the third card bears the letter P,
  (iii) the three cards bear the letters P, O, T in that order,
  (iv) the three cards bear the letters P, O, T in any order.
  (C)

2 Four people were chosen at random from a group of 8 which comprised 4 husbands and their 4 wives. Find the probability that the sample contained:
  (a) one person from each married couple (called event A);
  (b) two males and two females (called event B).
  Find also the probability that *both* events A and B occurred.
  Deduce, or otherwise find, $P(B|A)$ (the probability that event B happened if it is known that event A happened). (Answers may be given as fractions in their lowest terms.)
  (O & C)

3 (a) A and B play a game as follows: an ordinary die is rolled and if a six is obtained then A wins and if a one is obtained then B wins. If neither a six nor a one is obtained then the die is rolled again until a decision can be made. What is the probability that A wins on (i) the first roll, (ii) the second roll, (iii) the rth roll? What is the probability that A wins?
  (b) A bag contains 4 red and 3 yellow balls and another bag contains 3 red and 4 yellow. A ball is taken from the first bag and placed in the second, the second bag shaken and a ball taken from it and placed in the first bag. If a ball is now taken from the first bag what is the probability that it is red? (You are advised to draw a tree diagram.) *(S)*

4 An unbiased die is thrown six times. Calculate the probabilities that the six scores obtained will
  (i) consist of exactly two 6's and four odd numbers,
  (ii) be 1, 2, 3, 4, 5, 6 in some order,
  (iii) have a product which is an even number,
  (iv) be such that a 6 occurs *only* on the last throw and that exactly three of the first five throws result in odd numbers. *(J)*

Index numbers

A set of data may be reduced to relative values by comparing it with a fixed (base) number. These relative values are called percentage relatives or **simple index numbers**. If the **percentage relatives** refer to prices they are called **price relatives**.

A percentage relative can be calculated using $\frac{q_n}{q_0} \times 100$

where q_0 is the quantity in a base year, and q_n is the quantity in another year.

In situations which have many contributory factors, more complicated index numbers are found by using **weighted averages** of the percentage relatives of the contributory factors. If the percentage relatives are $r_1, r_2, \ldots, r_n$ with respective weights $w_1, w_2, \ldots, w_n$, then the **weighted index** is $\frac{\Sum r_n w_n}{\Sum w_n}$.

The expenditure of a household over a three year period is shown below.

Item	Year 1	Year 2	Year 3	Weight
House	3000(100)	2400(80)	2550(85)	110
Food	2000(100)	2200(110)	2400(120)	360
Fuel	800(100)	880(110)	950(119)	90
Travel	800(100)	900(113)	900(113)	80
Others	1100(100)	1500(136)	1600(145)	360
Total	7700(100)	7880(102.3)	8400(109.1)	

The figures in brackets are percentage relatives with year 1 as base. Verify these.

e.g. for total expenditure for Year 2

$$= \frac{7880}{7700} \times 100 = 102.3$$

Index numbers for the total expenditure as weighted averages of the percentage relatives are 100, 116.3, 124.5.

Crude and standardised rates

The **crude death rate** for a given district is the number of deaths per thousand population,

i.e. crude death rate $= \frac{\text{total number of deaths}}{\text{total population}} \times 1000$

Crude death rates are poor for comparing different areas because they do not take into account the age structure of the populations under consideration. To do this a standardised death rate is used.

A **standardised death rate** is a weighted average in which the weights are related to the age distribution of the population of the entire country.

Crude and standardised rates can also be obtained for births, marriages and unemployment figures.

Calculation of crude and standardised death rate.

Age group	Pop.	Deaths in group	% of UK pop. in gp. (W)	Group deaths per 1000 pop. (D)	WD
0–4	4000	52	7	13	91
5–14	5000	4	17	0.8	13.6
15–29	4200	14	26	3.3	85.8
30–59	9000	74	38	8.2	311.6
60+	2600	104	12	40	480.0
	24800	248	100		982.0

Crude death rate $= \frac{248}{24800} \times 1000 = 10$ deaths per 1000.

Standardized death rate $= \frac{982}{100} = 9.82$ deaths per 1000.

Moving averages and their use in time series

Given a set of numbers $x_1, x_2, \ldots$ the **moving average** of order n is given by the following set of arithmetic means:

$$\frac{x_1+x_2+\ldots+x_n}{n}, \frac{x_2+x_3+\ldots+x_{n+1}}{n}, \frac{x_3+x_4+\ldots+x_{n+2}}{n},$$

If the data is monthly data, then the average is known as the **n month moving average**, and is usually centred on the period to which it refers.

Moving averages are used in **time series analysis**. In this analysis it is usual to distinguish between the following types of variation:

(a) the **secular** or **general trend** with a cycle of several decades,

(b) **cyclical variations**, which are fluctuations in the general trend usually of a 5–10 year period. They may be removed by subtracting suitably chosen moving averages,

(c) **seasonal variations** which recur annually due to the season of the year and may be removed by subtracting 4-quarterly or 12-monthly moving averages,

(d) **residual variations** are those fluctuations which remain when the above have been taken into account.

Given the numbers 2, 0, 1, 7, 4, 2, 2, 8, find the moving averages of order 4 and 5.

First moving average of order 4 is $\frac{2+0+1+7}{4} = 2.5$

Second moving average of order 4 is $\frac{0+1+7+4}{4} = 3$

Summarising:

	2	0	1	7	4	2	2	8
Order 4		2.5	3	3.5	3.75	4		
Order 5			2.8	2.8	3.2	4.6		

Calculation of 3-monthly moving averages as used in the analysis of time series.

Month	1	2	3
Quarter 1	9	11	12
Quarter 2	11	12	14
$\frac{Q_2 - Q_1}{3}$	0.67	0.33	0.67

First 3-monthly moving average $\frac{9+11+12}{3} = 10.67$

Adding the quantities in the final row of the table gives the sequence of moving averages:

10.67, 11.34, 11.67, 12.34

Index Numbers and Moving Averages
Worked examples and Exam questions.

 (a) *Using 1980 as base year, the price index of a particular commodity in 1981 is 110. Using 1981 as base year, the price index for the same commodity in 1982 is 120. Calculate the index number for 1982 taking 1980 as base year.*
(b) *Calculate a composite index number for the following data.*

Index Number	127	118	96	112
Weight	2	1	6	3

(a) With an obvious notation

$$\frac{P_{81}}{P_{80}} \times 100 = 110 \text{ and } \frac{P_{82}}{P_{81}} \times 100 = 120$$

Multiplying gives,

$$\frac{P_{81}}{P_{80}} \times \frac{P_{82}}{P_{81}} \times 100 \times 100 = 110 \times 120$$

$$\text{i.e. } \frac{P_{82}}{P_{80}} \times 100 = \frac{110 \times 120}{100} = 132$$

∴ the index number for 1982 with 1980 as base is 132.

(b) The composite index number is
$$\frac{127 \times 2 + 118 \times 1 + 96 \times 6 + 112 \times 3}{2+1+6+3} = \frac{1284}{12} = 107$$

 A petrol filling station, open seven days a week, had the following daily sales of petrol, in gallons, during a two week period.

	Mon	Tue	Wed	Thu	Fri	Sat	Sun
Week 1	700	360	590	620	680	710	350
Week 2	520	280	460	530	510	650	290

Plot these sales.
Calculate the values of the seven-day moving averages and superimpose these on the graph.
From the graph, estimate the next value of the moving average and hence estimate the sales for Monday of Week 3.

See the graph for the plot of the sales.
To calculate the moving averages the working is set out in tabular form.

	Mon	Tue	Wed	Thu	Fri	Sat	Sun
Week 1	700	360	590	620	680	710	350
Week 2	520	280	460	530	510	650	290
W2 − W1	−180	−80	−130	−90	−170	−60	−60
$\frac{W2-W1}{7}$	−25.7	−11.4	−18.6	−12.9	−24.3	−8.6	−8.6

The first seven-day moving average is
$$\frac{700+360+590+620+680+710+350}{7} = 572.9$$

Adding the quantities in the final row of the table gives the following sequence of seven-day moving averages, 572.9, 547.2, 535.6, 517.2, 504.3, 480.0, 471.4, 462.8.
See the graph for the superimposition of the values.
The estimate from the graph of the next moving average is 445.
Note, the 'best line' through the moving averages has been estimated by eye.

$$\therefore 445 = \frac{280+460+530+510+650+290+M3}{7}$$

$$\therefore M3 = 7 \times 445 - 2720$$
$$= 3115 - 2720$$
$$= 395$$

∴ the estimated sales for Monday of Week 3 are 395 gallons.

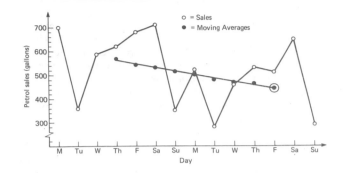

○ = Sales
● = Moving Averages

1

Commodity	1976	Price (£) 1977	1978
A	4	5	7
B	10	12	15
C	8	8	10

Use the above data to complete the following table of price relatives (1976 = 100).

Commodity	Price Relatives (1976 = 100) 1977	1978
A	125	
B		
C		

Using weights of 5, 3 and 2 for commodities *A*, *B* and *C*, respectively, show that the weighted index of price relatives (1976 = 100) for 1977 is 118.5. Obtain the weighted index of price relatives for 1978.
Using the same weights, determine the weighted index of price relatives (1977 = 100) for 1978.

(S)

2 The table below refers to the mean quarterly rainfall, in cm, for the years 1975 and 1976.

	Jan.–Mar.	Apr.–June	July–Sept.	Oct.–Dec.
1975	26	14	33	*a*
1976	*b*	18	23	28

The 4-point moving averages for the above data are 29.5, 28.25, *c*, 26.75, *d*. Calculate the values of *a*, *b*, *c* and *d*. If rainfall were subject to seasonal variation only, what would you expect of the values of the moving averages? State, and explain briefly, any other types of variation that may affect the quarterly rainfall figures.

(C)

3 Explain briefly the reasons for using moving averages.
A set of 4-point moving averages is calculated for seven successive values of a certain variable. The first three values of the variable are 3, 7, 5 and the first four moving averages are 6, 8, 7, 9. Calculate the last four values of the variable. Illustrate these data by drawing graphs, on the same diagram, of the values of the variable and the values of the moving averages.

(C)

S9 Discrete Probability Distributions
Definitions, Expectation, Variance, Two random variables.

Definitions

Suppose the outcome set S of an experiment is divided into n mutually exclusive and exhaustive events $E_1, E_2, \ldots, E_n$. A variable, X, which can assume exactly n numerical values each of which corresponds to one and only one of the events is called a **random variable**.

Two random variables are independent if any value that either may take is unaffected by any value of the other.

Let X be a discrete variable taking only the values $x_1, x_2, \ldots, x_n$ with probabilities $p_1, p_2, \ldots, p_n$ respectively.

X is called a **discrete random variable** if $\sum_{i=1}^{n} p_i = 1$.

The **probability density function** (pdf) of a discrete random variable X is a function that allocates probabilities to all the distinct values that X can take.
Let $P(X=x)$ be the pdf for a random variable X defined for the discrete values of X.
Then $\sum_{all\,x} P(X=x) = 1$.

A bag contains 6 blue and 4 red counters. 3 counters are drawn at random and not replaced. Find the probability distribution for the number of red counters drawn.

Let the random variable X be 'the number of red counters drawn'.

$P(X=0) = P(\text{no red counters}) = P(B_1 . B_2 . B_3)$
$\qquad = P(B_1) \times P(B_2|B_1) \times P(B_3|B_2 \text{ and } B_1)$
$\qquad = \dfrac{6}{10} \times \dfrac{5}{9} \times \dfrac{4}{8} = \dfrac{1}{6}$

$P(X=1) = P(R_1 . B_2 . B_3 \text{ or } B_1 . R_2 . B_3 \text{ or } B_1 . B_2 . R_3)$
$\qquad = \left(\dfrac{4}{10} \times \dfrac{6}{9} \times \dfrac{5}{8}\right) + \left(\dfrac{6}{10} \times \dfrac{4}{9} \times \dfrac{5}{8}\right) + \left(\dfrac{6}{10} \times \dfrac{5}{9} \times \dfrac{4}{8}\right)$
$\qquad = \dfrac{1}{2}$

$P(X=2) = P(R_1 . R_2 . B_3 \text{ or } R_1 . B_2 . R_3 \text{ or } B_1 . R_2 . R_3)$
$\qquad = \dfrac{3}{10}$

$P(X=3) = P(R_1 . R_2 . R_3) = \dfrac{1}{30}$

Hence the probability distribution for X is:

x	0	1	2	3
$P(X=x)$	$\frac{1}{6}$	$\frac{1}{2}$	$\frac{3}{10}$	$\frac{1}{30}$

Note: The sum of the probabilities is 1.

Expectation

For a discrete random variable X with pdf $P(X=x)$ the **expectation** of x is $E[X] = \sum_{all\,x} xP(X=x)$.
$E[X]$ is interpreted as the mean value μ of X.

Properties of E
$\qquad E[a] = a$ where a is constant
$\qquad E[aX] = aE[X]$
$\qquad E[G(X)] = \sum_{all\,x} G(X)\,P(X=x)$
Where $F(X)$ and $G(X)$ are any two functions of X,
$E[F(X) + G(X)] = E[F(X)] + E[G(X)]$.

For the situation above:

$E[X] = \sum_{x=0}^{3} xP(X=x)$
$\qquad = \left(0 \times \dfrac{1}{6}\right) + \left(1 \times \dfrac{1}{2}\right) + \left(2 \times \dfrac{3}{10}\right) + \left(3 \times \dfrac{1}{30}\right) = 1.2$

$E[X^2] = \sum_{x=0}^{3} x^2 P(X=x)$
$\qquad = \left(0 \times \dfrac{1}{6}\right) + \left(1 \times \dfrac{1}{2}\right) + \left(4 \times \dfrac{3}{10}\right) + \left(9 \times \dfrac{1}{30}\right) = 2$

$E[3X^2 - 2X] = 3E[X^2] - 2E[X] = 6 - 2.4 = 3.6$

Variance

The **variance** of a probability distribution associated with the random variable X is
$Var[X] = E[(X-\mu)^2]$ where $\mu = E[X]$
Computational formula:
$Var[X] = E[X^2] - (E[X])^2$

Properties of Var
If a and b are constants:
$\qquad Var[a] = 0$
$\qquad Var[aX] = a^2\,Var[X]$
$\qquad Var[aX+b] = a^2\,Var[X]$

For the situation above:

$Var[X] = E[X^2] - (E[X])^2$
$\qquad = 2 - (1.2)^2$
$\qquad = 0.56$

For the situation above:

$Var[3X] = 3^2\,Var[X] = 9 \times 0.56 = 5.04$

Two random variables

If X and Y are any two random variables and a and b are constants, then
$\qquad E[aX+bY] = aE[X] + bE[Y]$
If X and Y are also independent, then
$\qquad Var[aX+bY] = a^2\,Var[X] + b^2\,Var[Y]$
From this last result
$\qquad Var[X+Y] = Var[X-Y] = Var[X] + Var[Y]$

If X and Y are two independent random variables with $E[X]=0.4$, $E[Y]=0.7$, $Var[X]=0.2$ and $Var[Y]=0.3$, find (a) $E[2X+3Y]$, (b) $Var[X-Y]$.

(a) $E[2X+3Y] = 2E[X] + 3E[Y] = 2 \times 0.4 + 3 \times 0.7 = 2.9$

(b) $Var[X-Y] = Var[X] + Var[Y] = 0.2 + 0.3 = 0.5$

Discrete Probability Distributions
Worked example, Guided example and Exam questions.

 The discrete random variable, X, has the following probability distribution.

x	0	1	2
$P(X=x)$	$\frac{1}{8}$	$\frac{3}{4}$	$\frac{1}{8}$

Find the mean and variance of X.
If two independent random variables, X_1 and X_2, have the same distribution as X, find the distribution of $X_1 - X_2$, and give its mean and variance.

By symmetry $E[X] = 1$
$Var[X] = E[X^2] - E^2[X]$

$$E[X^2] = \sum_{x=0}^{2} x^2 P(X=x) = 0 \times \frac{1}{8} + 1 \times \frac{3}{4} + 4 \times \frac{1}{8} = \frac{5}{4}$$

$Var[X] = \frac{5}{4} - 1 = \frac{1}{4}$

Let $Y = X_1 - X_2$
The tree diagram below shows the possible values y of Y and the associated probabilities $P(Y=y)$.

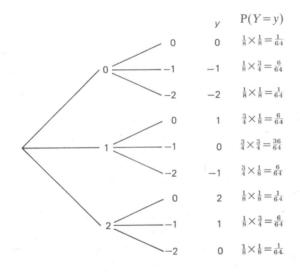

The probability distribution for Y is

y	-2	-1	0	1	2
$P(Y=y)$	$\frac{1}{64}$	$\frac{12}{64}$	$\frac{38}{64}$	$\frac{12}{64}$	$\frac{1}{64}$

$E[X_1] = 1 \qquad Var[X_1] = \frac{1}{4}$
$E[X_2] = 1 \qquad Var[X_2] = \frac{1}{4}$
$E[X_1 - X_2] = E[X_1] - E[X_2] = 1 - 1 = 0$
$Var[X_1 - X_2] = Var[X_1] + Var[X_2] = \frac{1}{4} + \frac{1}{4} = \frac{1}{2}$

GE *The faces of an ordinary die are re-numbered so that the faces are 1, 2, 2, 3, 3, 3. This die and an ordinary, unaltered die are thrown at the same time. The score, X, is the sum of the numbers on the uppermost faces of the two dice. Show*

that the probability of X being 3 is $\dfrac{1}{12}$ and of X being 4 is $\dfrac{1}{6}$.

List the values that X can take and determine their respective probabilities. Hence, obtain the expected value of X, correct to three decimal places.
If the dice are thrown three times, determine the probability, correct to three significant figures, that none of the three values of X exceeds 3.

Let A be the score on the altered die and U the score on the unaltered die, then $X = A + U$ and the possible score combinations for a score of 3 are:

A	U
1	2
2	1

Thus $P(X=3) = P(A=1)P(U=2) + P(A=2)P(U=1)$
The probabilities on the RHS are easily found and hence $P(X=3)$ can be evaluated.
A similar approach can be used for $P(X=4)$.

A tree diagram shows that the range of values of X is the integral values 2 to 9 inclusive, and also assists in the calculation of the respective probabilities.
$P(X \text{ does not exceed } 3) = P(X=2 \text{ or } 3)$, and this probability is easily found from the probability distribution of X and so $P(X \text{ does not exceed } 3$ in three throws of the dice) can be evaluated.

 1 Jane earns £40 for a five-day week. She works every fourth Sunday, for which she is paid double-time, and three Saturdays in every four, for each of which she is paid time and a half. Draw up a table showing the probability distribution of her wage on a day chosen at random and hence find the mean and variance of her daily wage. Find also the mean and variance of her weekly wage assuming that the Sundays on which she works fall in weeks *not* containing a 'working' Saturday. What would be the mean of her weekly wage if her 'working' Sundays fall in weeks also containing a 'working' Saturday?

(W)

2 In a game, a player rolls two balls down an inclined plane so that each ball finally settles in one of five slots and scores the number of points allotted to that slot as shown in the diagram below.

2	4	7	4	2

It is possible for both balls to settle in one slot and it may be assumed that each slot is equally likely to accept either ball. The player's score is the sum of the points scored by each ball. Draw up a table showing all the possible scores and the probability of each. If the player pays 10p for each game and receives back a number of pence equal to his score, calculate the player's expected gain or loss per 50 games.

(C)

3 In a certain gambling game a player nominates an integer x from 1 to 6 inclusive and he then throws three fair cubical dice. Calculate the probabilities that the number of x's thrown will be 0, 1, 2 and 3.
The player pays 5 pence per play of the game and he receives 48 pence if the number of x's thrown is three, 15 pence if the number of x's thrown is two, 5 pence if only one x is thrown and nothing otherwise. Calculate the player's expected gain or loss per play of the game.

(J)

4 A random variable X has the probability distribution given in Table 1, and $2Y = X - 18$. Find $E(Y)$ and $E(Y^2)$. Deduce the values of $E(X)$ and $Var(X)$.

Table 1

X	12	16	18	20	24
$P(X)$	$\frac{1}{15}$	$\frac{4}{15}$	$\frac{1}{3}$	$\frac{1}{5}$	$\frac{2}{15}$

(L)

S10 Continuous Probability Distributions
Definitions, Expectations, Variance, Two random variables, Cumulative distribution function.

Definitions

Let X be a continuous variable taking only values in the ranges x_1 up to x_2, x_2 up to x_3, . . . , x_n up to x_{n+1}, with probabilities $p_1, p_2, \ldots, p_n$ respectively.

X is called a **continuous random variable** if $\sum_{i=1}^{n} p_i = 1$.

The **probability density function** (pdf) of a continuous random variable X is a function that allocates probabilities to all of the ranges of values that X can take.

Let $f(x)$, the pdf for the random variable X, be defined over the range x_1 to x_2 only. Then

$$P(a \leqslant X \leqslant b) = \int_a^b f(x)\, dx.$$

and $\int_{x_1}^{x_2} f(x)\, dx = 1$.

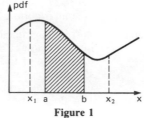

Figure 1

ⓘ *Construct the probability distribution for the ranges 0 to 1, 1 to 2, 2 to 3, for the continuous distribution defined by the pdf, $f(x) = \frac{2}{9}x(3-x)$, $0 \leqslant x \leqslant 3$.*

$$P(0 \leqslant X \leqslant 1) = \int_0^1 \frac{2}{9}x(3-x)\, dx = \frac{2}{9}\left[\frac{3x^2}{2} - \frac{x^3}{3}\right]_0^1 = \frac{7}{27}$$

$$P(1 \leqslant X \leqslant 2) = \int_1^2 \frac{2}{9}x(3-x)\, dx = \frac{2}{9}\left[\frac{3x^2}{2} - \frac{x^3}{3}\right]_1^2 = \frac{13}{27}$$

$$P(2 \leqslant X \leqslant 3) = \int_2^3 \frac{2}{9}x(3-x)\, dx = \frac{2}{9}\left[\frac{3x^2}{2} - \frac{x^3}{3}\right]_2^3 = \frac{7}{27}$$

So the probability distribution for X is

Range of X	0 up to 1	1 up to 2	2 up to 3
Probability	$\frac{7}{27}$	$\frac{13}{27}$	$\frac{7}{27}$

Note: The sum of the probabilities is 1.

Expectation

For a continuous random variable X with pdf $f(x)$, the **expectation** of X is $E[X] = \int_{\text{all }x} x f(x)\, dx$.

$E[X]$ is interpreted as the mean value μ of X.

Properties of E

$$E[a] = a \text{ where } a \text{ is constant}$$
$$E[aX] = aE[X]$$

$$E[G(X)] = \int_{\text{all }x} G(x) f(x)\, dx$$

$$E[F(X) + G(X)] = E[F(X)] + E[G(X)]$$
where $F(X)$ and $G(X)$ are any two functions of X.

ⓘ For the situation above:

$$E[X] = \int_0^3 x \cdot \frac{2}{9}x(3-x)\, dx = \frac{2}{9}\left[x^3 - \frac{x^4}{4}\right]_0^3 = \frac{3}{2}$$

$$E[X^2] = \int_0^3 x^2 \cdot \frac{2}{9}x(3-x)\, dx = \frac{2}{9}\left[\frac{3x^4}{4} - \frac{x^5}{5}\right]_0^3 = \frac{27}{10}$$

$$E[3X^2 - 2X] = 3E[X^2] - 2E[X]$$
$$= 3(2.7) - 2(1.5) = 5.1$$

Variance

The **variance** of a probability distribution is $\text{Var}[X] = E[(X - \mu)^2]$ where $\mu = E[X]$.
Computational formula: $\text{Var}[X] = E[X^2] - (E[X])^2$.

Properties of Var
If a and b are constants: $\text{Var}[a] = 0$
$\text{Var}[aX] = a^2\, \text{Var}[X]$ $\text{Var}[aX + b] = a^2\, \text{Var}[X]$

ⓘ For the situation above:

$$\text{Var}[X] = E[X^2] - (E[X])^2$$
$$= 2.7 - (1.5)^2 = 0.45$$

ⓘ For the situation above:
$$\text{Var}[4X - 8] = 4^2\, \text{Var}[X] = 16 \times 0.45 = 7.20$$

Two random variables

If X and Y are any two random variables and a and b are constants, then
$$E[aX + bY] = aE[X] + bE[Y]$$
If X and Y are also independent, then
$$\text{Var}[aX + bY] = a^2\, \text{Var}[X] + b^2\, \text{Var}[Y]$$
From this last result:
$$\text{Var}[X + Y] = \text{Var}[X - Y] = \text{Var}[X] + \text{Var}[Y]$$

ⓘ *If X and Y are two independent random variables with $E[X] = 0.3$, $E[Y] = 0.4$, $\text{Var}[X] = 0.2$ and $\text{Var}[Y] = 0.3$, find: (a) $E[4X - 3Y]$ (b) $\text{Var}[4X - 3Y]$.*

(a) $E[(4X - 3Y] = 4E[X] - 3E[Y]$
$= 4 \times 0.3 - 3 \times 0.4 = 0$

(b) $\text{Var}[4X - 3Y] = 4^2\text{Var}[X] + 3^2\text{Var}[Y] = 5.9$

Cumulative distribution function

The **cumulative distribution function** is defined by

$$A = \int_{-\infty}^{a} f(x)\, dx$$

where $f(x)$ is the pdf.
As a varies so does A, i.e. $A = F(a)$

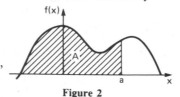

Figure 2

So $F(a) = \int_{-\infty}^{a} f(x)\, dx = P(X \leqslant a)$

$F(a)$ is the cumulative distribution function
Clearly $f(x) = F'(x)$.
If M, Q_1, Q_3 are the median, lower and upper quartiles of x, then

$$F(M) = \frac{1}{2}, \quad F(Q_1) = \frac{1}{4}, \quad F(Q_3) = \frac{3}{4}.$$

ⓘ For the random variable X with pdf
$$p(x) \begin{cases} = \dfrac{1}{3} & 0 < x < 3 \\ = 0 & \text{otherwise} \end{cases}$$

the cumulative distribution function is

$$F(x) = \int_{-\infty}^{x} p(x)\, dx$$

which gives $F(x) = \begin{cases} 0 & x \leqslant 0 \\ \frac{1}{3}x & 0 < x < 3 \\ 1 & x \geqslant 3 \end{cases}$

The graph of $F(x)$ against x is shown.

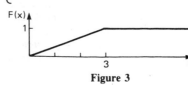

Figure 3

Continuous Probability Distributions
Worked example and Exam questions.

 A continuous random variable X has a probability density function defined by

$$f(x) = \frac{3x^2}{a^3}, \quad 0 \leq x \leq a$$
$$= 0, \quad otherwise.$$

(a) Find the variance of X.
(b) Find the cumulative distribution function of X.

(c) If $Y = 1 - \dfrac{X}{a}$ find

   (i) $P(Y > X)$,
   (ii) the probability density function of Y.

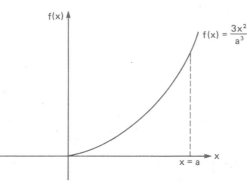

(a)
$$\text{Var}[X] = E[X^2] - E^2[X]$$

$$E[X] = \int_0^a xf(x)dx = \int_0^a \frac{3x^3}{a^3}dx = \frac{3}{4a^3}\left[x^4\right]_0^a = \frac{3a}{4}$$

$$E[X^2] = \int_0^a x^2 f(x)dx = \int_0^a \frac{3x^4}{a^3}dx = \frac{3}{5a^3}\left[x^5\right]_0^a = \frac{3a^2}{5}$$

$$\text{Var}[X] = \frac{3a^2}{5} - \left(\frac{3a}{4}\right)^2 = \frac{3\times16 - 9\times5}{80}a^2 = \frac{3a^2}{80}$$

(b) Let $F(x) = \displaystyle\int_0^x f(t)dt$ be the cumulative distribution function of X.

$$F(x) = \int_0^x \frac{3t^2}{a^3}dt = \frac{1}{a^3}\left[t^3\right]_0^x = \frac{x^3}{a^3}$$

(c)
(i) $Y = 1 - \dfrac{X}{a}$

$$P(Y > X) = P(Y - X > 0)$$

$$Y - X = 1 - \frac{X}{a} - X = \frac{a - X - aX}{a} > 0$$

i.e. $a > X(1 + a)$

i.e. $X < \dfrac{a}{1+a}$

$$\therefore P\left(X < \frac{a}{1+a}\right) = \int_0^{\frac{a}{1+a}} f(x)dx = \int_0^{\frac{a}{1+a}} \frac{3x^2}{a^3}dx$$

$$= \frac{1}{(1+a)^3}$$

(ii) $P(Y < t) = P\left(1 - \dfrac{X}{a} < t\right) = P(X > a(1-t))$

$$= 1 - P(X < a(1-t))$$

$$P(X < a(1-t)) = \int_0^{a(1-t)} f(x)dx = \int_0^{a(1-t)} \frac{3x^2}{a^3}dx$$

$$= (1-t)^3$$

$$\therefore P(Y < t) = 1 - (1-t)^3$$

If $F_Y(x)$ is the cumulative distribution function for Y, then $F_Y(x) = P(Y < x) = 1 - (1-x)^3$ and if $f_Y(x)$ is the probability density function for Y, then $f_Y(x) = \dfrac{d}{dx}F_Y(x) = 3(1-x)^2$

---

 1 A continuous random variable X can assume values only between 0 and 2 inclusive and its probability density function is given by $f(x) = k(4x - x^2)$, $0 \leq x \leq 2$, where k is a positive constant.
   (i) Using the fact that $P(0 \leq x \leq 2) = 1$, find the value of k. Using this value of k, find
   (ii) the mean value of X,
   (iii) the variance of X, and
   (iv) the probability that the value of X exceeds 1.0, i.e. $P(X > 1.0)$.   *(W)

2 A continuous random variable X can assume values only between 0 and 4 inclusive and its probability density function is given by $f(x) = \frac{1}{2} - ax$ $(0 \leq x \leq 4)$, where a is a constant.
   (i) Calculate, in terms of a, the value of $P(0 \leq x \leq 4)$.
   (ii) Using the result of (i) above, determine the value of a.
   (iii) Find the mean and variance of the random variable X.
   (iv) Find the probability that the value of X lies between 1 and 2.   *(W)

3 The random variable X has a probability density function given by

$$P(x) = \begin{cases} kx(1-x^2) & (0 \leq x \leq 1), \\ 0 & \text{elsewhere}, \end{cases}$$

k being a constant. Find the value of k and find also the mean and variance of this distribution. Find the median of the distribution.   *(O & C)*

4 The lifetime T, in hours of a certain type of electric lamp is a random variable with distribution

$$f(t) = Ae^{-t/1200}, \quad 0 \leq t < \infty,$$
$$= 0, \quad t < 0.$$

Find the value of A and show that the mean and standard deviation of T are both 1200 hours. To test the reliability of the production a random sample of 40 bulbs was tested and found to have a mean life of 1020 hours. Does this indicate at the 5% level of significance that the batch from which the sample was taken was sub-standard?   *(S)*

5 The random variable X has probability density function given by

$$f(x) = \begin{cases} \dfrac{1}{(b-a)} & a \leq x \leq b \\ & \qquad\qquad \text{where } b > a. \\ 0 & \text{otherwise} \end{cases}$$

Show that the mean is $(b+a)/2$, and the variance is $(b-a)^2/12$ for this distribution. Given that the mean equals 1 and the variance equals 4/3 find:
   (i) $P(X < 0)$,
   (ii) the value of z such that $P(X > z + \sigma_x) = \frac{1}{4}$, where σ_x is the standard deviation of X.   *(A)*

6 A continuous random variable, X, has probability density function $\lambda \sin x$ $(0 \leq x \leq \pi)$, and zero outside this range. Find a value of the constant λ, the mean, the variance, the median, the quartiles. What is the probability that a random observation lies within one standard deviation of the mean?   *(OLE)*

S11 The Binomial Distribution

Definition, Binomial situations, Expectation and variance, Binomial recurrence formula, Fitting a binomial distribution.

Definition

A discrete random variable X having a probability density function (pdf) of the form:

$$P(X=x) = \binom{n}{x} p^x (1-p)^{n-x} \text{ where } x = 0, 1, 2, \ldots, n$$

is said to have a **binomial distribution**.

We write X is Bin(n, p).
n and p are called the **parameters of the distribution**.
n is a positive integer and $0 \leq p \leq 1$.

ⓘ Bin $(4, \frac{1}{2})$ has $n=4$ and $p=\frac{1}{2}$.

$$P(X=x) = \binom{4}{x}\left(\frac{1}{2}\right)^x\left(\frac{1}{2}\right)^{4-x} = \binom{4}{x}\left(\frac{1}{2}\right)^4$$

Verifying this gives the following probability table:

x	0	1	2	3	4
$P(X=x)$	$\frac{1}{16}$	$\frac{4}{16}$	$\frac{6}{16}$	$\frac{4}{16}$	$\frac{1}{16}$

Binomial situations

Any situation having only two possible, mutually exclusive outcomes, often labelled 'success'/'failure', is called a **binomial situation**. The probability of a 'success' (or 'failure') is usually known.

ⓘ *Seeds have a probability of germinating of 0.9. If six seeds are sown what is the probability of five or more seeds germinating?*

This is a binomial situation with $n=6$ and $P(\text{success}) = P(\text{germination}) = 0.9$

$$\therefore P(X=x) = \binom{6}{x}(0.9)^x(0.1)^{6-x}$$

$P(5 \text{ or more germinations}) = P(X=5 \text{ or } 6)$
$= P(X=5) + P(X=6)$

$$= \binom{6}{5}(0.9)^5(0.1)^1 + \binom{6}{6}(0.9)^6(0.1)^0 = 0.88$$

Expectation and variance

If X is Bin(n, p), then:
the **expectation** of X is $E[X] = np$,
the **variance** of X is $Var[X] = np(1-p)$

ⓘ For Bin$(6, 0.9)$:
$E[X] = 6 \times 0.9 = 5.4$
$Var[X] = 6 \times 0.9 \times (1-0.9) = 0.54$

Binomial recurrence formula

The **binomial recurrence formula** is

$$P(X=x+1) = \frac{n-x}{x+1} \cdot \frac{p}{(1-p)} P(X=x)$$

This enables successive probabilities to be more easily calculated once the initial probability is known.

ⓘ For Bin$\left(4, \frac{1}{2}\right)$, $P(X=0) = \binom{4}{0}\left(\frac{1}{2}\right)^4\left(\frac{1}{2}\right)^0 = \frac{1}{16}$

By the binomial recurrence formula:

$$P(X=1) = \frac{4}{1} \cdot \frac{\frac{1}{2}}{\frac{1}{2}} \cdot P(X=0) = 4 \times \frac{1}{16} = \frac{4}{16}$$

$$P(X=2) = \frac{3}{2} \cdot 1 \cdot P(X=1) = \frac{3}{2} \times \frac{4}{16} = \frac{6}{16}$$

$$P(X=3) = \frac{2}{3} \cdot 1 \cdot P(X=2) = \frac{2}{3} \times \frac{6}{16} = \frac{4}{16}$$

$$P(X=4) = \frac{1}{4} \cdot 1 \cdot P(X=3) = \frac{1}{4} \times \frac{4}{16} = \frac{1}{16}$$

Fitting a binomial distribution

To fit a binomial distribution to a given frequency distribution:

(a) Find the values of the parameters n and p:
n is the largest value of x,
$p \approx \frac{\bar{x}}{n}$, since $\bar{x} \approx E[X] = np$.

(b) Generate the binomial probability distribution for X as Bin(n, p).

(c) Multiply the probabilities by the total frequency of the given distribution to find the expected frequencies.

ⓘ *Fit a binomial distribution to the following:*

x	0	1	2	3	4	Total
f	4	13	20	11	2	50

The largest value of x is 4. Take $n=4$.
$\Sigma fx = 94$, $\Sigma f = 50 \Rightarrow \bar{x} = 1.88$. Take $p \approx \frac{1.88}{4} = 0.47$.

Assume X is Bin$(4, 0.47)$.

$$P(X=x) = \binom{4}{x}(0.47)^x(0.53)^{4-x}$$

$$P(X=0) = \binom{4}{0}(0.47)^0(0.53)^4 = 0.0789$$

By the binomial recurrence formula:
$P(X=1) = 0.2799$, $P(X=2) = 0.3723$,
$P(X=3) = 0.0488$, $P(X=4) = 0.0488$.

$\Sigma f = 50$ gives this table of expected frequencies:

x	0	1	2	3	4	Total
f_E	4	14	19	11	2	50

The Binomial Distribution
Cumulative binomial tables.
Worked examples and Exam questions.

Cumulative binomial tables	These are most useful when calculating the probabilities which involve a summation of many terms. Two parameters are required, the probability p of success and the number of trials n.

 If X is Bin $(15, 0.3)$, find $P(6 \leq X \leq 9)$.
$$P(X \geq 6) = 1 - 0.7216 = 0.2784$$
$$P(X \geq 10) = 1 - 0.9963 = 0.0037$$
So $P(6 \leq X \leq 9) = 0.2784 - 0.0037 = 0.2747$

 The probability that a marksman will hit a target is $\frac{5}{6}$. He fires 9 shots. Calculate, correct to three decimal places, the probability that he will hit the target (i) at least 7 times, (ii) no more than 6 times. If he hits the target exactly 6 times, calculate the probability that the three misses are with 3 successive shots.

$$P(\text{hitting target}) = P(\text{success}) = \frac{5}{6}$$

$$P(\text{not hitting target}) = P(\text{failure}) = \frac{1}{6}$$

Taking the nine shots to be independent events the probability distribution of X, 'the number of targets hit' is

$\text{Bin}\left(9, \frac{5}{6}\right)$, and so $P(X=x) = \binom{9}{x}\left(\frac{5}{6}\right)^{x}\left(\frac{1}{6}\right)^{9-x}$

(i) $P(\text{at least 7 targets hit}) = P(X=7) + P(X=8) + P(X=9)$

$$= \frac{9 \times 8}{1 \times 2}\left(\frac{5}{6}\right)^{7}\left(\frac{1}{6}\right)^{2} + 9\left(\frac{5}{6}\right)^{8}\left(\frac{1}{6}\right) + \left(\frac{5}{6}\right)^{9}$$

$$= \left(\frac{5}{6}\right)^{7}\left[\frac{36}{36} + \frac{45}{36} + \frac{25}{36}\right] = \left(\frac{5}{6}\right)^{7} \times \frac{106}{36}$$

$$= 0.822$$

(ii) $P(\text{no more than 6 targets})$
$$= P(X=0) + P(X=1) + P(X=2) + \ldots + P(X=6)$$
$$= 1 - P(X=7) - P(X=8) - P(X=9)$$
$$= 1 - 0.822 = 0.178$$

The number of ways of hitting the target exactly six times is $^{9}C_{6} = 84$. The three misses happening with three successive shots can occur in 7 ways i.e. 123, 234, 345, 456, 567, 678 or 789.

$\therefore P(\text{6 targets and 3 misses with successive shots}) = \frac{7}{84} = \frac{1}{12}$.

 Groups of 5 people are chosen at random and the number, x, of people in each group who normally wear spectacles is recorded. The results obtained for 400 groups of 5 are shown in the table.

x	0	1	2	3	4	5
f	34	106	130	90	36	4

Calculate, from the above data, the mean value of x. Assuming that the situation can be modelled by a binomial distribution having the same mean as the one calculated above, state the appropriate values for the parameters n and p. Calculate the theoretical frequencies corresponding to those in the table.

$$\bar{x} = \frac{\Sigma fx}{\Sigma f} = 2$$

$$n = 5, \ p = \frac{\bar{x}}{n} = \frac{2}{5}$$

The probability distribution of X, 'number in group wearing spectacles' is $\text{Bin}\left(5, \frac{2}{5}\right)$, and $P(X=x) = \binom{5}{x}\left(\frac{2}{5}\right)^{x}\left(\frac{3}{5}\right)^{5-x}$

The theoretical probability distribution is shown in the table below

x	0	1	2	3	4	5
$P(X=x)$	0.078	0.259	0.346	0.230	0.077	0.010

The theoretical frequencies are found by multiplying each probability by 400, giving

x	0	1	2	3	4	5
f_T	31.2	103.6	138.4	92.0	30.8	4.0

 1 Previous experience indicates that, of the students entering upon a particular diploma course, 90% will successfully complete it. One year, 15 students commence the course. Calculate, correct to 3 decimal places, the probability that:
  (i) all 15 successfully complete the course;
  (ii) only 1 student fails;
  (iii) no more than 2 students fail;
  (iv) at least 2 students fail.   *(C)*

2 (i) There are 8 red apples and 2 green apples in a bag. If 2 apples are taken out at random, determine the probability that just one of them will be red.
(ii) It is found by experience that 20% of the electric toasters made by a certain manufacturer are faulty. The toasters are packed in boxes, each box containing 10 toasters. Calculate the probability that in a box selected at random (a) just 3 will be faulty; (b) just 2 will be faulty. Determine the most likely number of faulty toasters to be found in a box chosen at random.   *(OLE)*

3 State the conditions necessary for a Binomial Distribution to result when a series of events occurs. Illustrate your answer by means of an example.
Four ordinary dice are thrown. Find:
(a) the probability that at least one of the dice shows a six;
(b) the probability that the highest score showing is a two.   *(S)*

4 A company has ten telephone lines. At any instant the probability that any particular line is engaged is 1/5. State the expected number of free telephone lines. Calculate for any instant, correct to two significant figures, the probability that
  (i) all the lines are engaged,
  (ii) at least one line is free,
  (iii) exactly two lines are free.   *(A)*

5 (a) Berg and Korner have a long rivalry in tennis: in the last 25 games, Berg has won 15 times. They start a new series of 8 games. Assuming that the binomial model may be applied, what is the probability that Berg will win at least 6 of these?
(b) Prove that the mean of the binomial distribution is np. A set of 100 pods, each containing 4 peas, was examined to see how many of the peas were good. the following were the results:

No. of good peas in pod	0	1	2	3	4
No of pods	7	20	35	30	8

  (i) What is the probability of getting a good pea?
  (ii) Calculate the theoretical frequencies of 0, 1, 2, 3, 4 good peas, using the associated theoretical binomial distribution.   *(S)*

6 Prove that the mean number of successes in a series of n independent trials, each of which has a probability p of success, is np. Show that the standard deviation is $\sqrt{\{np(1-p)\}}$.   *(O & C)*

S12 The Poisson Distribution
Definitions, Uses, Poisson or binomial, Additive property.

Definitions

A discrete random variable X having a probability density function (pdf) of the form

$$P(X=x)=e^{-\mu}\cdot\frac{\mu^x}{x!} \text{ where } x=0,1,2,\ldots$$

is said to have a **Poisson distribution**.
We write X is $Po(\mu)$
$\mu(>0)$ is the **parameter of the distribution.**

Note: There is no upper limit to the value of x. This is usually determined by practical considerations.

If X is $Po(\mu)$, then $E[X]=\mu$ and $Var[X]=\mu$.

The **Poisson recurrence formula** is

$$P(X=x+1)=\frac{\mu}{x+1}P(X=x) \text{ for } x=0,1,\ldots$$

This enables successive probabilities to be more easily calculated once the initial probability is known.

$\boxed{i}$ For $Po(1.5)$, $\mu=1.5$

$$P(X=x)=e^{-1.5}\cdot\frac{(1.5)^x}{x!} \text{ where } x=0,1,2,\ldots$$

This gives the following probability table:

x	0	1	2	3	4	5 or more
$P(X=x)$	0.223	0.335	0.251	0.126	0.047	0.018

$\boxed{i}$ For $Po(1.5)$, $E[X]=1.5$ and $Var[X]=1.5$.

$\boxed{i}$ For $Po(1.5)$, $P(0)=0.223$.
By the Poisson recurrence formula:

$$P(1)=\frac{1.5}{0+1}P(0)=1.5\times0.223=0.335$$

etc.

Uses

There are two main uses of the Poisson distribution.

1. Estimation of probabilities of random events which have a small probability of occurrence. Typical applications of this are telephone calls arriving at a switchboard, insurance claims, accident rates, flaws in manufactured material.
Usually the mean rate of occurrence per unit time will be given, although this may be scaled accordingly.

2. Approximation to a binomial distribution with the same mean, i.e. $\mu=np$, and usually $n>50$ and $p<0.1$.

$\boxed{i}$ *Telephone calls arrive at a switchboard at the rate of 50 per hour. Find the probabilities of 0, 1 or 2 calls arriving in any 5 minute period.*

The average rate of calls per 5 minute period
$=50\div12=4.17$ calls
If the random variable X is 'the number of calls in any 5 minute period', then X is $Po(4.17)$.

$$P(X=x)=e^{-4.17}\cdot\frac{(4.17)^x}{x!}$$

$P(X=0)=0.02$, $P(X=1)=0.06$, $P(X=2)=0.13$

$\boxed{i}$ *A large population has 0.5% defective. A sample of 200 is taken at random. Using a Poisson approximation find the probabilities of 0, 1 or 2 defectives in the sample.*

This is a binomial situation with $n=200$, $p=0.005$.
So $\mu=np=200\times0.005=1.00$
If X is 'the number of defectives', then X is $Po(1)$.

$$P(X=x)=e^{-1}\cdot\frac{(1)^x}{x!}$$

$P(X=0)=0.37$, $P(X=1)=0.37$, $P(X=2)=0.18$

Poisson or binomial

Given a frequency distribution of the binomial/Poisson type, the decision on whether to fit a binomial or Poisson distribution is often made by considering the mean and variance of the distribution.
The closer these two are in value the more likely a Poisson distribution is applicable.

$\boxed{i}$ The expected frequencies for a theoretical binomial and Poisson fit are compared with a given distribution below.

x	0	1	2	3	4	total
f	21	18	7	3	1	50
f_B	18	21	9	2	0	50
f_P	20	18	8	2	1	50

For the given distribution $\bar{x}=0.9$ and $s^2=0.97$.
The Poisson fit is more appropriate.

Additive property

The **additive property of the Poisson distribution:**
if X is $Po(x)$ and Y is $Po(y)$,
then $X+Y$ is $Po(x+y)$.

$\boxed{i}$ An item is made of two manufactured parts A and B. Flaws in A occur randomly and with a mean rate of 7.8 per 1000, while flaws in B also occur randomly (and independently of those in A) with a mean rate of 5.6 per 1000. Assuming Poisson distributions for the flaws in A and B, the item composed of A and B will have flaws distributed $Po(7.8+5.6)=Po(13.4)$.

The Poisson Distribution
Worked example, Guided example and Exam questions.

Telephone calls reach a switchboard independently and at random, external ones at a mean rate of 1 in any 5 minute period, and internal ones at a mean rate of 2 in any 5 minute period.
Calculate the probability that there will be more than 2 calls in any period of 2 minutes.

Let the random variable E be 'the number of external calls per 2 minute period', E is Po(0.4).
Let the random variable I be 'the number of internal calls per 2 minute period', I is Po(0.8).
Using the additive property of Poisson distributions, $E+I$ is Po(0.4+0.8) i.e. Po(1.2).
$P(E+I>2) = 1 - P(E+I=0) - P(E+I=1) - P(E+I=2)$
$P(E+I=0) = e^{-1.2} = 0.301$
$P(E+I=1) = e^{-1.2} \times \dfrac{1.2}{1} = 0.361$
$P(E+I=2) = e^{-1.2} \times \dfrac{(1.2)^2}{2!} = 0.271$
$\therefore\ P(E+I>2) = 1 - 0.301 - 0.361 - 0.217$
$\qquad = 0.121$
$\therefore$ P(more than 2 calls in any 2 minute period) $= 0.121$

The frequency distribution of the number of accidents in each week in a period of 104 weeks in a factory is given in the table.

Number of accidents(x)	0	1	2	3	4	5
Frequency(f)	30	45	20	6	2	1

Fit a Poisson distribution to these data, calculating the frequencies it predicts.

Calculate $\bar{x}$ the mean number of accidents per week. Then the random variable X 'the number of accidents per week' is Po($\bar{x}$).
Calculate $P(X=0) = e^{-\bar{x}}$ and then use the Poisson recurrence formula to find $P(X=1)$ to $P(X=5)$.
Multiplying each of these probabilities by 104 will give the predicted frequencies using a Poisson model.

---

1 Sketch the frequency polygon of a Poisson distribution with mean 2. Telephone calls arrive at a switchboard at random intervals at an average rate of 24 calls per hour. Find the probability of receiving:
(a) no calls in 5 minutes;
(b) more than 4 calls in 5 minutes;
(c) Estimate the probability of receiving more than 50 calls in $1\frac{1}{2}$ hours. *(O & C)*

2 The frequency distribution of the number of accidents in each week in a period of 2 years (104 weeks) in a factory is given in the table.

Number of accidents	0	1	2	3	4	5
Frequency	33	42	19	8	1	1

Fit a Poisson distribution to these data, calculating the frequencies it predicts. State why the binomial distribution is not appropriate in this case. *(A)*

3 Show that the variance of a Poisson distribution is equal to the mean. The number of bacteria in 1 ml of inoculum has a Poisson distribution with mean 2.0. If at least 3 bacteria are needed for a dose to be infective, find the probability that a dose of 1 ml will cause infection. Find approximate limits, symmetrical about the mean, between which lies 95% of the distribution of the number of bacteria in 100 ml of inoculum. *(O & C)*

4 Define the Poisson distribution and derive its mean and variance. In the first year of the life of a certain type of machine, the number of times a maintenance engineer is required has a Poisson distribution with mean four. Find the probability that more than four calls are necessary. The first call is free of charge and subsequent calls cost £20 each. Find the mean cost of maintenance in the first year.
(J)

5 A footballer finds that the number of goals he scores in a match has a Poisson distribution with mean $\frac{1}{4}$. What is the distribution of the number of goals he scores in n matches? How many matches must he play in order to be 95% sure of scoring at least 20 goals? *(OLE)*

6 A random variable X has a Poisson distribution given by $P(X=r)=p_r=e^{-\lambda}\lambda^r/r!$, $r=0, 1, 2, \ldots$ Prove that the mean of X is λ. Give two examples (other than that suggested below) of situations where you would expect a Poisson distribution to occur.
The number of white corpuscles on a slide has a Poisson distribution with mean 3.2. By considering the values of r for which $p_{r+1}/p_r>1$ find the most likely number of white corpuscles on a slide. Calculate correct to 3 decimal places the probability of obtaining this number. If two such slides are prepared what is the probability, correct to 3 decimal places, of obtaining at least two white corpuscles in total on the two slides? *(S)*

7 Derive the mean and the variance of a Poisson distribution. Two types of flaw, A and B, may occur in a manufactured cloth. The numbers of flaws of type A and of type B occurring per metre length of the cloth are independent random variables having Poisson distributions with means 0.5 and 1, respectively.
(a) Find the probabilities, to three significant figures, that a length of 1 metre of the cloth will have:
(i) 2 or fewer flaws of type A,
(ii) no flaw of either type.
(b) Show that the probability of a length of 1 metre of the cloth containing 1 flaw only is exactly three times that of it containing 1 flaw of each type.
(c) Removing a type A flaw from the cloth costs 8 pence and removing a type B flaw costs 2 pence. Find the mean and the standard deviation of the cost of removing flaws per 1 metre length of cloth. *(W)*

8 Explain under what conditions it is appropriate to apply a Poisson model to describe a distribution. Referring to your project work if you wish, give brief details of two situations in which you used this model. It is known that 0.1% of people having an influenza injection of type A suffer an adverse reaction. If 2250 people are to receive the injection, what is the probability that
(a) exactly two people will suffer an adverse reaction;
(b) more than 3 people will suffer an adverse reaction?
Given that 2000 people receive an injection of type B and no one suffers an adverse reaction to this injection, is this sufficient evidence to suggest that there is a smaller probability of an adverse reaction to type B than to type A? Give reasons for your answer. *(L)*

9 A large number of screwdrivers from a trial production run is inspected. It is found that the cellulose acetate handles are defective on 1% and that the chrome steel blades are defective on $1\frac{1}{2}$% of the screwdrivers, the defects occurring independently.
(a) What is the probability that a sample of 80 contains more than two defective screwdrivers?
(b) What is the probability that a sample of 80 contains at least one screwdriver with both a defective handle and a defective blade? *(O & C)*

S13 The Normal Distribution
Definition, Standard normal distribution, Use of tables, Using the standard variable.

Definition

A continuous random variable X having a probability density function (pdf) of the form

$$f(x) = \frac{1}{\sigma\sqrt{2\pi}} \exp\left[-\frac{(x-\mu)^2}{2\sigma^2}\right], \quad -\infty < x < \infty$$

is said to have a **normal distribution**.
We write X is $N(\mu, \sigma^2)$.
$\mu(-\infty < \mu < \infty)$ and $\sigma(>0)$ are the **parameters of the distribution**.
$E[X] = \mu$ and $\text{Var}[X] = \sigma^2$

The normal distribution curve is a characteristic 'bell shape' symmetrical about $x = \mu$ (the mean).

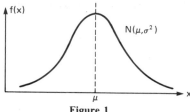

The area under the normal curve is unity (1).

Figure 1

Standard normal distribution

The normal distribution with $\mu = 0$, $\sigma = 1$ is called a **standard normal distribution**. The corresponding variable is usually denoted by Z, so Z is $N(0, 1)$.

The pdf for Z is $\phi(x) = \frac{1}{\sqrt{2\pi}} \exp\left(\frac{-x^2}{2}\right)$

By definition

$$P(Z < x) = \int_{-\infty}^{x} \phi(x)\, dx = \int_{-\infty}^{x} \frac{1}{\sqrt{2\pi}} \exp\left(\frac{-x^2}{2}\right) dx$$

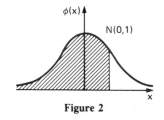

Figure 2

$P(Z < x)$ is the shaded area in the diagram. It is usually referred to as $\Phi(x)$. The integral which gives this area under the curve is difficult to evaluate but it is given in normal distribution tables.

Use of tables

Most normal distribution function tables are given only for $x \geq 0$. Other probabilities are derived by suitable transformations. When evaluating probabilities using these tables, draw a sketch to ensure that the correct quantity is being evaluated.

For a given $a \geq 0$,
$P(Z < a) = \Phi(a)$
This is simply the value in the table at $x = a$

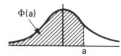

$P(Z > a) = 1 - \Phi(a)$
since the total area under the curve is equal to 1.

$P(Z > -a) = \Phi(a)$
$P(Z < -a) = 1 - \Phi(a)$
by the symmetry of the normal curve

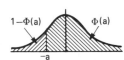

For $b < c$,
$P(b < Z < c) = \Phi(c) - \Phi(b)$

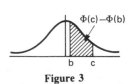

Figure 3

The tables may also be used 'in reverse' to find z if $\Phi(z)$ is known.

ℹ️ *Find the values of*:
(a) $\Phi(1.85)$ (b) $\Phi(-0.63)$ (c) $P(Z > -1.5)$
(d) $P(0.5 < Z < 1.8)$ (e) $P(-2.1 < Z < 1.6)$

(a) $\Phi(1.84) = 0.9671$
direct from tables

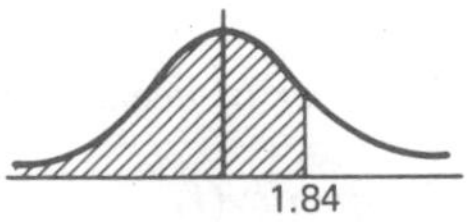

(b) $\Phi(-0.63) = 1 - \Phi(0.63)$
$\qquad = 1 - 0.7357$
$\qquad = 0.2643$

(c) $P(Z > -1.5) = 1 - \Phi(-1.5)$
$\qquad = 1 - (1 - \Phi(1.5))$
$\qquad = \Phi(1.5)$
$\qquad = 0.9332$

(d) $P(0.5 < Z < 1.8)$
$\qquad = \Phi(1.8) - \Phi(0.5)$
$\qquad = 0.9641 - 0.6915$
$\qquad = 0.2726$

(e) $P(-2.1 < Z < 1.6)$
$\qquad = \Phi(1.6) - \Phi(-2.1)$
$\qquad = \Phi(1.6) - (1 - \Phi(2.1))$
$\qquad = 0.9452 - (1 - 0.9821)$
$\qquad = 0.9273$

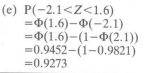

Figure 4

Using the standard variable

Probabilities associated with any given normal distribution may be found by using the standard variable as follows.

1. Transform the given random variable X, which is $N(\mu, \sigma^2)$, into the standard variable Z, which is $N(0, 1)$ using:

$$Z = \frac{X - \mu}{\sigma}$$

2. Use the standard normal distribution function tables to find the probabilities of the transformed values as shown above.

ℹ️ *An industrial process mass produces an item whose weights are normally distributed with mean 18.5 kg and standard deviation 1.5 kg. What is the probability that an item chosen at random weighs more than 21.5 kg?*

The weights are $N(18.5, 2.25)$.

The standard variable is $Z = \dfrac{W - 18.5}{1.5}$.

$\therefore P(W > 21.5) = P\left(Z > \dfrac{21.5 - 18.5}{1.5}\right)$

$= P(Z > 2) = 1 - \Phi(2)$
$\qquad = 0.0227$

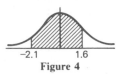

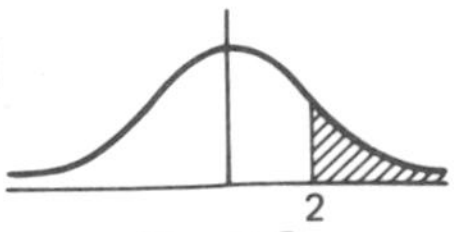

Figure 5

The Normal Distribution
Worked example, Guided example and Exam questions.

 An industrial process mass produces items which are normally distributed. 11.55% of them weigh over 20 kg and 5.89% weigh under 10 kg. Calculate the mean weight and standard deviation for this distribution.

Let W be the weight statistic for the items and Z the standardized variable. $W \sim N(\mu, \sigma^2)$ and $Z = (W - \mu)/\sigma \sim N(0, 1)$, where μ and σ are the mean and standard deviation of the distribution for W.

When $W = 20$, $\Phi(z_{20}) = 1 - 0.1155 = 0.8845$, where z_{20} is the value of the standard variable Z for $W = 20$.

i.e. $z_{20} = 1.198$ (from tables)
hence $1.198 = (20 - \mu)/\sigma$ [1]

When $W = 10$, $\Phi(z_{10}) = 0.0589$
i.e. $\Phi(-z_{10}) = 1 - 0.0589 = 0.9411$
so $-z_{10} = 1.564$ (from tables)
hence $1.564 = -(10 - \mu)/\sigma$ [2]

Solving [1] and [2] for μ and σ gives $\mu = 15.66$ and $\sigma = 3.62$

GE *Eggs are classified by weight according to the following table:*

Class	2	3	4	5	6
Weight (grams)	65–70	60–65	55–60	50–55	45–50

100 *hens of breed A are found to lay eggs at the rate of* 180 *per day, the eggs being of mean weight* 63 g *with standard deviation* 5 g. 100 *hens of breed B lay* 210 *eggs per day of mean weight* 52 g *and standard deviation* 6 g. *What ratio of hens of breed A to hens of breed B should be kept in order that equal numbers of eggs of class 3 and class 5 should be produced daily? Assume that the weights of eggs from each breed of hen are normally distributed.*

Summarising diagrammatically the information for breed A, and breed B gives:

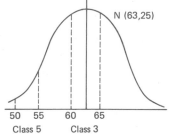
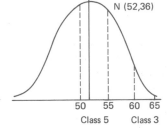

$$Z_A = \frac{w_A - 63}{5} \qquad Z_B = \frac{w_B - 52}{6}$$

Calculating the probability of obtaining a class 3 egg gives
$P(-0.6 \leqslant Z_A \leqslant 0.4) + P(1.33 \leqslant Z_B \leqslant 2.17)$
$\Phi(0.4) - (1 - \Phi(0.6)) + \Phi(2.17) - \Phi(1.33)$
$0.6554 - 1 + 0.7257 + 0.9850 - 0.9082$
$0.3811 + 0.0768$
∴ the number of class 3 eggs will be
     $0.3811 \times 180 + 0.0768 \times 210 = 68.6 + 16.1$
per 200 hens, 100 of each breed.

A similar calculation shows that the number of class 5 eggs will be
     $0.3208 \times 210 + 0.0491 \times 180 = 67.4 + 8.8$
per 200 hens, 100 of each variety.

For the same number of class 3 eggs and class 5 eggs we require
$68.6A + 16.1B = 67.4B + 8.8A$

where A = number of breed A in units of 100
and B = number of breed B in units of 100.
From this equation we obtain the required ratio, $A : B = 0.86 : 1$

EX

1 Observation of a very large number of cars at a certain point on a motorway establishes that the speeds are normally distributed. 90% of cars have speeds less than 75.7 mph and only 5% have speeds less than 60 mph. Determine the mean speed μ and the standard deviation σ. Give your answers correct to 2 decimal places. Because of a fuel economy drive the mean speed of motorists is reduced. Assuming that the standard deviation σ has remained unchanged and that 2% now exceed 75 mph, find the new mean speed. What percentage of motorists now exceed the 70 mph speed limit?
(W)

2 In a given manufacturing process, components are rejected if they have a particular dimension greater than 60.4 mm or less than 59.7 mm. It is found that 3% are rejected as being too large and 5% are rejected as being too small. Assuming the dimension is Normally distributed, find the mean and standard deviation of the distribution of the dimension, correct to 1 decimal place. use the mean and standard deviation you have calculated to estimate the percentage of rejects if the limits for *acceptance* are changed to 59.6 mm and 60.3 mm.
(W)

3 The length of an engine part must be between 4.81 cm and 5.20 cm. In mass production it is found that 0.8% are too short and 3% are too long. If these lengths are normally distributed about mean μ with standard deviation σ, find two equations of the form $\mu + A\sigma = B$. Solve these equations to find the mean and standard deviation. Each part costs £4 to produce; those that turn out to be too long are shortened, at an extra cost of £2; those that turn out to be too short have to be scrapped. Find the expected total cost of producing 100 parts that meet the specification.
(O & C)

4 A sample of 100 apples is taken from a load. The apples have the following distribution of sizes.

Diameter to nearest cm	6	7	8	9	10
Frequency	11	21	38	17	13

Determine the mean and standard deviation of these diameters.

Assuming that the distribution is approximately normal with this mean and this standard deviation find the range of size of apples for packing, if 5% are to be rejected as too small and 5% are to be rejected as too large.
(O & C)

5 A machine packs flour into bags which nominally contain 1 kg but there is a variation in the actual weight (kg), which is described by a normal random variable of mean μ and variance σ^2. Previous investigations indicate that $\sigma = 0.03$ kg and that the probability that a bag is underweight is 0.02. Find the value of μ at which the machine is operating. An attempt is made to improve the machine with the hope that, while it operates with the same value of μ, σ will be reduced. Find the value of σ which is required to ensure that the probability that a bag is underweight is 0.001. Assuming this improved value of σ to have been achieved, show that the new probability that a random bag will weigh more than 1.1 kg is just less than 0.03.
(L)

S14 Uses of the Normal Distribution

Fitting a normal distribution, Normal approximation to binomial, Normal approximation to Poisson.

Fitting a normal distribution

There are two cases to consider when fitting a normal distribution.

1. Given a frequency distribution

(a) Calculate $\bar{x}$ and s^2 from the given data. Use them as estimates of μ and σ^2.

(b) Note the upper class bound for each class.

(c) Standardise the upper class bounds using
$$z = \frac{x - \bar{x}}{s}.$$

(d) Find $\Phi(z)$ for each standardised upper class bound. This gives a set of cumulative probabilities.

(e) Obtain class probabilities by subtracting successive Φs.

(f) Calculate expected frequencies by multiplying each probability by the total given frequency.

2. Given μ and σ^2

(a) Determine a practical range, i.e. $\mu - 3\sigma$ to $\mu + 3\sigma$.

(b) Divide this range into about 10 classes.

(c) Proceed as in 1.

ℹ️ *Fit a normal distribution to this data:*

class	up to 15	15 up to 20	20 up to 25	25 up to 30	30 up to 35	35 and over
f	5	12	26	34	16	7

Take the first class as 10 up to 15 and the last class as 35 up to 40.
Using mid-class values:
$\Sigma fx = 2575$, $\Sigma f = 100 \Rightarrow \bar{x} = 25.75$
$\Sigma fx^2 = 70075 \Rightarrow s^2 = 37.7$ and $s = 6.14$.
The upper class bounds are:
$$15, 20, 25, 30, 35, \infty$$
The standardised upper class bounds are:
$$-1.74, -0.94, -0.12, 0.89, 1.51, \infty$$
Φ for each standardised upper class bound:
$$0.0409, 0.1736, 0.4522, 0.7549, 0.9345, 1$$
The probabilities for each class are:
$$0.0409, 0.1327, 0.2786, 0.3027, 0.1796, 0.0655$$
$\Sigma f = 100$, so the expected frequencies are:
$$4, 13, 28, 30, 18, 7 \text{ (total 100)}$$

Normal approximation to binomial

The normal distribution may be used to approximate the binomial distribution when n is large ($n > 50$) and p is not too big or small ($0.2 \leqslant p \leqslant 0.8$). If n is very large, then the approximation is good even if p is near to 0 or 1.

If X is Bin(n, p), then X is approximately N$(np, np(1-p))$ since E$[X] = np$ and Var$[X] = np(1-p)$.

To compensate for the change from a discrete distribution (the binomial) to a continuous distribution (the normal), a continuity correction is made. The discrete integer value a in the binomial distribution becomes the class interval $[(a-0.5)$ up to $(a+0.5)]$ in the normal distribution.

So the discrete variable 3 becomes the class interval 2.5 up to 3.5, and the discrete value '>5' becomes '>5.5'.

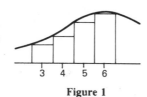

Figure 1

ℹ️ *A machine manufacturing nails makes approximately 15% that are outside set tolerance limits. If a random sample of 200 is taken, find the probability that more than 20 will be outside the tolerance limits.*

If the random variable X is 'number of nails outside limits', then X is Bin(200, 0.15).
E$[X] = 200 \times 0.15 = 30$ and Var$[X] = 30 \times 0.85 = 25.5$.
So X is approximately N(30, 25.5).
We require P$(X > 20.5)$ using the continuity correction.

Standard variable is $Z = \dfrac{X - 30}{5.05}$

$$\therefore P(X > 20.5) = P\left(Z > \frac{20.5 - 30}{5.05}\right) = P(Z > -1.88)$$

$$= P(Z < 1.88) = \Phi(1.88)$$

$$= 0.9699$$

i.e. It is almost certain that there will be more than 20 faulty nails in the sample of 200.

Normal approximation to Poisson

The normal distribution may be used to approximate the Poisson distribution when μ is large ($\mu > 20$).

If X is Po(μ), then X is approximately N(μ, μ) since E$[X] = \mu$ and Var$[X] = \mu$.

The continuity correction is also required because the Poisson distribution is discrete.

ℹ️ *An accident 'black-spot' averages 2 per week. Find the probability that there are 24 or more accidents in a 12 week period.*

Over a 12 week period the mean number of accidents would be $2 \times 12 = 24$.

If X is the random variable 'number of accidents in a 12 week period', then X is Po(24).
Use the normal approximation N(24, 24).

Standard variable is $Z = \dfrac{X - 24}{4.90}$

We require P$(X \geqslant 23.5)$ using the continuity correction.

$$P(X \geqslant 23.5) = P\left(Z > \frac{23.5 - 24}{4.90}\right) = P(Z > -0.102)$$

$$= P(Z < 0.102) = \Phi(0.102) = 0.541.$$

i.e. The required probability is 0.541.

Uses of the Normal Distribution
The 2 standard deviation check/test.
Worked example and Exam questions.

The 2 standard deviation test/check

If X is $N(\mu, \sigma^2)$, then

$$P(|X - \mu| < 2\sigma) = 0.95$$

i.e. $P(|Z| < 2) = 0.95$

where Z is the standard normal variable.

This says that the probability of X lying within 2 standard deviations of its mean is approximately 95%.

 Approximate the probability that a produced item weighs between 2 standard deviations of the mean. Then calculate exactly.

$$P(\mu - 2\sigma < W < \mu + 2\sigma) = P(-2\sigma < W - \mu < 2\sigma)$$
$$= P(|W - \mu| < 2\sigma) = 0.95$$

Calculating exactly gives (Z is the standard normal variable)

$$P\left(-2 < \frac{W - \mu}{\sigma} < 2\right) = P(-2 < Z < 2) = P(|Z| < 2)$$
$$= \Phi(2) - \Phi(-2) = 0.9772 - (1 - 0.9772)$$

Hence $P(|Z| < 2) = 0.9544$ exactly.

WE

(a) *Estimate the probability that a fair coin comes down heads more than 290 in 500 tosses.*

(b) *Assuming that a biased coin comes down heads with probability $\dfrac{290}{500}$, estimate the least integer value of r such that the probability of getting more than r heads in 500 tosses is less than $\dfrac{1}{1000}$.*

(a) $P(\text{success}) = P(\text{a head}) = \frac{1}{2}$
Let the random variable X be 'the number of heads in 500 tosses', then X is $\text{Bin}(500, \frac{1}{2})$
$np = 250$ and $np(1-p) = 125$
∴ since n is large and p is not too large or too small we take a normal approximation and let X be $N(250, 125)$ approximately.

The standard variable is $Z = \dfrac{X - \mu}{\sigma} = \dfrac{X - 250}{\sqrt{125}}$

∴ $P(X > 290) = P\left(Z > \dfrac{290.5 - 250}{\sqrt{125}}\right)$ Note, the continuity correction
$= P(Z > 3.622)$
$= 1 - \Phi(3.622)$
$= 0.00022$

(b) $P(\text{success}) = P(\text{a head}) = \dfrac{290}{500}$

Let the random variable X be 'the number of heads in 500 tosses', then X is $\text{Bin}\left(500, \dfrac{29}{50}\right)$

$np = 290$, $np(1-p) = 121.8$
∴ since n is large and p is not too large or too small we take a normal approximation and let X be $N(290, 121.8)$ approximately.

The standard variable is $Z = \dfrac{X - \mu}{\sigma} = \dfrac{X - 290}{\sqrt{121.8}}$

$P(X > r) = P\left(Z > \dfrac{r + 0.5 - 290}{\sqrt{121.8}}\right) = 1 - \Phi\left(\dfrac{r + 0.5 - 290}{\sqrt{121.8}}\right)$
< 0.001

i.e. $\Phi\left(\dfrac{r + 0.5 - 290}{\sqrt{121.8}}\right) > 0.999$

i.e. $\dfrac{r - 289.5}{\sqrt{121.8}} = 3.1$, and $r = 323.71$

Hence the least integer value of r is 324.

EX

1 (a) Estimate the probability that a fair coin would come down heads 270 times or more in 500 tosses.
(b) Assuming that a biased coin comes down heads with probability 270/500, estimate the least integer value of r such that the probability of getting r heads or more in 500 tosses is less than 1/1000.
(O & C)

2 The probability of success in each of 5 independent trials is p. Show that the mean number of successes is $5p$. (If you quote a formula for the mean of a binomial distribution, you should prove that it is correct.) A farmer has 5 cows in calf. Assuming these calves are equally likely to be bulls or heifers, find the probability that there will be at least 2 heifers. He estimates bulls to be worth £200 each and heifers to be worth £300 each. Find the expected value of the 5 calves. A second farmer has 50 cows in calf. Use the normal distribution to estimate the probability that they will produce at least 35 heifers.

(O & C)

3 One of two dice is loaded so that there is a probability of 0.2 of throwing a six with it, nothing being known about the other scores. The other die is fair. A person is given one of these dice (which is just as likely to be the fair as the biased one), together with the above information and is asked to discover which die it is. He decides to throw the die 10 times; if there are two or more sixes he will assert that the die is biased, otherwise he will assert that it is fair.

Calculate the probability of his asserting that the die is (i) biased when it is, in fact, fair; (ii) fair when it is, in fact, biased. What is the probability that his choice will be incorrect?

If, instead, he decided to throw the die 240 times and will assert that the die is biased if there are N or more sixes, use the Normal approximation to the Binomial distribution to estimate N if the probability of his asserting that it is fair when it is biased is to be 0.2.

(S)

4 Calculate the normal approximation to the probability of obtaining exactly 30 successes in 90 independent trials in each of which the probability of success is $\frac{1}{3}$. In a sequence of 100 independent identical trials the number of successes is 36. Estimate the probability of success at a given trial and the variance of the proportion of successes in 100 such trials. Is the observed proportion of successes significantly different from $\frac{1}{3}$?

(OLE)

5 A machine manufactures glass bottles of which, on average, 1 in 20 are found to be defective. If a random sample of five bottles is taken from the production line, calculate the probability that
 (i) there is at least one defective bottle,
 (ii) there are at most two defective bottles.
If a random sample of 1000 bottles is taken from the production line, calculate the probability that there are at least 35, but no more than 55, defective bottles.

(A)

S15 Sampling I

Populations, sampling units and sampling frames, Sampling types.

Populations, sampling units and sampling frames

The complete set of objects under study is called the **study population**. The study population is usually a subset of the total finite population about which we require information, the **target population**. Usually a certain **characteristic** of the population is obtained by the process of **statistical inference**.

A **sample** is a subset of a population (usually the study population).

The potential members of a sample are the **sampling units**. The sampling units can have different forms for the same population.

The set of sampling units from which the sample will be drawn is called the **sampling frame**.

i The target population about which information is required might be all 16 year olds in the United Kingdom. The study population might be all 16 year olds whose permanent address is in the area of our enquiry.

i If information about the production of rape seed oil in southern England is required, then a decision on the sampling units will have to be made; they could be either fields or farms, however these may be defined.

i If information about the health of mothers under the age of 25 years is required it might be easiest to ask doctors about young mothers who have recently consulted them. The doctors are the sampling units and the young mothers the sub-units. The set of doctors would be the sampling frame.

Sampling types

In **simple random sampling** each member of the population has an equal chance of being selected. Some form of random process, such as random numbers, is used to obtain the members of the random sample.

Advantage: Likely to be representative of the population as a whole.

Disadvantage: May not take stratification of the population into account.

In **systematic sampling** each member of a population is given a number and a 'system' is used to draw the sample, e.g., draw the first member at random, then take every seventh member after that.

Advantages: Easy to draw members of the sample. Distributes the sample more evenly over the population.

Disadvantages: May give a biased sample (if the population contains periodic variations). No reliable way to estimate standard error of the mean.

In **stratified sampling**, a population is divided into parts (strata) on the basis of known information. A sample is drawn independently from each part (stratum). The ratio of each 'stratum sample size' to the 'total sample size' must be the same as that of its 'stratum size' to the 'population size'.

Advantage: Chances of drawing a biased sample are reduced.

Disadvantage: Requires advance knowledge about the population.

In **stratified random sampling** a random sample of a predetermined size is drawn from each stratum as above.

In **cluster sampling**, the sampling unit is a natural group or cluster (e.g. a school) formed from the smaller units in which we are interested (e.g. the children).

Advantages: Cheap; easy to access data.

Disadvantage: May be unrepresentative of the population.

In **quota sampling**, the researcher chooses the sample size of the total sample and the quota, or proportion, of this sample to be taken for each identified category. Quotas are filled until the total sample size is reached.

Advantage: Data easily and quickly gathered.

Disadvantages: Not random. Cannot be modelled theoretically.

i *A random sample of size $n = 5$ is required from a class of 32 students. Use random number tables to collect the sample.*

Students are first numbered 00 to 31. Putting a pin onto a table of random numbers produced the following:

37 31 04 05 56 07 93 89 30 69 30 ...

Starting with 37 and ignoring numbers outside the range 00 to 31, the students numbered 31, 04, 05, 07, 30 form the random sample.

i *Draw a 10% sample from the 430 students in the sixth form at Cranstone College.*

First select a random number between 0 and 9.

Using the above list of random numbers, this would be 04. Start with the student numbered 04 and pick every 10th one thereafter. The 43 chosen would be numbered

04 14 24 34 ... 424.

i *The Secretary of Sewell Tennis Club wants to obtain the opinions of the members about the club's facilities. He decides to conduct a survey of 40 of the club's 246 members of whom 113 are men.*

Suggest a way in which this might be done.

A good way for the Secretary to conduct the survey is to use stratified random sampling.

He should first calculate the numbers of men and women he should question.

Of the club members, 113 are men so 133 are women. He needs:

$$\text{men:} \quad \frac{113}{246} \times 40 = 18$$

$$\text{women:} \quad \frac{133}{246} \times 40 = 22.$$

He could take a random sample of 18 men and 22 women, using random numbers and their club membership numbers.

Sampling I
Worked example, Exam questions.

 One sixth form class in the school of a small country town has 15 students. The fifteen records below indicate whether a student is male or female (M or F), lives in the town or in the country (T or C) and gives their GCSE points score (a number).

[M,C, 18], [M, T, 33], [M, C, 26], [M, C, 27], [M, C, 23], [M, C, 29], [M, C, 30], [M, T, 28], [M, T, 34], [F, T, 35], [F, T, 30], [F, C, 39], [F, C, 19], [F, T, 25], [F, C, 19]

A team of five students is needed to represent the class in an inter-school competition. Discuss the different ways in which stratified random sampling could be used to select the team.

This is an example of a population which is stratified in several ways:

(1) by sex (9 males and 6 females);

(2) by residence (6 town and 9 country);

(3) by GCSE points score (3 students < 20 points, 6 students 20 ≤ points < 30, 6 students 30 ≤ points < 40).

A stratified random sample of 5 team members, with proportional allocation would give:

For (1): males: $\frac{9}{15} \times 5 = 3$; females: $\frac{6}{15} \times 5 = 2$.

For (2): town students: $\frac{6}{15} \times 5 = 2$;

country students: $\frac{9}{15} \times 5 = 3$.

For (3): students with points score < 20: $\frac{3}{15} \times 5 = 1$,

students with 20 ≤ points < 30: $\frac{6}{15} \times 5 = 2$,

students with 30 ≤ points <40: $\frac{6}{15} \times 5 = 2$.

---

 1 (a) State a situation in which you would consider using (i) a systematic sample, (ii) a stratified sample, when sampling from a population. Give a specific example in each case.
(b) Give one advantage and one disadvantage associated with stratified sampling. *(L)*

2 (a) The two boxplots in the figure summarise the percentage unemployment rates for towns in two regions of Britain: the north-west and the south-west.

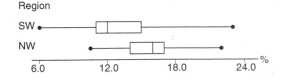

Region

(The data from which the box plots were drawn comes from Exploring Data by Catherine Marsh and has been printed here by kind permission of Polity Press.)

Use these boxplots to write two statements comparing the unemployment rates between the two regions.

(b) Suppose that there are 1000 residents who live in your area. You have been asked to obtain a random sample of 20 of these residents from your area. Give two reasons why you would reject a method which picks the first 20 people in your area in the telephone book.
(OLE)

3 (a) Explain briefly:
(i) why it is often desirable to take samples
(ii) what you understand by a sampling frame.
(b) Give an example of a sampling frame suitable for use in a survey of attitudes of pupils in a school to a proposal to start the school day 15 minutes earlier. *(L)*

4 (a) A village has 450 households. The landlord of the local pub wants to obtain the opinion of the villagers about the new licensing laws which allow greatly extended opening hours. He decides to conduct a 10% survey of the households. Describe briefly but clearly how he might select the households to survey.
Illustrate your description by using the following random digits to select the first three households in his sample.
08395   94760   26132.

(b) An insurance company receives a large number of claims for storm damage.
Following a spell of particularly stormy weather 42 claims were received on a single day. Sufficient staff were available to investigate only six of these. The claims were numbered 00 to 41 and several suggestions were made as to how the sample should be selected. Comment on each of the following methods including an explanation of whether it would yield a random sample or not. In each case six claims are required.
(i) Choose the six largest claims.
(ii) Select two-digit random numbers, ignoring any number greater than 41. When six have been obtained choose the corresponding claims.
(iii) Select two-digit random numbers. Divide each one by 42, take the remainder and choose the corresponding claims. (For example, if 44 is selected, claim number 03 would be chosen.)
(iv) As (iii) but when selecting the original random numbers ignore 84 and over.
(v) Select a single digit at random, ignoring 7 and over. Choose this and every seventh claim thereafter. (For example, if 3 is selected, choose claims numbered 03, 10, 17, 24, 31 and 38.) *(OLE)*

5 Consider the following scenario.

You are asked to carry out a survey to discover the career intentions of 700 students aged 16-19 in a sixth-form college. You have been given three lists, each giving the name, gender, date of birth, and the courses studied for the students on that list.
List I contains all 380 students who are studying at least one A level; List II contains all 170 students not on List I who are studying vocational courses; and List II contains all the remaining 150 students.
You are going to collect data using a questionnaire, and you can afford to survey only 50 students.

(a) With reference to this scenario, write brief notes about
(i) simple random sampling
(ii) stratified random sampling
(iii) quota sampling.
Your notes should include a brief description of how the sampling method might be used in this situation and either an advantage or a disadvantage it might have.

(b) Decide which is the most appropriate sampling method and give reasons for your choice. *(OLE)*

S16 Sampling II

Sample statistics, Sampling distributions, Sums and differences,
Finite population sampled without replacement, Finite population sampled with replacement.

Sample statistics

A **sample statistic** is any quantity which depends only on the data of the sample.

If a large number of random samples, of the same size, are taken from the same population, then the same statistic calculated for all of the samples will form a distribution, called the **sampling distribution** of the statistic.

The standard deviation of a sampling distribution is called the **standard error** of the sample statistic.

> **ℹ** A die was thrown 4 times and the mean score calculated. This was repeated 50 times and gave rise to the sampling distribution below.

$\bar{x}$	1–	1.5–	2–	2.5–	3–	3.5–	4–	4.5–	5–	5.5–
f	0	0	5	5	12	14	5	7	2	0

For this case $\sigma_{\bar{x}}^2 = 0.6256$
So the standard error is $\sigma_{\bar{x}} = 0.79$.

Sampling distributions

Mean: $\bar{x}$ is approximately $N\left(\mu, \dfrac{\sigma^2}{n}\right)$. This is the

Central Limit Theorem. If the parent population is normal this is an exact result. The standard variable $Z = \dfrac{\bar{x} - \mu}{\sqrt{\dfrac{\sigma^2}{n}}}$ is $N(0, 1)$ approximately.

Proportion: P is approximately $N\left(\Pi, \dfrac{\Pi(1-\Pi)}{n}\right)$ for $n \geqslant 30$ and Π is the population proportion.

The standard variable $Z = \dfrac{P - \Pi}{\sqrt{\dfrac{\Pi(1-\Pi)}{n}}}$ is $N(0, 1)$ approximately.

> **ℹ** *A sample of size 16 is drawn from a population with mean 52 and variance 64. Find the probability that the sample mean is greater than 55.*

The sampling distribution of sample means is approximately $N\left(52, \dfrac{64}{16}\right)$, i.e. $N(52, 4)$.

$$P(\bar{x} > 55) = P\left(Z > \dfrac{55 - 52}{2}\right)$$
$$= 1 - \Phi(1.5)$$
$$= 1 - 0.9332$$
$$= 0.0668$$

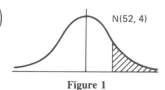

Figure 1

Sums and differences

If X and Y are two independent random variables which are $N(\mu_1, \sigma_1^2)$ and $N(\mu_2, \sigma_2^2)$ respectively, then $X + Y$ is $N(\mu_1 + \mu_2, \sigma_1^2 + \sigma_2^2)$ and $X - Y$ is $N(\mu_1 - \mu_2, \sigma_1^2 + \sigma_2^2)$.

This result readily extends to the X_i ($i = 1, \dots, n$) random variables which are $N(\mu_i, \sigma_i^2)$ respectively, then ΣX_i is $N(\Sigma \mu_i, \Sigma \sigma_i^2)$.

Difference of means; $\bar{x} - \bar{y}$ is approximately $N\left(\mu_1 - \mu_2, \dfrac{\sigma_1^2}{n_1} + \dfrac{\sigma_2^2}{n_2}\right)$ for $n \geqslant 30$.

The standard variable $Z = \dfrac{(x - y) - (\mu_1 - \mu_2)}{\sqrt{\dfrac{\sigma_1^2}{n_1} + \dfrac{\sigma_2^2}{n_2}}}$

is $N(0, 1)$ approximately.

> **ℹ** *A girl travels to college by walking part of the way and travelling the rest by train. Over a period of time she estimates that the walking time and train time are approximately $N(12, 3)$ and $N(20, 6)$ minutes respectively. Find the probability that if she leaves home 40 minutes before a lecture starts that she will be late.*

Assume the two components are independent. The distribution of the total journey time is $N(12 + 20, 3 + 6) = N(32, 9)$

$$P(T > 40) = P\left(Z > \dfrac{40 - 32}{3}\right)$$
$$= 1 - \Phi(2.33)$$
$$= 0.0099$$

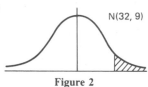

Figure 2

Finite population sampled without replacement

If a sample of size n is taken from a finite population of size N and the sampling is **without replacement**, then for the sample mean $\bar{x}$,

$$E[\bar{x}] = \mu \quad \text{and} \quad \text{Var}[\bar{x}] = \dfrac{\sigma^2}{n} \cdot \dfrac{(N - n)}{N}$$

where μ and σ^2 are the population mean and variance.

> **ℹ** *A random sample of size 20 is taken from a population of size 80 without replacement. Find the expectation and variance of the sample if the population mean is 2.85 and the standard deviation is 0.07.*

For the sample mean $\bar{x}$,

$$E[\bar{x}] = \mu = 2.85$$
$$\text{Var}[\bar{x}] = \dfrac{\sigma^2}{n} \cdot \dfrac{(N - n)}{N} = \dfrac{(0.07)^2}{20} \cdot \dfrac{(80 - 20)}{80} = 0.00018$$

Finite population sampled with replacement

If a sample of size n is taken from a finite population of size N and the sampling is **with replacement**, then for the sample mean $\bar{x}$,

$$E[\bar{x}] = \mu \quad \text{and} \quad \text{Var}[\bar{x}] = \dfrac{\sigma^2}{n} \cdot \dfrac{(N - 1)}{N}$$

where μ and σ^2 are the population mean and variance.

> **ℹ** *A random sample of size 20 is taken from a population of size 80 with replacement. Find the expectation and variance of the sample if the population mean is 2.85 and the standard deviation is 0.07.*

For the sample mean $\bar{x}$,

$$E[\bar{x}] = \mu = 2.85$$
$$\text{Var}[\bar{x}] = \dfrac{\sigma^2}{n} \cdot \dfrac{(N - 1)}{N} = \dfrac{(0.07)^2}{20} \cdot \dfrac{(80 - 1)}{80} = 0.00024$$

Sampling II
Worked example, Guided example and Exam questions.

The inside diameters of bearings supplied by a factory have a mean of 21.04 mm *and a standard deviation of* 0.03 mm. *The diameters of axles supplied by a second factory have a mean value of* 20.92 mm *and a standard deviation of* 0.05 mm. *What is the mean and standard deviation of the random variable defined to be the diameter of a bearing less the diameter of an axle? Assuming that both dimensions are normally distributed, what percentage of axles and bearings taken at random will not fit?*

Let D_B be the random variable 'diameter of a bearing', $\mu_B = 21.4$ and $\sigma_B = 0.03$

Let D_A be the random variable 'diameter of an axle', $\mu_A = 20.92$ and $\sigma_A = 0.05$

Then the random variable $D_B - D_A$ is 'the diameter of a bearing less the diameter of an axle' and

$E[D_B - D_A] = E[D_B] - E[D_A] = \mu_B - \mu_A = 21.04 - 20.92$
$\qquad = 0.12$ mm

$\text{Var}[D_B - D_A] = \text{Var}[D_B] + \text{Var}[D_A] = \sigma_B^2 + \sigma_A^2$
$\qquad = 0.03^2 + 0.05^2 = 0.0034$ mm^2

Assuming D_B is $N(21.04, 0.03^2)$ and D_A is $N(20.92, 0.05^2)$ then $(D_B - D_A)$ is $N(0.12, 0.0034)$ with standard variable

$Z = \dfrac{(D_B - D_A) - 0.12}{0.0583}.$

If axle and bearing do not fit $D_B - D_A < 0$, i.e. the axle is bigger than the bearing.

$P(D_B - D_A < 0) = P\left(Z < \dfrac{-0.12}{0.0583}\right)$

$\qquad = P(Z < -2.058)$
$\qquad = 1 - \Phi(2.058)$
$\qquad = 1 - 0.9802$
$\qquad = 0.0198$

∴ 1.98% of bearings and axles will not fit.

The random number 482 *is obtained from a table of random digits. Use it to obtain a random observation from each of the following distributions, quoting as many significant figures as are justified in each answer.*
(a) Poisson with mean 1.6.
(b) Normal with mean 4 *and variance* 4.

(a) We assign the random digits 000 to 999 to the distribution Po(1.6) in proportion to the probabilities corresponding to the values of X, the random variable which is Po(1.6).
The working is set out in tabular form below, with the first two rows only shown.

Probability	Cumulative probability (to 3 d.p.)	Allocation of random numbers
$P(X=0) = e^{-1.6}$ $\quad = 0.2019$	0.202	001–202
$P(X=1) = e^{-1.6} \times \dfrac{1.6}{1!}$ $\quad = 0.3323$	0.525	203–525

The random number 482 is in the range 203–525 corresponding to the value 1 of the random variable X which is Po(1.6).

(b) The distribution to be considered is $N(4, 4)$.
Take 4 ± 6 (approximately $\mu \pm 3\sigma$) i.e. −2 to 10 as an effective range. Divide this range into 8 classes. Find the upper class bounds, the standardised upper class bounds and the cumulative probability corresponding to each of the

standardised upper class bounds (as in the method of Unit S13, Uses of the normal distribution). The random numbers are then allocated as above. It will be easy to see the interval in which the random observation lies, simple proportion in this interval gives an estimate of the random observation.

---

 1 The number 1437 is obtained from a table of random digits. Use it to select an observation at random from each of the following distributions. Your method should be clearly indicated by your written working, and your solution should contain as many significant figures as the given random number permits.
(a) Rectangular distribution with range 13 to 15.
(b) Binomial distribution with parameters 4, $\frac{3}{4}$.
(c) Poisson distribution with mean 2.5.
(d) Normal distribution with mean 11, variance 4.

(*OLE*)

2 A discrete random variable X has probability distribution given by $P(X=0) = 0.1$, $P(X=0 \text{ or } 1) = 0.3$; $P(X=0 \text{ or } 1 \text{ or } 2) = 0.7$, $P(X=0 \text{ or } 1 \text{ or } 2 \text{ or } 3) = 1.0$. Obtain the expectation and variance of X. Describe how you would use a table of single-figure random numbers to generate a random sample of size n from the above distribution.
Use your procedure, for the case $n = 10$, with the random numbers given below, to obtain unbiased estimates of the expectation and variance of X.
Random numbers: 0, 9, 3, 3, 3, 7, 4, 7, 5, 6.

(C)

3 In a packaging factory, the empty containers for a certain product have a mean weight of 400 g with a standard deviation of 10 g. The mean weight of the contents of a full container is 800 g with a standard deviation of 15 g. Find the expected total weight of 10 full containers and the standard deviation of this weight, assuming that the weights of containers and contents are independent.
Assuming further that these weights are normally distributed random variables, find the proportion of batches of 10 full containers which weigh more than 12.1 kg. If 1% of the containers are found to be holding weights of product which are less than the guaranteed minimum amount, deduce this minimum weight.

(O & C)

4 A population of size N has mean μ and variance σ^2. Random samples of size n are taken without replacement. Write down the expectation and the variance of the means of these samples.
In the game of bridge hands of size 13 are dealt to each of four players in such a way that each hand can be considered to be a random sample without replacement from a standard pack of 52 cards.
Each player has to decide upon a 'bid' for his hand, and to help him to do this one particular player decides to allot points to his cards. An ace receives 4 points, a king 3 points, a queen 2 points and a jack 1 point; all others receiving 0 points. He thus arrives at a total score for this hand. Calculate the expectation and variance of the mean score and deduce the expectation and variance of the total. Assuming that the distribution of this total is normal, calculate the probability of a total score greater than 18.

(A)

S17 Estimation
Point estimation, Interval estimation.

Point estimation

Point estimation involves using a statistic from a random sample to find an estimator for the corresponding population parameter.

Note: 'Estimator' is used for a statistic; 'estimate' is used for the numerical value of that statistic.

An **unbiased estimator** is a sample statistic whose expectation is equal to the population parameter.

The **best** or **most efficient estimator** is the unbiased estimator which has the smallest variance.

ℹ Some important results are:

	sample statistic	best estimator for population
mean	$\bar{x}$	$\bar{x}$ for μ
variance	s^2	$\dfrac{ns^2}{n-1}$ for σ^2
proportion	r	r for Π

Interval estimation

Interval estimation involves using the data from a random sample to find an interval within which an unknown population parameter is expected to lie with a given degree of confidence (probability).

The interval is called a **confidence interval** and the two extreme values are called the **confidence limits**.

If $\bar{x}$ is the mean of a random sample of size n from $N(\mu, \sigma^2)$, where σ^2 is known, then a symmetric $B\%$ confidence interval for μ

is given by $\bar{x} \pm z.\dfrac{\sigma}{\sqrt{n}}$

i.e. $\bar{x} - z.\dfrac{\sigma}{\sqrt{n}} < \mu < x + z.\dfrac{\sigma}{\sqrt{n}}$

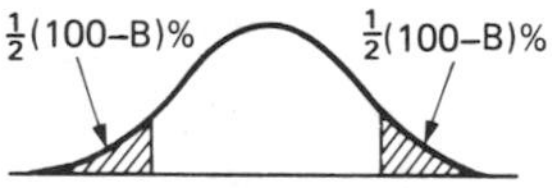

$\frac{1}{2}(100-B)\%$ $\frac{1}{2}(100-B)\%$

Figure 1

where z is the $\frac{1}{2}(100-B)\%$ point of $N(0, 1)$.

If a large sample ($n \geqslant 30$) from any distribution has a sampling distribution which is approximately normal $N(\mu, \sigma^2/n)$, where μ is the mean and σ^2 the variance of the parent population, both unknown, then a symmetric $B\%$ confidence interval for μ is

$$\bar{x} - z.\frac{s}{\sqrt{n}} < \mu < \bar{x} + z.\frac{s}{\sqrt{n}}$$

where $\bar{x}$, s^2 are the mean and variance of the sample and z is the $\frac{1}{2}(100-B)\%$ point of $N(0, 1)$.

If r is the proportion of a random sample of size n from a population that has a particular property, then an approximate $B\%$ confidence interval for the population proportion Π having the property is

$$r - z\sqrt{\frac{r(1-r)}{n}} < \Pi < r + z\sqrt{\frac{r(1-r)}{n}}$$

where z is the $\frac{1}{2}(100-B)\%$ point of $N(0, 1)$.

ℹ *The weights of each of ten specimens of a certain type of beetle were found to be (in grams):* 14.3, 13.8, 13.6, 14.6, 15.4, 14.8, 13.1, 14.2, 16.8, 15.1

Given that the weights are approximately normally distributed with variance 1.44, construct a 95% confidence interval for μ, the mean of the population weights.

$$\bar{x} = \frac{\Sigma x}{n} = \frac{145.7}{10} = 14.57$$

$\sigma^2 = 1.44$, so $\sigma = 1.2$

For a 95% confidence interval, z is the $\frac{1}{2}(100-95)\%$ $= 2.5\%$ point of $N(0, 1)$.
$\Phi(z) = 1 - 0.025 = 0.975 \Rightarrow z = 1.96$
∴ a 95% confidence interval for μ is given by:

$$14.57 - 1.96 \times \frac{1.2}{\sqrt{10}} < \mu < 14.57 + 1.96 \times \frac{1.2}{\sqrt{10}}$$

i.e. $13.83 < \mu < 15.31$

ℹ *Before a by-election, for which there are two candidates A and B, a survey was made of 350 voters, chosen at random, and it was found that 198 of them intend to vote for A. Give 95% confidence limits for the percentage of voters favourable to A at the time of the survey.*

Using proportions the property to be considered is 'is an A voter'.

Assuming that the total population votes for either A or B, the sample proportion is given by

$$r = \frac{198}{350} = 0.566$$

For a 95% confidence level, z is the $\frac{1}{2}(100-95)\%$ $= 2.5\%$ point of $N(0, 1)$.
$\Phi(z) = 1 - 0.025 = 0.975 \Rightarrow z = 1.96$
∴ a 95% confidence interval for Π is given by

$$0.566 \pm 1.96 \sqrt{\frac{0.566(1-0.566)}{350}}$$

i.e. $0.514 < \Pi < 0.618$
∴ between 51.4% and 61.8% of voters would vote for A.

Estimation
Worked examples and Exam questions.

 A bag contains 10 *balls of which* 3 *are blue and* 7 *are yellow. A random sample of* 3 *balls is taken, without replacement, and* $\hat{p}$ *denotes the proportion of blue balls in the sample.*

Tabulate the probability distribution of $\hat{p}$, *and hence verify that* $\hat{p}$ *is an unbiased estimate of the population proportion.*

Let the random variable X be 'the number of blue balls in a sample of 3'.

$P(X=0) = P(\bar{B}\bar{B}\bar{B}) = \frac{7}{10} \times \frac{6}{9} \times \frac{5}{8} = \frac{35}{120}$

$P(X=1) = P(B\bar{B}\bar{B}) + P(\bar{B}B\bar{B}) + P(\bar{B}\bar{B}B) = 3 \times \frac{3}{10} \times \frac{7}{9} \times \frac{6}{8} = \frac{63}{120}$

$P(X=2) = P(BB\bar{B}) + P(B\bar{B}B) + P(\bar{B}BB) = 3 \times \frac{3}{10} \times \frac{2}{9} \times \frac{7}{8} = \frac{21}{120}$

$P(X=3) = P(BBB) = \frac{3}{10} \times \frac{2}{9} \times \frac{1}{8} = \frac{1}{120}$

$\therefore$ the probability distribution of $\hat{p}$ is

x	0	$\frac{1}{3}$	$\frac{2}{3}$	1
$P(\hat{p}=x)$	$\frac{35}{120}$	$\frac{63}{120}$	$\frac{21}{120}$	$\frac{1}{120}$

$E[\hat{p}] = \Sigma x P(\hat{p}=x)$

$= 0 \times \frac{35}{120} + \frac{1}{3} \times \frac{63}{120} + \frac{2}{3} \times \frac{21}{120} + 1 \times \frac{1}{120} = \frac{36}{120}$

$= 0.3$, the population proportion.

$\therefore$ $\hat{p}$ is an unbiased estimator for the population proportion.

 A certain city has about 1 million *adult inhabitants of whom an unknown proportion p have never spent a holiday in a foreign country. A random sample of* 1000 *of the adult inhabitants is taken, and* 735 *people in the sample are found never to have spent a holiday in a foreign country. Find a* 95% *confidence interval for p.*

The attribute of interest is 'has never spent a holiday in a foreign country'.

The sample proportion is $\frac{735}{1000} = 0.735$.

The 95% confidence interval for p is

$$p_s - 1.96 \sqrt{\frac{p_s(1-p_s)}{n}} < p < p_s + 1.96 \sqrt{\frac{p_s(1-p_s)}{n}}$$

where $p_s = 0.735$
$n = 1000$

Substituting and evaluating leads to
$0.708 < p < 0.762$ as the 95% confidence interval for the population proportion p.

---

 1 Explain briefly what the standard error of the mean is used for. Among the first 150 customers at a new snack bar 90 order coffee. Assuming that this is a random sample from the population of future customers, estimate 95% confidence limits for the proportion of future customers who will order coffee. If the proportion of future customers who order coffee is exactly 60%, find the probability that 2, 3 or 4 of the next 5 customers will order coffee.

(O & C)

2 X is a random variable. Define var (X), the variance of X, in terms of $E(X)$ and $E(X^2)$. Deduce that var$(aX+b) = a^2$ var(X), where a and b are constants. The weights in grams of the contents of 200 packets of soap powder are summarised in the table below.

Weight (Centre of Interval)	899	900	901	902
Frequency	40	90	58	12

Find the mean and the standard deviation of these measurements. Assuming they are a random sample from a normal distribution, find 99% confidence limits for the population mean, correct to the nearest 0.02 g.

(O & C)

3 A point whose coordinates are (X, Y) with respect to rectangular axes is chosen at random where $0 < X < 1$ and $0 < Y < 1$. What is the probability that the point lies inside the circle whose equation is $x^2 + y^2 = 1$? In a computer simulation 1000 such points were generated and 784 of them lay inside the circle. Obtain an estimate for π and give an approximate 90% confidence interval for your estimate. Show that about 290 000 points need to be selected in order to be 90% certain of obtaining a value for π which will be in error by less than 0.005. *(S)*

4 In the production of an item of furniture, part A fits into part B. For part A, the relevant outer dimension is x, and for B the corresponding inner dimension is y. Both x and y are normally distributed, having means μ_x, μ_y and standard deviations σ_x, σ_y respectively. State the mean and variance of $y - x$.
It is given that $\mu_x = 2.05$ cm, $\mu_y = 2.10$ cm, $\sigma_x = 0.03$ cm, $\sigma_y = 0.04$ cm. In assembly, a part A is selected at random and an attempt is made to fit it into a part B, also selected at random. Find the percentage of pairs so selected which must be rejected because part A is too large to fit into part B.
In order to reduce this percentage, the setting of the machine which produces part A is adjusted so that the mean μ_x is altered, the variance remaining unchanged. A sample of 50 of part A has a mean value for x of 2.01 cm. Write down a symmetrical two-sided 99% confidence interval for the new value of μ_x, giving the limits to two decimal places. Calculate the corresponding range of values of the percentage of pairs for which part A is too large to fit into part B. *(J)*

5 There are n_0 fish in a lake. A random sample of m of these fish is taken. The fish in this sample are tagged and released unharmed back into the lake. After a suitable interval, a second random sample of size n is taken. The random variable R is the number of fish in this second sample that are found to have been tagged. Assuming that the probability that a fish is captured is independent of whether it has been tagged or not, and that n_0 is sufficiently large for a binomial approximation to be used, obtain the expectation of R in terms of m, n and n_0. Suppose that $m = 100$, $n = 4000$ and that the observed value of R is 20. Obtain an approximate symmetric 98% confidence interval for the proportion of fish in the lake which are tagged. Deduce an approximate 98% confidence interval for n_0. *(C)*

6 Distinguish between the expressions $\frac{\Sigma(x-\bar{x})^2}{n}$ and $\frac{\Sigma(x-\bar{x})^2}{n-1}$, both of which are used in connection with variance for a set of observations. A random sample of 100 observations is taken from a distribution. The sum of the observations is 1000 and the sum of their squares is 19 900.
(a) Explain how you would estimate the mean and the variance of the distribution from which the random sample was taken, and give the values of these estimates.
(b) Estimate the mean and the variance of the distribution of the mean of random samples of size 100 from the original distribution.
(c) Construct a 95% confidence interval for the mean of the distribution, and use it to test whether this mean could be 9. *(OLE)*

S18　Hypothesis Testing

Statistical hypotheses, Critical regions, Types of error.

Statistical hypotheses

A **statistical hypothesis** is an assumption about the value of a statistic of a distribution.

A **null hypothesis**, H_0, is a statistical hypothesis which can be tested in some way.

An **alternative hypothesis**, H_1, is the one which is accepted if the null hypothesis is rejected.

A **test of a null hypothesis**, or **significance test**, is a rule, based on the results of a random sample, whereby acceptance or rejection of H_0 is decided.

ℹ The sample distribution of the mean is $N(\mu, \sigma^2/n)$ with standardised variable $z = \dfrac{\bar{x} - \mu}{\sigma/\sqrt{n}}$

Typically H_0 will be an assumption about μ, the population mean, for instance $H_0: \mu = \mu_0$. The value $\bar{x}$, obtained from a sample, is tested on this assumption.

Possible alternative hypotheses in this case are:
$H_1: \mu \neq \mu_0$; $H_1: \mu > \mu_0$; $H_1: \mu < \mu_0$.

Critical regions

The **critical region** corresponding to every test must be found.

If the sample value falls in the critical region, then H_0 is rejected, otherwise it is accepted.

A test statistic is said to be **significant** if it falls in the critical region, otherwise it is **non-significant.**

The critical region depends upon:

(a) the significance levels of the test,

(b) the nature of H_1, the alternative hypothesis.

The **significance level** of the test gives the probability assigned to rejecting H_0.

There are two types of alternative hypothesis, **one-tailed** and **two-tailed,** which give rise to two types of test. A one-tailed test considers only an increase or only a decrease in the parameter and there is only one critical region whose area is equal to the level of significance. A two-tailed test considers any change in the parameter and there are two equal critical regions whose area sum is equal to the level of significance.

Consider the following tests based on H_0; $\mu = \mu_0$.

(i) $H_0: \mu = \mu_0$
　$H_1: \mu \neq \mu_0$
Significance level $\alpha\%$
A two-tailed test since any change in μ is considered.

(ii) $H_0: \mu = \mu_0$
　$H_1: \mu > \mu_0$
Significance level $\alpha\%$
A one-tailed test since only an increase in μ is considered.

(iii) $H_0: \mu = \mu_0$
　$H_1: \mu < \mu_0$
Significance level $\alpha\%$
A one-tailed test since only a decrease in μ is considered.

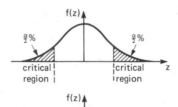
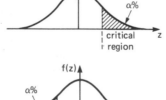

Figure 1

ℹ *Nails produced by a machine have a mean length of 1.50 in. A random sample of 100 nails has a mean length of 1.51 in with a standard deviation of 0.05 in. Do these results indicate that the mean length of nails produced has changed at the 5% significance level?*

The sampling distribution of the mean $\bar{x}$ is $N(1.50, \sigma^2/n)$.

Since σ^2 is unknown, estimate $\hat{\sigma}^2 = \dfrac{ns^2}{(n-1)}$

where s is the sample standard deviation.

So $\dfrac{\hat{\sigma}^2}{n} = \dfrac{(0.05)^2}{99}$ ∴ $\dfrac{\hat{\sigma}}{\sqrt{n}} = \dfrac{0.05}{\sqrt{99}} = 0.005$

Take $\bar{x} \sim N(1.50, 0.005^2)$

with standardised variable $Z = \dfrac{\bar{x} - 1.50}{0.005}$.

The null hypothesis is $H_0: \mu = 1.50$.
The alternative hypothesis is $H_1: \mu \neq 1.50$.
Significance level is 5%.
This is a two-tailed test since any change in μ is to be considered.

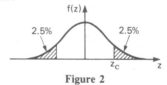

Figure 2

The sample mean $\bar{x} = 1.51$ in.

$z_{\text{test}} = \dfrac{1.51 - 1.50}{0.005} = 4.12 \, (2 \text{ d.p.})$

$\Phi(z_c) = 1 - 0.025 = 0.975$

$z_c = 1.96$

∴ $-1.96 < z_{\text{test}} < 1.96$
$z_{\text{test}} = 4.12 > 1.96$, which is significant so H_0 is rejected.

Types of error

A **Type I error** is made when the null hypothesis H_0 is rejected when it should have been accepted. The probability of making this type of error is the level of significance of the test. We write: $P(\text{Type I error}) = \alpha$.

A **Type II error** is made when the null hypothesis H_0 is accepted when it should have been rejected. The probability of making this type of error is not usually easy to calculate. We write: $P(\text{Type II error}) = \beta$.

The **power function** of a test of some statistic is the value of $(1 - \beta)$ and indicates the **power** of the test to reject a wrong hypothesis.

Hypothesis Testing
Testing the parameter p from a binomial distribution, Testing the mean of a Poisson distribution.
Worked example and Exam questions.

Testing the parameter p from a binomial distribution

Let $X_1, X_2, \ldots X_n$ be a sample of size n, which takes values 1 for a success and 0 for a failure. If Y counts the number of successes in n trials, Y is Bin(n, p).

Suppose the observed value is y and we find from cumulative binomial tables, using n and p, the probability $P(Y \geq y)$.

In testing $H_0 : p_y = p$ against $H_1 : p_y \neq p$ at a particular significance level α,

- if $P(Y \geq y) \leq \dfrac{\alpha}{2}$, we reject H_0 in favour of H_1, and

- if $P(Y \geq y) > \dfrac{\alpha}{2}$, we accept H_0.

> **i** *An unbiased coin is thrown* 16 *times and lands on heads* 13 *times. Assuming the number of heads is binomial, test the hypothesis that at the 5% significance level the coin is biased.*

Test is $H_0 : p = 0.5$ against $H_1 : p \neq 0.5$.

Let Y count the number of heads in 16 trials, so Y is Bin(16, 0.5) under H_0.

From cumulative binomial tables
$$P(Y \geq 13) = 1 - P(Y \leq 12) = 1 - 0.9894 = 0.0106$$

Since $P(Y \geq 13) = 0.0106 < 0.025$, this suggests that the true proportion is not 0.5, and that we should reject H_0 in favour of H_1.

Thus we conclude that the coin is biased.

Testing the mean of a Poisson distribution

Let x be an observation from a random variable X which has a Poisson distribution with mean λ.

Suppose the value observed is x, and we find from cumulative Poisson tables using the mean λ, the probability $P(X \geq x)$.

In testing $H_0 : \lambda_x = \lambda$ against $H_0 : \lambda_x \neq \lambda$ at a particular significance level, α,

- if $P(X \geq x) \leq \dfrac{\alpha}{2}$, we reject H_0 in favour of H_1, and

- if $P(X \geq x) > \dfrac{\alpha}{2}$, we accept H_0.

> **i** *A firm manufactures batches of compact discs which consist of* 5000 *CDs. The number of faults per batch follows a Poisson distribution. The firm claims the mean of faults per batch is* 1.6. *A batch is selected at random and is found to contain* 4 *faults. Is this evidence that the firm's claim is wrongly stated? Test at the 5% significance level.*

We test $H_0 : \lambda = 1.6$ against $H_1 : \lambda > 1.6$.

Let X be Po(1.6). X counts the number of faults in a batch.
From cumulative Poisson tables,
$$P(X \geq 4) = 1 - P(x \leq 3) = 1 - 0.9212 = 0.0788$$

Since $0.0788 > 0.05$, we accept H_0 and conclude that the data suggests the true mean is 1.6 as claimed by the firm.

WE *The top forms of two junior schools both took the same examination on transfer to secondary school. In school X there were* 32 *pupils and the mean mark obtained was* 51. *In school Y there were* 37 *pupils and the mean mark was* 46. *The standard deviation for marks in this examination, calculated from a large number of primary school candidates, was* $\sigma = 11.5$.
Test the hypothesis that the pupils from school X were better than those from school Y, using a 5% significance level.

Let μ_X and μ_Y be the population mean marks for the examination candidates from the two schools.

We have $H_0 : \mu_X = \mu_Y$, $H_1 : \mu_X > \mu_Y$ (the test is one-tailed)

The test statistic is $Z = \dfrac{(\bar{x}_X - \bar{x}_Y) - (\mu_X - \mu_Y)}{\sqrt{\dfrac{\sigma_X^2}{n_X} + \dfrac{\sigma_Y^2}{n_Y}}}$

where $\bar{x}_X = 51$ and $n_X = 32$
$\qquad \bar{x}_Y = 46$ and $n_Y = 37$
$\qquad \sigma_X^2 = \sigma_Y^2 = 11.5$
and $\mu_X - \mu_Y = 0$ if H_0 is true.

$z_{\text{test}} = \dfrac{51 - 46}{11.5\sqrt{\dfrac{1}{32} + \dfrac{1}{37}}} = 1.801$ and $z_{5\%} = 1.65$

Since $z_{\text{test}} = 1.801 > 1.65$ the result is significant at the 5% level and we reject H_0 in favour of H_1.

Thus is can be considered that the pupils from school X performed significantly better than those from school Y.

EX

1 The mass of jam in a jar is x grams, the mass of the jar is y grams and the mass of the lid is z grams. x, y and z are independent and normally distributed with means 502, 90 and 10 and standard deviations 0.60, 0.24 and 0.07 respectively. Deduce the mean and standard deviation of the total mass of the jar full of jam, complete with lid. These full jars are packed in boxes of 25. Find the mean and

standard deviation of the mass of the total contents of a box.
The average mass of jam per jar in a box is found to be 502.2 grams. Test, at the 5% level, whether or not this is
  (i) significantly different from the expected value,
  (ii) significantly greater than the expected value. $\qquad$ (J)

2 When you are testing a hypothesis, explain the conditions under which you would use (a) a one-tailed test and (b) a two-tailed test. Give an example of a typical problem for each of (a) and (b), referring to your projects if you wish. The breaking strengths of a particular brand of thread are known to have a normal distribution with mean μ and standard deviation 1.4 units. A random sample of 36 newly produced pieces of thread are found to have a mean breaking strength of 9.3 units. Test, at the 5% level of significance, the null hypothesis that $\mu = 9.7$ units against the alternative hypothesis that $\mu < 9.7$ units. We are given that x is a typical breaking strength for the above random sample and that $\Sigma(x^2) = 3240$. Assuming that neither the mean nor the standard deviation of the population of breaking strengths had in fact been known, find estimates of the population mean and variance. $\qquad$ (L)

3 Assuming that the mean and variance of a random variable X having a Binomial distribution with parameters n and p are np and $np(1-p)$ respectively, prove that the mean and variance of a proportion based on a sample of size n are p and $p(1-p)/n$ respectively, where p is the true proportion. Of a random sample of 50 shoppers in a certain city store 13 stated that they lived more than 10 miles from the city centre. Of a random sample of shoppers from another store in the same city 9 lived more than 10 miles from the city centre. Stating your null and alternative hypotheses and using a significance level of 5%
  (i) test that the true proportion in both stores could be 0.15;
  (ii) show that the two samples do not offer evidence of a difference in proportions between the two stores.
$\qquad$ (S)

The Student *t*-distribution
Definition, Hypothesis testing.

Definition

A continuous random variable X having a probability density function (pdf) of the form

$$f(x) = T_v\left(1 + \frac{x^2}{v}\right)^{-\frac{v+1}{2}} \quad \text{for } -\infty < x < \infty,$$

where T_v is a constant depending on v, is said to have a *t*-distribution.

The parameter, v, is integral valued and called the **degrees of freedom**.

For a particular value of v, the appropriate *t*-distribution is denoted by $T(v)$.

The frequency curves for $f(x)$ resemble 'squashed' versions of the normal distribution curve. They are bell-shaped and centred about 0. The *t*-distribution is more spread out and this spread decreases as n increases. As $v \to \infty$, the *t*-distribution curve gets closer and closer to the standard Normal distribution curve, shown by the broken line.

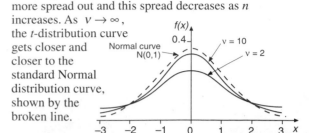

Hypothesis testing

In Unit S18 the Z statistic was used to test for differences between means of samples (or between a mean of a sample and a population). The *z*-test is only valid for large samples ($n > 30$). The *t*-test is used for small samples (say $5 \le n \le 30$).

Single sample

Let $X_1, X_2, ..., X_n$ be a small random sample with mean $\bar{x}$ and variance s^2. To test whether this sample has been drawn from a Normal population with known mean μ and unknown variance σ^2, use the statistic

$$T = \frac{\bar{x} - \mu}{\frac{s}{\sqrt{n-1}}}$$ which is distributed as $T(n-1)$ under the

null hypothesis that the true population mean is μ.

Two unmatched samples

Let $X_1, X_2, ..., X_m$ be a random sample with mean $\bar{x}$ and variance s_x^2 drawn from a Normal population with mean μ_x and variance σ_x^2 (both unknown).

Let $Y_1, Y_2, ..., Y_n$ be a random sample with mean $\bar{y}$ and variance s_y^2 (both unknown) drawn from another Normal population with mean μ_y and variance σ_y^2.

To use a *t*-test to test the null hypothesis that the two unknown population means are identical, we test $H_0 : \mu_x = \mu_y$. We assume that the Xs and Ys are independent of each other and that the two unknown population variances are identical, i.e.

$$\sigma_x^2 = \sigma_y^2 = \hat{\sigma}^2, \text{ where } \hat{\sigma}^2 = \frac{ms_x^2 + ns_y^2}{(m-1)+(n-1)} \text{ is the}$$

estimate of the common population variance.

Use the statistic $T = \frac{\bar{X} - \bar{Y}}{\hat{\sigma}\sqrt{\frac{1}{m} + \frac{1}{n}}}$ which is distributed as

$T[(m-1)+(n-1)]$ under the null hypothesis $\mu_x = \mu_y$. (See the Worked example.)

Paired differences

Let $(X_1, Y_1), (X_2, Y_2), ..., (X_n, Y_n)$ be n independently selected pairs of values and $D_1 = X_1 - Y_1$, $D_2 = X_2 - Y_2$, ..., $D_n = X_n - Y_n$ be the n paired sample differences.

To test whether the two random samples ($X_1, X_2, ..., X_n$ and $Y_1, Y_2, ..., Y_n$) are drawn from the same theoretical Normal population with unknown variance use the

statistic $T = \frac{\bar{D}}{\frac{s}{\sqrt{n-1}}}$ which is distributed as $T(n-1)$

under the null hypothesis that both samples are drawn from Normal populations having the same mean and variance.

Here, $\bar{D}$ and s are the mean and standard deviation respectively of the paired sample differences.

[i] *Seedlings have a mean height of 30 mm when watered in the normal way for a month. A sample of ten seedlings was watered more frequently and after one month their mean height was found to be 38 mm with standard deviation 13.5 mm. Is there evidence at the 1% level of a significant increase in height?*

Here, $\mu = 30$, $\bar{x} = 38$, $s = 13.5$.

Use a one-tailed test since we are looking for a significant increase in order to reject a true population mean height of 30 mm.

We test $H_0 : \mu \le 30$ against $H_1 : \mu > 30$.

Using $T = \frac{\bar{x} - \mu}{\frac{s}{\sqrt{n-1}}}$ gives $t_{\text{test}} = \frac{38 - 30}{\frac{13.5}{\sqrt{9}}} = 1.778$.

To find the critical value of t, look in *t*-tables at $P = 2\%$ (since we have a one-tailed test at 1% level) and $v = 10 - 1 = 9$. This gives $t_{\text{crit}} = 2.821$.

Since $t_{\text{test}} < t_{\text{crit}}$ i.e. $1.778 < 2.821$, we must accept H_0 and conclude there is no evidence at the 1% level of significance to assume that there has been an increase in the mean height of the seedlings.

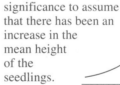
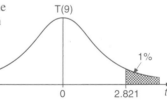

[i] *A group of 8 diabetics were given a special diet and it was desired to test the weight gained in kg at the end of a 2-week period. The weights are shown below.*

Person	A	B	C	D	E	F	G	H
Before	82.27	78.18	86.36	85.00	95.45	75.45	83.18	83.64
After	82.87	79.54	87.36	86.10	94.99	75.48	83.54	82.15
Diff.	0.60	1.36	1.00	1.10	–0.46	0.03	0.36	–1.49

Is there evidence at the 5% level that the diet has resulted in a significant weight gain?

From the given data, using
D = Weight after – Weight before,

$\bar{d} = 0.313$ and $s = 0.8804$.

Use a one-tailed test since we are looking for a significant weight gain in order to reject a null hypothesis.

The test involves the hypotheses $H_0 : \mu_D \le 0$ against $H_1 : \mu_D > 0$ using the test statistic for T (see opposite) where $v = 8 - 1 = 7$.

Here $t_{\text{test}} = \frac{0.313}{\frac{0.8804}{\sqrt{7}}} = 0.828$.

At the 5% level (one-tailed test), $t_{\text{crit}} = 1.895$, hence t_{test} is not significant and we accept H_0.

The Student t-distribution
Confidence intervals.
Worked example and Exercise.

Confidence intervals

If a population is at least approximately normally distributed with mean μ and variance σ^2 (both unknown), then a confidence interval can be obtained for μ, based on a small random sample of size n, using the t-distribution.

A symmetric $B\%$ confidence interval for μ is

$$\bar{x} - t.\frac{s}{\sqrt{n-1}} < \mu < \bar{x} + t.\frac{s}{\sqrt{n-1}}$$ where $\bar{x}$ and s^2 are the sample mean and variance and t is the $\frac{1}{2}(100 - B)\%$ point of $T(n - 1)$.

A symmetric $B\%$ confidence interval may also be calculated for the two-sample case and for paired differences.

Two sample case: the confidence interval for $\mu_x - \mu_y$ (where μ_x and μ_y are the assumed population means) is:

$$(\bar{x} - \bar{y}) - t.\hat{\sigma}\sqrt{\frac{1}{m} + \frac{1}{n}} < \mu_x - \mu_y < (\bar{x} - \bar{y}) + t.\hat{\sigma}\sqrt{\frac{1}{m} + \frac{1}{n}}$$

Paired differences: the confidence interval for μ_D (the assumed mean of the population of differences) is

$$\bar{d} - t.\frac{s}{\sqrt{n-1}} < \mu_D < \bar{d} + t.\frac{s}{\sqrt{n-1}}.$$

---

i *The weights of each of ten specimens of a certain type of beetle were found to be (in grams):*

14.3 13.8 13.6 14.6 15.4 14.8 13.1 14.2 16.8 15.1

Given that the weights are approximately normally distributed with unknown mean and variance, construct a 95% confidence interval for μ, the mean of the population weights.

From tables, we need to find the value of t such that the interval $(-t, t)$ encloses the central 95% of a $T(10 - 1)$ (i.e. $T(9)$) distribution.

From tables, $t = 2.262$.

From the given sample data we compute:

$\bar{x} = 14.57$, $s = 0.995$

$\therefore$ a 95% confidence interval for μ is

$$14.57 - 2.262.\frac{0.995}{\sqrt{9}} < \mu < 14.57 + 2.262.\frac{0.995}{\sqrt{9}}$$

i.e. $13.82 < \mu < 15.32$.

WE *Nine observations of surface-soil pH were made at each of two different locations, A and B, at a local farm. It is suspected that the true mean soil pH values differ at the two locations. Here are the data:*

A: 8.43 8.52 8.11 8.32 7.98 7.81 8.02 7.92 7.85

B: 7.83 7.69 7.74 7.21 7.19 7.44 7.54 7.89 7.81

Test an appropriate hypothesis, making clear any assumptions you make.

The different locations suggest that the pH values at A and B are independent. We also assume that the data are taken from two populations which have independent normal distributions with unknown means μ_A and μ_B and a common unknown variance $\hat{\sigma}^2$.

From the given data $n_A = 9$, $n_B = 9$ and

$\bar{x}_A = 8.107$, $s_A{}^2 = 0.05924...$, $\bar{x}_B = 7.953$, $s_B{}^2 = 0.06197...$,

Use a t-test to test for a difference between the two population means, μ_A and μ_B (both unknown).

Test, $H_0 : \mu_A = \mu_B$ against $H_1 : \mu_A \neq \mu_B$.

The test statistic for this hypothesis, based on our assumptions, is $T = \dfrac{\bar{x}_A - \bar{x}_B}{\hat{\sigma}\sqrt{\frac{1}{n_A} + \frac{1}{n_B}}}$ which is distributed as

$T[(9 - 1) + (9 - 1)]$, i.e. $T(16)$, under H_0.

Here,

$$\hat{\sigma} = \sqrt{\frac{n_A s_A{}^2 + n_B s_B{}^2}{(n_A - 1) + (n_B - 1)}} = \sqrt{\frac{9 \times 0.05924... + 9 \times 0.06197...}{(9 - 1) + (9 - 1)}}$$

$$= 0.261\,127...$$

Hence $t_{\text{test}} = \dfrac{8.107 - 7.593}{0.261127...\sqrt{\frac{1}{9} + \frac{1}{9}}} = 4.176$ (3 d.p.).

At the 5% level (two-tailed test), $t_{\text{crit}} = 2.120$.

Since $t_{\text{test}} > t_{\text{crit}}$ the result is significant at the 5% level, so we reject H_0 in favour of H_1. The data suggest (strongly) that the true mean surface pH at location A is different from the true mean pH level at location B.

EX

1 The average life span of a certain brand of electric light bulb is claimed to be 18 500 hours. A sample of fifteen electric light bulbs of this brand were tested and gave the following results (in units of 1000 hours).

18 17 19 20 15 18 16 21 19 17 15 17 17 21 19

What is the appropriate hypothesis and is the result of the experiment significant?

2 The heights of a random sample of 1250 Welshmen had a mean of 1.6898 m with a standard deviation of 0.0602 m. A random sample of 5872 Englishmen gave an average height of 1.7129 m with a standard deviation of 0.0646 m. Is this difference significant?

3 The densities of two samples A and B of an acid were measured. Four determinations of sample A were made and six determinations of the other sample. Do the results lead to the rejection of the hypothesis that the acids have the same density?

Sample A	42	46	43	43		
Sample B	48	43	46	47	47	45

4 In an agricultural experiment a certain variety of root crop was subjected to different growing conditions by using two different types of fertiliser. The yields of sixteen samples from each of the crops grown using the different fertilisers were measured to the nearest 0.1 kg. Do the results of the experiment lead to a rejection of the hypothesis that the fertilisers produce crops with the same mean weight?

Sample from fertiliser A

2.1	2.3	1.9	2.2	2.1	2.3	2.0	2.2
1.7	2.6	2.0	1.9	1.8	2.0	2.0	2.4

Sample from fertiliser B

2.5	2.1	2.2	2.0	2.4	1.8	2.2	2.0
1.9	2.3	2.1	1.7	2.5	2.4	2.6	1.8

Observations and errors

A **linear relationship** between two variables x and y can be represented mathematically as $y = \alpha + \beta x$. In many practical situations x, the independent variable, can be measured with little or no error, while y, the dependent variable, is subject to **random experimental error**. These random experimental errors may be due to limitations in any experimental apparatus used and/or random fluctuations in experimental conditions.

If an experiment is performed for n values of x, x_i for $i = 1, 2, \ldots, n$, then there will be n corresponding equations for y, given by $y_i = \alpha + \beta x_i + \varepsilon_i$.

The ε_i are error terms which take into account random experimental errors, and are usually considered to be independent (the error of one experiment has no effect on the error of another experiment) and to be distributed normally with zero mean and known variance.

Method of least squares

If the n pairs (x_i, y_i) for an experiment are plotted on a graph, then the points are scattered about a straight line.

The **method of least squares** 'fits' the 'best' line AB to the points by making $\Sigma(P_iQ_1)^2$ a minimum (i.e. minimising the sum of the squared deviations of each point from the 'best' line). This is called the **line of regression of y on x**.

If $\Sigma(P_iR_i)^2$ is minimised, then the corresponding line of best fit is called the **line of regression of x on y**.

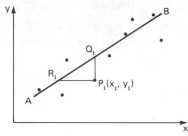

Figure 1

Equations of the lines of regression

The line of regression of y on x (used for predicting y-values given x-values) is

$$y - \bar{y} = \frac{C_{xy}}{C_{xx}}(x - \bar{x})$$

where

$$\bar{y} = \frac{\Sigma y_i}{n}, \; \bar{x} = \frac{\Sigma x_i}{n}, \quad C_{xy} = \Sigma xy - n\bar{x}\bar{y}, \quad C_{xx} = \Sigma x^2 - n\bar{x}^2.$$

Note: Since $C_{xx} = ns_x^2$, i.e. $s_x^2 = \dfrac{C_{xx}}{n}$ is the variance of x,

$\dfrac{C_{xy}}{n} = s_{xy}$ is called the **covariance of x and y**.

The **line of regression of x on y** (used for predicting x-values given y-values) is

$$x - \bar{x} = \frac{C_{xy}}{C_{yy}}(y - \bar{y}) \qquad \text{where } C_{yy} = \Sigma y^2 - n\bar{y}^2.$$

Since $(\bar{x}, \bar{y})$ satisfies both equations for the lines of regression, it follows that both lines pass through the point $(\bar{x}, \bar{y})$.

$b = \dfrac{C_{xy}}{C_{xx}}$ and $a = \bar{y} - b\bar{x}$ are often referred to as the **least squares estimates** for β and α in the equation $y_i = \alpha + \beta x_i + \varepsilon_i$.

Suppose there is a large number N of independent sets of n experimental pairs (x_i, y_i) and from each set determine estimates a and b for α and β. The set of values of a so formed will have a sampling distribution, as will the set of values of b.

It can be shown that with the four assumptions made above about the errors ε_i, then

$$\frac{b - \beta}{\sigma/\sqrt{C_{xx}}} \sim N(0, 1), \; \frac{a - \alpha}{\sigma\sqrt{\dfrac{1}{n} + \dfrac{\bar{x}}{C_{xx}}}} \sim N(0, 1)$$

$\boxed{\mathbf{i}}$ *For the following set of bivariate data*

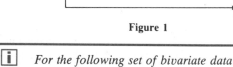

x	4	15	22	27
y	3.2	6.7	11.3	12.5

(a) *calculate the two least squares regression lines,*
(b) *calculate an estimate for x when $y = 7$.*

(a) $\Sigma x = 68 \quad \bar{x} = \dfrac{68}{4} = 17$

$\Sigma y = 33.7 \quad \bar{y} = \dfrac{33.7}{4} = 8.425$

$\Sigma x^2 = 1454 \quad \Sigma y^2 = 339.07 \quad \Sigma xy = 699.4$
$C_{xx} = \Sigma x^2 - n\bar{x}^2 = 1454 - 4 \times 17^2 = 298$
$C_{yy} = \Sigma y^2 - n\bar{y}^2 = 339.07 - 4 \times 8.425^2 = 55.148$
$C_{xy} = \Sigma xy - n\bar{x}\bar{y} = 699.4 - 4 \times 17 \times 8.425$
$\qquad = 126.5$

The line of regression of y on x is given by

$$(y - 8.425) = \frac{126.5}{298}(x - 17)$$

i.e. $y = 0.42x - 1.21$

The line of regression of x on y is given by

$$(x - 17) = \frac{126.5}{55.148}(y - 8.425)$$

i.e. $x = 2.29y - 2.33$

(b) Use the line of regression of x on y.
When $y = 7$, $x = 2.29(7) - 2.33 = 13.70$.

Residuals

Calculating and plotting the residuals is a check for the adequacy of the model used. The ith **fitted value** is called y_i, which is calculated from the linear equation in x. The ith **observed value** is called Y_i, which matches the respective x_i.

The ith **residual** r_i is the difference between the observed value and the fitted value.

$$r_i = Y_i - y_i \text{ for } i = 1, 2, \ldots n$$

If the plot of residuals against x shows a random scatter, this is a good indication that the model is adequate.

Linear Regression
Guided example and Exam questions..

 In a heathland region there are a large number of silver birch trees where the ground is dry but very few where the ground is marshy. The number x of silver birch trees and the ground moisture content y are found in each of 10 equal areas (which have been chosen to cover the range of x in all such areas). The following is a summary of the results of the survey:

$\Sigma x = 495$, $\Sigma y = 425$, $\Sigma x^2 = 31475$, $\Sigma xy = 17300$, $\Sigma y^2 = 20125$.

Find the equation of the regression line of y on x. Estimate the ground moisture content in an area equal to one of the chosen areas which contains 60 silver birch trees.

The equation of the line of regression of y on x is

$$y - \bar{y} = \frac{C_{xy}}{C_{xx}}(x - \bar{x})$$

where $C_{xy} = \Sigma xy - n\bar{x}\bar{y}$ and $C_{xx} = \Sigma x^2 - n\bar{x}^2$

Using the given information C_{xy} and C_{xx} can be calculated and hence the required regression line found.
Substituting $x = 60$ in the regression line gives the corresponding value of y, the ground moisture content.

 1 The principle of least squares is used to find the regression line of y on x. Illustrate the distances the sum of whose squares is minimised on a rough sketch showing the x- and y-axes with a few points and their regression line. From 20 pairs of values of x and y the following were calculated:
$\Sigma x = 50$, $\Sigma x^2 = 140$, $\Sigma xy = 27$, $\Sigma y = 24$.
(a) Find the mean values of x and y.
(b) Find the line of regression of y on x in the form $y = a + bx$.
(c) Draw a graph showing this regression line for the range $0 \leq x \leq 5$. *(O & C)

2 Eight candidates sat examinations in Mathematics and Physics. Their corresponding marks were:

Mathematics (x)	63	72	41	56	44	89	70	45
Physics (y)	48	71	50	46	35	92	42	48

(i) Plot these points on a scatter diagram.
(ii) Calculate the equation of the regression line of y on x by the method of least squares.
(iii) Calculate the coordinates of the points at which this regression line intersects the lines $x = 10$ and $x = 90$.
(iv) Hence plot the regression line on your diagram.
*(A)

3 The maximum value, in parts per million (PPM), of atmospheric carbon dioxide in Hawaii for each given year is shown in the table below.

Year (x)	PPM of carbon dioxide (y)
1958	318
1961	320
1964	322
1967	325
1970	329
1973	333
1976	335

Plot a scatter diagram, and obtain the equation of the regression line of y on x by the method of least squares. Show this line on your diagram. Use your equation to estimate the mean annual increase in atmospheric carbon dioxide and the year in which the proportion of carbon dioxide may be expected to reach 350 PPM, if present trends continue. * (A)

4 The values of the dependent variable y corresponding to values of the independent variable x are shown in the following table:

x	0	1	2	3	4
y	2	3	5	4	6

Find the equation of the line of regression of y on x and hence estimate the value of y when $x = 3.5$. Explain in what sense the line of regression is a line of best fit to the data. (O & C)

5 (X_i, Y_i), $i = 1, 2, \ldots, n$ is a sample from a bivariate population. The least-square regression lines of Y on X and X on Y are calculated. Why would you not expect the two lines to coincide? Under what circumstances would they coincide? In the table, Y_i is the mass (in grammes) of potassium bromide which will dissolve in 100 grammes of water at a temperature of $X_i°C$.

X	10	20	30	40	50
Y	61	64	70	73	78

Find the equation of the regression line of Y on X. Find, also, the product-moment correlation coefficient between X and Y. (S)

6 In an investigation into prediction using the stars and planets, a celebrated astrologist Horace Cope predicted the ages at which thirteen young people would first marry. The complete data, of predicted and actual ages at first marriage, are now available and are summarised in the following table:

Person	Predicted age x (years)	Actual age y (years)
A	24	23
B	30	31
C	28	28
D	36	35
E	20	20
F	22	25
G	31	45
H	28	30
I	21	22
J	29	27
K	40	40
L	25	27
M	27	26

(i) Draw a scatter diagram of these data.
(ii) Calculate the equation of the regression line of y on x and draw this line on the scatter diagram.
(iii) Comment upon the results obtained, particularly in view of the data for person G. What further action would you suggest? (A)

7 To each value of x, there corresponds a value y of a random variable Y. Forty observations (x, y) are summarised thus:
$\Sigma x = 96$, $\Sigma y = 26$, $\Sigma x^2 = 270$, $\Sigma xy = 58$, $\Sigma y^2 = 18$.
(a) Find the line of regression of Y on x in the form $y = a - bx$.
(b) Draw a graph for $0 \leq x \leq 6$ showing the regression line; show also on your graph the point $(\bar{x}, \bar{y})$. Indicate roughly on your graph a region in which you would expect almost all the observations (x, y) to lie.
(c) For what value of x would the mean value of the corresponding Y be zero? (O & C)

S21 Correlation

Bivariate distributions, Correlation coefficients, Fisher's transformation, t-test.

Bivariate distributions

A population with two variables gives rise to **bivariate distributions.**

In such distributions it is often necessary to know any interdependence or correlation.

If the variables are plotted in the xy-coordinate plane, the result is a **scatter diagram.**

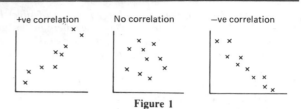

Figure 1

Correlation coefficients

The **product moment correlation coefficient** is given by

$$r = \frac{C_{xy}}{\sqrt{C_{xx}C_{yy}}}$$

where $C_{xy} = \Sigma xy - n\bar{x}\bar{y}$,
$C_{xx} = \Sigma x^2 - n\bar{x}^2$,
$C_{yy} = \Sigma y^2 - n\bar{y}^2$.

r takes the sign of C_{xy}.
It can be shown that $-1 \leq r \leq 1$.
$r = 1$ for perfect positive correlation.
$r = 0$ for no correlation.
$r = -1$ for perfect negative correlation.

Spearman's rank correlation coefficient is given by

$$r_s = 1 - \frac{6\Sigma d^2}{n(n^2-1)}$$

where d is the rank difference for each pair of values. For tied ranks it is conventional to give both places the average rank of the equal values.

ℹ *For the data given below, calculate:*
(a) The product moment correlation coefficient,
(b) Spearman's rank correlation coefficient.

x	1	2	3	4	5
y	2	1	3	3	6

(a) From the above data:

$\Sigma x = 15$, $\Sigma y = 15$, $\Sigma x^2 = 55$, $\Sigma y^2 = 59$, $\Sigma xy = 55$.

From their definitions:

$\bar{x} = 3$, $\bar{y} = 3$, $C_{xx} = 10$, $C_{yy} = 14$, $C_{xy} = 10$.

So $r = \dfrac{10}{\sqrt{10 \times 14}} = 0.845$ (+ve because C_{xy} is +ve)

(b) s and t are the ranks of x and y and $d = (s - t)$

s	5	4	3	2	1
t	4	5	2.5	2.5	1
d^2	1	1	0.25	0.25	0

$r = 1 - \dfrac{6(2.5)}{5(24)}$
$= 0.875$

Fisher's transformation

Fisher's transformation, z, of r is given by

$$z = \text{Fi}(r) = \frac{1}{2}\ln\frac{(1+r)}{(1-r)} = \tanh^{-1} r$$

and z is approximately $N(\tanh^{-1}\rho, 1/(n-3))$.
To test hypotheses about the population correlation coefficient, ρ:

(a) Transform r and ρ to obtain z_r and z_ρ.

(b) Calculate $z_{\text{test}} = \dfrac{z_r - z_\rho}{\sqrt{1/(n-3)}}$.

(c) Test z_{test} against $N(0, 1)$.

If r_1 and r_2 are the correlation coefficients of two independent random samples, then $z_1 = \text{Fi}(r_1)$ and $z_2 = \text{Fi}(r_2)$ are approximately $N(\tanh^{-1}\rho_1, 1/(n_1 - 3))$ and $N(\tanh^{-1}\rho_2, 1/(n_2 - 3))$

and $z_1 - z_2$ is $N\left(\tanh^{-1}(\rho_1 - \rho_2), \dfrac{1}{(n_1-3)} + \dfrac{1}{(n_2-3)}\right)$

approximately.
To test the hypothesis that two samples come from the same population:

(a) Transform r_1 and r_2 to obtain z_1 and z_2

(b) Calculate $z_{\text{test}} = \dfrac{z_1 - z_2}{\sqrt{\dfrac{1}{(n_1-3)} + \dfrac{1}{(n_2-3)}}}$.

(c) Test z_{test} against $N(0, 1)$.

ℹ *A random sample of size 45 is taken from a bivariate normal distribution and has a value of $r = 0.78$.*
Test H_0: $\rho = 0.65$ against H_1: $\rho > 0.65$.

$z_r = \text{Fi}(r) = \text{Fi}(0.78) = 1.045$
$z_\rho = \text{Fi}(\rho) = \text{Fi}(0.65) = 0.7675$

$$z_{\text{test}} = \frac{1.045 - 0.7675}{\sqrt{\dfrac{1}{42}}} = 1.798$$

From tables, $\Phi(1.64) = 0.95$.
$\therefore z_{\text{test}} = 1.798 > 1.64$
Reject H_0.

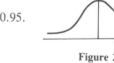

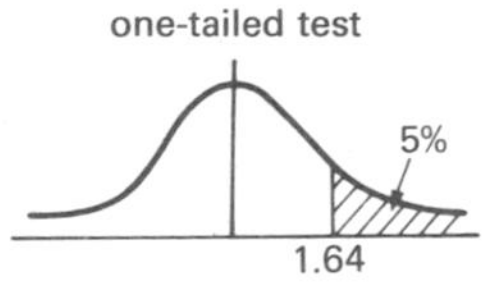

one-tailed test

Figure 2

ℹ *The correlation coefficients from two independent samples of sizes $n_1 = 50$ and $n_2 = 45$ are $r_1 = 0.65$ and $r_2 = 0.45$. Test H_0: $\rho_1 = \rho_2$ against H_1: $\rho_1 \neq \rho_2$.*

$z_1 = \text{Fi}(r_1) = 0.7675$ and $z_2 = \text{Fi}(r_2) = 0.485$.

$$z_{\text{test}} = \frac{0.7675 - 0.485}{\sqrt{\dfrac{1}{47} + \dfrac{1}{42}}} = 1.33$$

From tables, $\Phi(1.96) = 0.975$
$\therefore z_{\text{test}} = 1.33 < 1.96$.
Accept H_0.

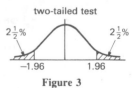

two-tailed test

Figure 3

---

t-test

The **t-test** is used to test the hypothesis that the true population correlation coefficient is zero ($\rho = 0$).

(a) Calculate $t = \sqrt{\dfrac{r^2(n-2)}{(1-r^2)}}$, n is the sample size.

(b) Test against $t_{\alpha\%}(n-2)$ where $\alpha\%$ is the level of significance, and is the α percentage point of the t-distribution.

ℹ *For the data of the first* **ℹ** *above test the null hypothesis H_0: $\rho = 0$ at the 1% level.*

$$t = \sqrt{\frac{0.845^2(5-2)}{(1-0.845^2)}} = 7.49, \quad t_{1\%}(3) = 5.84$$

Since $7.49 > 5.84$ reject H_0: $\rho = 0$ at the 1% level.

Correlation
Worked example and Exam questions.

x	1.1	1.9	3.0	4.2	5.1	5.8	7.0	8.3	9.3	10.0	10.9	12.1
y	5	7	6	6	8	9	11	12	14	20	43	60

(i) Calculate the product moment correlation coefficient for these data.

(ii) Assuming that the above data comprise a random sample from a population with a bivariate normal distribution, test the hypothesis $H_0: \rho = 0.95$, where ρ is the true population correlation coefficient. Use a 5% level of significance.

(iii) Calculate Spearman's rank correlation coefficient.

(i) $r^2 = \dfrac{C_{xy}}{C_{xx}C_{yy}}$ where $C_{xy} = \Sigma xy - n\bar{x}\bar{y}$

$\qquad\qquad\qquad\qquad C_{xx} = \Sigma x^2 - n\bar{x}^2$

$\qquad\qquad\qquad\qquad C_{yy} = \Sigma y^2 - n\bar{y}^2$

$\bar{x} = \dfrac{\Sigma x}{12} = 6.56$, $\bar{y} = \dfrac{\Sigma y}{12} = 16.75$

$\Sigma xy = 1856.5$, $\Sigma x^2 = 660.71$, $\Sigma y^2 = 6601$

$C_{xy} = 1856.5 - 12 \times 6.56 \times 16.75 = 537.94$

$C_{xx} = 660.71 - 12 \times 6.56^2 = 144.31$

$C_{yy} = 6601 - 12 \times 16.75^2 = 3234.25$

$r^2 = \dfrac{537.94^2}{144.31 \times 3234.25} = 0.62,$

$r = 0.79$ (positive $\therefore C_{xy}$ is positive)

(ii) Let $z = \mathrm{Fi}(r)$; $H_0: \rho = 0.95$, $H_1: \rho \neq 0.95$ (two-tailed test)

$z_r = \mathrm{Fi}(0.79) = 1.072$, from tables

$z_p = \mathrm{Fi}(0.95) = 1.83$, from tables

z_r is $\mathrm{N}\left(\tanh^{-1}\rho, \dfrac{1}{n-3}\right)$ with standardised variable

$$\dfrac{z_r - z_p}{\sqrt{\dfrac{1}{n-3}}}$$

$$z_{\text{test}} = \dfrac{1.072 - 1.83}{\sqrt{\dfrac{1}{9}}} = -2.297$$

The critical value for a two-tailed test with a 5% significance level is ± 1.96. Since $z_{\text{test}} = -2.297 < -1.96$ the result is significant so we reject H_0 that the sample comes from a population with correlation coefficient $\rho = 0.95$.

(iii)

x	1.1	1.9	3.0	4.2	5.1	5.8	7.0	8.3	9.3	10.0	10.9	12.1
r	12	11	10	9	8	7	6	5	4	3	2	1
y	5	7	6	6	8	9	11	12	14	20	43	60
s	12	11	$9\frac{1}{2}$	$9\frac{1}{2}$	8	7	6	5	4	3	2	1
d	0	0	$-\frac{1}{2}$	$\frac{1}{2}$	0	0	0	0	0	0	0	0

Note: $d = r - s$

$R = 1 - \dfrac{6\Sigma d^2}{n(n^2-1)} = 1 - \dfrac{6 \times \frac{1}{2}}{12 \times 143} = 0.999$

1 The moisture contents in per cent and the crushing loads in tonnes of 10 test specimens are given in the following table:

Moisture	Crushing load
0.6	1.5
7.2	4.1
3.1	4.3
5.4	4.6
9.6	2.1
1.2	1.8
2.5	2.9
8.4	2.3
7.7	3.0
5.9	3.8

Convert these data to ranks and find Spearman's rank correlation coefficient. Plot a scatter diagram of the original data. Comment on your results. Is there a relationship between the crushing load and the moisture content?

*(O & C)

2 In the two papers of an A-level Higher Mathematics examination, ten candidates gained the marks shown in the table below.

Candidate	A	B	C	D	E	F	G	H	I	J
Paper I	95	83	74	92	84	89	36	71	49	71
Paper II	78	92	72	84	81	93	63	63	66	73

Calculate: (a) the product-moment correlation coefficient; (b) Spearman's coefficient of correlation by ranks.

*(A)

3 (a) The marks of eight candidates in English and Mathematics are:

Candidate	1	2	3	4	5	6	7	8
English (x)	50	58	35	86	76	43	40	60
Mathematics (y)	65	72	54	82	32	74	40	53

Rank the results and hence find a rank correlation coefficient between the two sets of marks.

(b) Using the data in part (a), obtain the product-moment correlation coefficient. To assist in the lengthy calculation, you may use the information $S_x = 16.67$.

(S)

4 The heights h, in cm, and weights W, in kg, of 10 people are measured. It is found that $\Sigma h = 1710$, $\Sigma W = 760$, $\Sigma h^2 = 293\,162$, $\Sigma hW = 130\,628$ and $\Sigma W^2 = 59\,390$. Calculate the correlation coefficient between the values of h and W. What is the equation of the regression line of W on h?

(O & C)

5 The items in a sample each have associated with them the variables X and Y. Explaining any symbols that you use, write down a formula for the sample product-moment correlation coefficient between X and Y and the equation of the regression line of Y on X.

State the conclusions that you would draw if you obtained values for the correlation coefficient of (i) 0, (ii) -1.

For a sample of 100 such items, the following data are known.

$\Sigma x = 36$, $\Sigma y = 25$, $\Sigma xy = 21$,
$\Sigma x^2 = 1012.96$, $\Sigma y^2 = 366.25$.

(x, y are actual values taken by the variables respectively.)

Representing the mean values of X and Y for the data by $\bar{x}$ and $\bar{y}$ respectively, calculate $\Sigma(x-\bar{x})(y-\bar{y})$, $\Sigma(x-\bar{x})^2$, $\Sigma(y-\bar{y})^2$ and the sample product-moment correlation coefficient between X and Y.

Given that the equation of the regression line of Y on X for the data is $y = a + bx$, calculate a and b.

(J)

χ^2 distribution

In many statistical situations **observed frequencies,** O, are compared with **expected frequencies,** E.

In such cases it is possible to calculate the statistic $\chi^2 = \sum \dfrac{(O-E)^2}{E}$.

The χ^2 **distribution** is a function of ν, the number of **degrees of freedom.** ν is an **integral valued parameter.** For a particular value of ν, the appropriate χ^2 distribution is denoted by $\chi^2(\nu)$.

Tables

The χ^2 distribution is tabulated as percentage points.

A **percentage point** of a χ^2 distribution is that value of χ^2 which has a specified percentage of the distribution lying to its right.

The $p\%$ point of $\chi^2(\nu)$ is written $\chi^2_{p\%}(\nu)$ and is that value of $\chi^2(\nu)$ which has $p\%$ of the distribution lying to its right (see diagram).

The tables for the χ^2 distribution are usually given for those selected values of ν and p which are found to be adequate for most practical purposes.

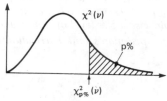

Figure 1

ℹ️ *From suitable tables verify* (a) $\chi^2_{5\%}(4)=9.49$, (b) $\chi^2_{1\%}(4)=11.34$ (c) $\chi^2_{10\%}(1)=2.71$.

To calculate $\chi^2_{5\%}(\nu)$ for $\nu>100$, use the result
$$\chi^2_{5\%}(\nu)=\tfrac{1}{2}(1.645+\sqrt{2\nu-1})^2$$

ℹ️
$$\begin{aligned}\chi^2_{5\%}(110)&=\tfrac{1}{2}(1.645+\sqrt{220-1})^2\\ &=135.20 \text{ (2 d.p.)}\end{aligned}$$

Goodness of fit

The χ^2 distribution is used to test the **goodness of fit** of a given table of observed frequencies to a theoretical model. It is often used to test whether or not a given distribution is binomial, Poisson or normal.

To apply the test it is usual to have a total frequency of at least 50 and a minimum class frequency of 5.

If class frequencies fall below this minimum level, then two or more adjacent classes should be combined.

For a given distribution, which is thought to be binomial, Poisson or normal, proceed as follows.

(a) Calculate the expected frequencies, E, under H_0, the null hypothesis that the distribution is binomial, Poisson or normal.

(b) Combine any adjacent classes so that no expected frequency is less than 5. If this has to be done combine the corresponding classes of the observed frequencies.

(c) Calculate $\dfrac{(O-E)^2}{E}$ for each class.

(d) Calculate the statistic $\chi^2_{\text{test}}=\sum \dfrac{(O-E)^2}{E}$, where the sum is over all classes.

(e) Determine ν. In general $\nu =$ number of classes (n) − number of restrictions.
For a binomial distribution:
(i) if p is known (by hypothesis), then $\nu=n-1$,
(ii) if p has to be estimated (using $\bar{x}=np$) from the observed frequencies, then $\nu=n-2$.
For a Poisson distribution:
(i) if λ is known, then $\nu=n-1$,
(ii) if λ has to be estimated (using $\bar{x}=\lambda$) from the observed frequencies, then $\nu=n-2$.
For a normal distribution:
(i) if μ and σ are known, then $\nu=n-1$,
(ii) if μ and σ have to be estimated from the observed frequencies, then $\nu=n-3$.

(f) Find $\chi^2_{\alpha\%}(\nu)$ from tables, where $\alpha\%$ is the significance level assigned to the test.

(g) Compare χ^2_{test} with $\chi^2_{\alpha\%}(\nu)$.
If $\chi^2_{\text{test}}>\chi^2_{\alpha\%}(\nu)$, then reject H_0, otherwise accept it.

ℹ️ *Four identical coins were tossed* 160 *times and the observed frequencies of the number of heads per toss is shown in the table.*

Number of heads	0	1	2	3	4
Observed frequency (O)	10	46	54	37	13

Test at the 5% level if the coins are biased.

Let H_0: $P(H)=\tfrac{1}{2}$ i.e. the cons are unbiased.
The random variable X 'the number of heads per toss' is Bin$(4,\tfrac{1}{2})$. This probability distribution is calculated (see Binomial Distribution p. 194) and given below.

x	0	1	2	3	4
$P(X=x)$	0.0625	0.25	0.375	0.25	0.0625

Multiplying each of these probabilities by 160 gives the following table of expected frequencies.

Number of heads	0	1	2	3	4
Expected frequency (E)	10	40	60	40	10

The calculation of χ^2 is set out below.

x	0	1	2	3	4
O	10	46	54	37	13
E	10	40	60	40	10
$(O-E)$	0	6	−6	−3	3
$\dfrac{(O-E)^2}{E}$	0	0.9	0.6	0.225	0.9

$$\chi^2_{\text{test}}=\sum \dfrac{(O-E)^2}{E}=2.625$$

$\nu=4$ since there are 5 classes with one restriction, the total frequency.
So test $\chi^2_{\text{test}}=2.625$ against $\chi^2_{5\%}(4)=9.49$.

Since $\chi^2_{\text{test}}=2.625<9.49$ this is not significant so do not reject H_0, i.e. accept it.
There is no evidence that the coins are biased.

For a period of three months 100 similar gerbils were given a new type of food. The table below shows the recorded changes in mass.

Change in mass (g) x	Observed frequency f
$-\infty < x \leqslant -15$	2
$-15 < x \leqslant -10$	3
$-10 < x \leqslant -5$	8
$-5 < x \leqslant 0$	14
$0 < x \leqslant 5$	16
$5 < x \leqslant 10$	24
$10 < x \leqslant 15$	15
$15 < x \leqslant 20$	9
$20 < x \leqslant 25$	6
$25 < x < \infty$	3

It is thought that these data follow a normal distribution, with mean 5 and standard deviation 10. Use the χ^2 distribution at the 5% level of significance to test this hypothesis.

Describe how the test would be modified if the mean and standard deviation were unknown.

Let the random variable X be 'change in mass over three months', $H_0 : X$ is $N(5, 10^2)$ and $H_1 : X$ is not $N(5, 10^2)$. Assuming H_0 the expected frequencies for the given class intervals can be calculated. This calculation is set out in tabular form below.

If X is $N(5, 10^2)$ then the standardised variable is

$$Z = \frac{X-5}{10}$$

Class	Observed frequency	Upper class bound.	Standard upper class bound.	$\Phi(z)$	Class prob.	Expected class frequency
$-\infty < x \leqslant -15$	2	-15	-2.0	0.0228	0.0228	2.3
$-15 < x \leqslant -10$	3	-10	-1.5	0.0668	0.0440	4.4
$-10 < x \leqslant -5$	8	-5	-1.0	0.1587	0.0919	9.2
$-5 < x \leqslant 0$	14	0	-0.5	0.3085	0.1498	15.0
$0 < x \leqslant 5$	16	5	0.0	0.5000	0.1915	19.2
$5 < x \leqslant 10$	24	10	0.5	0.6915	0.1915	19.2
$10 < x \leqslant 15$	15	15	1.0	0.8413	0.1498	15.0
$15 < x \leqslant 20$	9	20	1.5	0.9332	0.0919	9.2
$20 < x \leqslant 25$	6	25	2.0	0.9773	0.0441	4.4
$25 < x < \infty$	3	∞	∞	1.0000	0.0227	2.3

Combining adjacent cells where necessary so that no cell has a frequency less than 5 gives rise to the following table of observed and expected frequencies.

O	5	8	14	16	24	15	9	9
E	6.7	9.2	15.0	19.2	19.2	15.0	9.2	6.7
$O-E$	-1.7	-1.2	-1.0	-3.2	4.8	0	-0.2	2.3
$\dfrac{(O-E)^2}{E}$	0.431	0.157	0.067	0.533	1.200	0	0.004	0.790

$$\chi^2_{\text{test}} = \sum \frac{(O-E)^2}{E} = 3.182$$

We test this against $\chi^2_{5\%}(7) = 14.07$

Note: there are 7 degrees of freedom, 8 cells less 1 restriction. $\chi^2_{\text{test}} = 3.182 < 14.07$, $\therefore$ we do not reject H_0 that the data follow a normal distribution with mean 5 and standard deviation 10.

If the mean and standard deviation were unknown they would be estimated from the given data and used to recalculate the expected frequencies; the test would be as above except that there would be two degrees of freedom less.

1 (a) A gambler threw 15 ones and 45 larger numbers in 60 throws of a 6-sided die. Use χ^2 and a 5% significance level to test his assertion that this die is biased.
(b) Whatever the result of your test, assume that the die is biased and find approximate 95% confidence limits for the probability of obtaining a one in a single throw.

(O & C)

2 Over a period of 50 weeks the numbers of road accidents reported to a police station are shown in the table below.

No. of accidents	0	1	2	3
No. of weeks	23	13	10	4

Find the mean number of accidents per week. Use this mean, a 5% level of significance, and your table of χ^2 to test the hypothesis that these data are a random sample from a population with a Poisson distribution.

(O & C)

3 A manufactured article can be made by three different methods A, B, C. The numbers of defective articles found in random samples taken from trials of each method are shown in the table:

Method	A	B	C	Total
Defective	14	11	5	30
Total	30	40	30	100

Use χ^2 and a 5% significance level to determine whether there is evidence that the percentage of defectives is not the same for all three methods.

(O & C)

4 For a period of six months 100 similar hamsters were given a new type of feedstuff. The gains in mass are recorded in the table below:

Gain in mass (g) x	Observed frequency f	Gain in mass (g) x	Observed frequency f
$-\infty < x \leqslant -10$	3	$10 < x \leqslant 15$	16
$-10 < x \leqslant -5$	6	$15 < x \leqslant 20$	14
$-5 < x \leqslant 0$	9	$20 < x \leqslant 25$	8
$0 < x \leqslant 5$	15	$25 < x \leqslant 30$	3
$5 < x \leqslant 10$	24	$30 < x \leqslant \infty$	2

It is thought that these data follow a normal distribution, with mean 10 and variance 100. Use the χ^2 distribution at the 5% level of significance to test this hypothesis. Describe briefly how you would modify this test if the mean and variance were unknown.

(A)

5 Analysis of the goals scored per match by a certain football team gave the following results:

No. of goals per match:	0	1	2	3	4	5	6	7
No. of matches:	14	18	29	18	10	7	3	1

Calculate the mean of the above distribution and the frequencies (each correct to 1 decimal place) associated with a Poisson distribution having the same mean. Perform a χ^2 goodness of fit test to determine whether or not the above distribution can be reasonably modelled by this Poisson distribution.

(S)

Definitions

A **contingency table** is an array which displays data relating to two factors.

A table with m rows and n columns is called an $m \times n$ contingency table.

factor B

		b_1	b_2	.	.	.	b_n
factor	a_1	f_{11}	f_{12}	.	.	.	f_{1n}
A	a_2	f_{21}	f_{22}	.	.	.	f_{2n}
	.	.	.				.
	.	.					.
	.	.					.
	a_m	f_{m1}	f_{m2}	.	.	.	f_{mn}

[i] Two schools enter their pupils for a mathematics test with the results shown in the table

School

		X	Y
Test	Pass	75	63
result	Fail	21	26

This is a 2×2 contingency table.

One factor, which relates to the schools, is shown as the column headings. The other factor, which relates to the test result is shown as the row headings.

Testing for independence

To test if the two factors are independent in a **2×2 contingency table.**

(a) State the null hypothesis H_0: the two factors are independent.

(b) Calculate the row totals, column totals and the grand total (=sum of the row totals=sum of the column totals).

(c) Calculate the expected frequency E for each cell of the table using

$$E = \frac{\text{cell row total} \times \text{cell column total}}{\text{grand total}}$$

(d) Calculate $(O-E)$ for each cell of the table where O is the observed frequency.

(e) Calculate the value of χ^2_{test} using

$$\chi^2_{\text{test}} = \Sigma \frac{(|O-E|-0.5)^2}{E}$$

(see χ^2 p. 212).

(f) State the number of degrees of freedom ν. For a 2×2 contingency table $\nu=1$. This is because, although there are 4 variables (the expected frequencies), there are 3 restrictions (3 of the four row and column totals must be given), so $\nu = 4-3=1$.

(g) Compare the χ^2_{test} value with the $\chi^2(1)$ distribution (since $\nu=1$) at the appropriate significance level.

(h) Apply **Yates' continuity correction** if necessary. When the χ^2 test is applied to a situation with only one degree of freedom, i.e. $\nu=1$, Yates' continuity correction should be applied. It gives

$$\chi^2_c = \Sigma \frac{(|O-E|-0.5)^2}{E}$$

Since χ^2_c is always less than χ^2 it is not necessary to apply the correction if H_0 is accepted. If an uncorrected χ^2 would reject H_0 while χ^2_c would accept H_0, then it usually indicates that a larger sample should be taken.

To test if the two factors are independent in a **$m \times n$ contingency table.**

Proceed as with the 2×2 contingency table but the number of degrees of freedom is given by

$$\nu = (m-1)(n-1)$$

Yates' continuity correction is not needed here since $\nu \neq 1$.

[i] *For the above 2×2 contingency table, test if the factors 'School' and 'Test result' are independent at the 5 per cent level of significance.*

Null hypothesis H_0: the two factors 'School' and 'Test result' are independent.

The totals are given in the table below.

	X	Y	
Pass	75	63	138
Fail	21	26	47
	96	89	185

The expected frequencies are given in the table below.

	X	Y	
Pass	$\frac{96 \times 138}{185} = 72$	$\frac{89 \times 138}{185} = 66$	138
Fail	$\frac{96 \times 47}{185} = 24$	$\frac{89 \times 47}{185} = 23$	47
	96	89	185

$(O-E)$ values are given in the table below.

	X	Y
Pass	$75-72=3$	$63-66=-3$
Fail	$21-24=-3$	$26-23=3$

Using $\chi^2_{\text{test}} = \Sigma \frac{(O-E)^2}{E}$

$$= \frac{3^2}{72} + \frac{(-3)^2}{66} + \frac{(-3)^2}{24} + \frac{3^2}{23}$$

$$= 1.03 \ (2 \ \text{d.p.})$$

Since it is a 2×2 contingency table $\nu=1$

$\chi^2_{5\%}(1) = 3.81$. So $\chi^2_{\text{test}} = 1.03 < 3.81$.

$\therefore$ Accept H_0, i.e. the two factors 'School' and 'Test result' are independent at 5% significance level. Yates' continuity correction is not necessary because H_0 is accepted.

Contingency Tables
Worked example and Exam questions.

Four machines are used to manufacture items which are then graded into three categories. A summary of the production for a given period is shown in the table below.

Grade	Machine			
	A	B	C	D
Top	16	29	23	42
Ordinary	11	6	7	26
Reject	3	15	10	12

Find the expected frequencies on the hypothesis that there is no difference in the quality of the product from each machine. Use the χ^2 distribution and a 5% level of significance to test the above hypothesis.

Let H_0: grade and machine are independent.
In the table of expected frequencies shown below the row and column totals are first computed, then the total of the row totals (which is also the total of the column totals) is also recorded.
Each expected frequency is then calculated using the standard result

$$\frac{\text{cell row total} \times \text{cell column total}}{\text{grand total}}$$

where grand total means total of row totals.
So, for example, the expected frequency for top grade items from machine A is $\frac{110 \times 30}{200} = 16.5$.

Expected Frequencies	Machine				
	A	B	C	D	Totals
Top	16.5	27.5	22.0	44.0	110
Ordinary	7.5	12.5	10.0	20.0	50
Reject	6.0	10.0	8.0	16.0	40
Totals	30	50	40	80	200

The following table records observed frequency minus expected frequency for each cell.

O−E	Machine			
	A	B	C	D
Top	−0.5	1.5	1.0	−2.0
Ordinary	3.5	−6.5	−3.0	6.0
Reject	−3.0	5.0	2.0	−4.0

Thus from the tables above we can calculate

$$\chi^2_{\text{test}} = \sum \frac{(O-E)^2}{E} = 13.45$$

This value is tested against $\chi^2_{5\%}(6) = 12.59$

Note: there are 6 degrees of freedom, a 3×4 contingency table has $(3-1) \times (4-1)$ degrees of freedom.

$\chi^2_{\text{test}} = 13.45 > 12.59$

$\therefore$ there is some evidence to suggest that we should reject H_0, i.e. that there is some association between grade and machine.

1 Fifty people were chosen at random in each of two towns and asked whether they had watched a certain TV programme. Their replies are summarised in the table below.

	Watched Programme	Did Not Watch	Totals
Town A	24	26	50
Town B	16	34	50
Totals	40	60	100

If the numbers of people who watched this programme bear the same proportion to the total population in each of these towns, show that the number in the town A sample who would be expected to have watched this programme is 20. Hence or otherwise use χ^2 to show that it is reasonable to assume that the proportion of people who watched this programme was the same in both towns. Find approximate 95% confidence limits for this proportion.

(O & C)

2 A random sample of 100 housewives were asked by a market research team whether or not they used Sudsey Soap. 58 said yes and 42 said no. In a second random sample of 80 housewives, 62 said yes and 18 said no. By considering a suitable 2×2 contingency table, test whether these two samples are consistent with each other.

(O & C)

3 Children from five schools are entered for an examination in which four grades are awarded. The table gives the frequency distribution of the results.

School	Ackney	Beetham	Cramham	Dotheboys	Egonham
Grade A	55	45	55	40	55
Grade B	45	60	50	40	55
Grade C	50	90	55	10	45
Grade D	50	105	40	10	45

Test whether the proportion of entrants obtaining the various grades varies significantly among the schools. If the schools are of equal size and can be assumed to enter their best pupils, explain why your test does not give a fair comparison of academic standards in the schools. Do you think the above data provide any information about relative standards? If you do, conduct a test and state your conclusions.

(OLE)

4 Inflatia, in common with many other Western countries, is in the middle of an economic recession. As part of a nationwide enquiry into which economic measures will be most acceptable to the general public, a survey was undertaken in the town of Tucville. The responses to the question 'Would you support an incomes policy based on a flat rate increase of £500 per annum for every worker?' are summarised below, together with the employment status of the respondents.

Response	Employment Status			
	Skilled and Union Member	Skilled and non Union Member	Unskilled and Union Member	Unskilled and non Union Member
Yes	7	7	9	12
No	24	21	9	11
Don't Know	29	27	17	27

Use the χ^2 distribution and a 5% level of significance to test the hypothesis that there is no association between response to the above question and employment status. Form a new 2×2 contingency table from the above data by omitting all the "Don't know" responses and then pooling the remaining responses to obtain one column for "Skilled" and one column for "Unskilled". Use a 5% level of significance to test the hypothesis of no association between the factors in this new table. *(A)*

Logarithmic graph paper

Logarithmic graph paper uses scales which are graduated logarithmically. By plotting original data on a logarithmic scale, logarithms are automatically taken and plotted in a single process.

A logarithmic scale may have one or more cycles. Each cycle is graduated from 1 to 10 and may be used to represent 10^n to 10^{n+1}, where n is an integer.

The number of cycles used and the values to be marked on them are determined by the range of the data.

There are two basic types of logarithmic graph paper.

1. **Full logarithmic paper** (or **log–log paper**)
On this paper both axes are marked with logarithmic scales. A relation of the form $y = ax^n$ gives a straight line if x is plotted against y on log–log paper since $\log y = \log a + n \log x$. The gradient is n and the intercept on the y-axis is a.

Note: Use an ordinary ruler to measure the distances used to calculate the gradient. Do not use the numbers marked on the logarithmic scales.

2. **Semi-logarithmic paper** (or **log–linear paper**)
On this paper one scale is linear and the other is logarithmic. A relation of the form $y = ab^x$ gives a straight line if x is plotted on the linear scale and y on the logarithmic scale since $\log y = \log a + x \log b$. The gradient is $\log b$ and the intercept on y-axis is a.

Note: Use an ordinary ruler to find the gradient as before. The length of one cycle is taken as one unit of length on the logarithmic scale.

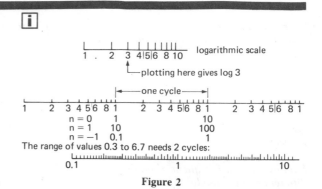

Figure 2

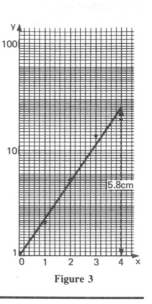

$\boxed{i}$ *The given data are thought to behave as $y = a^x$. Use log paper to estimate a.*

x	y
0	1
1	2.1
2	5.29
3	13.82
4	19.45

From the graph:
4.1 cm ≈ 1 log cycle
5.8 cm ≈ 1.4 cycles
$\therefore \log a \approx \dfrac{1.4}{4} = 0.35$
$\Rightarrow a \approx 2.24$

Figure 3

Poisson probability chart

The **Poisson probability chart** is used to find $P(X \geqslant c)$ for a distribution which is $Po(a)$. It gives the probabilities for different values of a and c. The chart is used in the following way.

(a) Determine a (using $a = np$). Find its position on the 'a scale'.

(b) Find where the ordinate at a cuts the curve marked c.

(c) read the corresponding value of p on the 'p scale'. This gives the probability for $x \geqslant c$.

Figure 1

$\boxed{i}$ *A company making microprocessor parts has 1% of its production faulty. What is the probability of getting at least 5 defectives in a box of 200?*

$n = 200$, $p = 0.01$, so $a = np = 2$.
Verify on a Poisson chart that for $a = 2$ and $c = 5$,
$p = 0.015$.
So the probability of getting at least 5 defectives in a box of 200 is 0.015.

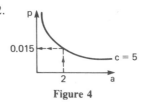

Figure 4

Arithmetic probability graph paper

Arithmetic probability graph paper has one linear and one non-linear scale. It is designed so that when the cumulative frequency of a normal distribution is plotted (on the non-linear scale) against a variable the result is a straight line. This gives a method of testing if a sample is from a normal population.

Note: If the distribution has been transformed, then the transformed variable must be used.

Skewed distributions result in curved lines as shown.

The mean μ can be estimated since it is the value of the variable corresponding to 50% cumulative frequency.

The standard deviation can be estimated using
$$4\sigma = x(97.72) - x(2.28)$$
$$\text{or} \quad 3\sigma = x(93.32) - x(6.68)$$
where $x(97.72)$ is the value of the variable corresponding to 97.72% cumulative frequency, etc.

The range of values of the variable determines which of these results is used but the first is preferred.

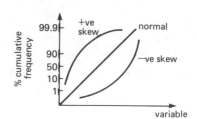

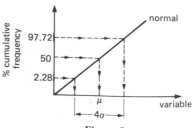

Figure 5

Special Graph Papers
Worked example and Exam questions.

 The following is a random sample of size 20, which it is believed may be from a normal population.

11.4, 18.0, 12.4, 22.5, 17.0, 0.1, 31.1, 20.4, 34.6, 18.5, 26.8, 2.6, 1.1, 7.0, 21.0, 7.6, 19.6, 36.4, 36.3, 21.9.

Plot this sample on arithmetic probability paper.
Estimate from this graph the mean and variance of the sample.

Inspecting the given set of values indicates 0 to 40 as a suitable range, this range is divided into eight equal classes each of width 5. A frequency, cumulative frequency and percentage cumulative frequency table is constructed as shown below.

Class	0–	5–	10–	15–	20–	25–	30–	35–40
Frequency	2	3	2	4	4	1	2	2
Cumulative frequency	2	5	7	11	15	16	18	20
Percentage cumulative frequency	10	25	35	55	75	80	90	100

The percentage cumulative frequency is plotted on arithmetic probability paper as shown below. On the assumption that the sample is from a normal population an estimate for the mean of the sample is obtained by reading the value of the variable corresponding to 50% cumulative frequency, and this is estimated to be 18.2 from the graph.

We use

$$s = \frac{x(93.32) - x(6.68)}{3}$$ to estimate s, the standard deviation of

the sample, where $x(93.32)$ is the value of the variable corresponding to 93.32% percentage cumulative frequency, and similarly for $x(6.68)$.

From the graph $s = \dfrac{34.5 - 1.5}{3} = 11$, so the variance of the

sample is estimated to be 121.

∴ the sample has estimated mean 18.2 and estimated variance 121. (See graph overleaf.)

---

 1 The frequency distribution of 200 masses, each recorded to the nearest gram, is given in the table.

Mass (g)	11	12	13	14	15
Frequency	16	28	118	22	16

Use arithmetic probability paper to fit a normal distribution to the data, stating its mean and standard deviation. Find the frequencies predicted by the fitted distribution for the groups in the table.

*(A)

2 The number of cosmic particles per minute arriving at an apparatus was recorded over a period of 1000 minutes and these observations are tabulated below.

No. of particles	0	1	2	3	4	5	6
No. of minutes	300	372	201	97	25	4	1

Use Poisson probability paper to estimate the mean rate of arrival of cosmic particles. State the variance and find the probability that, in any given interval of one minute, the rate of arrival has a value which is more than five standard deviations from the mean. Also determine the probability that, in any given interval of three minutes:
(i) no particles arrive,
(ii) no more than two particles arrive. *(A)*

3 (a) Nine men of similar build were given x standard units of alcohol, allowed to rest for one hour, and then asked to complete a simple task. The time y, taken to complete this task was measured, in seconds, for each man. The results are given below.

Amount of alcohol x	Time y
1.1	1.4
1.8	4.5
3.3	11.2
3.9	19.0
5.2	31.4
6.5	45.9
6.7	55.6
8.0	76.8
9.1	97.1

It is thought that the model for these data is of the form $y = ax^b$. Verify that this is a reasonable assumption by plotting the above data on log–log paper. Estimate the parameters a and b from your graph. Indicate briefly how the method of least squares might have been used to find estimates of a and b.

(b) The table below gives the masses, in kilograms, of 150 working coalminers of similar height.

Mass (kilograms)	Frequency
50–54	4
55–59	8
60–64	25
65–69	33
70–74	35
75–79	27
80–84	9
85–89	5
90–94	4

Using arithmetical probability paper, verify that it is reasonable to assume that these data came from an underlying normal population. Estimate from your graph the mean and standard deviation of this distribution. *(A)*

4 (a) All schools in the county of Kentwall were involved in a "Sponsored Pumpkin Grow" during the summer of 1980. Each pupil was given two pumpkin seeds and asked to come back at the end of the summer at which time the mass of their largest pumpkin was recorded in kilograms. The table below gives the results for two random samples of pupils, one from the Much Wopping School and one from Markum School.

Much Wopping Primary School

6.07, 8.32, 9.40, 6.68, 4.24, 8.45, 10.00, 7.79, 5.79

Markum High School

5.86, 2.78, 6.61, 4.57, 6.50, 7.72, 2.30, 8.45, 4.41, 5.86, 3.35

Using the *same* sheet of arithmetical probability paper:
(i) plot the sample from Much Wopping Primary School,
(ii) plot the sample from Markum High School. Compare the distributions.

(b) The number of misprints on 200 randomly selected pages from the 1981 editions of the Daily Planet, a quality newspaper, were recorded. The table below summarises these results.

Number of misprints per page

Number of misprints per page x	0	1	2	3	4	5	6	7	8	more than 8
Frequency f	5	12	31	40	38	29	22	14	5	4

Use Poisson probability paper to verify that the Poisson distribution with mean 4 is a reasonable model for these data. Determine graphically an estimate for the probability of more than 11 misprints on a page. *(A)*

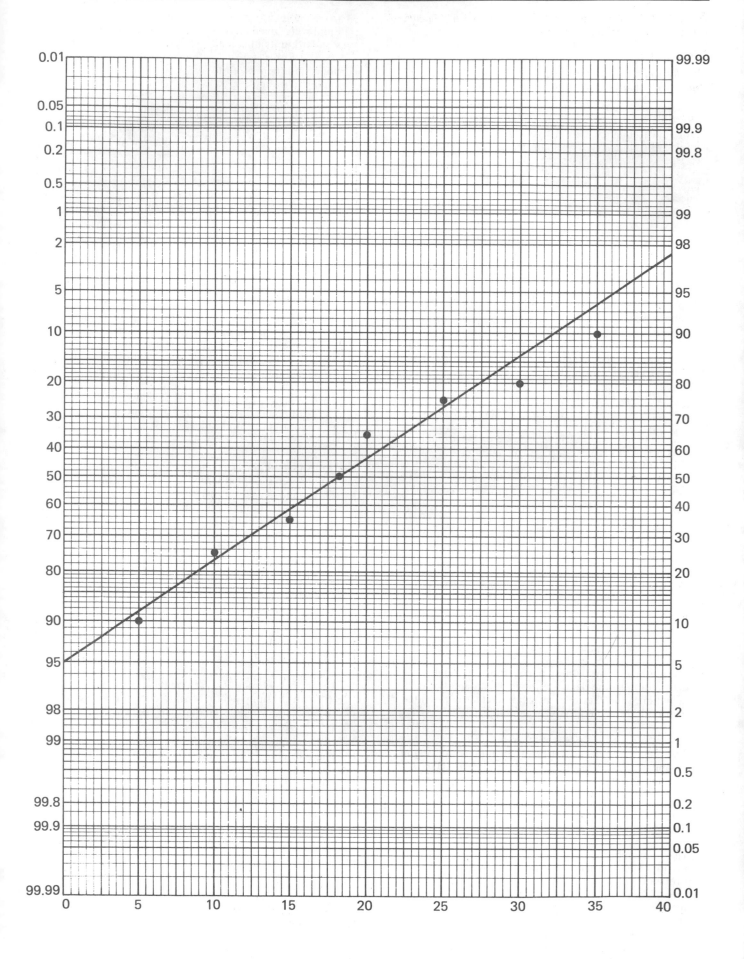

STATISTICS QUESTION BANK

Answers are given on pages 243–249. **A** and **AS** denote A-level and AS-level questions, respectively.

1 A 6 mins
The following data summarise the expenditure by a county council during a particular year.

Service	Expenditure (£m)
Education	160.2
Highways & Public Transport	35.7
Police	28.9
Social Services	27.9
Other	24.5

These data are to be represented by a pie chart of radius 5 cm. Calculate, to the nearest degree, the angle corresponding to each of the five classifications. (DO NOT DRAW THE PIE CHART.)
The following year the county council spent £305.2m.
Find the radius of a comparable pie chart which could be used to represent this second set of data.

(L)

2 AS 9 mins
The times, to the nearest second, taken by 100 students to solve a given problem are shown in the table below.

Time (seconds)	30–49	50–64	65–69	70–74	75–99
Number of students	10	30	25	20	15

(i) For the class 50–64, state the class boundaries and the class width.
(ii) Draw a histogram to illustrate this distribution.

(C)

3 AS 6 mins
The heights of 100 boys in a particular age group were measured, correct to the nearest cm, and the frequencies tabulated as follows:

Height (cm)	159–160	161–162	163–164	165–166	167–168	169–170	171–172
Frequency	2	14	28	26	19	9	2

State
(i) the modal group,
(ii) the upper and lower limits of the true heights in the group containing 9 boys.
Estimate, showing your method clearly,
(iii) the mean height of the 100 boys, correct to one decimal place.

(C)

4 A 7 mins
The table below shows the lifetimes of a random sample of 200 mass produced circular abrasive discs.

Lifetime (to nearest hour)	Number of discs
690–709	3
710–719	7
720–729	15
730–739	38
740–744	41
745–749	35
750–754	21
755–759	16
760–769	14
770–789	10

Without drawing the cumulative frequency curve, calculate estimates of the median and quartiles of these lifetimes.

(A)

5 A 22 mins
In a germination experiment, two hundred rows of seeds, with ten seeds per row, were incubated. The frequency distribution of the number of seeds which germinated per row is shown below.

Number of seeds germinated	Frequency
0	4
1	10
2	16
3	28
4	34
5	44
6	32
7	16
8	10
9	6
10	0

(a) Calculate the mean and the standard deviation of the number of seeds germinating per row.
For another 50 rows an analysis shows that the mean is 4.4 seeds and the standard deviation is 2.2 seeds.
(b) Determine the mean and, to 2 decimal places, the standard deviation for the 250 rows.

(L)

6 AS 11 mins
A random sample of 120 broad bean seeds was collected. Each seed was weighed to the nearest 0.01 g and the results are summarised below.

Weight (g)	Number of beans
1.10–1.29	7
1.30–1.49	24
1.50–1.69	33
1.70–1.89	32
1.90–2.09	14
2.10–2.29	8
2.30–2.49	1
2.50–2.69	1

Calculate an estimate for the mean and standard deviation of the weights of these broad bean seeds, giving your answers to 3 decimal places.

(L)

7 AS 6 mins
(a) In 1990, the index number of the value of a commodity was 135 when 1988 was taken as the base year. The value of the commodity in 1990 was £54 and in 1989 was £46. Find
(i) the value of the commodity in 1988,
(ii) the index number of the value of the commodity in 1989 when 1988 was taken as the base year.
(b) The cost of servicing a car depends on three items – cost of materials, cost of labour and cost of overheads. The price relatives of these items in 1990, using 1988 as the base year, are shown below, together with the weights attached to them.

	Materials	Labour	Overheads
Price relative	115	110	x
Weight	2	5	3

Given that the cost of servicing a car was £50 in 1988 and £57 in 1990, find the value of x.

(C)

8 AS 30 mins
A market stallholder sells clothes on three days a week – Tuesday (T), Friday (F) and Saturday (S). Her takings over a five week period were as follows:

Week	1			2			3			4			5		
Day	T	F	S	T	F	S	T	F	S	T	F	S	T	F	S
Takings, £	196	210	343	267	274	336	168	279	315	160	258	310	154	242	312

(a) Plot the data together with a suitable moving average.
(b) On one of the 15 days a nearby clothes stall was closed. Suggest which day this was.
(c) On another day the stallholder overslept and opened late. Suggest which day this was.
(d) Forecast the takings on Tuesday of week 6. Indicate how

you have made the forecast and discuss whether or not your method would be suitable for forecasting the takings on Tuesday of week 26.

(L)

9 A 7 mins
Three cards are to be drawn at random without replacement from a pack of ten cards. Six of the cards in the pack are red and numbered from 1 to 6, respectively, while the other four cards are blue and numbered from 1 to 4, respectively. Calculate the probabilities that
(i) exactly two red cards will be drawn,
(ii) exactly one 2 will be drawn.

(W)

10 AS 4 mins
A and B are two independent events such that $P(A) = \alpha$ and $P(A \cup B) = \beta$, $\beta > \alpha$.
Show that
$$P(B) = \frac{\beta - \alpha}{1 - \alpha}.$$

(L)

11 A 11 mins
The discrete random variables X and Y have the joint probability distribution shown in the following table.

			x	
		0	1	2
	0	α	β	α
y	1	β	0	β
	2	α	β	α

(i) Express β in terms of α.
(ii) Show that $E(XY) = 1$.
(iii) Given that $Var(XY) = 2$, find the values of α and β.

(W)

12 AS 9 mins
The random variable X has probability function
$$P(X = x) = \begin{cases} \dfrac{c}{x} & x = 1, 2, ..., 6, \\ 0 & \text{otherwise} \end{cases}$$
where c is a constant.
Find the value of
(a) c,
(b) $E(X)$,
(c) $Var(X)$.

(L)

13 A 30 mins
A teacher travels to work by car and the journey time, t hours, has the probability density function
$$f(t) = \begin{cases} 10ct^2 & 0 \leq t < 0.6 \\ 9c(1 - t) & 0.6 \leq t \leq 1.0 \\ 0 & \text{otherwise} \end{cases}$$
where c is a constant.
(a) Find the value of c and sketch the graph of this distribution.
(b) Write down the most likely journey time taken by the teacher.

(c) Find the teacher's expected journey time.

(d) Determine the probability that the journey time will be
- (i) more than 48 minutes,
- (ii) between 24 and 48 minutes.

(A)

14 A   11 mins

The continuous random variable X is distributed with probability density function f given by

$f(x) = 12x^2(1 - x),$ for $0 \leq x \leq 1,$

$f(x) = 0,$ otherwise

Evaluate the mean and the variance of X. Deduce the mean and the variance of $Y = 6 - 5X$.

(W)

15 A   5 mins

Team A has probability $\frac{2}{3}$ of winning whenever it plays. Given that A plays 4 games, find the probability that A wins more than half of the games.

(L)

16 AS   7 mins

Over a long period of time, 15% of motorists given a breathalyser test between 11 p.m. and midnight fail the test. Find, to 3 decimal places, the probability that in a random sample of five motorists breathalysed between these hours, more than one will fail the test.

(L)

17 A   27 mins

The numbers, X and Y, of two types of bacteria A and B, respectively, in a given volume of a solution are independent random variables having Poisson distributions. The mean number of type A bacteria per litre of the solution is 3.6, while the mean number of type B bacteria per litre of the solution is 1.24.

(a) Find, correct to three decimal places, the probabilities that a sample of 1 litre of the solution will contain
- (i)   exactly 4 bacteria of type A,
- (ii) 3 or fewer bacteria of type B,
- (iii) exactly 2 bacteria of type A and exactly 2 bacteria of type B.

(b) Let $W = XY$.
- (i)   Find, correct to three decimal places, the probability that for a sample of 1 litre of the solution the value of W is zero.
- (ii) Evaluate the mean and the variance of W.

(W)

18 AS   6 mins

The number of accidents per week at a factory is a Poisson random variable with parameter 2.

(a) Find the probability that in any week chosen at random exactly 1 accident occurs.

The factory is observed for 100 weeks.

(b) Determine the expected number of weeks in which 5 or more accidents occur.

(L)

19 A   9 mins

The random variable X is normally distributed with mean μ (> 0) and standard deviation 0.1μ.

(i) If $\mu = 5$ find the probability, correct to three decimal

places, that a randomly observed value of X will be greater than 5.5.

(ii) Find the value of μ, correct to two decimal places, if the probability of a randomly observed value of X being greater than 30 is equal to 0.4.

(W)

20 AS   6 mins

Jam is packed in tins of nominal weight 1 kg. The actual weight of jam delivered to a tin by the filling machine is normally distributed about the mean weight set on the machine with a standard deviation of 12 g.

The average filling of jam is 1 kg.

(a) Find the probability that a tin chosen at random contains less than 985 g.

It is a legal requirement that no more than 1% of tins contain less than the nominal weight.

(b) Find the minimum setting of the filling machine which will meet this requirement.

(L)

21 A   11 mins

Independently for each seed of a particular variety of flower that is sown, the probability that the seed will germinate is 0.8.

(i) Twenty such seeds are sown. Use tables to find the probability that the number that will germinate lies between 14 and 18, inclusive.

(ii) Use a normal approximation to find the probability that exactly 324 of 400 seeds sown will germinate, giving your answer correct to two decimal places.

(W)

22 A   11 mins

A random sample of 16 observations is to be drawn from a normal distribution having mean 11 and standard deviation 3. Let $\overline{X}$ denote the sample mean. Find, correct to three decimal places,

(i) the probability that $\overline{X}$ will have a value between 9.2 and 12.2,

(ii) the value of c for which $P(\overline{X} < c) = 0.03$.

(W)

23 A   15 mins

The lengths, in cm, of the leaves of willow trees are known to be normally distributed with variance 1.33 cm². A sample of 40 willow tree leaves is found to have a mean of 10.20 cm.

(a) Estimate, giving your answer to three decimal places, the standard error of the mean. Use this value to estimate symmetrical 95% confidence limits for the mean length of the population of willow tree leaves, giving your answer to 2 decimal places.

(b) Find the minimum size of the sample of leaves which must be taken if the width of the symmetrical 98% confidence interval for the population mean is at most 1.50 cm.

(L)

24 AS   5 mins

A machine is regulated to dispense liquid into cartons in such a way that the amount of liquid dispensed on each occasion is normally distributed with a standard deviation of 20 ml. Find 99% confidence limits for the mean amount of liquid dispensed if a random sample of 40 cartons had an average content of 266 ml.

(L)

25 A   17 mins

A garage sells both leaded and unleaded petrol. The distribution of the values of sales for each type is normal. During 1990 the standard deviation of individual sales of each type of petrol is £3.25. The mean of the individual sales of leaded petrol during this time is £8.72.

A random sample of 100 individual sales of unleaded petrol gave a mean of £9.71.

Calculate

(a) an interval within which 90% of the sales of leaded petrol will lie,

(b) a 95% confidence interval for the mean sales of unleaded petrol.

The mean of the sales of unleaded petrol for 1989 was £9.10. Using a 5% significance level, investigate whether there is sufficient evidence to conclude that the mean of all the 1990 unleaded sales was *greater* than the mean of the 1989 sales.

(L)

26 A   19 mins

As part of a physics practical course, groups of students were each required to design, construct and calibrate a thermometer without the aid of other thermometers. On completion of their work, each thermometer was assessed for accuracy over a range of temperatures by comparison with an accurately calibrated standard thermometer. The results, in degrees Celsius, for group A's thermometer are shown below.

Temperature (°C)	
Standard thermometer (x)	Group A's thermometer (y)
15	20
18	24
27	33
31	37
37	42
45	56
54	60
60	64
68	77
75	87

$\sum x = 430$ $\sum x^2 = 22398$ $\sum xy = 25685$ $\sum y = 500$

(i) State why a regression line of y on x, but not of x on y, is appropriate.

(ii) Using a scale of 2 cm to represent 10°C on each axis, plot a scatter diagram of these data.

(iii) Calculate the equation of the least squares regression line of y on x and draw this line on your graph.

(J)

27 AS   18 mins

A company monitored the number of days (x) of business trips taken by executives of the company and the corresponding claims (£y) they submitted to cover the total expenditure of these trips.

A random sample of 10 trips gave the following results.

x (days)	10	3	8	17	5	9	14	16	21	13
y (£)	116	39	85	159	61	94	143	178	225	134

(a) Plot these data on a scatter diagram.
    Give a reason to support the calculation of a regression line through these points.

(b) Find an equation of the regression line of y on x, in the form $y = a + bx$.
    (Use $\sum x^2 = 1630$; $\sum xy = 17\,128$)

(c) Interpret the slope b and intercept a of your line.

(d) Find the expected expenditure of a trip lasting 11 days.

(e) State, giving a reason, whether or not you would use the line to find the expected expenditure of a trip lasting 2 months.

(L)

28 A   11 mins

The ages, in months, and the weights, in kg, of a random sample of 9 babies are shown below.

Baby	A	B	C	D	E	F	G	H	I
Age (x)	1	2	2	3	3	3	4	4	5
Weight (y)	4.4	5.2	5.8	6.4	6.7	7.2	7.6	7.9	8.4

(a) Calculate, to 3 decimal places, the product moment correlation coefficient between weight and age for these babies. Give a brief interpretation of your result.

A boy who does not know the weights or ages of these babies is asked to list them, by guesswork, in order of increasing weight. He puts them in the order

A C E B G D I F H.

(b) Obtain, to 3 decimal places, a rank correlation coefficient between the boy's order and the true weight order.

(L)

29 AS   16 mins

The length of service and the gross annual earnings for 1990 of eleven employees of a large oil company were as follows:

Employee	A	B	C	D	E	F	G	H	I	J	K
Length of service (months)	14	18	36	24	13	83	108	41	33	17	79
Gross earnings (hundred £)	121	117	124	118	104	60	74	52	54	47	64

(a) Calculate Spearman's rank correlation coefficient for the data, giving your answer to 3 significant figures.

(b) The company statistician found the result of (a) surprising. Explain why she was surprised.

(L)

30 A   11 mins.

In a certain town an investigation was carried out into accidents in the home to children under 12 years of age. The numbers of reported accidents and the ages of the children concerned are summarised in the following table.

Group	A	B	C	D	E	F
Age of child (yrs)	0 to < 2	2 to < 4	4 to < 6	6 to < 8	8 to < 10	10 to < 12
No. of accidents	42	52	28	20	18	16

An investigator believes that children in the groups *A, B, C, D, E, F* are likely to have accidents in the home in the ratios 2:2:1:1:1:1 respectively. Use a χ^2 test at a 5% significance level to decide whether or not this belief is justified.

(L)

31 AS   18 mins

The table summarises the numbers of eggs laid by the hens on a small egg farm in one week.

Monday	Tuesday	Wednesday	Thursday	Friday	Saturday	Sunday
247	232	257	284	275	199	214

(a) Under the assumption that the day of the week does not affect the number of eggs laid, calculate the numbers of eggs expected on any given day.

(b) Use the χ^2 test to assess whether or not the difference between the observed and expected numbers of eggs laid is significant at the 5% level.

(L)

32 A   9 mins

A research worker studying the ages of adults and the number of credit cards they possess obtained the results shown below.

Age	Number of cards possessed	
	≤ 3	> 3
< 30	74	20
≥ 30	50	35

Use the χ^2 statistic and a significance test at the 5% level to decide whether or not there is an association between age and number of credit cards possessed.

(L)

33 AS   3 mins

When analysing the results of a 3×2 contingency table it was found that

$$\sum_{i=1}^{6} \frac{(O_i - E_i)^2}{E_i} = 2.38.$$

Write down the number of degrees of freedom and the critical value appropriate to these data in order to carry out a χ^2 test of significance at the 5% level.

(L)

Question Bank Answers

1 A

Total expenditure = £277.2m so, to the nearest degree,

Education is represented by $\dfrac{160.2}{277.2} \times 360° = 208°$

Highways and Public Transport $\dfrac{35.7}{277.2} \times 360° = 46°$

Police $\dfrac{28.9}{277.2} \times 360° = 38°$

Social Services $\dfrac{27.9}{277.2} \times 360° = 36°$

Other $\dfrac{24.5}{277.2} \times 360° = 32°$

The area of the pie chart represents the total so the radius of the pie chart for the following year (r) is given by

$$\frac{\pi r^2}{\pi 5^2} = \frac{305.2}{277.2} \Rightarrow r = 5.25 \ (2 \ \text{d.p.})$$

2 AS

(i) For the class 50–64, the u.c.b. is 64.5 and the l.c.b. is 49.5. The class width is 15.

(ii)

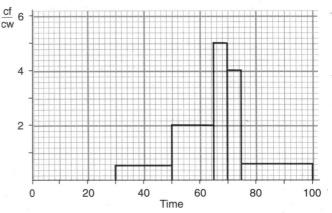

3 AS

(i) The highest frequency is 28 so the modal group is 163–164 cm.

(ii) The upper limit of true heights is 170.5 cm and the lower limit is 168.5 cm.

(iii) Using the midpoint of each group width to represent all the heights in that group, an estimate for the mean height is $\dfrac{1}{100}\big\{(2 \times 159.5) + (14 \times 161.5) + (28 \times 163.5)$

$+ (26 \times 165.5) + (19 \times 167.5) + (9 \times 169.5) + (2 \times 171.5)\big\}$

$= 165.1$ cm

4 A

The class containing the halfway point in the data is 740–744. The median lies in this class. An estimate of the median M is

$$M = 739.5 + \left(\frac{100 - 63}{41}\right)(5) = 744$$

The lower quartile is one-quarter of the way along the data and the upper quartile is three-quarters of the way along

Statistics Question Bank: Answers

the data. Therefore, estimates are

$$\text{lower quartile} = 729.5 + \left(\frac{50-25}{38}\right)(10) = 736.1$$

$$\text{upper quartile} = 749.5 + \left(\frac{150-139}{21}\right)(10) = 754.7$$

5 A

(a) $\bar{x} = \dfrac{\sum fx}{\sum f} = \dfrac{920}{200} = 4.6$

$$\sigma = \sqrt{\frac{\sum fx^2}{\sum f} - \bar{x}^2} = \sqrt{\frac{5032}{200} - (4.6)^2} = 2$$

(b) For the additional 50 rows $\bar{x} = \dfrac{\sum fx}{\sum f} \Rightarrow \dfrac{\sum fx}{50} = 4.4$

$$\Rightarrow \sum fx = 220$$

$$\sigma = \sqrt{\frac{\sum fx^2}{\sum f} - \bar{x}^2} \Rightarrow 2.2 = \sqrt{\frac{\sum fx^2}{50} - (4.4)^2}$$

$$\Rightarrow \sum fx^2 = 1210$$

Hence for the 250 rows, $\sum f = 200 + 50 = 250$

$\sum fx = 920 + 220 = 1140$, $\sum fx^2 = 5032 + 1210 = 6242$

So $\bar{x} = \dfrac{\sum fx}{\sum f} \Rightarrow \bar{x} = \dfrac{1140}{250} = 4.56$

$$\sigma = \sqrt{\frac{\sum fx^2}{\sum f} - \bar{x}^2} = \sqrt{\frac{6242}{250} - (4.56)^2} = 2.04$$

6 AS

Using the midpoint of each class to represent the data, estimates for $\bar{x}$ and σ are

$$\bar{x} = \frac{\sum fx}{\sum f} = \frac{202.4}{120} = 1.687 \ \text{(3 d.p.)}$$

$$\sigma = \sqrt{\frac{\sum fx^2}{\sum f} - \bar{x}^2} = \sqrt{\frac{350.493}{120} - (1.687)^2} = 0.274 \ \text{(3 d.p.)}$$

7 AS

(a) (i) 1990 index $= 135 \Rightarrow$ 1988 index $= 100$

1990 value $= £54 \Rightarrow$ 1988 value $= £54 \times \dfrac{100}{135} = £40$

(ii) 1989 value $= £46$ and 1988 value $= £40$

$$\Rightarrow \text{1989 index} = \frac{46}{40} \times 100 = 115$$

(b) The price relative in 1990 is $\dfrac{57}{50} \times 100 = 114$

The weighted index for car servicing in 1990 is

$$\frac{2(115) + 5(110) + 3x}{10} = \frac{3x + 780}{10}$$

So $\dfrac{3x + 780}{10} = 114 \Rightarrow x = 120$

8 AS
(a)

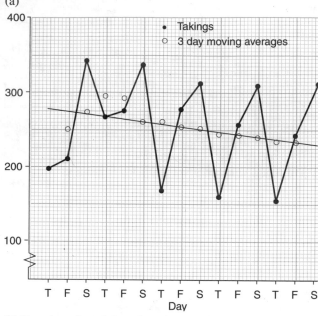

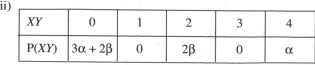

(b) Tuesday of week 2 as the sales are significantly higher than on other Tuesdays.

(c) Friday of week 1 as the sales are noticeably lower than on other Fridays.

(d) The trend line shows a reduction in takings of about £10 between corresponding days each week. A reasonable forecast for Tuesday of week 6 would be £144. This method would not be suitable for forecasting the takings in week 26 as the trend line would indicate negative takings at that time.

9 A

(i) $P(2 \text{ Reds}) = 3\left(\dfrac{6}{10} \times \dfrac{5}{9} \times \dfrac{4}{8}\right) = \dfrac{1}{2}$

(ii) $P(\text{one 2 only}) = P(\text{one 2 and two non-2s})$

$$= 3\left(\frac{2}{10} \times \frac{8}{9} \times \frac{7}{8}\right) = \frac{7}{15}$$

10 AS

$$P(A \cup B) = P(A) + P(B) - P(A \cap B)$$
$$= P(A) + P(B) - P(A).P(B)$$

$$\therefore \beta = \alpha + P(B) - \alpha P(B)$$
$$= \alpha + (1 - \alpha)P(B)$$

So $P(B) = \dfrac{\beta - \alpha}{1 - \alpha}$.

11 A

(i) Total of all row and column entries $= 1$ so

$$4\alpha + 4\beta = 1 \Rightarrow \beta = \frac{1}{4} - \alpha$$

(ii)

XY	0	1	2	3	4
P(XY)	$3\alpha + 2\beta$	0	2β	0	α

$$E[XY] = (0)(3\alpha + 2\beta) + (1)(0) + (2)(2\beta) + (3)(0)$$
$$+ (4)(\alpha)$$
$$= 4\beta + 4\alpha = 1$$

(iii) $\text{Var}[XY] = E\left[(XY)^2\right] - \left(E(XY)\right)^2$

$2 = \{(0)^2(3\alpha + 2\beta) + (1)^2(0) + (2)^2(2\beta) + (3)^2(0) + (4)^2(\alpha)\} - 1^2$

$= 8\beta + 16\alpha - 1$

So $16\alpha + 8\beta = 3$

Solving the simultaneous equations $16\alpha + 8\beta = 3$

$4\alpha + 4\beta = 1$

gives $\alpha = \beta = \dfrac{1}{8}$

12 AS

(a)

x	1	2	3	4	5	6
$P(X=x)$	c	$\dfrac{c}{2}$	$\dfrac{c}{3}$	$\dfrac{c}{4}$	$\dfrac{c}{5}$	$\dfrac{c}{6}$

Summing the probabilities gives $\sum\limits_{x=1}^{6} P(X = x) = 1$ so

$c + \dfrac{c}{2} + \dfrac{c}{3} + \dfrac{c}{4} + \dfrac{c}{5} + \dfrac{c}{6} = 1 \Rightarrow c = \dfrac{20}{49} = 0.408$

(b) $E(X) = \sum\limits_{x=1}^{6} x P(X = x) = \sum\limits_{x=1}^{6} x\left(\dfrac{c}{x}\right) = \sum\limits_{x=1}^{6} c = 6c = 2.45$

(c) $\text{Var}(X) = E\left(X^2\right) - \left[E(X)\right]^2$

$E\left(X^2\right) = \sum\limits_{x=1}^{6} x^2 P(X = x) = (1)(c) + (4)\left(\dfrac{c}{2}\right) + (9)\left(\dfrac{c}{3}\right)$

$\qquad + (16)\left(\dfrac{c}{4}\right) + (25)\left(\dfrac{c}{5}\right) + (36)\left(\dfrac{c}{6}\right)$

$= 21c = 8.57$

$\therefore \text{Var}(X) = 8.57 - (2.45)^2 = 2.57 \ \ (2 \text{ d.p.})$

13 A

(a)

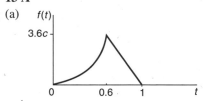

$f(t)$ is a p.d.f. $\Rightarrow$ area under curve $= 1$

For $0 \le t < 0.6$, area $= \displaystyle\int_0^{0.6} 10ct^2 \, dt = \left[\dfrac{10}{3} ct^3\right]_0^{0.6} = 0.72c$

For $0.6 \le t \le 1$, area $= \dfrac{1}{2}(0.4)(3.6c) = 0.72c$

$\therefore 0.72c + 0.72c = 1 \Rightarrow c = 0.694$

(b) The most likely journey time is 0.6 hours as this is where the graph of $f(t)$ is at a maximum.

(c) $E(t) = \displaystyle\int_0^1 tf(t) \, dt = \int_0^{0.6} 10ct^3 \, dt + \int_{0.6}^1 9ct - 9ct^2 \, dt$

$= \left[\dfrac{10}{4} ct^4\right]_0^{0.6} + \left[\dfrac{9}{2} ct^2 - 3ct^3\right]_{0.6}^1$

$= (0.324c) + (4.5c - 3c - 1.62c + 0.648c)$

$= 0.852c = 0.592$ hours

(d) (i) 48 minutes $= 0.8$ hours so

$P(t > 0.8) = \displaystyle\int_{0.80}^1 9c - 9ct \, dt = \left[9ct - 4.5ct^2\right]_{0.8}^1$

$= 9c - 4.5c - 7.2c + 2.88c$

$= 0.18c = 0.125$

(ii) 24 minutes $= 0.4$ hours so

$P(0.4 < t < 0.8) = 1 - P(t < 0.4) - P(t > 0.8)$

$P(t < 0.4) = \displaystyle\int_0^{0.4} 10ct^2 \, dt = \left[\dfrac{10}{3} ct^3\right]_0^{0.4} = 0.213c = 0.148$

$\therefore P(0.4 < t < 0.8) = 1 - 0.148 - 0.125 = 0.727$

14 A

$E(X) = \displaystyle\int_0^1 xf(x) \, dx = \int_0^1 12x^3 - 12x^4 \, dx$

$= \left[3x^4 - \dfrac{12}{5} x^5\right]_0^1 = 3 - \dfrac{12}{5} = \dfrac{3}{5}$

$\text{Var}(X) = E\left(X^2\right) - \left[E\left(X^2\right)\right] = \displaystyle\int_0^1 x^2 f(x) \, dx - \left(\dfrac{3}{5}\right)^2$

$= \displaystyle\int_0^1 12x^4 - 12x^5 \, dx - \dfrac{9}{25}$

$= \left[\dfrac{12}{5} x^5 - 2x^6\right]_0^1 - \dfrac{9}{25}$

$= \dfrac{12}{5} - 2 - \dfrac{9}{25} = \dfrac{1}{25}$

$E(Y) = E(6 - 5X) = 6 - 5E(X) = 6 - 5\left(\dfrac{3}{5}\right) = 3$

$\text{Var}(Y) = \text{Var}(6 - 5X) = \text{Var}(6) + \text{Var}(5X)$

$= 0 + 5^2 \text{Var}(X) = 25\text{Var}(X) = 25\left(\dfrac{1}{25}\right) = 1$

15 A

Let X be the random variable representing the number of wins and let $p = \dfrac{2}{3}$ be the probability of a win. X is Bin$(4, \tfrac{2}{3})$. The probability that team A wins more than half its games is

$P(X = 3) + P(X = 4) = \dbinom{4}{3} p^3 q + \dbinom{4}{4} p^4$

$= 4\left(\dfrac{2}{3}\right)^3\left(\dfrac{1}{3}\right) + \left(\dfrac{2}{3}\right)^4$

$= \dfrac{32}{81} + \dfrac{16}{81} = \dfrac{16}{27}$

16 AS

Let X be the random variable representing the number of motorists who fail the breathalyser test and let $p = 0.15$ be the probability of failing the test.

X is Bin$(5, 0.15)$

$P(X > 1) = 1 - P(X = 0) - P(X = 1)$

$= 1 - (0.85)^5 - 5(0.85)^4(0.15)$

$= 0.165$

17 A

(a) For A, X is Po(3.6) and for B, Y is Po(1.24)

(i) $P(X = 4) = e^{-3.6} \dfrac{(3.6)^4}{4!} = 0.191$

(ii) $P(Y \leq 3) = P(Y=0) + P(Y=1) + P(Y=2) + P(Y=3)$

$$= e^{-1.24} + 1.24e^{-1.24} + \frac{(1.24)^2}{2!}e^{-1.24} + \frac{(1.24)^3}{3!}e^{-1.24}$$

$$= 0.963$$

(iii) $P(X=2 \text{ and } Y=2) = P(X=2).P(Y=2)$

$$= \left[e^{-3.6}\frac{(3.6)^2}{2!} \right]\left[e^{-1.24}\frac{(1.24)^2}{2!} \right]$$

$$= 0.039$$

(b) (i) $P(W=0) = P(XY=0) = P(X=0 \text{ or } Y=0)$

$$= P(X=0) + P(Y=0) - P(X=0 \text{ and } Y=0)$$

$$= e^{-3.6} + e^{-1.24} - (e^{-3.6})(e^{-1.24})$$

$$= 0.309$$

(ii) Let $E(W) = Var(W) = \mu$

$P(W=0) = 0.309 \Rightarrow e^{-\mu} = 0.309 \Rightarrow \mu = 1.175$

$\therefore E(W) = Var(W) = 1.175$

18 AS
Let X be the random variable representing the number of accidents per week. X is Po(2).

(a) $P(X=1) = e^{-2}\frac{(2)^1}{1!} = 0.271$

(b) $P(X \geq 5) = 1 - P(X \leq 4)$

$P(X \leq 4) = P(X=0) + P(X=1) + P(X=2)$
$\qquad\qquad + P(X=3) + P(X+4)$

$$= e^{-2} + e^{-2}\frac{(2)^1}{1!} + e^{-2}\frac{(2)^2}{2!} + e^{-2}\frac{(2)^3}{3!} + e^{-2}\frac{(2)^4}{4!}$$

$$= 0.9473$$

$\therefore P(X \geq 5) = 1 - 0.9473 = 0.0527$

$\therefore$ In 100 weeks, the expected number of weeks with 5 or more accidents is $100 \times 0.0527 = 5.27$

19 A
(i) $\mu = 5 \Rightarrow \sigma = 0.1\mu = 0.5$

$P(X > 5.5) = P\left(Z > \frac{5.5-5}{0.5} \right) = P(Z > 1)$

$= 1 - P(Z < 1) = 1 - 0.841 = 0.159$

(ii) $P(X > 30) = 0.4 \Rightarrow P\left(Z > \frac{30-\mu}{0.1\mu} \right) = 0.4$

$\Rightarrow P\left(Z < \frac{30-\mu}{0.1\mu} \right) = 0.6$

From tables,

$P(Z < a) = 0.6 \Rightarrow a = 0.253$ so $\frac{30-\mu}{0.1\mu} = 0.253$

$\Rightarrow 30 - \mu = 0.0253\mu \Rightarrow \mu = 29.26$

20 AS
Let X be the random variable representing the weight of jam in a tin.
$\mu = 1 \text{ kg} = 1000 \text{ g}$ and $\sigma = 12$

(a) $P(X < 985) = P\left(Z < \frac{985-1000}{12} \right) = P(Z < -1.25)$

$= 1 - P(Z < 1.25) = 1 - 0.8944 = 0.1056$

(b)

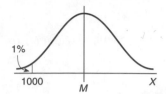

$P(X \leq 1000) \leq 0.01 \Rightarrow P\left(Z \leq \frac{1000-M}{12} \right) \leq 0.01$

From tables, $\frac{1000-M}{12} = 2.33$

so $M = 1028$ (to the nearest gram)

$\therefore$ The minimum setting of the machine is a mean weight of 1.028 kg.

21 A
Let X be the random variable representing the number of seeds that germinate.

(i) X is Bin(20, 0.8)

$P(14 \leq X \leq 18) = P(X \leq 18) - P(X \leq 13)$

Using tables we need to convert as follows:

$P(X \leq 18 | p = 0.8) = P(X \geq 2 | p = 0.2)$

$$= 1 - P(X \leq 1 | p = 0.2)$$

$$= 1 - 0.0692 = 0.9308$$

$P(X \leq 13 | p = 0.8) = P(X \geq 7 | p = 0.2)$

$$= 1 - P(X \leq 6 | p = 0.2)$$

$$= 1 - 0.9133 = 0.0867$$

$\therefore P(X \leq 18) - P(X \leq 13) = 0.9308 - 0.0867 = 0.8441$

(ii) When using a normal approximation,
$P(X = 324) = P(323.5 < X < 324.5)$ and

$\mu = np = 400 \times 0.8 = 320$

$\sigma = np(1-p) = \sqrt{400 \times 0.8 \times 0.2} = 8$

So $P(323.5 < X < 324.5)$

$$= P\left(\frac{323.5-320}{8} < Z < \frac{324.5-320}{8} \right)$$

$$= P(0.4375 < Z < 0.5625)$$
$$= P(Z < 0.5625) - P(Z < 0.4375)$$
$$= 0.7132 - 0.6691$$
$$= 0.04 \text{ (2 d.p.)}$$

22 A
X is N(11, 9) so $\bar{X}$ is $N\left(11, \frac{9}{16}\right)$ by Central Limit Theorem

$$P(9.2 < \bar{X} < 12.2) = P\left(\frac{9.2-11}{\sqrt{\frac{9}{16}}} < Z < \frac{12.2-11}{\sqrt{\frac{9}{16}}} \right)$$
$$= P(-2.4 < Z < 1.6)$$
$$= P(Z < 1.6) - P(Z < -2.4)$$
$$= P(Z < 1.6) - \{1 - P(Z < 2.4)\}$$
$$= 0.937$$

(ii) $P(\bar{X} < c) = 0.03 \Rightarrow P\left(Z < \frac{c-11}{0.75} \right) = 0.03$

$\Rightarrow \frac{c-11}{0.75} = -1.88 \Rightarrow c = 9.59$

23 A
Let X be the random variable representing the length of a willow leaf.

$\sigma^2 = 1.33$ and for a sample of 40 leaves, $\bar{x} = 10.20$.

(a) Standard error of the mean $= \sqrt{\dfrac{\sigma^2}{n}} = \sqrt{\dfrac{1.33}{40}} = 0.182$

Symmetrical 95% confidence interval for the mean μ is

$$\bar{x} - 1.96\sqrt{\dfrac{\sigma^2}{n}} \leq \mu \leq \bar{x} + 1.96\sqrt{\dfrac{\sigma^2}{n}}$$

$$10.2 - 1.96(0.182) \leq \mu \leq 10.2 + 1.96(0.182)$$

$$9.84 \leq \mu \leq 10.56$$

(b) From tables, $z = 2.33$ for 98% confidence interval so

$$10.2 - 2.33\sqrt{\dfrac{1.33}{n}} \leq \mu \leq 10.2 + 2.33\sqrt{\dfrac{1.33}{n}}$$

$$\therefore 2\left(2.33\sqrt{\dfrac{1.33}{n}}\right) \leq 1.50 \Rightarrow \sqrt{\dfrac{1.33}{n}} \leq 0.322$$

$$\Rightarrow n \geq 12.8 \Rightarrow n = 13 \text{ is the minimum sample size.}$$

24 AS

Let X be the random variable representing the quantity of liquid dispensed. X is $N(\mu, 400)$. For a random sample of 40 cartons, $\bar{x} = 266$ and $n = 40$, and for 99% confidence limits, $z = 2.575$.

$$\therefore \bar{x} - 2.575\left(\dfrac{\sigma}{\sqrt{n}}\right) \leq \mu \leq \bar{x} + 2.575\left(\dfrac{\sigma}{\sqrt{n}}\right)$$

$$266 - 2.575\left(\dfrac{20}{\sqrt{40}}\right) \leq \mu \leq 266 + 2.575\left(\dfrac{20}{\sqrt{40}}\right)$$

$$257.86 \leq \mu \leq 274.14$$

25 A

(a) Let X be the random variable representing the value of a sale of leaded petrol. X is $N\left(8.72, (3.25)^2\right)$.

From tables, $P(-a < Z < a) = 0.9 \Rightarrow a = 1.645$

so 90% of the sales lie in the interval $\bar{x} \pm 1.645\sigma$

∴ The interval is £8.72 ± 1.645(3.25)

i.e. from £3.37 to £14.07.

(b) Let $\bar{X}$ be the random variable representing the mean of random samples of 100 sales of unleaded petrol.

In 1990, $\bar{X}$ is $N\left(\mu, \dfrac{(3.25)^2}{100}\right)$ where μ is the mean

of the sales of unleaded petrol.

Then, for 95% confidence interval,

$$\bar{x} - 1.96\left(\dfrac{\sigma}{\sqrt{n}}\right) \leq \mu \leq \bar{x} + 1.96\left(\dfrac{\sigma}{\sqrt{n}}\right)$$

$$9.71 - 1.96\left(\dfrac{3.25}{10}\right) \leq \mu \leq 9.71 + 1.96\left(\dfrac{3.25}{10}\right)$$

$$£9.07 \leq \mu \leq £10.35$$

To test to see if $\mu > £9.10$, use the null hypothesis $H_0 : \mu = 9.1$ so $H_1 : \mu > 9.1$.

The test statistic is $z_{\text{test}} = \dfrac{\bar{x} - \mu}{\dfrac{\sigma}{\sqrt{n}}} = \dfrac{9.71 - 9.1}{\dfrac{3.25}{10}} = 1.877$

and for a one-tailed test at the 5% level, $z_c = 1.645$.

Since $z_{\text{test}} > z_c$, we reject H_0 and conclude that the mean of the 1990 unleaded sales was greater than the mean of the 1989 sales.

26 A

(i) The x values are a fixed scale to which the y values are being compared. The comparability of the y values in relation to the x values is being assessed so only the regression line of y on x is appropriate.

(ii)

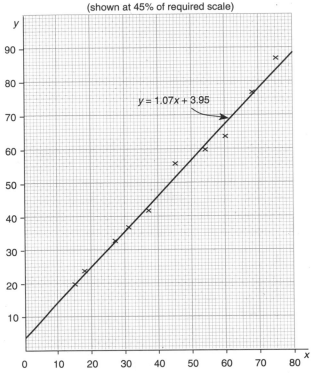

(shown at 45% of required scale)

(iii) The equation of the least squares regression line of y on x is

$$y - \bar{y} = \dfrac{C_{xy}}{C_{xx}}(x - \bar{x})$$

$$\bar{y} = \dfrac{\sum y}{n} = \dfrac{500}{10} = 50$$

$$\bar{x} = \dfrac{\sum x}{n} = \dfrac{430}{10} = 43$$

$$C_{xy} = \sum xy - n\bar{x}\bar{y} = 25685 - 10(43)(50) = 4185$$

$$C_{xx} = \sum x^2 - n\bar{x}^2 = 22398 - 10(43)^2 = 3908$$

∴ Equation is $y - 50 = \dfrac{4185}{3908}(x - 43)$

i.e. $y = 1.07x + 3.95$

[when plotting this line, make sure it passes through $(\bar{x}, \bar{y})$]

27 AS

(a)

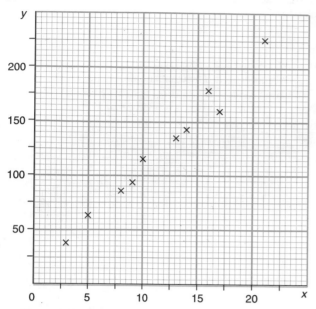

The trend in these data is clearly in a definite direction and all points would be relatively close to a straight line through them.

(b) The equation of the regression line of y on x is

$$y - \bar{y} = \frac{C_{xy}}{C_{xx}}(x - \bar{x})$$

$$\bar{y} = \frac{\sum y}{n} = \frac{1234}{10} = 123.4$$

$$\bar{x} = \frac{\sum x}{n} = \frac{116}{10} = 11.6$$

$$C_{xy} = \sum xy - n\bar{x}\bar{y} = 17128 - 10(11.6)(123.4) = 2813.6$$

$$C_{xx} = \sum x^2 - n\bar{x}^2 = 1630 - 10(11.6)^2 = 284.4$$

$\therefore$ Equation is $y - 123.4 = \dfrac{2813.6}{284.4}(x - 11.6)$

$$y = 9.89x + 8.64$$

(c) Slope b represents the rate of increase of expenses as the number of days increases.

$a = 8.64$ suggests that there is an initial expense of £8.64 for any visit.

(d) 11 days $\Rightarrow$ £117

(e) 2 months, i.e. 60 or 61 days, is well beyond the end of this range of samples so extrapolation so far ahead would not be valid.

28 A

(a)
$$r = \frac{C_{xy}}{\sqrt{C_{xx}C_{yy}}}$$

$$\bar{x} = \frac{\sum x}{n} = \frac{27}{9} = 3 \qquad \sum xy = 191.3$$

$$\bar{y} = \frac{\sum y}{n} = \frac{59.6}{9} = 6.6222$$

$$C_{xy} = \sum xy - n\bar{x}\bar{y} = 191.3 - 9(3)(6.6222) = 12.5$$

$$C_{xy} = \sum x^2 - n\bar{x}^2 = 93 - 9(9) = 12$$

$$C_{yy} = \sum y^2 - n\bar{y}^2 = 408.46 - 9(6.6222)^2 = 13.78$$

$$\therefore r = \frac{12.5}{\sqrt{(12)(13.78)}} = 0.972$$

As r is close to 1, the two sets of data show a high positive correlation.

(b)

	rank	rank	d^2
A	1	1	0
B	2	4	4
C	3	2	1
D	4	6	4
E	5	3	4
F	6	8	4
G	7	5	4
H	8	9	1
I	9	7	4

$\sum d^2 = 26$

$$r_s = 1 - \frac{6\sum d^2}{n(n^2 - 1)} = 1 - \frac{6(26)}{9(80)} = 0.783$$

29 AS

	Length of service	rank	Gross earnings	rank	d^2
A	14	10	121	2	64
B	18	8	117	4	16
C	36	5	124	1	16
D	24	7	118	3	16
E	13	11	104	5	36
F	83	2	60	8	36
G	108	1	74	6	25
H	41	4	52	10	36
I	33	6	54	9	9
J	17	9	47	11	4
K	79	3	64	7	16

$\sum d^2 = 274$

$$r_s = 1 - \frac{6\sum d^2}{n(n^2 - 1)} = 1 - \frac{6(274)}{11(120)} = -0.245$$

(b) One might expect earnings to rise in relation to length of service so a positive correlation value might have been expected.

30 A

Group	A	B	C	D	E	F
O	42	52	28	20	18	16
E	44	44	22	22	22	22

The expected values, E, are the total divided in the ratio 2:2:1:1:1:1.
The null hypothesis H_0 is that the differences between O and E values are not significant.

Group	A	B	C	D	E	F
$(O-E)^2$	4	64	36	4	16	36
$\dfrac{(O-E)^2}{E}$	0.09	1.45	1.64	0.18	0.73	1.64

$$\chi^2_{\text{test}} = \Sigma \frac{(O-E)^2}{E} = 5.73$$

5 classes and 1 restriction (totals agree) $\Rightarrow V = 4$
$\chi^2_{5\%}(4) = 9.49$ so as $\chi^2_{\text{test}} < \chi^2_{5\%}(4)$, do not reject H_0 and accept that the belief is justified.

31 AS

(a) Day of the week does not affect the number of eggs laid
$\Rightarrow$ number laid each day = $\dfrac{\text{weekly total}}{7} = 244$

(b)

	M	T	W	Th	F	S	Sun
O	247	232	257	284	275	199	214
E	244	244	244	244	244	244	244
$(O-E)^2$	9	144	169	1600	961	2025	900
$\dfrac{(O-E)^2}{E}$	0.04	0.59	0.69	6.56	3.94	8.30	3.69

$$\chi^2_{\text{test}} = \Sigma \frac{(O-E)^2}{E} = 23.81$$

7 classes and 1 restriction (totals agree) $\Rightarrow \chi^2_{5\%}(6) = 12.59$
Since $\chi^2_{\text{test}} > \chi^2_{5\%}(6)$, reject H_0. The difference is significant.

32 A

Observed values with row and column totals are

74	20	94
50	35	85
124	55	179

Using expected value = $\dfrac{(\text{row total})(\text{column total})}{\text{grand total}}$

Expected values are

65.12	28.88	94
58.88	26.12	85
124	55	179

2×2 table $\Rightarrow$ 1 degree of freedom so use Yates' continuity correction

O	E	$(\lvert O-E \rvert - 0.5)^2$	$\dfrac{(\lvert O-E \rvert - 0.5)^2}{E}$
74	65.12	70.22	1.078
20	28.88	70.22	2.432
50	58.88	70.22	1.193
35	26.12	70.22	2.689

$\Sigma = 7.39$

$\chi^2_{\text{test}} = 7.39$
$\chi^2_{5\%}(1) = 3.84$

Since $\chi^2_{\text{test}} > \chi^2_{5\%}(1)$, there is an association between age and the number of credit cards held.

33 AS

Number of degrees of freedom = $(m-1)(n-1)$
3×2 contingency table $\Rightarrow 2 \times 1 = 2$ degrees of freedom.
The critical value at 5% level of significance for these data is $\chi^2_{5\%}(2) = 5.99$.

Part III ANSWERS TO QUESTIONS IN STUDY UNITS

Answers to Guided Examples

PURE MATHEMATICS

P1 core Rational and irrational numbers

(a) $\frac{5}{6}$ (b) Example, $\sqrt{52} = 2\sqrt{13}$.

P2 core Errors and accuracy

(a) Absolute error in both height and radius is ±0.05 cm.
Absolute error in π is ±0.005.

(b) 5790 ± 50 cm².

P3 core Solving equations

$$A = \frac{C^2}{4\pi}.$$

P4 core Quadratics

$\alpha\beta = 5$
(i) $x^2 - 4x + 8 = 0$
(ii) $(x-5)(x^2 - 4x + 8) = 0$

P5 core Solving simultaneous equations

$x = \frac{1}{2}, y = \frac{1}{2}; x = 2, y = -1$.

P6 core Inequations

$x \leqslant 1$ or $x \geqslant 4$
$x \leqslant 1$ or $x \geqslant 4$ or $2 \leqslant x \leqslant 3$

P7 core Polynomials

$P = 4, Q = -4, c = 1$.

P13 core Trigonometrical functions

Perimeter = 43.98 cm (2 d.p.)
Area = 95.08 cm² (2 d.p.).

P15 core 3-D figures

642 m (to nearest metre).

P18 core Series

$$r = -\frac{1}{2}$$

$$S_\infty = \frac{2a}{3}$$

P19 core Binomial theorem

$1 + 10x + 34x^2 + 24x^3$

P20 core Differentiation

(a) $e^x(\cos x + \sin x)$ (b) $x^4(1 + 5\ln x) - \sin x$.

P21 core Further differentiation

$\frac{dy}{dx} = \sec^2 x > 0$ for $-\frac{\pi}{2} < x < \frac{\pi}{2}$.

P22 core Special points

Stationary points: Inflexion at $(0, 0)$, Minimum at $(3, -27)$;
Inflexion at $(2, -16)$.

P24 core Methods of integration I

$I = \frac{1}{13}e^{2x}[3\sin 3x + 2\cos 3x] + c$.

P26 Polynomial and fractions

$P(x) = 2x^2 + 3x - 2$
$x = \frac{1}{2}$ or -2

P27 Rational functions

1 $\frac{3}{4} - \frac{2n+3}{2(n+1)(n+2)}$

2 $\frac{1}{8} + \frac{3}{32}x + \frac{17}{128}x^2 + \frac{47}{512}x^3 + \ldots$

3 $\ln\frac{16}{15}$

4 $f(x) = \frac{2}{x-2} + \frac{3}{(x-2)^2}$
$f'(x) = \frac{-2}{(x-2)^2} - \frac{6}{(x-2)^3}$
$f''(x) = \frac{4}{(x-2)^3} + \frac{18}{(x-2)^4}$.

P29 Permutations and combinations

$\frac{6!}{2!3!} = 60$

$\frac{5!}{2!2!} + \frac{5!}{3!} + \frac{5!}{2!3!} = 60$

P31 Exponential and logarithmic series

$2x - 4x^2 + \frac{17}{3}x^3 - 8x^4; |x| < \frac{1}{2}$

P33 The circle

C_1 centre $(0, 8)$, radius $= 4\sqrt{2}$
C_2 centre $(9, -1)$, radius $= 5\sqrt{2}$
$(4, 4); 167°$

P35 Unknown curves

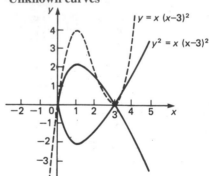

P36 More trigonometry

(a) $\tan^2 22\frac{1}{2}° = \tan^2\frac{\pi}{8} = \frac{1 - \sin\frac{\pi}{4}}{1 + \sin\frac{\pi}{4}}$
$= \frac{1 - \frac{1}{\sqrt{2}}}{1 + \frac{1}{\sqrt{2}}} = (\sqrt{2} - 1)^2$

Hence, $\tan 22\frac{1}{2}° = \sqrt{2} - 1$.

(b) $\theta = -90°$ or $36.9°$ (1 d.p.).

P37 Vectors

(a) $\overrightarrow{OU} = (\mu + \lambda)(\mathbf{i} + \mathbf{j})$
$\overrightarrow{ST} = (\mu - \lambda)(\mathbf{i} - \mathbf{j})$

(b) O is the centre of mass of triangle PQR.

P38 Vectors and geometry

$\lambda : \mu = 1 : 6$
$\mathbf{r} = \mathbf{i} - 2\mathbf{j} + \mathbf{k} + t(13\mathbf{i} + 4\mathbf{j} - 5\mathbf{k})$
$\mathbf{p} = -12\mathbf{i} - 6\mathbf{j} + 6\mathbf{k}$

P39 Matrices

$k = a^2 + bc$

P40 Complex numbers

(i) $1-i$ or $1+i$; $1+2i$ or $2+i$; $1-2i$ or $2-i$.

P41 Complex numbers and graphs

$$z = 2\left(\cos\frac{\pi}{4} + i\sin\frac{\pi}{4}\right),$$

$$w = 6\left(\cos\left(\frac{2\pi}{3}\right) + i\sin\left(\frac{2\pi}{3}\right)\right);$$

(i) $\dfrac{1}{2}\left(\cos\left(\dfrac{-\pi}{4}\right) + i\sin\left(\dfrac{-\pi}{4}\right)\right);$

(ii) $12\left(\cos\left(\dfrac{11\pi}{12}\right) + i\sin\left(\dfrac{11\pi}{12}\right)\right);$

(iii) $\dfrac{1}{3}\left(\cos\left(\dfrac{-5\pi}{12}\right) + i\sin\left(\dfrac{-5\pi}{12}\right)\right).$

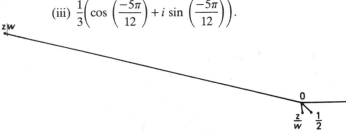

P43 Applications of differentiation

1%.

P44 Methods of integration II

(a) $k\ln\left|(x+2)\sqrt{x^2+3}\right|$

(b) $x - \frac{1}{2}\ln\left|\dfrac{x-1}{x+1}\right| + c$

(c) $\ln\left|x + \sqrt{1+x^2}\right| + c.$

P45 Applications of integration

(a) 64π cubic units; (b) 64π cubic units.

P46 Differential equations

$y = 2(x+1)$

MECHANICS

M3 Graphs in Kinematics

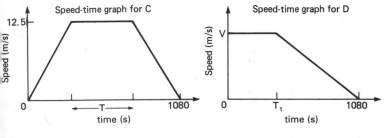

(a) 4500 m, (b) 13.3 m/s (48 km/h), (c) 0.0165 m/s² or 0.0592 km/h².

M4 Relative Motion

N31·4°E, 12.41 pm, 9·5 nautical miles.

M5 1-D Particle Dynamics

(a) 4930 J, (b) 680 N.

M7 Work and Energy

(i) 20 N m, (ii) 48 N m, (iii) 28 N m, (iv) $2\frac{1}{3}$ N; 5 m.

M9 Impulse and Momentum

790 kN; $\dfrac{1}{25}$ s.

M13 Motion in a Vertical Circle

$\sqrt{[2ag(1-\cos\theta)]}$; $mg(3\cos\theta - 2)$.

M14 Variable Forces

(ii) $v^2 = u^2(1 - e^{-2kx})$.

M15 Simple Harmonic Motion

$2\pi\sqrt{\dfrac{2a}{g}}$; a; $\dfrac{a}{2}$ above O.

M17 Coplanar Concurrent Forces

2 N along GP.

M18 Moments and Couples

(i) 5 kg; (ii) 2 kg.

M19 Equilibrium

Force from wall, $\dfrac{75\sqrt{3}}{4}$ N; force from ground, $168\frac{3}{4}$ N; force from rod, $37\frac{1}{2}$ N.

M20 Three Force Problems

Tension, 30 N; Reaction, 18 N.

M21 Friction

(a) $H = W\tan 2\alpha$; (b) $\theta = \alpha$.

M23 Equivalent Systems of Forces

(a) R = 5 N, S = 8 N; (b) R = 5 N, S = 2 N; $11\sqrt{3}$ N m.

M24 Centre of Mass

$\bar{x} = \dfrac{5r}{3}$, $\bar{y} = 0$.

M25 Suspending and Toppling

(a) 1 cm; (b) $(3, 3\frac{4}{3})$; (c) 38.3°

STATISTICS

S9 Discrete probability distributions

x	2	3	4	5	6	7	8	9
$P(X=x)$	$\dfrac{1}{36}$	$\dfrac{3}{36}$	$\dfrac{6}{36}$	$\dfrac{6}{36}$	$\dfrac{6}{36}$	$\dfrac{6}{36}$	$\dfrac{5}{36}$	$\dfrac{3}{36}$

$E[X] = 5\cdot833$
$P(X = 2$ or 3 for 3 throws$) = 0\cdot00137$

S12 The Poisson distribution

Predicted frequencies, $34\cdot1$, $38\cdot1$, $21\cdot2$, $7\cdot9$, $2\cdot2$, $0\cdot5$.

S16 Sampling II

For the 8 classes; less than -2, -2 up to 0, 0 up to 2, 2 up to 4, 4 up to 6, 6 up to 8, 8 up to 10, greater than 10, the allocation of the random numbers 001 to 000 to the classes is 001, 002–023, 024–159, 160–500, 501–841, 842–977, 978–999, 000.
The random observation is in the class 160–500 and simple proportion gives the random observation to be $3\cdot894$.

S20 Linear regression

$y = -0\cdot536x + 69\cdot033$
For $x = 60$, $y = 36\cdot873$

Answers to Exercises and Exam Questions

PURE MATHEMATICS

P1 core Rational and irrational numbers

1 (a) $\frac{1}{11}$ (b) $\frac{1}{74}$.

2 (a) $5\sqrt{2}$ (b) $2\sqrt{5}$ (c) $\frac{\sqrt{2}}{4}$ (d) $\sqrt{6}$.

3 (a) $\sqrt{3}$ (b) $67-12\sqrt{7}$ (c) $28-\sqrt{5}$ (d) $3-\sqrt{2}$.

4 (a) $\frac{5}{2}+\frac{5}{2}\sqrt{3}$ (b) $2+\sqrt{3}$ (c) $\frac{34}{19}-\frac{11}{19}\sqrt{5}$.

5 They all simplify to $6\sqrt{7}$.

6 (a) $2\sqrt[3]{2}$ (b) $2\sqrt[3]{3}$ (c) $2\sqrt[4]{5}$ (d) $3\sqrt[5]{2}$.

7 (a) The square root of any one of 17, 18, 19, 20, 21, 22, 23, 24 suitably simplified will do, e.g.
$\sqrt{18}=3\sqrt{2}$, $\sqrt{24}=2\sqrt{6}$, etc.
(b) The square root of any integer from 290 to 323 inclusive, suitably simplified, would do.
(c) Similarly, $-2\sqrt{6}$, $-2\sqrt{3}$, etc. will do.

8 $\frac{5p-2q}{2p+5q}$.

9 (a) $\sin 30°=\frac{1}{2}$, $\cos 30°=\frac{\sqrt{3}}{2}$, $\tan 30°=\frac{\sqrt{3}}{3}$.

(b) $\sin 60°=\frac{\sqrt{3}}{2}$, $\cos 60°=\frac{1}{2}$, $\tan 60°=\sqrt{3}$.

(c) $\sin 45°=\frac{\sqrt{2}}{2}$, $\cos 45°=\frac{\sqrt{2}}{2}$, $\tan 45°=1$.

10 $2\sqrt{6}$ metres.

11 (a) $x=1\pm\sqrt{6}$ (b) $x=\frac{3}{2}\pm\frac{\sqrt{7}}{2}$.

12 (a) $\frac{\sqrt{3}}{4}l^2$ square units

(b) (i) $31\,250\sqrt{3}$ m^2 (ii) $7200(2\sqrt{3}-3)$ m^2.

P2 core Errors and accuracy

1 (a) 6.18 ± 0.01 (b) -0.96 ± 0.01 (c) 9.32 ± 0.04
(d) 0.731 ± 0.003.

2 (a) 3.28 ± 0.02 (b) 5.90 ± 0.05 (c) -2.63 ± 0.07.

3 3.3%.

4 (a) 14.5 ± 0.4 cm^2 (b) 13.1 ± 0.4 cm^2.
Greatest possible relative error is approximately 2.5%.

5 (a) 0.0052
(b) 0.0050.
The choice of value for π makes no difference to the accuracy of a calculated value for A.
$A=17.20\pm0.08$.

6 (i) Lower bound 0.4, upper bound 0.6
(ii) Lower bound 5.583, upper bound 8.625.

7 (i) Greatest value = 659.7 (1 d.p.), least value = 632.7 (1 d.p.) (ii) 0.021 or 2.1%.

P3 core Solving equations

1 (a) 13 (b) 1.5 (c) 16 (d) 7 (e) 8 (f) 4 (g) 1.5 (h) $-\frac{1}{4}$.

2 (a) 0, $\frac{1}{8}$ (b) $\pm\frac{7}{3}$ (c) 4, 5 (d) 2, -6 (e) $\frac{5}{4},\frac{3}{2}$ (f) $\frac{9}{5},-\frac{1}{4}$.

3 (a) 8.2, -0.2 (b) 0.5, -5.5 (c) 4.5, -0.5 (d) 1.2, -0.4.

4 (a) -7.16, -0.84 (b) -1.13, 0.53 (c) -1.19, 4.19
(d) 0.23, 1.43.

5 (a) 12.5 (b) 3 (c) 2 (d) 68 (e) 9.5 (1 d.p.) (f) 5.5.

6 (a) $y=-\frac{2}{5}x+3$ (b) $3y+x-6=0$
(c) $3x^2+9x-8=0$ (d) $x^2+4x=3$.

7 (a) $b=\frac{V}{lh}$ (b) $\frac{P-2l}{2}$ (c) $\frac{2A-ha}{h}$ (d) $\frac{S-2lh}{2(l+h)}$.

8 (a) $\frac{C}{2\pi}$ (b) $\sqrt{\frac{3V}{\pi h}}$ (c) $\sqrt[3]{\frac{3V}{4\pi}}$ (d) $\sqrt{\frac{\pi R^2-A}{\pi}}$ (e) $\frac{S}{1+S}$

(f) $100\left(1-\sqrt{\frac{A}{P}}\right)$.

P4 core Quadratics

1 $-4\leqslant x\leqslant4$; $q=3$ or 4.

2 $qx^2+px+1=0$.

3 (a) $2<k<6$. (b) -7, 11. (c) $11x^2-27x+11=0$.

4 (a) (i) 2. (ii) 5. (iii) $4x^2-21x+1=0$.

(b) 5/2; $m=-5/2$; $n=\frac{1}{2}$.

5 ±2.

6 (i) $-11/4$. (ii) $4x^2+11x+9=0$.

7 (a) $4<x<5$. (b) $-6<k<6$.

8 $n>3$ or $n<-3$.

P5 core Solving simultaneous equations

1 (a) $\frac{1}{2}$ (b) $-$ (c) $x=1.3$, $y=2.7$.

2 $(\frac{13}{5},\frac{11}{5})$.

3 (a) $x=\frac{3}{2}$, $y=\frac{5}{2}$ (b) $a=-\frac{1}{2}$, $b=-4$ (c) $p=2$, $q=-1$
(d) $x=3$, $y=-1$.

4 (a) $x=\frac{3}{5}$, $y=\frac{4}{5}$; $x=1$, $y=0$
(b) $x=\frac{1}{3}$, $y=12$; $x=8$, $y=\frac{1}{2}$
(c) $x=-2$, $y=-3$; $x=0$, $y=1$
(d) $x=\frac{4}{9}$, $y=-\frac{2}{3}$; $x=1$, $y=1$.

5 (a) Not possible. Lines parallel.
(b) Not possible. Lines coincident.
(c) Not possible. No intersection point.
(d) Line and curve meet at a single point, (2, 1).

6 $p=7$, $q=\frac{6}{5}$; A $(\frac{6}{5}$, 7), B $(\frac{11}{5}$, 12).

7 $(-5, 0)$, $(\frac{7}{2}, 0)$, $(\frac{16}{7}, \frac{17}{7})$.

8 $m=3$, $c=-4$.

9 $(-7, -4)$ and $(7, 3)$

10 $x=\frac{1}{5}$, $y=\frac{13}{10}$; $x=\frac{1}{3}$, $y=\frac{3}{2}$.

11 $x=1$, $y=-1$; $x=4$, $y=2$.

12 $x=-\frac{1}{3}$, $y=\frac{7}{3}$; $x=3$, $y=-1$.

13 $x=-\frac{1}{3}$, $y=2$; $x=-\frac{3}{2}$, $y=-5$.

14 $x=-\frac{3}{2}$, $y=-4$; $x=\frac{3}{2}$, $y=4$;
$x=-2$, $y=-3$; $x=2$, $y=3$.

15 $x=16$, $y=8$.

16 $x=2$, $y=4$.

17 $x=\frac{1}{9}$, $y=3^{\frac{3}{2}}$; $x=27$, $y=\frac{1}{3}$.

P6 core Inequations

1 (a) $\frac{1}{2}<x<2\frac{1}{2}$. (b) $-1<x<1$ or $x>2$.

2 (i) $x\geqslant-2$; (ii) $-2\leqslant x\leqslant-1$ or $x\geqslant1$.

3 $x=0$ or -1; $x>0$ or $x<-1$

4 (i) $x<-1$ or $x>2/3$; (ii) $x<-1$ or $0<x<2/3$;
(iii) $-1<x<0$ or $x>2/3$.

5 $-4<x<4$.

6 $-\frac{3}{4}<x<3$.

7 $5/6+\ln 4$.

P7 core Polynomials

1 $11x^6+2x^5+5x^4+3x+7$.

2 $2x^7+2x^5+11x-12$.

3 $8x^5-12x^4+14x^3-x^2-25$.

4 $2x^3-7x^2+2x+4$.

5 $2x^7-4x^6+6x^5-7x^4+14x^3-23x^2+17x-4$.

6 $18x^9+6x^8-12x^7-4x^6-9x^5+42x^4+20x^3-21$.

7 (a) $3x^2(2x^3+3x-5)$ (b) $(5-2x^3)(5+2x^3)$
(c) $(x+4)^2$ (d) $(x-5)^2$ (e) $5(x+1)^2$ (f) $3x(x-1)^2$
(g) $(x-1)(x+4)$ (h) $(x-3)(2x-1)$
(i) $(10-3x^2)(100+30x^2+9x^4)$
(j) $(x^3+4)(x^6-4x^3+16)$.

8 (a) $a=-21$, $b=8$ (b) $P=6$, $Q=-8$, $c=4$.

9 $k = -34$; $(2x-1)(2x+5)(2x-3)$.

10 $(3-x)(1-x)^2$; $x = 1$ or $x \geq 3$.

11 $a = b = -1$, $c = 0$.

12 (a) – (b) $a = 1$, $b = 0$, $c = -2$ (c) $x = \pm\sqrt{2}, 3$
  (d) $x = \pm\sqrt{2} - 1$.

13 (a) – (b) $(x+2)(x-3)(2x-1)$ (c) -2, $\frac{1}{2}$, 3
  (d) $x < -2$, $\frac{1}{2} < x < 3$.

14 $x < 2$, $3 < x < 4$.

15 $a = -5$, $b = 19$.

16 _____

P8 core Indices and logarithms

1 (a) (i) $z = 3$; (ii) $z = \frac{1}{4}$; (iii) $x = \frac{1}{16}$; (iv) $y = -1$.

  (b) $z^2 - 4z + 3 = 0$, $y = 0$ or 1.
  (c) 1.

2 (a) $\dfrac{x+1}{x(x-1)}$.

  (b) (i) $\frac{1}{2}$; (ii) $-\frac{3}{2}$.

3 (i) 5; (ii) $\frac{1}{125}$.

4 (a) 2; (b) $v = x^{\frac{1}{2}(p-q)}$.

5 (a) $x = 625$ or $(625)^{-1}$; (b) $y = 2$, $-\frac{1}{3}$.

6 (i) $x = -2.06$; (ii) $y = 8$.

7 (a) $xy = 3^{2p+\frac{q}{2}}$, $\dfrac{x^2}{y} = 3^{4p-\frac{q}{2}}$.

  (b) $x = \ln 2$.

8 (a) (i) 0; (ii) 3.

  (b) $x = \ln\left(\frac{5}{2}\right)$, $y = -\ln 6$.

9 $(x,y) = (3,9)$ or $(9,3)$.

10 (i) $k = 2{\cdot}303$, $\dfrac{dy}{dx} = 10^x \ln 10$;

  (ii) $g(x) = \ln x$, $\dfrac{dy}{dx} = x^x(1 + \ln x)$.

P9 core Exponential growth and decay

1 Distance $= 20(1.1)^{n-1}$. In week 18.

2 $k = 7499$, $\lambda = 0.22$, £3875 or £3840.

3 (a) 40 (b) 28 minutes.

4 (i) 1.65 or 65% increase (ii) Approximately 0.5 (iv) 0.5.

5 (a)

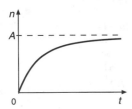

  (d) $y = 0.5$ or 1 (e) 20 000.

P10 core Coordinates and graphs

1 (ii) Area $= 25$; (iii) $PR = 5\sqrt{5}$;
  perpendicular distance $= 2\sqrt{5}$.

2 $x = 1.18$; 3.71; $x^3 - 4x^2 + 4 = 0$.

3 $X(10,0)$ $Y(0,5)$; Area $= 25$.

4 $(1,1)$ $y = 18 - 2x$.

5 $D(2,-4)$.

6 (a) $2y = 5x + 11$; (b) $16y = 3(x+1)^2 + 32$; (c) $xy = 2$
  (d) $y^2 = x^3$; (e) $(x-1)^2 + (y-3)^2 = 16$; (f) $y = x - 3$
  (g) $(x-a)^2 + y^2 = a^2$; (h) $x^2 - y^2 = 4$.

P11 core Functions

1 (a) Max $= 5$. (b) $(-\infty, 5)$.

2 (i) fg; (ii) g^{-1}; (iii) g^2; (iv) g^2f; (v) gf^{-1}.

3 (a) $f: x \to 2 - \frac{1}{x}$, $x \neq 0$. (b) (i) $\frac{1}{3}$; (ii) $5/3$.

4 _____

5 (a) $f(0) = 0$; $f(1) = 56$. (b) $9^{2n+2} - 5^{2n+2}$.

6 $(-\infty, \infty)$ $g \neq 0$; $g \circ f = \dfrac{1}{\log_a x}$ $(x \in \mathbb{R}_+, x \neq 1)$;

  $f^{-1}: x \to a^x$ $(x \in \mathbb{R}_+, a > 1)$; g^{-1}:

  $x \to \dfrac{1}{x}$ $(x \in \mathbb{R}_+)$; h^{-1}; $x \to a^{-x} \Rightarrow h^{-1}(x) + f^{-1}(x) = a^{-x} + a^x \neq 0$.

7 $x = 1$; $1/5$.

8 Periods π, π, π Range $[-1, 1]$.

9 _____

10 $b > -9$; $x = 11$, -5; Non-commutative.

11 $x \to \sin x$; domain D.

P12 core Simple curves

1 (a)

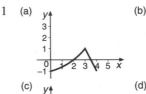

(b)

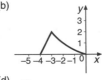

(c)

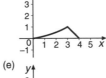

(d)

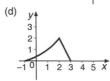

(e)

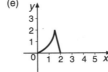

2 $f(x+1) + 2 = \dfrac{1}{x+1} + 2 = \dfrac{2x+3}{x+1}$

(a)

(b)

(c)

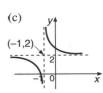

Symmetrical about $(-1, 2)$. (For clarity, three separate graphs are drawn here.)

3 (a)

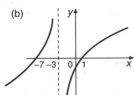

(b)

4

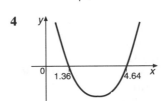

(b) $x = 3$, $a = -3$ (c) $b = -2.6896$.

5 (a) (i) π (ii) 10 (iii) $x = \dfrac{\pi}{4}$.

  (b) A stretch parallel to the y-axis, scale factor 10.
  A stretch parallel to the x-axis, scale factor 0.5.
  The order does not matter.

6 Coordinates of A: $(\ln(\frac{2}{3}), 0)$, coordinates of B: $(0, -1)$.

Transformations:
(i) Reflection in the y-axis
(ii) Stretch parallel to the y-axis, scale factor 2
(iii) Translation parallel to the y-axis, 3 units down.

P13 core Trigonometrical functions

1 Angle $AOB = 2$ rad; area sector $AOB = 9$ cm².

2 (a) $\frac{3}{5}, \frac{4}{5}$; $-\frac{3}{5}, -\frac{4}{5}$ (b) $\frac{3}{4}, \frac{3}{5}$; $-\frac{3}{4}, -\frac{3}{5}$
 (c) $\frac{7}{25}, \frac{24}{7}$; $-\frac{7}{25}, -\frac{24}{7}$

3 (a) $\frac{1}{6}\pi$, $\frac{5}{6}\pi$ (b) $-36.9°$, $143.1°$ (c) $33°$, $327°$
 (d) 0.445, 5.84, 2.70, 3.59
 (e) $-127.5°$, $-97.5°$, $-37.5°$, $-7.5°$, $52.5°$, $82.5°$, $142.5°$, $172.5°$
 (f) $-35°$, $25°$, $85°$ (g) $26.5°$ (h) $71.5°$, $228.5°$
 (i) 0.653, -2.488, -0.981, 2.223

4 0.04 rad.

P14 core Plane triangles

1 (a) $53\cdot1°$; $126\cdot9°$.
2 (i) $2\sqrt{117}$; (ii) $16\cdot1°$.
3 (i) $22°$, $98°$; (ii) $30°$, $270°$.
4 $58\cdot1°$, $121\cdot9°$; $13\cdot8$ cm, $3\cdot2$ cm.·
5 $\pi/6$, $5\pi/6$.
6 (b) $\pi/2$.
7 $111°$; $1\cdot58$ m.
8 _____
9 (i) 242 m; (ii) 306 m.
10 $124°$, $28°$, $28°$.
11 $AP^2 = a^2 + c^2 - 2ac \cos(B + 60°)$; $\lambda = \frac{1}{2}$, $\mu = 2\sqrt{3}$.

P15 core 3-D figures

1
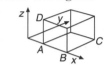

 (b) $(1, 3, 0)$, $(1, 3, 2)$, $(6, 0, 2)$, $(6, 3, 2)$ (c) $(3\frac{1}{2}, 1\frac{1}{2}, 1)$.
2 (a) (i) For example: $(3, 4, 24)$, $(15, 4, 12)$, $(3, 16, 12)$
 (ii) A sphere, centre Q, radius 12 units
 (b) (i) 13 units (ii) $(0, 0, 24)$ (iii) $134.8°$ (1 d.p.)
3 (a) $OC = \sqrt{17}$ units, $OD = \sqrt{21}$ units
 (b) $CD = \sqrt{18}$ units
 (c) $C\hat{O}D = 58°$, $O\hat{D}C = 56°$, $D\hat{C}O = 66°$ (each to nearest 1°).
4 (a) $PQ = \sqrt{18}$ units, $QR = \sqrt{36}$ units, $RP = \sqrt{18}$ units
 (b) $Q\hat{P}R = \cos^{-1}\left(\frac{18 + 18 - 36}{2\sqrt{18}\sqrt{18}}\right) = \cos^{-1}0 = 90°$.
5 420.5 m.
6 62 m.
7 (i) 11.5 m (ii) $73.9°$.
8 69.8 m.
9 219.8 m; 138.6 m; 326.6 m; area $11\,668$ m².
10 $51.2°$; 7.79 cm; $70.5°$.

P16 core Trigonometrical identities

1 $A = 54.7°$, $125.3°$, $234.7°$, $305.3°$; $k < 1$.
2 (i) $60°$, $120°$, $240°$, $300°$ (ii) $31°$, $211°$
 (iii) $30°$, $150°$, $210°$, $330°$ (iv) $0°$, $109.5°$, $250.5°$, $360°$.
3 (a) $-\frac{12}{13}$ (b) $-\frac{12}{5}$ (c) $\frac{5}{12}$ (d) $-\frac{13}{12}$.
4 (i) $5°$, $45°$, $125°$, $165°$, $245°$, $285°$
 (ii) $19.5°$, $160.5°$, $210°$, $330°$.
5 $x = 108°$, $-108°$.
6 (a) $\frac{1}{3}$ or $-\frac{1}{2}$ (b) $285.5°$, $430.5°$, $240°$, $480°$.
7 $15°$, $75°$, $195°$, $255°$.
8 _____
9 $\theta = 0°$, $180°$, $360°$ or $\theta = 30°$, $150°$ or $\theta = 210°$, $330°$.

P17 core Sequences

1 (a) $4, 8, 12, 16, 20$ (b) $1, 4$ $7, 10, 13$ (c) $3, 9, 19, 33, 51$
 (d) $1, 2, 4, 8, 16$ (e) $-\frac{1}{2}, \frac{4}{3}, -\frac{9}{4}, \frac{16}{5}, -\frac{25}{6}$.
2 (a) $2, 7, 17, 37, 77$ (b) $5, \frac{3}{2}, \frac{23}{20}, \frac{223}{200}, \frac{2223}{2000}$
 (c) $0, \frac{1}{5}, \frac{5}{24}, \frac{24}{115}, \frac{115}{551}$ (d) $0, 1, 2, 3, 4$
 (e) $1, 3, 7, 15, 31$.

3 (a) $f: k \mapsto \dfrac{1}{k+1}$ $(k \in N)$ (b) $f: k \mapsto 2k - 1$ $(k \in N)$
 (c) $f: k \mapsto \dfrac{1}{2^k}$ $(k \in N)$ (d) $f: k \mapsto (-1)^{k+1}k$ $(k \in N)$
 (e) $f: k \mapsto (-1)^k \dfrac{1}{k^2}$ $(k \in N)$.

4 (a) $u_1 = 2$; $u_k = u_{k-1} + 2$ $(k = 2, 3, 4, \ldots)$
 (b) $u_1 = 2$; $u_k = 3u_{k-1}$ $(k = 2, 3, 4, \ldots)$
 (c) $u_1 = 1$; $u_k = 2u_{k-1} + 1$ $(k = 2, 3, 4, \ldots)$
 (d) $u_1 = 1$; $u_k = 3u_{k-1} - 1$ $(k = 2, 3, 4, \ldots)$

5
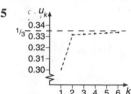

The sequence is convergent with limit $\frac{1}{3}$.
6 The sequence is convergent with limit $\sqrt{10}$.
 $\sqrt{10} = 3.162\,278$ (to 6 d.p.).
7 (a) $3, 3k, 3k^2, 3k^3, 3k^4$ (b) $u_n = 3k^{n-1}$ $(n \in N)$.
8 (a) $m = 2$, $c = 1$ (b) $u_3 = 7$.
9 (i) $u_1 = 0$; sequence oscillates between 0 and -1
 $u_1 = 1$; sequence oscillates between 0 and -1 from u_2 onwards
 $u_1 = 2$; sequence is divergent (all terms positive)
 (ii) $\frac{1}{2} \pm \frac{1}{2}\sqrt{5}$.
10 (a) Convergent with limit 1 (b) Periodic with period 3.

P18 core Series

1 $c = -8$, $r = \dfrac{1}{2}$.

2 6273.
3 (a) $d = 2$, $a = 3$. (b) $1,1,1$ or $4,6,9$.
4 (i) £1656.03. (ii) $n = 500\,001$.
5 $-\cos 2\alpha$.

6 $x + 1$ valid if $x > -\dfrac{1}{2}$

7 $\dfrac{\pi}{4} < |\theta| < \dfrac{3\pi}{4}$

8 _____

9 $d = \dfrac{1}{2}$ $a = -2\frac{1}{2}$; 205.

10 100; 2046; 2146.
11 (i) $7(p + 1)$ (ii) $7(p + 1)(10p + 11)$.

P19 core Binomial theorem

1 (a) $1 - 12x + 54x^2 - 108x^3 + 81x^4$
 (b) $1 + \frac{5}{2}x^2 + \frac{5}{4}x^4 + \frac{5}{16}x^6 + \frac{5}{16}x^8 + \frac{1}{32}x^{10}$.
2 (a) $8x^3 + 36x^2y + 54xy^2 + 27y^3$
 (b) $\dfrac{16}{625}p^4 - \dfrac{48}{125}\dfrac{p^3}{q} + \dfrac{54}{25}\dfrac{p^2}{q^2} - \dfrac{27}{5}\dfrac{p}{q^3} + \dfrac{81}{16}\dfrac{1}{q^4}$
3 (a) $-262\,440$ (b) $22\,680$.
4 $1 + 3a + 6a^2 + 7a^3 + 6a^4 + 3a^5 + a^6$
5 -3
6 $32 - 40x + 20x^2 - 5x^3 + \frac{5}{8}x^4 - \frac{1}{32}x^5$; 31.208.
7 $-192x^3 - 432x$.
8 $256 - 3072x + 16\,128x^2$; 253.
9 $32 - 80x + 80x^2$; 32.808.
10 -280.
11 $a = 2$.
12 $1 + 5x + 10x^2 + 10x^3 + 5x^4 + x^5$; 30.
13 240.

P20 core Differentiation

1 (a) $12x + 1$ (b) $4x^3 - 2 - \dfrac{2}{x^3}$ (c) $\dfrac{3(2x+1)}{4x^{\frac{5}{4}}}$.

2 ――――――

3 (a) $-\dfrac{3}{2x^{\frac{5}{2}}}$ (b) $2x(3x+2)$ (c) $3 + \dfrac{2}{x^3}$.

4 (a) $x^2(3\ln x + 1)$. (b) $\dfrac{-x\sin x - 1 - \cos x}{x^2}$.

5 $\dfrac{dy}{dx} = \dfrac{6x}{(2x^2+1)^2} > 0$ for $x > 0$; $-1 \leqslant y \leqslant 0$.

6 $\dfrac{dy}{dx} = \dfrac{2(x^2+4)}{(x^2-4)^2}$; $\dfrac{1}{3} \leqslant y \leqslant \dfrac{5}{3}$.

7 (i) (a) $6x(x^2+1)^2$. (b) $12\sin^3 3x \cos 3x$. (c) $\dfrac{3x+1}{(2x+1)^{\frac{1}{2}}}$.

(ii) $\dfrac{-(x^2+2)\sin x}{x^3}$

8 (i) $2x\cos 3x - 3x^2 \sin 3x$, (ii) $e^x\left(\dfrac{1}{x} + \ln x\right)$, (iii) $6x(x^2+2)^2$,

(iv) $\dfrac{3+x}{\left(x^2+1\right)^{\frac{3}{2}}}$

9 (i) $8\tan^3 2x \sec^2 2x$; (ii) $-\dfrac{1}{(2x-3)^2}$; (iii) $x(2\ln x + 1)$.

P21 core Further differentiation

1 ――――――

2 (a) $-2e^{-t}$ (b) $3 - x$.

3 2800 m$^{2!}$ s^{-1}.

4 (a) 0.12π cm^2/s (b) 0.05 cm.

5 100π cm^3 s^{-1}.

6 (i) $\dfrac{dx}{dy} = 2y$, $\dfrac{dy}{dx} = \dfrac{1}{2y}$ (ii) $\dfrac{dy}{dx} = \dfrac{1}{2\sqrt{x-4}}$

(iii) Answer is the same as in (ii) (iv) $x \geqslant 4$.

7 $\dfrac{dy}{dx} = 3\left((x - \frac{1}{3})^2 + \dfrac{2}{9}\right) > 0$ for all x.

8 4 cm^2 s^{-1}.

9 (a) 10π m^2 s^{-1} (b) $\dfrac{x}{y} = \dfrac{3}{2}$ (c) 3 s.

10 $2T$.

11 (a) $\frac{1}{3}$ second (b) 0.28 m s^{-1} (c) 4.

12 (a) 4.58 (b) (i) $-100e^{-\frac{1}{5}t}$ (ii) $-$.

P22 Special points

1 (i) $p = 2$, $q = 1$; (ii) 6.

2 $a = -2$, $b = 4$.

3 Depth: $32x^{-2}$ cm; width 3.42 cm, length 13.68 cm, depth 2.74 cm.

4 $x = \dfrac{1}{3}$, maximum.

5 (a) $x = 0$, maximum; $x = -4$, minimum.

6 $\dfrac{dy}{dx} = 2t(1+t)\,e^t$; $\dfrac{d^2y}{dx^2} = 2(1+t)(1+2t+2t^2+2t^3)\,e^t$; minimum at $(0, 1)$.

7 $\left(-1, \dfrac{1}{3}\right)$.   **8** (i) min $(a, 0)$, max $\left(x = \dfrac{a+2}{3}\right)$;

(ii) max $(a, 0)$, min $\left(x = \dfrac{a+2}{3}\right)$.

9 ――――――

10 $0 < V < \dfrac{32}{81}\pi a^3$.

P23 core Integration

1 $\frac{9}{8}$.

2 (a) $4\left(2x - \dfrac{1}{x^2}\right)\left(1 + \dfrac{1}{x^3}\right)$ (b) $13\frac{1}{2}$.

3 (a) (i) $4x - \dfrac{4}{3}x^3 + \dfrac{x^5}{5} + c$ (ii) $\dfrac{2}{3}x^{\frac{3}{2}} + 2x^{\frac{1}{2}} + c$ (b) $-\dfrac{8}{3}$.

4 $a = 3$.

5 (a) $\dfrac{3x^2}{2} - \dfrac{x^3}{3} + c$ (b) $4\frac{1}{2}$ square units.

6 (i) A $(0, 2)$, B $(\frac{2}{3}, 0)$ (ii) $-$ (iii) $\dfrac{10}{3}$ square units.

7 $6\frac{2}{3}$ square units.

8 (i) $-$ (ii) Area $ABCD = -e^{-n}(1 - e^{-1})$.

P24 core Methods of integration

1 $\frac{5}{36}$.

2 0.16.

3 (a) (i) $\frac{1}{2}\ln 2$ (ii) $\dfrac{2e^3+1}{9}$ (b) $-2e^{-\sqrt{x}} + c$.

4 (a) (i) $-4\frac{1}{2}$ (ii) 156 (iii) $-\dfrac{2}{3\pi}$.

5 (i) $\dfrac{(x^4-3)^6}{24} + c$ (ii) $\ln|\sec x| + c$ (iii) $\dfrac{e^{x^2}}{2} + c$.

6 $-\cos x - \dfrac{\cos^3 x}{3} + c$.

7 $\dfrac{\sin 2x}{4} - \dfrac{x\cos 2x}{2} + c$.

8 (a) $\frac{3}{2}x^2(1+x^3)^{-\frac{1}{2}}$ (b) $\frac{4}{3}$.

9 (i) $8(3+2x)^3$ (ii) 68 (iii) $-$.

10 (i) $\frac{1}{2}\ln(x^2+4) + c$ (ii) $-$

(iii) $f'(x) = -\dfrac{4}{(2x+1)^2} - \dfrac{4-x^2}{(x^2+4)^2}$

$f'(0) = -4.25$, $f'(8) = -0.000\,865$

(iv) $\dfrac{8-x}{(2x+1)(x^2+4)}$.

P25 Numerical solution of equations

1 2.93.

2 2 roots; 3.98; -1.06.

3 $2.0145 = 2.01$(2d.p.).

4 1.179747.

5 0.53.

6 18.5.

7 $\alpha = 2.218$, $x = 2(1 + e^{-x})$.

8 $f(1) = -2$, $f(2) = 2 \implies 1 < \alpha < 2$

(a) $\alpha = 1.733$ (b) $\sqrt[3]{x^2+2}$, $x_2 = 1.613$, $x_3 = 1.663$.

P26 Polynomials and fractions

1 (a) $(x^3 + 2x^2 + 3x + 4)$

(b) $(2x^4 + x^3 - 5)$

(c) $(x^4 - 3x + 6)$

(d) $(x^5 - 2x^2 + 1)$.

2 (a) Quotient: $x^3 - 3x^2 + 6x - 18$; remainder: 61

(b) quotient: $3x^2 - 5x$; remainder: $-2x^2 + 5x + 1$.

3 (a) $x - 1 + \dfrac{(x-5)}{(x^2-1)}$ (b) $2x^3 - 4x^2 + 8x - 19 + \dfrac{(38x+1)}{(x^2+2x)}$

4 $a = -9$, $b = 7$; $(x-2)(x-3)(2x+1)$.

5 $a = -1$, $b = 6$.

6 (i) -12; (ii) -60; (iii) 0; $2x+1$ is factor; $(x-3)(x+1)$.

7 See text; $a = -10$.

8 $a = -9$, $b = 2$, $c = 8$.

9 (a) $k = 1$, $-\dfrac{1}{2} \pm \sqrt{\dfrac{3}{4}}$. (b) $2x + 3$.

10 $3x - 2$; $x - 1$.

11 $A = \frac{3}{2}$, $B = -\frac{1}{2}$.

12 (a) $\dfrac{2}{2+x} + \dfrac{1}{1-2x}$ (b) $\dfrac{3}{1-3x} - \dfrac{2}{1-2x}$

(c) $\dfrac{1}{x+7} - \dfrac{1}{x+9}$ (d) $\dfrac{1}{x+2} + \dfrac{1}{x+3}$.

13 (a) $1 + \dfrac{3}{x+4} + \dfrac{5}{x-2}$ (b) $(x-3) - \dfrac{1}{x+1} + \dfrac{8}{x+2}$.

P27 Rational functions

1. $\dfrac{2}{(2+x)} - \dfrac{1}{(1+x^2)}$.

2. $\dfrac{2}{(x-1)} + \dfrac{3}{(x+2)} - \dfrac{5}{(x+2)^2}$.

3. $\dfrac{1}{(1+x)} + \dfrac{2x}{(1-2x^2)}$.

4. $\dfrac{4}{(1+2x)} + \dfrac{2}{(1-x)} + \dfrac{3}{(1-x)^2}$.

5. $\dfrac{3}{(x+1)} - \dfrac{2}{(x+)^2}$.

6. $\dfrac{-4}{9(x+1)} + \dfrac{4}{9(x-2)} + \dfrac{2}{3(x-2)^2}$.

7. $\dfrac{-1}{3(1+2x)} + \dfrac{5}{3(x+2)} - \dfrac{4}{(x+2)^2}$.

8. $\dfrac{-1}{(x+1)} + \dfrac{x}{(x^2+1)}$.

9. $\dfrac{1}{2(x-1)} + \dfrac{x+1}{2(x^2+1)}$.

10. (i) $\dfrac{1}{3y} + \dfrac{1}{3(3-y)}$ (ii) $\frac{1}{3}\ln\left(\dfrac{y}{3-y}\right) + k$.

   (iii) $y = \dfrac{3x^3}{(4+x^3)}$.

11. (a) $\dfrac{1}{(1-2x)} + \dfrac{1}{(1-x)^2} - \dfrac{1}{(1-x)}$

   (b) $1 + 3x + 6x^2 + 11x^3 + \ldots$ (c) $|x| < \frac{1}{2}$.

12. (a) $\dfrac{3x}{(1+x^2)} - \dfrac{1}{(1+x^2)} + \dfrac{4}{(2-x)}$

   (b) Use of $\left[\frac{3}{2}\ln(1+x^2) - \tan^{-1}x - 4\ln(2-x)\right]_0^1$.

P28 More about series

1. (a) (i) $\frac{1}{6}n(n+1)(4n-1)$. (ii) $2x(1-(2x)^n)/(1-2x)$.

   (b) (i) $2^{n+1} - 2 - n$; (ii) 6.

2. 73710.

3. ——————

4. ——————

5. ——————

6. $8n^2 + 8n + 1$.

7. ——————

P29 Permutations and combinations

1. (i) 40320; (ii) 6720; (iii) 907200; (iv) 1152

2. (a) 5040. (b) 1440. (c) 144.

3. 840; 96.

4. (a) 120; (b) 60.

5. 3240.

6. 50.

7. 10080; 30.

8. (i) 12; (ii) 12.

9. 9! or 362880; (i) 9!/5! or 3024; (ii) 5!×4! or 2880.

P30 Binomial series

1. (a) $1 - 2x - 2x^2 - 4x^3$; $-\frac{1}{4} < x < \frac{1}{4}$; 3.91918. (b) ±8.

2. $1 - 6x + 24x^2 - 80x^3$.

3. $2 + \dfrac{2x^2}{9} + \dfrac{2x^4}{81}$.

4. $1 + \frac{1}{2}x + \frac{3}{8}x^2 + \frac{5}{16}x^3$.

5. (i) $1 + \frac{1}{2}x - \frac{1}{8}x^2$; (ii) $1 + \frac{1}{2}x + \frac{3}{8}x^2$; $1 + x + \frac{1}{2}x^2$; 3.315.

6. (a) $1 - x - \frac{1}{2}x^2 - \frac{1}{2}x^3 - \frac{5}{8}x^4$, valid for $|x| < \frac{1}{2}$
   (b) Put $x = 0.1 \Rightarrow \sqrt{0.8} = 0.8944$ (4 d.p.).

P31 Exponential and logarithmic series

1. $1 - \frac{8}{3}x^3$; $|x| < \frac{1}{2}$.

2. $1 + \dfrac{x^2}{2!} + \dfrac{x^4}{4!} + \dfrac{x^6}{6!} + \ldots + \dfrac{x^{2n}}{(2n)!} + \ldots$; $\dfrac{x^n}{(2n)!}$.

3. (a) $1 + x + \dfrac{x^2}{2!} + \dfrac{x^3}{3!} + \ldots + \dfrac{x^n}{n!} + \ldots$.

   (b) $1 - \frac{3}{2}x + \frac{11}{8}x^2$.

4. (a) $-2x - 2x^2 - \frac{8}{3}x^3$; (b) $-3x - \frac{9}{2}x^2 - 9x^3$;

   $3x^2 + 10x^3$; $\frac{1}{n}(2(3)^n - 3(2^n))$; $|x| < \frac{1}{3}$.

5. (a) $x + \frac{5}{24}x^3 - \frac{1}{8}x^4$; $a = -\frac{1}{4}$ $-1 \leq x \leq 1$. (b) 0.099 504.

6. $4x + \dfrac{16}{3}x^3 + \dfrac{64}{5}x^5$; 0.510 82.

P32 The straight line

1. (i) $y = 3x - 6$; (ii) (2,0).

2. $k = 1, -2$.

3. $k = 9$.

4. $a = 2\sqrt{5}$, $b = 4\sqrt{5}$.

5. $3y = 2x + 11$.

6. $24x + 32y = 600$; $x^2 + y^2 - 30x - 15y + 225 = 0$; 9,12.

7. (i) $\frac{3}{4}$; (ii) 3.

P33 The circle

1. $x^2 + y^2 - 6x + 8y = 0$; $P(6,0)$ $Q(-1,-7)$; $7\sqrt{2}$

2. 10 units; $x^2 + y^2 - 6x - 2y - 15 = 0$.

3. Pt of contact (3,2).

4. $2y = x + 9$; $3y = 16 - x$; $x^2 - 2x + y^2 - 10y + 1 = 0$; $x^2 + y^2 - 7x = 144$.

5. $x^2 - 4x + y^2 - 12y + 32 = 0$; $x^2 - 12x + y^2 - 4y + 32 = 0$. Tangents: $y = x$, $y = 4 - x$, $y = 12 - x$.

6. (i) $x^2 - 8x + y^2 - 6y = 0$;
   (ii) $x^2 - 4x + y^2 - 4y + 4 = 0$.

P34 Experimental laws

1. $a = 2.5$, $k = 0.18$.

2. $n = 1.4$, $a = 0.7$, $y = 1.6$.

3. $b = 1.56$, $a = 0.78$.

4. $\log y = \log a + k \log x$; $k = 1.5$, $a = 2.5$. (a) 2.5. (b) 14.

5. $a = 30$, $b = -4$, $x \leq 7.5$.

6. $a = 0.25$, $b = 2.3$.

7. (a) $2y + 3x = 4$. (b) $\ln 5 + \ln x = y \ln 6$.

8. $a = 7$, $b = 5$.

9. $b = 0.35$, $a = 140$.

10. (i) $\log y = \log a + (x+1) \log b$; (ii) $px = 1 - q\left(\dfrac{y}{x}\right)$.

P35 Unknown curves

1. ——————

2. $x = 0$ or -2; minimum at (0, 0), maximum at $(-2, -4)$.

3. (i) Inflexion at (0, 0), maximum at $\left(\dfrac{3}{4}, \dfrac{27}{256}\right)$;

   (ii) asymptote $x = -2$, maximum at $\left(0, \dfrac{1}{4}\right)$.

4. (i) $y \to 1$ as $x \to \pm\infty$; (ii) $\frac{2}{3} < y < 2$;

   (iv) maximum at $(-1, 2)$, minimum at $\left(1, \dfrac{2}{3}\right)$.

5. (a) minimum at (0, 0), maximum at $\left(\dfrac{2}{3}, \dfrac{4}{27}\right)$.

   (b) $-\infty < y < 1$. (c) asymptotes $x = 0$ and $y = \pm 1$.

6 Minimum $\left(\dfrac{7\pi}{4}, -\dfrac{1}{\sqrt{2}}\, e^{-\frac{7\pi}{4}}\right)$; maximum $\left(\dfrac{3\pi}{4}, \dfrac{1}{\sqrt{2}}\, e^{\frac{3\pi}{4}}\right)$.

7 $y \to 0$ as $x \to \pm\infty$, $y \to \pm\infty$ as $x \to \pm1$;

maximum at $\left(-\dfrac{1}{2}, -4\right)$, minimum at $(-2, -1)$.

8 $\dfrac{dy}{dx} = 8x^3 - 2x$; maximum at $(0, 1)$, minima at $\left(-\dfrac{1}{2}, \dfrac{7}{8}\right)$

and $\left(\dfrac{1}{2}, \dfrac{7}{8}\right)$.

9 (ii) $\dfrac{dy}{dx} = -\dfrac{1}{x^2(1-x^2)^{\frac{1}{2}}} < 0$ for all x; (iii) 2.

P36 More trigonometry

1 (a) – (b)(i) $-\frac{7}{25}$ (ii) $\frac{1}{2}$.
2 $7t^2 - 10t + 3 = 0$, $46.4°$.
3 (a) – (b)(i) $5\sin(\theta - 36.9)°$ (ii) $\frac{1}{15}$, $\frac{1}{5}$.
4 $x = 2n\pi \pm \frac{\pi}{3}$.
5 $R = \sqrt{2}$, $A = \frac{\pi}{4}$.
  (a) $x = 2n\pi$, $x = 2n\pi + \frac{\pi}{2}$ (b) $\sqrt{2}$.
6 (i) $\alpha = 31.0°$ (ii) $x = 15.7°$, $282.3°$
  (iii) $7.9°$, $141.2°$, $187.9°$, $321.2°$.

P37 Vectors

1 $|\mathbf{p}+\mathbf{q}| = 11{\cdot}5$ units.

2 $\mathbf{m} = \frac{1}{2}(\mathbf{a}+\mathbf{b})$; $\mathbf{t} = \frac{2}{3}(\mathbf{a}+\mathbf{b})$; $OM:OT = 3:4$.

3 $AB = \mathbf{b}-\mathbf{a}$, $\mathbf{PQ} = \frac{1}{10}(5\mathbf{b}-3\mathbf{a})$;

  (i) $\frac{n}{10}(5\mathbf{b}-3\mathbf{a})$; (ii) $\frac{1}{2}(1+2k)\mathbf{b}-\frac{1}{2}\mathbf{a}$; $n = \frac{5}{3}$, $k = \frac{1}{3}$.

4 $AB:BC = 1:2$; $\overrightarrow{OD} = 6\mathbf{q}-4\mathbf{p}$; $\overrightarrow{OE} = -3\mathbf{q}+5\mathbf{p}$.

5 (a) $\mathbf{x} = \frac{1}{2}(3\mathbf{b}-\mathbf{a})$; (b) $\mathbf{y} = \frac{1}{4}(\mathbf{c}+3\mathbf{b})$; (d) $XY:YZ = 1:1$.

6 (a) $\overrightarrow{OM} = \frac{1}{2}\mathbf{b}$; (b) $\overrightarrow{OT} = \frac{1}{3}(\mathbf{a}+2\mathbf{b})$; (c) $\overrightarrow{OX} = \frac{1}{6}(8\mathbf{a}+\mathbf{b})$;

  (d) $\overrightarrow{OY} = \frac{1}{9}(8\mathbf{a}+\mathbf{b})$.

7 $\mathbf{q} = \frac{1}{5}(\mathbf{r}+4\mathbf{p})$; $PQ:QR = 1:4$.

P38 Vectors and geometry

1 (i) $\frac{1}{5}\binom{3}{4}$; (ii) $m = 5$, $n = 1$; $\mathbf{a}.\mathbf{b} = -4$; $\dfrac{-2\sqrt{5}}{25}$.

2 $\binom{4}{2}$; $3\sqrt{2}$; $s\binom{1}{-2}$; $t\binom{2}{2}$; $\dfrac{-\sqrt{10}}{10}$.

3 (a) $AC:CB = 5:3$.

4 $54{\cdot}7°$; $\overrightarrow{OP} = \mathbf{i}+3\mathbf{j}-2\mathbf{k}$; $\mathbf{r}.(4\mathbf{i}+3\mathbf{j}-3\mathbf{k}) = 19$.

5 (i) $30°$; $\overrightarrow{PQ} = \begin{pmatrix} 2+q-2p \\ -3+p \\ 5+q-p \end{pmatrix}$; $p = 1$, $q = -2$.

6 (a) $3\mathbf{j}+4\mathbf{k}$; (b) $\mathbf{r}.(3\mathbf{j}+4\mathbf{k}) = 0$; (c) $\left(\dfrac{\sqrt{26}}{26}\right)$.

P39 Matrices

1 (i) $M^2 = \begin{pmatrix} 3 & -5 \\ 5 & 8 \end{pmatrix}$, $M^3 = \begin{pmatrix} 1 & -18 \\ 18 & 19 \end{pmatrix}$; $M^{-1} = \frac{1}{7}\begin{pmatrix} 3 & 1 \\ -1 & 2 \end{pmatrix}$;

  $x = 2$, $y = 1$;

  (ii) $\begin{pmatrix} 0 & -2 \\ -2 & 0 \end{pmatrix}$, $(-1, -3)$.

2 (i) $(-3, 11)$, (ii) $\frac{1}{10}\begin{pmatrix} 3 & -1 \\ -2 & 4 \end{pmatrix}$, (iii) $a = 2$, $b = 3$,

  (iv) $(5\alpha, 5\alpha)$, (v) $y = x$.

3 (a) I. (b) $\begin{pmatrix} 1 & -1 & -1 \\ -1 & 3 & -1 \\ 0 & 1 & 3 \end{pmatrix}$.

4 (a) $m_2 = \dfrac{m_1}{1+m_1}$, $y = 0$.

5 $4x+5y = 0$; $y = 2x$; $x+2y = 0$.

P40 Complex numbers

1 $32+47i$; $32-47i$; $(6-5i)(6+5i)(7+2i)(7-2i)$.

2 0, $\pm\sqrt{3}$, $\pm\dfrac{\sqrt{3}}{3}$.

3 $z = 2-i$, $w = 2+3i$.

4 (a) $-\frac{1}{2}(1+\sqrt{3}i)$. (b) $p = 6$, $q = 25$.

5 $a = \pm\dfrac{\sqrt{2}}{2}$, $b = \pm\dfrac{\sqrt{2}}{2}$; $z = \dfrac{\sqrt{2}}{2}-1+i\dfrac{\sqrt{2}}{2}$ or

  $-\dfrac{\sqrt{2}}{2}-1-i\dfrac{\sqrt{2}}{2}$.

6 $\dfrac{x}{x^2+y^2} - i\dfrac{y}{x^2+y^2}$.

7 (a) $z^2 = x^2+y^2+i\,2xy$; $\sqrt{i} = \pm\dfrac{\sqrt{2}}{2}(1+i)$.

  (b) $\dfrac{7+24i}{5}$; $5x^2-14x+125 = 0$.

8 $p = -5-4i$, $q = 1+7i$; $a = -3$, $b = -1$.
9 z^2+2z+5.
10 x^2-2x+2; $(1+i)$ or $(1-i)$ or $(-1+2i)$ or $(-1-2i)$.
11 $p = 3$, $q = 5$; $2-i$.
12 $\pm(3+2i)$ and $\pm(3-2i)$; $z = 5+3i$ or $2+i$; $5-3i$ or $2-i$.
13 $p = 3$, $q = 1$ or $p = -3$, $q = -1$.
14 $A = B = -1$.

P41 Complex numbers and graphs

1 (a) $a = b = \pm1$; $z_1 = 2\left(\cos\dfrac{\pi}{2}+i\sin\dfrac{\pi}{2}\right)$,

  $z_2 = \sqrt{2}\left(\cos\dfrac{\pi}{4}+i\sin\dfrac{\pi}{4}\right)$,

  $z_3 = \sqrt{2}\left[\cos\left(\dfrac{-3\pi}{4}\right)+i\sin\left(\dfrac{-3\pi}{4}\right)\right]$.

  (b) $2+i\,2\sqrt{3}$; $z_4 = 2\left[\cos\dfrac{\pi}{6}+i\sin\dfrac{\pi}{6}\right]$;

  $z_4^2 = 4\left[\cos\dfrac{\pi}{3}+i\sin\dfrac{\pi}{3}\right]$;

  $z_5 = 2\left[\cos\left(\dfrac{-5\pi}{6}\right)+i\sin\left(\dfrac{-5\pi}{6}\right)\right]$.

2 $\frac{1}{2}\left[\cos\left(\dfrac{-\pi}{3}\right)+i\sin\left(\dfrac{-\pi}{3}\right)\right]$.

3 (a) $4\left(\cos\dfrac{\pi}{3}+i\sin\dfrac{\pi}{3}\right)$. (b) $\frac{1}{2}\left[\cos\left(\dfrac{-\pi}{6}\right)+i\sin\left(\dfrac{-\pi}{6}\right)\right]$.

4 (a) $1, \theta$; $2\cos\dfrac{\theta}{2}, \dfrac{\theta}{2}$; $2\sin\dfrac{\theta}{2}, \dfrac{\pi}{2}+\dfrac{\theta}{2}$.

5 (i) disc, centre $(0, 0)$, radius 1;
  (ii) disc, centre $(1, 1)$, radius 2.
6 (a) $127°$. (b) (i) circle, centre $(1, 1)$, radius 1;
  (ii) perpendicular bisector of line joining $(1, 0)$ to $(0, -1)$;
  (iii) half line, $x = 1$ $(y > 0)$.
7 (i) 1; (ii) $2+2i$.
8 (a) $-2+4i$. (b) $\dfrac{2-i}{30}$; $P\hat{O}Q = 90°$
9 $x^2+y^2+10x+16 = 0$; $P\left(\dfrac{-16}{5}, \dfrac{-12}{5}\right)$.

10 1, $\tan^{-1}\left(\dfrac{3}{4}\right)-\pi$; radius 1, centre $(0,0)$.

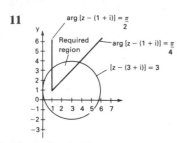

11

arg $[z-(1+i)] = \frac{\pi}{2}$

Required region

arg $[z-(1+i)] = \frac{\pi}{4}$

$[z-(3+i)] = 3$

P42 Methods of differentiation

1 (a) $\frac{x}{y}$ (b) $\frac{3x^2}{4y}$ (c) $\frac{2x^3-y}{2y^3+x}$ (d) $-\frac{x+3y}{3x+y}$.

2 (a) $\frac{t^2-1}{2t}$ (b) $t=\pm 1$, $(2, -2)$ and $(2, 2)$.

3 $\frac{dy}{dx}=\frac{9(t-2)^2}{4(t-3)^2}$ (a) 3 (b) 2 (c) 0, $\frac{12}{5}$.

4 (a) $\frac{1}{(x^2-1)}\sqrt{\frac{x-1}{x+1}}$ (b) $x^{\sin x}\left[\frac{\sin x}{x}+\cos x\ln x\right]$

(c) $x^{e^x}e^x\left[\ln x+\frac{1}{x}\right]$ (d) $\frac{4x^2-12x+7}{(2x-1)^{\frac{1}{2}}(2x-2)^{\frac{1}{2}}(2x-3)^{\frac{3}{2}}}$.

5 (i) $\frac{\sin t}{1-\cos t}=\cot\frac{t}{2}$ (ii) –.

6 (i) $y=-3x-3$ and $y=-12x$ (ii) $(\frac{1}{3}, -4)$.

7 ————

8 (i) $\frac{y(x+1)e^x+1}{(x+1)(2y-e^x)}$ (ii) $x+y=2$.

P43 Applications of differentiation

1 -5 m s^{-1}.

2 (i) $v=3(t^2-6t+8)$; $2s$, $4s$ (ii) 4 m
(iii) -6 m s^{-1}, 6 m s^{-1} (iv) 18 m.

3 (i) $\delta P=0.0008x\,\delta x$ (ii) – (iii) approx 1%.

4 $-\frac{3}{4}$.

5 $\frac{\sqrt{3}}{2}-\frac{\pi}{3}$.

6 (i) $\ln e=1$ (ii) $\frac{1}{e}$ (iii) $ey=x$ (iv) –.

7 $y=x-\frac{\pi}{2}+2$; $y=\frac{\pi}{2}-x$.

P44 Methods of Integration II

1 33.4 (b) $\frac{2}{3}$ (c) $\ln(\frac{7}{5})$.

2 (i) $\frac{1}{x-2}+\frac{3}{5-x}$ (ii) $4\ln 2$.

3 (i) $\sqrt{2x+1}+c$ (ii) $\frac{x}{2}-\frac{1}{4}\ln|2x+1|+c$

(iii) $\frac{1}{4}\ln\left|\frac{t+2}{t-2}\right|+c$.

4 (a) $\frac{\pi}{4}$ (b) $xe^{2x}-\frac{e^{2x}}{2}+c$ (c) $\frac{1}{x-1}+\ln\left|\frac{x-1}{2x+1}\right|+c$.

5 $\frac{1}{x}+\frac{1}{x^2}-\frac{1}{x+1}$; $\ln\left|\frac{x}{x+1}\right|-\frac{1}{x}+c$.

6 $\frac{1}{2}\ln 3=\ln\sqrt{3}$.

7 $\frac{\pi}{12}$.

8 (a) $A=1$, $B=-1$, $C=2$.

9 $\frac{1}{4}(\sqrt{3}-1)$.

P45 Applications of integration

1 (a) Inflexion at $(0, 0)$, minimum at $\left(-\frac{3}{4}, -\frac{27}{128}\right)$
(b) $(-1, 0)$, $(0, 0)$ (c) $\frac{1}{10}$.

2 $\frac{179}{6}\pi$ cubic units.

3 (i) $(1, -4)$ and $(25, 20)$ (ii) 144 square units.

4 A $(6, 8)$, B $(-6, 8)$; 80.35 square units; $\frac{544}{3}\pi$ cubic units.

5 (i) $\frac{14}{3}$ (ii) $\frac{188}{5}\pi$.

6 (a) (i) $12\ln\left(\frac{3}{2}\right)$ (ii) 12π
(b) (i) 1.5 seconds (ii) 7.5 m s^{-2} (iii) $30(1-\cos\frac{1}{2}t)$.

P46 Differential equations

1 $y=\frac{2x}{5-2x}$.

2 $\ln y=\frac{x^2}{2}\ln x-\frac{x^2}{4}+\frac{1}{4}$.

3 $2y=\ln\left(x^2+x+1\right)$.

4 $\frac{e^{-2y}}{2}+e^{-y}=\frac{3}{2}-\frac{x}{2}-\frac{\sin 2x}{4}$.

5 $\tan y=\ln(1+x)+1$.

6 $y=\frac{e^x}{1+e^x}$.

7 $\ln\left(\frac{y}{20}\right)=\frac{1}{(1+t)^2}-1$; as $t\to\infty$, $y\to\frac{20}{e}$.

8 $t=\frac{1}{\beta V}\ln 3$, $m=\frac{Ve^{\beta Vt}}{a(3+e^{\beta Vt})}$.

P47 Numerical integration

1 10/9.

2 $0\cdot 467$; $0\cdot 475$; $0\cdot 476$; $3\cdot 114$.

3 $-0\cdot 026$.

4 $57\cdot 3$; $57\cdot 29$.

5 $0\cdot 867$.

6 $3\cdot 69$; $6\cdot 71$.

7 $0\cdot 815$; $0\cdot 815$.

8 $0\cdot 160$.

9 $2\cdot 4948$.

MECHANICS

M1 Force diagrams

1

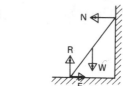

W – weight
N, R – normal reactions
F – friction

2 (a)

W – weight of ladder
N, R – normal reactions
F – friction
P – normal reaction
between man and
ladder.

(b)

w – weight of man
P – normal reaction

3

P – pull
W – weight
N – normal reaction
F – friction

4

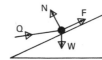

Q – push
W – weight
N – normal reaction
F – friction

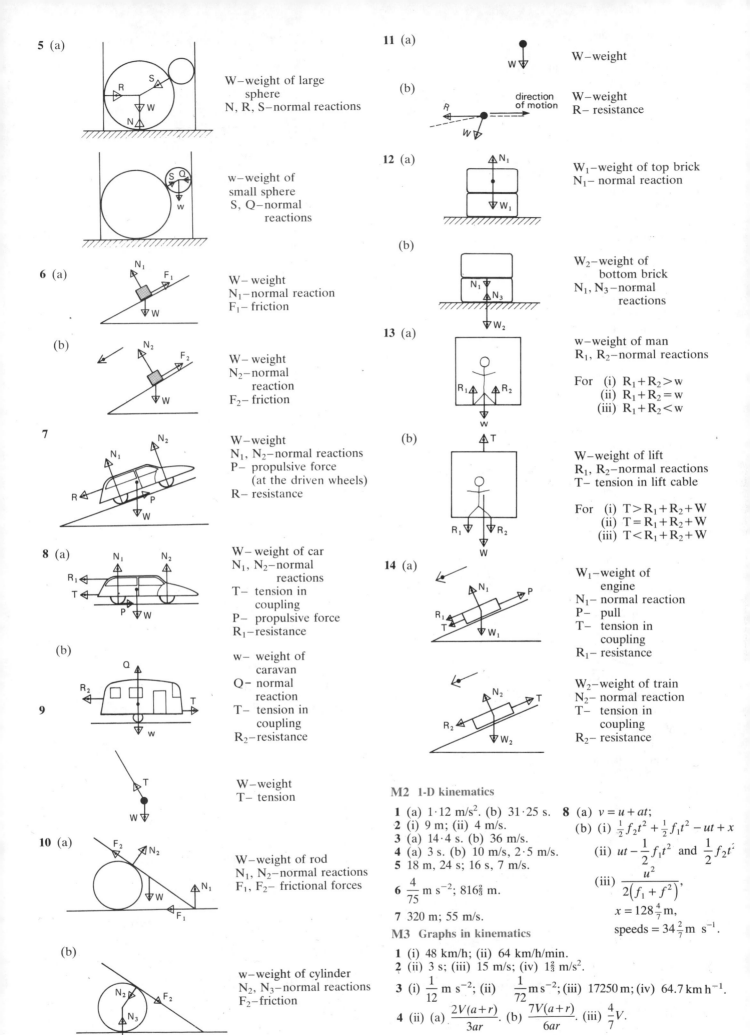

5 (a)

W–weight of large sphere
N, R, S–normal reactions

w–weight of small sphere
S, Q–normal reactions

6 (a)

W– weight
N_1–normal reaction
F_1– friction

(b)

W– weight
N_2–normal reaction
F_2– friction

7

W–weight
N_1, N_2–normal reactions
P– propulsive force (at the driven wheels)
R– resistance

8 (a)

W– weight of car
N_1, N_2–normal reactions
T– tension in coupling
P– propulsive force
R_1–resistance

(b)

w– weight of caravan
Q– normal reaction
T– tension in coupling
R_2–resistance

9

W– weight
T– tension

10 (a)

W– weight of rod
N_1, N_2–normal reactions
F_1, F_2– frictional forces

(b)

w–weight of cylinder
N_2, N_3–normal reactions
F_2–friction

11 (a)

W– weight

(b)

direction of motion

W–weight
R– resistance

12 (a)

W_1–weight of top brick
N_1– normal reaction

(b)

W_2–weight of bottom brick
N_1, N_3–normal reactions

13 (a)

w–weight of man
R_1, R_2–normal reactions

For (i) $R_1 + R_2 > w$
(ii) $R_1 + R_2 = w$
(iii) $R_1 + R_2 < w$

(b)

W–weight of lift
R_1, R_2–normal reactions
T– tension in lift cable

For (i) $T > R_1 + R_2 + W$
(ii) $T = R_1 + R_2 + W$
(iii) $T < R_1 + R_2 + W$

14 (a)

W_1–weight of engine
N_1– normal reaction
P– pull
T– tension in coupling
R_1– resistance

W_2–weight of train
N_2– normal reaction
T– tension in coupling
R_2– resistance

M2 1-D kinematics

1 (a) $1 \cdot 12$ m/s². (b) $31 \cdot 25$ s.
2 (i) 9 m; (ii) 4 m/s.
3 (a) $14 \cdot 4$ s. (b) 36 m/s.
4 (a) 3 s. (b) 10 m/s, $2 \cdot 5$ m/s.
5 18 m, 24 s; 16 s, 7 m/s.
6 $\dfrac{4}{75}$ m s⁻²; $816\tfrac{2}{3}$ m.
7 320 m; 55 m/s.

8 (a) $v = u + at$;
(b) (i) $\tfrac{1}{2} f_2 t^2 + \tfrac{1}{2} f_1 t^2 - ut + x$
(ii) $ut - \dfrac{1}{2} f_1 t^2$ and $\dfrac{1}{2} f_2 t^?$
(iii) $\dfrac{u^2}{2(f_1 + f^2)}$,
$x = 128\tfrac{4}{7}$ m,
speeds $= 34\tfrac{2}{7}$ m s⁻¹.

M3 Graphs in kinematics

1 (i) 48 km/h; (ii) 64 km/h/min.
2 (ii) 3 s; (iii) 15 m/s; (iv) $1\tfrac{2}{3}$ m/s².
3 (i) $\dfrac{1}{12}$ m s⁻²; (ii) $\dfrac{1}{72}$ m s⁻²; (iii) 17250 m; (iv) 64.7 km h⁻¹.
4 (ii) (a) $\dfrac{2V(a+r)}{3ar}$. (b) $\dfrac{7V(a+r)}{6ar}$. (iii) $\dfrac{4}{7}V$.
5 (i) $\dfrac{4T}{3}$; (ii) $\dfrac{2VT}{3}$.

M4 Relative motion

1 6 m s^{-1} from S60°E; from S41°E.
2 11·1 knots on bearing 339°; 340·6°.
3 2·7 h, 2·6 h, 1·4 h.
4 $P(30t-10, 0)$, $Q(0, 10-40t)$, $PQ = 10\sqrt{(25t^2-14t+2)}$, approximately 17 minutes past noon, 50 km per hour at S36·9°W.

M5 1-D particle dynamics

1 5·6 N.
2 (i) $9\frac{3}{8}$ m/s^2; (ii) 16·25 N; (iii) 95 m.
3 (i) 167·5 N; (ii) 2·58 m s^{-2}.
4 (i) $4\frac{1}{6}$ s; (ii) $10\frac{5}{12}$ m.
5 (i) 0·2 m s^{-2};
   (ii) 25 m; 612 N, 600 N 576 N.
6 1·2 kg, 5 m/s^2.
7 0·4, 0·225 m s^{-2}.

M6 Connected particles

1 (i) $13\frac{1}{3}$ N; (ii) $\dfrac{3\sqrt{10}}{10}$ s.

2 (a) 2 m s^{-2}. (b) 3 m s^{-1}. (c) 3·6 m.
3 (a) 1·4 m/s^2. (b) 2·52 N. (c) 3 s. (d) 4·2 m/s.

4 (i) $\dfrac{g}{2}$; (ii) $\dfrac{3mg}{2}$; (iii) $\dfrac{3}{2}mgh$; (iv) $\dfrac{5h}{2}$, $3\sqrt{\dfrac{h}{g}}$; (v) $\dfrac{\sqrt{hg}}{4}$.

5 3·92 ms^{-2}, 42 N; $\dfrac{4}{7}$ s.

M7 Work and energy

1 52 J; (i) $25d$ J; (ii) $40d$ J; $d = 0·8$ m.
2 (i) 10·08 kJ (ii) 24 kJ; 82·8 N

3 (i) mgd; (ii) $\sqrt{2gd}$; (iii) $\dfrac{2}{5}mgd$; (iv) $3mgd$.

4 $x = \dfrac{2E}{mg}$, $\lambda = \dfrac{m^2g^2l}{2E}$.

M8 Power

1 400 N.
2 (i) 840 N, 240 N; (ii) 3590 N, 990 N; (iii) 12·6 kW.
3 (i) 1500 N; (ii) (a) 0·05 m s^{-2}; (b) 1650 N,
   (c) 24·75 kW; (iii) 33·33 kW.
4 500 N, 15 kW.
5 10 m s^{-1}, 0·2 m s^{-2}.

6 1·8 kW; $\dfrac{1}{15}$ m s^{-2}; 25 minutes.

M9 Impulse and momentum

1 (i) 6 m/s; (ii) 24 Ns; (iii) 5832 J.
2 (a) 2120 Ns. (b) 10·6 kN.

3 $x = \dfrac{u}{6}$, $y = \dfrac{u}{4}$.

4 $u, 2u$.
5 (i) 15 m s^{-1}, 900 m s^{-1}; (ii) 6 m s^{-1}; (iii) 0 m s^{-1};
   (iv) 94·5 kJ, 9000 Ns.

M10 Impact

1 1·5 m s^{-1}; (i) 25 s, 30 s; (ii) $6\frac{7}{8}$ m.

2 $\dfrac{1}{2}$.

3 $e^{-\frac{1}{2}}$.

4 (i) $\dfrac{1}{2}$.

5 $4V$, $45\, mV^2$; $-V$, $14V$.

6 $v_A = \dfrac{u}{3}(7-8e)$; $v_B = \dfrac{u}{3}(16e+7)$; $\dfrac{1}{8}$, $\dfrac{3u}{1+k}$; $k > \dfrac{1}{2}$.

M11 Projectiles

1 (i) 39·3 m; (ii) 60 m; (iii) $4\sqrt{3}$ s; (iv) 98·6 m.
2 (a) 27 m. (b) 24 m. (c) 72°.
3 75·3 m; 29·9 m s^{-1}.

4 $\sqrt{\dfrac{5a}{2g}}$.

5 $\tan \alpha + \tan \beta = \dfrac{5}{x}$, $\tan \alpha \tan \beta = \dfrac{5y+x^2}{x^2}$, $\tan(\alpha+\beta) = \dfrac{-x}{y}$

M12 Motion in a horizontal circle

1 $\dfrac{1}{2}$ kg; 76·4 revs/min.

2 (a) $\sqrt{\dfrac{3ag}{2}}$ (b) ——————

3 $m(g \cos \alpha + l\omega^2 \sin^2 \alpha)$, $\omega^2 = \dfrac{g}{l \cos \alpha}$.

4 $\dfrac{5mu^2}{9a} + \dfrac{5}{8}mg$; $\dfrac{5mu^2}{9a} - \dfrac{5}{8}mg$.

5 $2\pi\sqrt{\dfrac{ma}{F}} \approx 1·60$ h.

M13 Motion in a vertical circle

1 60° to upward vertical; $h = \dfrac{27a}{16}$.

2 (ii) $u^2 = \dfrac{7ag}{2}$, $v = \sqrt{\dfrac{ag}{2}}$.

3 $\sqrt{\dfrac{2ag}{3}}$.

4 ——————

5 $v = \sqrt{[2ag(1+\sin \theta)]}$ (b) $\theta = 30°$, $v = \sqrt{3ag}$; $\sqrt{\dfrac{a}{g}}$.

6 0·994 m; clock gains 8 minutes; new length 1·005 m.
7 $\sqrt{[2gr(1-\cos \theta)]}$ towards the centre.

M14 Variable forces

1 $\left(\dfrac{g}{k} + \dfrac{e^{-2kx}}{k}(kw^2 - g)\right)^{\frac{1}{2}}$.

2 (i) 482 m; (ii) 24 s.

3 (i) $v = Ue^{k(a-x)}$; $v = \dfrac{U}{1+Ukt}$; (iii) $x = a + \dfrac{1}{k}\ln(1+Ukt)$.

4 $\dfrac{dv}{dt} = -g\left(1+\dfrac{v^2}{V^2}\right)$.

5 (i) 2·77; (ii) $v = \dfrac{e^{\frac{t}{2}}}{4+e^{\frac{t}{2}}}$; $x_{0·8} = 4\ln 2$, $x_{0·6} = 2\ln 2$.

6 $\left(\dfrac{g}{k} + u\right)e^{-kt} - \dfrac{g}{k}$.

M15 Simple harmonic motion

1 (i) (a) $\sqrt{10}$ m; (b) π s; (c) $2\sqrt{10}$ m/s; (d) $\dfrac{\pi}{4}$ s;

   (ii) (a) -8 m/s^2. (b) 64 N; (iii) $x = \sqrt{10} \sin 2t$ m,

   $t_1 = \frac{1}{2}\sin^{-1}\left(\dfrac{\sqrt{10}}{10}\right)$ s, $t_2 = \frac{1}{2}\sin^{-1}\left(\dfrac{\sqrt{10}}{5}\right)$ s,

   $\frac{1}{2}\sin^{-1}\left(\dfrac{\sqrt{10}}{5}\right) - \frac{1}{2}\sin^{-1}\left(\dfrac{\sqrt{10}}{10}\right)$ s.

2 (i) $x = 3$, $v = -12$; (ii) $x = 5$.   3 $OE = \dfrac{5}{3}a$.

4 (i) 0·08 m; (ii) 0·6 m s^{-1}; 3 N.
5 $\ddot{x} = -5$ m s^{-2}; 7 cm.

M16 Vectors in dynamics

1 $\begin{pmatrix} \frac{1}{2}t^2 \\ 3t \end{pmatrix}$, $\begin{pmatrix} 2+\frac{1}{6}t^3 \\ 2+\frac{3}{2}t^2 \end{pmatrix}$; $\begin{pmatrix} 1/(6\times10^4) \\ 3/(2\times10^4) \end{pmatrix}$; 6 s.

2 $2\sqrt{5}$ N, $8\mathbf{i}+16\mathbf{j}$, $12\mathbf{i}+18\mathbf{j}$, $\dfrac{2\sqrt{13}}{13}\mathbf{i} + \dfrac{3\sqrt{13}}{13}\mathbf{j}$; $4\mathbf{i}+6\mathbf{j}$ m s^{-2}; $2\sqrt{13}$ m s^{-1}.

3 (i) $3\mathbf{i}+4\mathbf{j}$, $\dfrac{4}{\sqrt{(1+\lambda^2)}}\mathbf{i} - \dfrac{4\lambda}{\sqrt{(1+\lambda^2)}}\mathbf{j}$;

   (ii) $3t\mathbf{i}+4t\mathbf{j}$; $\dfrac{4t}{\sqrt{(1+\lambda^2)}}\mathbf{i} - \dfrac{4\lambda t}{\sqrt{(1+\lambda^2)}}\mathbf{j}$,

   $\left(\dfrac{4t}{\sqrt{(1+\lambda^2)}} - 1 - 3t\right)\mathbf{i} + \left(8 - \dfrac{4t\lambda}{\sqrt{(1+\lambda^2)}} - 4t\right)\mathbf{j}$; 5s.

4 (i) $(1+4t)\mathbf{i}+(4+4t)\mathbf{j}$, $(4+t^2)\mathbf{i}+(1+2t+t^2)\mathbf{j}$; (ii) 1 h, 4 km; (iii) 3 h; (iv) 10 km h^{-1}, in direction $\tan^{-1}(4/3)$ N of E.

5 ——————

6 $-\frac{1}{2}mv\mathbf{i}+\dfrac{\sqrt{3}}{6}mv\mathbf{j}$; $\dfrac{\sqrt{3}}{9}v$, at 30° clockwise from x-axis.

7 (i) $\mathbf{F}.\mathbf{v}$; (ii) $\displaystyle\int_0^T \mathbf{F}.\mathbf{v}\,dt$; $-4a\sin 2t\,\mathbf{i}+2a\cos 2t\,\mathbf{j}$;

$-8ma\cos 2t\,\mathbf{i}-4ma\sin 2t\,\mathbf{j}$; $P=12ma^2\sin 4t$; $6a^2m$; $\dfrac{\pi}{4}$.

M17 Coplanar concurrent forces
1 $P=24$ N, $Q=12\sqrt{3}$ N.
2 $8\cdot83$ N at 316° 34′; $P=8\cdot83$ N, $Q=0\cdot24$ N.
3 $P=10$ N, Resultant at 090°; Direction 226.1°, Resultant 18.0 N
4 (i) $302\cdot4$ N at 41° 24′; (ii) $Q=3P$.
5 $\mathbf{F}_1=9\mathbf{i}+12\mathbf{j}$, $\mathbf{F}_2=3\mathbf{i}-3\mathbf{j}$, $\mathbf{F}_3=8\mathbf{i}+4\mathbf{j}$,
$\mathbf{F}_R=20\mathbf{i}+13\mathbf{j}$; moment -1 Nm.
6 (a) (i) $\overrightarrow{AC}=\mathbf{a}+\mathbf{b}$; (ii) $\overrightarrow{AD}=2\mathbf{b}$; (iii) $\overrightarrow{AE}=2\mathbf{b}-\mathbf{a}$;
(iv) $\overrightarrow{AF}=\mathbf{b}-\mathbf{a}$. (b) $7\mathbf{i}-\mathbf{j}$; $\overrightarrow{OA}=4\mathbf{i}+3\mathbf{j}$;
$\overrightarrow{OB}=14\mathbf{i}-2\mathbf{j}$, $\overrightarrow{CO}=-6\mathbf{i}+8\mathbf{j}$; 15 N.

M18 Moments and couples
1 $\mathbf{F}_1=3\mathbf{i}+6\mathbf{j}$, $\mathbf{F}_2=\mathbf{i}-2\mathbf{j}$, $\mathbf{F}_R=4\mathbf{i}+4\mathbf{j}$; moment is zero.
2 $X=25$ g, 65 g, 45 g.
3 5 kg, 10 kg; (i) 300 N; (ii) $1\cdot5$ m.
4 $2\cdot75$ m from A; $20\cdot5$ kg, $39\cdot5$ kg.
5 (a) $14\frac{2}{7}$ N. (b) $171\frac{3}{7}$ N.
6 $P=\dfrac{w(6-y)}{12-x-y}$, $Q=\dfrac{w(6-x)}{12-x-y}$; (ii) 3 cm.
7 (a) 3; (b) 50 N and 100 N.
8 (a) 10 N. (b) $\tan^{-1}\left(\dfrac{1}{3\sqrt{3}}\right)=10°\,54′$. (c) $10\sqrt{7}$ N;

90 Nm anticlockwise.

9 $\dfrac{3W}{4}$, c of g at $\dfrac{7a}{3}$ from A; $\dfrac{W}{2}$ and $\dfrac{W}{4}$.

M19 Equilibrium
1 (i) $15\sqrt{6}$ N, 30 N (twice), $30\sqrt{3}$ N;
(ii) $1\cdot5(\sqrt{3}-1)$ kg, 3 kg.
2 (a) $\dfrac{W\sqrt{3}}{6}$ (b) $\sqrt{\dfrac{13}{12}}\,W$ at 73° 53′ to horizontal.
(c) $\dfrac{W}{3}$. (d) 71° to horizontal.
3 $\dfrac{1160\sqrt{3}}{3}$ N; $X=\dfrac{580\sqrt{3}}{3}$ N; $Y=280$ N (down).

M20 Three force problems
1 (i) $4g$ N (ii) 60.3° ≈ 40 N.
2 (i) 22°; (ii) 28 N and $41\cdot5$ N.
3 (i) $40\cdot9°$; (ii) $50\sqrt{7}$ N.
5 $\dfrac{38}{65}$.

M21 Friction
1 $\dfrac{8}{27}$.
2 $7\cdot5$ N; 5 m s^{-2}.
3 $\dfrac{W\sqrt{3}}{6}$; W.
4 (i) $\dfrac{P}{mg}$.

M22 Bodies in contact
1 Equilibrium broken at C.
2 (i) C; (ii) $\dfrac{W}{2}\sqrt{(1+9\mu^2)}$ at $\tan^{-1}(3\mu)$ to vertical;
(iii) $\tan^{-1}\left(\dfrac{2}{3\mu}\right)$.
3 $\dfrac{1}{\sqrt{3}}$.

M23 Equivalent systems of forces
1 7 N at $38\cdot2°$ to AC; $4\cdot5$ m.
2 (a) $2\sqrt{10}$ N at $\tan^{-1}3$ to x-axis. (b) $71\cdot6°$.
(c) $a=8\frac{2}{3}$ m, $y=3x-26$.
3 48 Nm in sense $ABCD$.
4 $\sqrt{65}$ N at $\tan^{-1}8$ to OA; line of action $\dfrac{3}{8}$ m from O in
direction OA and 3 m from O in direction CO so $y=8x+3$;
3 N in direction BA.
5 $k=\dfrac{35}{6}$; $43\cdot2$ cm.
6 (i) $10\,P$; (ii) $\dfrac{4}{3}$; (iii) $\dfrac{9a}{4}$; (iv) ——————
(v) $20Pa$ in sense $ABCD$. (vi) $6P$ N, $3\frac{1}{2}P$ N, $4\frac{1}{2}P$ N.

M24 Centres of mass
1 (a) $3\frac{1}{2}$ cm. (b) $1\frac{2}{3}$ cm.
2 (a) $\dfrac{40}{59}$ mm from O. (b) $\bar{x}=10$, $\bar{y}=6$.
3 5.75 cm.
4 $\left(\dfrac{7a}{18},\dfrac{4a}{9}\right)$.

M25 Suspending and toppling
1 $\dfrac{2}{3}$.
2 $\dfrac{14b}{15}$ from AB, $\dfrac{19a}{15}$ from AD; 45°.
3 $\sin\beta=\dfrac{3+k}{3(k-8)}$.

STATISTICS

S1 core Pictorial representation

1 307.5°, 18.5°, 15.5°, 12.5°, 6.0° to nearest half degree.
2 UK: 144°; WE: 67°; Am: 48°; Aus: 39°; Others: 62°.
3 ──────────
4 A: 66°; B: 156°; C: 24°; D: 42°; E: 72°; 5·48 cm 6 cm 50°.
5 ──────────

S3 core Mode and means

1 5·65 cm.
2 51·6.
3 1011·3 millibars.
4 (a) (i) 3·5; (ii) 2·994.
5 ──────────
6 (i) $\bar{a}+\bar{b}$; (ii) $\frac{1}{2}(\bar{a}+\bar{b})$; (iii) $100+10\bar{a}+\bar{b}$; (iv) AB;
   (v) A^2B^3.
7 (a) (i) 5.

S4 core Median and quantiles

1 (i) 46·25; (ii) 29·80, 9·125%.
2 (b) 233 thou. (d) 2·165 tonnes. (e) 516 250 tonnes.
3 (ii) 35 years; (iii) Mean = 38·75.
4 6·6, 4, 9·25.
5 437, 412·5, 453 kNm^{-2}.

S5 core Measures of dispersion

1 Mean 21·25 kg, s.d. 2·5 kg.
2 38·7 g, 6·67 g; 42·7 g, 6·67 g.
3 Mean 16, s.d. 6 (i) – (ii) Mean 15, s.d. 7.
4 (a) 0.687 (b) 4.44 cm.
5 Mean 25.9 years, s.d. 1.99 years.
6 Median 89.3 g, Q_3 93.6 g, 16 animals, mean 89.7 g, s.d. 6.51 g.

S6 core Comparing frequency distributions

1 Estimated means and standard deviations are:
(a) 1992: mean 38.2 years, s.d. 22.9 years
(b) 2030: mean 42.9 years, s.d. 24.1 years.
It is estimated by the year 2030 the mean age will have increased and there will be a greater spread of ages. There will be fewer people in the under 45 age group and more in the 45 and over age group.
2 Type A: mean = 2.92 beans per pod, s.d.1.32
Type B: mean = 2.85 beans per pod, s.d. 1.34.
Therefore there is no significant difference.
3 Estimated means and standard deviations are:
males: mean 36.7 years, s.d. 22.5 years
females: mean 40.0 years, s.d. 24.0 years.
The mean age of the female population is greater than that of the male because the female population does not fall as rapidly as the male population after the age of 65 years.

S7 core Probability

1 (i) 1/9; (ii) 1/5; (iii) 1/120; (iv) 1/20.
2 (a) 8/35. (b) 18/35; 3/35, 3/8.
3 (a) (i) 1/6; (ii) 1/9; (iii) $(2/3)^{r-1}(1/6)$; 1/2. (b) 31/56.
4 (i) 5/192; (ii) 5/324; (iii) 63/64; (iv) 5/216.

S8 Index numbers and moving averages

1 125, 120, 100; 175, 150, 125; 157·5, 132·5.
2 $a=45$, $b=21$, $c=29·25$, $d=22·5$.
3 9, 11, 3, 13.

S9 Discrete probability distributions

1 Mean £7·57 Variance 12·96; £53, 3·00; £53, 99·0.
2 4, 4/25; 6, 8/25; 8, 4/25; 9, 4/25; 11, 4/25; 14, 1/25, 7·6 pence; £1·20 loss.
3 125/216, 75/216, 15/216, 1/216; 2 pence loss.
4 2/15, 34/15, 274/15, 2024/225.

S10 Continuous probability distributions

1 (i) 3/16; (ii) 5/4; (iii) 19/80; (iv) 11/16.
2 (i) $2-8a$; (ii) $\frac{1}{8}$; (iii) mean $\frac{4}{3}$, variance $\frac{8}{9}$; (iv) $\frac{5}{16}$.
3 $k=4$; mean 8/15; variance 11/225; median 0·541.
4 $A = 1/1200$, result not significant.
5 (i) $\frac{1}{4}$; (ii) $z=\frac{2}{3}(3-\sqrt{3})$.
6 $\lambda=\frac{1}{2}$, mean $\frac{\pi}{2}$, variance $\frac{\pi^2}{4}-2$, median $\frac{\pi}{2}$, quartiles $\frac{\pi}{3},\frac{2\pi}{3}$; $\sin\left(\frac{\pi^2}{4}-2\right)$. Probability $=\sin\sqrt{\frac{\pi^2}{4}-2}$.

S11 The binomial distribution

1 (i) 0·206; (ii) 0·343; (iii) 0·816; (iv) 0·451.
2 (i) 16/45; (ii) (a) 0·201. (b) 0·302; 2.
3 (a) 671/1296. (b) 15/1296.
4 8; (i) 0·00000010; (ii) 1·00; (iii) 0·000074.
5 (a) 0·315. (b) (i) 0·53 Fit 0·049, 0·22, 0·37, 0·28, 0·079.
6 ──────────

S12 The Poisson distribution

1 (a) 0·135. (b) 0·0527. (c) 0·00783.
2 Frequencies 35, 38, 21, 8, 2, 0.
3 0·143; limits 172·3, 227·7.
4 0·371, £60.34.
5 113 matches.
6 3, 0·223, 0·988.
7 (a) (i) 0·986; (ii) 0·223. (c) 6 pence per metre, s.d. 2.45p.
8 (a) 0·267. (b) 0·191 Insufficient evidence.
9 (a) 0·323. (b) 0·0119.

S13 The Normal distribution

1 Mean 68·82 mph, s.d. 5·36; new mean 63·98 mph, 13·1%.
2 Mean 60·0 mm, s.d. 0·2 mm, 9·0%.
3 Mean 5·03 cm, s.d. 0·09 cm, £409·27.
4 Mean 8 cm, s.d. 1·16 cm, Range 6·09 to 9·91 cm.
5 1·06, 0·020.

S14 Uses of the Normal distribution

1 (a) 0·0404. (b) $r=305$.
2 $P(x>2)=0.8125$; £1250, 0·0036.
3 (i) 0·515; (ii) 0·376; 0·445 $N=43$.
4 0·089; $p=0.36$; $\sigma\hat{p}=4.8$; not significant.
5 (i) 0·226; (ii) 0·9988; 0·7752.

S15 Sampling I

1 See text for answers.
2 (a) The median unemployment for the towns in the NW is greater than for the SW.
The spread for the NW is much less than for the SW.
(b) This method avoids children, and only picks those members of households whose name appears in the telephone book.
3 See text for answers.
4 (a) Sampling frame → 45 randomly selected households, e.g. 083 → 83; 959 too large; 476 → 26; 026 repeat; 132 → 132.
(b) (i) Not random but might 'pay off'.
(ii) Random, not efficient.
(iii) Random, but not equally likely.
(iv) Random, equal likelihood.
(v) Subsets not equally likely.
5 (a) *Simple random sampling*: randomly choose 50 from 700.
Each student has an equal chance of being chosen. Need to interview each student.
Stratified random sampling: treat each list as a separate stratum and randomly choose $\frac{50}{700}\times 380 = 27$ from List I. Similarly 12 from List II and 11 from List III.
Need to interview those chosen. More precise result.

Quota sampling: choose the first 27 from List I, the first 12 from List II and the first 11 from List III.
Quick to find respondents. Not random. Cannot be modelled theoretically.
(b) The stratified random sampling. This is the only way you can be sure to choose 11 students from List III; the simple random sample could leave this group under-represented.
Quota sampling cannot be modelled theoretically *or* list may be in an order which affects results.

S16 Sampling II

1 (a) 13·2874. (b) 2. (c) 1. (d) 8·872 (other answers possible).
2 Mean 1·9, Variance 0·89; mean 1·9, variance 0·54.
3 Mean 12000 g, s.d. 57·01 g; 0·0397; 765·1 g.
4 Mean score 0·769, 0·101. Total score 10, 17·07; 0·0198.

S17 Estimation

1 limits 0·521, 0·678; 0·835.
2 900·21, 0·83 limits 900·06, 900·36 g.
3 $\pi/4$, $\pi = 3.136$, limits 3·05, 3.22.
4 0.05 cm; 0.0025 cm^2; 15.9%; C.I. 2·00, 2·02
Range 2·28 to 5·48.
5 Interval for proportion 0·00241, 0·00759;
for number 13168, 41563.
6 (a) 10, 100. (b) 10, 1. (c) Interval 8·04, 11·96
Mean could be 9.

S18 Hypothesis testing

1 602 g, 0·65 g; box 15050 g, 3·25 g. (i) Not significant;
(ii) significant.
2 Mean < 9·7; Mean 9·3 units, Variance 3·61.
3 (i) 1st significant, 2nd not significant.

S19 The student *t*-distribution

1 $H_0: \mu = 18\,500$ versus $H_1: \mu \neq 18\,500$. There is insufficient evidence at the 5% level to reject H_0.
2 The difference between the mean heights is highly significant.
3 $t_{\text{test}} = 2.191$, $t_{\text{crit}} = 2.306$ (two-tailed test, $v = 8$, $P = 5\%$). So results do not lead to a rejection of the null hypothesis.
4 Assuming the samples are unmatched,
$t_{\text{test}} = 0.609$, $t_{\text{crit}} = 2.042$ (two-tailed test, $v = 30$, $P = 5\%$). So results do not lead to a rejection of the hypothesis.

S20 Linear regression

1 (a) 2·5, 1·2, $y = 6·7 - 2·2\,x$.
2 (ii) $y = 0·855\,x + 2·668$. (iii) 11·23, 79·62.
3 $y = x - 1641$; mean annual increase $y = 1·00$ ppm; incorrect use of information.
4 $y = 0·9\,x + 2·2$; $y = 5·35$;
5 $Y = 0·43\,X + 56·3$; $r = 0·9949$.
6 (ii) $y = 1·03\,x + 0·533$.
7 (a) $y = 0·917 - 0·11\,x$. *(b)* $\bar{x} = 2·4$; $\bar{y} = 0·65$. (c) $x = 8·3$.

S21 Correlation

1 0·188; $\mu_s = 0·34$, not significant.
2 (a) 0·753. (b) 0·767.
3 (a) 0·143. (b) 0·152.
4 0·603. $W = 0·888\,h - 75·9$.
5 $\sum(x - \bar{x})(y - \bar{y}) = 12$; $\sum(x - \bar{x})^2 = 1000$; $\sum(y - \bar{y})^2 = 360$
$r = 0.02$; $a = 0.246$; $b = 0.012$.

S22 χ^2

1 (a) $\chi^2_{\text{test}} = 3$, $\chi^2_{5\%}(1) = 3·84$, not biased. (b) 95% CI 0·140, 0·360.
2 Mean 0.9; $\chi^2_{\text{test}} = 3.215$, $\chi^2_{5\%}(1) = 3.84$, Poisson population.
3 $\chi^2_{\text{test}} = 4.501$; 6.63% defective is not the same.
4 3·24. Accept hypothesis.
5 Mean = 2·3 goals/match; frequencies 10·0, 23·1, 26·5, 20·3, 11·7, 5·4, 2·1, 0·7. Accept Poisson hypothesis; $\chi^2_{\text{test}} = 4·426$; $\chi^2_{5\%}(4) = 9·49$.

S23 Contingency tables

1 2·67; Not significant, proportion the same 95% CI 0·304, 0·496.
2 Significant at 1%. Not consistent.
3 Different proportions, highly significant.
4 8·45. Not significant. No association; 8·03 Significant.

S24 Special graph papers

1 Mean = 13 $s = 0·95$. Frequencies 13, 48, 78, 48, 13.
2 Mean 1·19, Variance 1·19; 0·00024; (i) 0·028 (ii) 0·308.
3 (a) $a = 1·16$, $b = 2$; (b) Mean 70·4, s.d. 8·43.
4 (b) 0·0009.

Index